CARBON-14

VERNON F. RAAEN
Chemistry Division
Oak Ridge National Laboratory
Oak Ridge, Tennessee

GUS A. ROPP
Professor of Chemistry
Coker College
Hartsville, South Carolina

HELEN P. RAAEN
Analytical Chemistry Division
Oak Ridge National Laboratory
Oak Ridge, Tennessee

McGRAW-HILL BOOK COMPANY
New York   St. Louis
San Francisco
Toronto   London
Sydney

CARBON-14

Library of Congress Catalog Card Number 67-20178

51085

1234567890 MAMM 7432106987

PREFACE

For almost two decades, "Isotopic Carbon" by Calvin, Heidelberger, Reed, Tolbert, and Yankwich has served, and will continue to serve, as an authoritative monograph. The prediction by its authors that isotopic carbon would "very soon find its place as a routine tool in many kinds of scientific laboratories" was realized during that period. Curiously, in its series of monographs, the National Academy of Sciences–National Research Council Subcommittee on Radiochemistry did not review work on carbon-14 "since that nuclide, its uses and applications, seem to be almost completely within the province of the organic chemist."

In chemical applications of carbon isotopes, the emphasis has shifted from techniques of counting and methods of synthesis to the study of reaction mechanisms and the use of carbon-14 as a powerful and elegant analytical tool. Also, the health hazard of carbon-14 has come to be considered in its proper perspective; the excessive concern that existed earlier appears to have been unjustified. These and other advances indicate the need for a concise up-to-date treatise on the principles of use, experimental techniques, and typical applications of carbon-14 in organic chemistry. This book was designed to meet that need. The information included is basic to work with carbon-14 and therefore is useful in any discipline in which organic chemical reactions are of interest. The book should be of value to the biochemist, who uses carbon-14 far more extensively than does the organic chemist.

It is impossible to make individual acknowledgments to all persons who have helped to create this volume. Our associations with former and present members of the research staff of the Oak Ridge National Laboratory (operated by the Union Carbide Corporation for the U.S. Atomic Energy Commission) and with consultants and visitors to this laboratory have been a source of inspiration and enrichment in knowledge. To them we make particular acknowledgment.

We are especially indebted and grateful to Mrs. Inez W. Hodge, who expertly typed the entire manuscript, and to Mr. B. Samuel Dunlap, who prepared many of the original illustrations.

Vernon F. Raaen
Gus A. Ropp
Helen P. Raaen

CONTENTS

PART
ONE
INTRODUCTION

CHAPTER

1

THE RADIOISOTOPE CARBON-14

1-1 HISTORY

Shortly after the discovery[1] that tritium is a product of the bombardment of water with deuterons, Ruben and Kamen[2] announced that a carbon isotope of mass number 14 had been produced by bombarding carbon with deuterons in a cyclotron. These discoveries came on the heels of other conclusions which indicated that no radioactive isotope of hydrogen or carbon would have a half-life long enough to warrant its use as a tracer. The $^{13}C(d,p)^{14}C$ reaction has been superseded by the reaction $^{14}N(n,p)^{14}C$, which takes place in a nuclear reactor and which is one of the few known slow-neutron reactions that emit a proton. It has been stated[3] that the large graphite reactor at Harwell produces hundreds of times more carbon-14 each day by the (n,p) reaction than five large cyclotrons could produce during one year's operation. Kamen[4] has written an interesting account of the early history of carbon-14.

1-2 METHODS OF PRODUCTION

Reactor production of carbon-14 is achieved by neutron bombardment of solid beryllium nitride, solid aluminum nitride, solid calcium nitrate, or a saturated solution of ammonium nitrate. Other target materials are also used. Because the thermal neutron cross section for nitrogen is small (1.8 barns), the irradiation periods are long. Thus, it is not unusual to irradiate aluminum nitride for periods as long as 1 to 3 years.[5,6]

In the United States it has been the practice to irradiate beryllium nitride, although a switch to aluminum nitride is under way. The amount of nitrogen converted to carbon-14 is relatively small. In a typical irradiation, four 40-g cylinders of beryllium nitride contained as an aluminum-jacketed slug are irradiated with neutrons; about 1.2 curies (0.28 g) of carbon-14 is obtained. Usually fifteen slugs are processed at one time. The jackets are removed from the irradiated slugs by radio-frequency heating.

The carbon-14 is then recovered from the beryllium nitride target by dissolving the target in 9 M sulfuric acid (8 ml per gram of target). Much hydrogen is evolved and acts as a carrier for the carbon-14-labeled gases, which are monitored by an ionization chamber located immediately following the reaction vessel. The effluent gases from the ionization chamber are passed into a sodium hydroxide scrubber, which removes the carbon-14 dioxide as well as small amounts of sulfur dioxide. About 10% of the total carbon-14 is trapped in the sodium hydroxide; the carbonate obtained is about 30 atom percent carbon-14. Mass spectral analysis seems to indicate that the remaining gas is almost pure methane. It, together with the hydrogen, is passed over heated copper oxide to oxidize the hydrogen and most of the methane. Because methane is resistant to oxidation, the copper oxide combustion tube is followed by another combustion tube that is filled with the more efficient oxidant, cobaltous cobaltic oxide. The carbon-14 dioxide is then absorbed by aqueous sodium hydroxide solution and is finally converted to barium carbonate-^{14}C by the addition of a carbonate-free solution of barium hydroxide. The methane-^{14}C and the barium carbonate obtained from it have a very high carbon-14 content, usually 85 to 90 atom percent. Methane-^{14}C can be purified conveniently on a molecular-sieve column; if demand for labeled methane were sufficiently great, it could be isolated at very high specific activity and sold inexpensively.[6] The multitude of other labeled compounds previously reported[7] as products of the irradiation and processing of beryllium nitride do not appear to be present or are not present in significant amounts.

The shipment of 409.5 curies of carbon-14 in 4992 shipments from the Oak Ridge National Laboratory alone in the period from 1954 to January 1967 is evidence of the great demand for this radionuclide. Quantities of carbon-14 shipped from The Radiochemical Centre, Amersham, England, and from the Labeled Molecules Section, Department of Radioelements, Saclay, France, would add significantly to these figures.

I-3 NATURAL OCCURRENCE

It is interesting that carbon-14 was unknown in nature until after its systematic preparation in the laboratory, as was the case with tritium and many other isotopes. Natural carbon contains small but measurable quantities of carbon-14, that is, about 1×10^{-12} g per gram of carbon. Although this level of radioactivity is usually negligible as a source of background radiation, it is nevertheless enough to permit the determination of the age of biogeochemical material by a rather elegant technique.[8,9] Naturally occurring carbon-14 is thought to result from the interaction of cosmic-ray neutrons with atmospheric nitrogen. The ^{14}C/^{12}C ratio is by no means constant in nature; it is very dependent on the changes in the amounts of carbon in the various exchangeable reservoirs. The ratio within a given reservoir (especially the atmosphere) has likewise been affected by the vicissitudes of man's progress. First, the ratio decreased considerably (2 to 3%)[10,11] when great quantities of inactive carbon dioxide were produced during the industrial revolution by the combustion of fossil fuels. Then, more recently, the ratio increased (by 10%)[12] as a result of nuclear testing. The overall effect is a recent overcompensation for the dilution by the combustion of fossil fuels.

I-4 NUCLEAR PROPERTIES

The half-life of carbon-14 has been measured by the use of absolute counting rates together with mass spectrometric determinations; the National Bureau of Standards average value is 5745 ± 50 y.[13] The effect of this new value on the Cambridge average[14] would be to raise it from 5730 to 5735 y.[13] The anomalously long half-life of carbon-14 is 10^5 times longer than the expected value of a few weeks,[15] which is based on theoretical calculations.

Carbon-14 is a β-particle emitter that yields nitrogen. The limiting value for the β-ray energy is 0.156_1 Mev,[16] which is equivalent to a range of about 28 mg/cm^2, that is, about 22 cm in air. The radiation is hard enough to permit easy monitoring of samples and apparatus with a thin-window Geiger-Müller (G-M) counter.

A radioactive nuclide decays according to the exponential law

$$N = N_0 e^{-\lambda t}$$

where N is the number of unchanged atoms at time t, N_0 is the number of atoms at time $t = 0$, and λ is the characteristic decay constant for the nuclide. If $t_{1/2}$ is the time interval required for N to change from any particular value to one-half that value, then

$$t_{1/2} = \frac{\ln 2}{\lambda} = \frac{0.693}{\lambda} \qquad (1\text{-}1)$$

The amount of a radioactive substance needed to obtain a millicurie of activity varies with its atomic or molecular weight and with its half-life; the longer the half-life, the greater the quantity needed. The relation

of weight to half-life is illustrated by calculating the weight in grams, W, of one millicurie of isotopically pure barium carbonate-^{14}C, whose molecular weight is 199. From the exponential decay equation (Eq. 1-1) and the half-life value 5745 y,

$$\lambda = \frac{0.693}{(5745)(365)(24)(60)(60)} = 3.83 \times 10^{-12} \text{ sec}^{-1}$$

Since the number of atoms disintegrating is proportional to the number of atoms present, the simple equation for the first-order reaction applies, and

$$-\frac{dN}{dt} = \lambda N = \lambda \frac{W}{199} (6.02 \times 10^{23})$$
$$= 1.16 \times 10^{10} W \text{ sec}^{-1}$$

For one millicurie, $-dN/dt = 3.700 \times 10^7$ disintegrations per sec, then

$$W = \frac{3.70 \times 10^7}{1.16 \times 10^{10}} = 3.19 \times 10^{-3} \text{ g} = 3.19 \text{ mg}$$

If the enrichment in atom percent were 50, then the weight of one millicurie would be slightly less than twice 3.19 mg (actually 6.35 mg), because nonradioactive barium carbonate has a molecular weight of 197.

Table 1-1 lists some of the more important nuclear properties of carbon-14 together with those of the other known

Table 1-1   Carbon nuclides

Nuclide	Isotopic mass ($^{12}C = 12.00000$)	Decay mode	Maximum energy, Mev	Half-life[a]	Natural abundance, %
^{10}C	10.0170_7	β^+	1.9	191 s	—
^{11}C	11.01114_3	β^+	$0.98(\beta^+)$	20.4 m	—
^{12}C	12.00000_0	Stable	—	—	98.89
^{13}C	13.00335_7	Stable	—	—	1.11
^{14}C	14.00324_9	β^-	0.156_1	5.7×10^3 y	0 to 10^{-10}
^{15}C	15.0094_0	β^-, γ	$9.8(\beta^-), 5.3(\gamma)$	2.3 s	—
^{16}C	16.00963	—	—	0.74 s	—

[a] s, second; m, minute; y, year.

Table 1-2   Radionuclides of use in organic chemistry[a]

Nuclide	Decay modes	Maximum energy,[b] Mev	Half-life[c]	Production form	Cost,[d] \$/mc
^3H	β^-	0.0180	12.26 y	$^3H_2$	0.002
^{14}C	β^-	0.156_1	5.7×10^3 y	$BaCO_3$	6.50
^{32}P	β^-	1.70_8	14.3_0 d	H_3PO_4 (HCl soln.)	1.30
^{35}S	β^-	0.167	$87._1$ d	S (benzene soln.)	15.00
^{36}Cl	β^-	0.71_4	3.2×10^5 y	HCl (soln.)	350.00
^{82}Br	γ	1.31	35.9 h	KBr (H_2O soln.)	3.75
^{131}I	β^-, γ	0.608 (β), 0.637 (γ)	8.05 d	NaI (Na_2SO_3 soln.)	0.45

[a] Data from Sullivan.[16]

[b] Maximum β or γ energy that occurs to an extent of 5% or more.

[c] s, second; m, minute; h, hour; d, day; y, year.

[d] There is a minimum order charge of \$25.00 (\$50.00 for ^{32}P).

carbon nuclides. Table 1-2 gives practical information about several radionuclides, including carbon-14, of use in organic chemistry. The prices quoted were furnished by the Isotope Sales Department, Oak Ridge National Laboratory, in January 1966; price changes are frequent. Packaging and handling charges must be paid by the customer and are often much greater than the cost of the isotope. Unless an isotope is needed in moderately large quantities, it may be less expensive to purchase it from one of the suppliers listed in Apx. II.

I-5 ADVANTAGES OF CARBON-14 AS A TRACER

Carbon-14 has many of the properties of an ideal tracer element. Because of its very long half-life, compounds of carbon-14 can be prepared and stored for an indefinite period if the precautions necessary to prevent damage under self-irradiation are taken. Many chemical supply houses keep a large stock of a wide variety of carbon-14-labeled compounds. Consequently, experimenters can obtain most of the carbon-14 compounds they need without recourse to the laborious syn-

theses, beginning with barium carbonate-^{14}C, that were once necessary.

The fact that carbon-14 emits only low-energy beta particles makes tracer studies with this radionuclide at moderate specific activities safe and simple. At specific radioactivities up to about 100 $\mu c/g$, most nonvolatile carbon-14-labeled organic materials can be handled by much the same techniques as those used with unlabeled chemicals. Even at very high levels of specific radioactivity, carbon-14 compounds can be safely handled in glass vessels if reasonable precautions are taken.

The price of carbon-14 in the form of barium carbonate-^{14}C (\$6.50/mc up to 1000 mc) is now low enough so that the cost of the nuclide itself is rarely if ever a barrier to its use in tracer studies, particularly for those who are willing to synthesize the needed carbon-14-labeled compounds. Furthermore, the cost of the counting instruments and accessories necessary to the use of carbon-14 in tracer studies is relatively small in comparison with that of much of the equipment found in most modern chemical laboratories.

Carbon-14 is already in much more general use than carbon-13 for chemical and biological tracer studies. It has been implied[17] that tritium-labeling may take the place of carbon-14-labeling, thereby providing a simple route to isotopically labeled biochemicals. However, this suggestion has little merit. Clearly, both tritium and carbon-14 have their own uses, and neither can supplant the other. For two reasons, carbon-14 is generally a more reliable tracer nuclide for carbon-12 than tritium is for hydrogen. First, many tritium-labeled molecules may undergo exchange reactions that result in a decrease in their tritium content. By comparison, the exchange of a labeled carbon atom for another carbon atom in an organic molecule is indeed a very rare occurrence under ordinary chemical conditions. Second, carbon-14 isotope effects on reaction rates and equilibria are almost negligible in their influence on tracer studies, whereas tritium isotope effects are often two orders of magnitude or more larger than carbon-14 isotope effects. Consequently, the possibility of isotope effects cannot be ignored in drawing conclusions from studies in which tritium is used as a tracer.

Carbon-14 tracer experiments and tritium tracer experiments supplement each other most effectively, and the equipment for counting and handling these two nuclides is very similar. For these reasons, much of the information given in Chap. 11, "Assay of Carbon-14 Compounds," also applies to tritium. It is possible to count both carbon-14 and tritium in a single sample of an organic compound labeled with both these nuclides. This fact makes convenient the determination, by a single experiment, of the disposition of both carbon-14 atoms and tritium atoms during a reaction.

CITED REFERENCES

[1] L. W. Alvarez and R. Cornog, *Phys. Rev.*, **56**, 613 (1939).

[2] S. Ruben and M. D. Kamen, *Phys. Rev.*, **57**, 549 (1940); M. D. Kamen and S. Ruben, *Phys. Rev.*, **58**, 194 (1940).

[3] G. E. Francis, W. Mulligan, and A. Wormall, "Isotopic Tracers," p. 37, The Athlone Press, London, 1954.

[4] M. D. Kamen, *J. Chem. Educ.*, **40**, 234 (1963).

[5] R. Pljewski, *Nukleonika*, **2**, 631 (1957).

[6] Personal communication, E. H. Acree, Oak Ridge National Laboratory.

[7] P. E. Yankwich and W. R. Cornman, Jr., *J. Am. Chem. Soc.*, **78**, 1560 (1956).

[8] W. F. Libby, "Radiocarbon Dating," 2d ed., University of Chicago Press, Chicago, Ill., 1955.

[9] W. B. Loosemore, *At. Nucl. Energy*, **8**, 97 (1957).

[10] H. E. Suess, *Science*, **122**, 415 (1955).

[11] G. J. Fergusson, *Proc. Roy. Soc. (London)*, Ser. A, **243**, 561 (1958).

[12] E. Segre, G. Friedlander, and W. E. Meyerhoff, "Annual Review of Nuclear Science," vol. 8, p. 246, Annual Reviews, Inc., Palo Alto, Calif. (1958).

[13] E. E. Hughes and W. B. Mann, *Intern. J. Appl. Radiation Isotopes*, **15**, 97 (1964).

[14] H. Godwin, *Nature*, **195**, 984 (1962).

[15] W. M. Vissher and R. A. Ferell, *Phys. Rev.*, **107**, 781 (1957).

[16] W. H Sullivan, "Trilinear Chart of Nuclides," United States Government Printing Office, Washington, D.C. (1957), and revisions.

[17] From material presented at the "Symposium on Tritium in Tracer Applications," New York, November 22, 1957; *Nucleonics*, **16**, 62 (1958).

PART
TWO
APPLICATIONS
OF CARBON-14

CHAPTER

2

ISOTOPE DILUTION AND RELATED ANALYTICAL METHODS

2-1 INTRODUCTION

Although the basis for isotope-dilution analysis was laid by Hevesy and Hofer in 1934,[1] Paneth had suggested in his lectures at Cornell University in 1926 that "In certain cases it is found advantageous to mix a certain amount of the radio-element with a sample of the inactive element in order that an otherwise indeterminable fraction of the original quantity may be detected and determined electroscopically."[2] Thus, a method is available for the quantitative determination of organic compounds in mixtures. The method is based on the fact that a compound which is labeled with an isotope is inseparable from its normal analog by the usual isolation procedures. If, for example, acetic-^{14}C acid is added to a mixture of isotopically normal fatty acids (including acetic acid), and then the acetic acid is isolated, this isolated sample will be representative of the mixture of the added acetic-^{14}C acid and the unlabeled acetic acid. If the labeled acetic acid added had a radioactivity of 2 mc/mole and if the reisolated acetic acid had a radioactivity of 1 mc/mole, then it is obvious that the amount of normal acetic acid in the mixture equaled the amount of acetic-^{14}C acid added to it.

The rediscovery of isotope-dilution analysis by Rittenberg and Foster[3] was followed by application of the technique to studies of a wide variety of substances, especially in the broad field of biology, involving the gamut from cockroach population studies to the determination of steroid yields.

Quantitative analysis of the products from an organic reaction is frequently difficult, especially if the products are similar, because quantitative recovery is rarely commensurate with purity. With the isotope-dilution method the requirement of quantitative recovery is removed; all that is needed is a sample sufficiently pure for isotopic assay. The specific radioactivities and the quantities of radioactivity needed to identify products for the determination of yields are very small. The position of labeling is not important provided the position is not reactive under the conditions of analysis. The compounds used for isotope-dilution analysis may therefore be labeled with the most convenient isotope and by the most efficient route. Generally, they may be prepared at relatively low specific radio-activities by conventional laboratory methods without fear of radiation damage or hazard. Material sufficient for hundreds of dilution assays can be obtained from a single prep-aration. In radioactive tracer work of this nature, the concentration of radioactive isotope is so small that no molecular-weight correction is needed.[4]

In addition to the requirement of a non-reactive label, certain other conditions must be met. First, uniform mixing of the labeled and nonlabeled forms must be ensured. This requirement poses no problem in the assay of ordinary reaction mixtures but may be a source of difficulty in work with natural products or polymeric materials. Second, the procedure for isolating the diluted component must yield a pure or assayable product that is free from traces of contaminants of high specific radioactivity. A source of error, contingent upon the second requirement, is the variation of the reactivity of a chemical with the mass involved. Although such isotope effects rarely occur in normal analytical procedures, the ever-increasing sensitivity of analytical methods is likely to cause oc-casional invalidation of the tracer method. Such discrimination between labeled and unlabeled molecules has been reported[5] in the chromatography of carbon-14-labeled amino acids; passage of the acids over an ion-exchange resin resulted in a slight sep-aration of the labeled and unlabeled molecules. Also, an isotope effect has been reported to occur during the countercurrent distribution of arabinose-^{14}C.[5a] There is always the possibility that such isotope effects are only *apparent* isotope effects that result from inadequate purification of labeled compounds or from radiation decomposition (especially

of amino acids) following initial purification, or from both. Differences in the degree of anomerization, racemization, tautomerization, etc., in the labeled compound as compared with the nonlabeled compound used to dilute it can likewise result in apparent—but unreal—isotope effects. The method for determining radioactivity must also be free from errors, such as those caused by gradual changes in self-absorption or degree of quenching.

The general method of isotope dilution is versatile and has achieved considerable popularity; it is likely that the possibilities for use of it in deriving analytical information are by no means exhausted. In the discussion given below of the various specific methods, the use of carbon-14 will receive major emphasis; this is not to say that many other isotopes, such as deuterium, tritium, carbon-13, chlorine-36, sulfur-35, and nitrogen-15, are not also useful.

2-2 NORMAL-ISOTOPE-ADDITION METHOD

If a multicomponent mixture is to be analyzed for a macro amount of an organic compound, it is necessary first to synthesize that com-pound labeled in any unreactive part of the molecule and then to add a known weight, a, of the labeled compound to a known fraction of the mixture. The isotope-dilution equation can be derived from the simple concept *total activity before mixing = total activity after mixing* at the equilibration stage. If the total radioactivity added is A, then the initial specific radioactivity, S_0, of the labeled compound is A/a. After thorough mixing and equilibration of the labeled compound with the fraction of the reaction mixture, a pure sample of the diluted labeled compound is isolated from the equilibrated mixture and is assayed for radioactivity. The specific radioactivity, S, of the diluted component will be equal to $A/(a + x)$. The weight, x, of the organic compound originally present in the known fraction of the mixture is then calculated from the simple relationship

$$\frac{S_0}{S} = \frac{A/a}{A/(a+x)} = \frac{a+x}{a} \qquad (2\text{-}1)$$

whence

$$x = \frac{a(S_0 - S)}{S} \qquad (2\text{-}2)$$

The calculation of the concentration of the compound originally present in the multi-component mixture is then straightforward. The accuracy of the normal isotope-addition method depends on the ratio x/a, errors in radioanalyses having proportionately less effect for proportionately larger values of x/a. Often, however, the addition of a fairly large amount of the labeled compound greatly simplifies the isolation of the desired component from chemically similar species; accuracy must then be weighed against practicality. Radin[5b] provides an excellent discussion of error limitations as they apply to isotope-dilution analysis.

For the equations given above, it is assumed that isolation and radioassay of the component sought have been made without resort to the preparation of derivatives. In many instances it may be desirable to convert the component and its labeled counterpart, after they are equilibrated, to a derivative that can be easily separated from the mixture and purified. For example, one may have a mixture of diphenylmethane, benzophenone, and benzoic acid. If one wishes to determine the amount of benzophenone in this mixture, it is a simple matter to add to the mixture first a weighed amount of ^{14}C-labeled benzophenone and then an excess of 2,4-dinitrophenylhydrazine reagent. The benzophenone 2,4-dinitrophenylhydrazone-^{14}C so prepared is easily separated from the other components and purified for radioanalysis. If more than one compound is present to react with the derivative-forming reagent, this procedure is still satisfactory provided the derivatives formed can be separated from each other in a subsequent step. In this way both methanol and ethyl alcohol have been determined in the same aqueous solution by adding carbon-14-labeled methanol or carbon-14-labeled ethyl alcohol, preparing the derivatives by use of 3,5-dinitrobenzoyl chloride in benzene, and chromatographically separating the derivatives on a column of silica gel.[6] Because the component sought and its derivative do not have the same molecular weight, it becomes necessary to express x and a in *gram moles*; S_0 and S therefore become molar radioactivities. For the small quantities of chemicals and radioactivities involved, it is possible and convenient to avoid large numbers of zeros and decimal points by keeping the data in terms of millimoles and microcuries.

2-3 CARRIER-ADDITION METHOD

A mixture that contains labeled components, each of known specific radioactivity, can be assayed for any one of the components by the addition of a known quantity of a nonradioactive counterpart of that component to act as carrier. This carrier-addition method of determining yields is the reverse of the method described above (and is sometimes referred to as "reverse isotope dilution") in that the radioactive component being determined in the mixture is diluted with a known amount of its nonradioactive counterpart (the carrier). As in the case of the isotope-addition method, it is then necessary to isolate only as much of the very carefully purified diluted component as is needed for radioactivity determinations.

In practice, a known amount, D, of the unlabeled component is added to and allowed to equilibrate with the radioactive mixture that contains its radioactive counterpart of known specific radioactivity, S_0. The diluted compound is isolated and purified; it is then radioassayed to determine its specific radioactivity, S. The amount, x, of the component sought can be determined by means of the following equations, which are similar to

Eqs. 2-1 and 2-2

$$\frac{S_0}{S} = \frac{D + x}{x} \qquad (2\text{-}3)$$

or

$$x = \frac{SD}{S_0 - S} \qquad (2\text{-}4)$$

In the case where D is very large with respect to x, Eq. 2-3 can be simplified to

$$x = \frac{SD}{S_0} \qquad (2\text{-}5)$$

Again it is necessary to bear in mind that, for the purpose of calculation, both the radioactivities and the amounts of compound must be expressed in the molar form if the compound sought was converted to a derivative. Ideally, the derivatization reaction should be free of isotope effect or it should be quantitative.

The carrier-addition method possesses some advantages over the isotope-addition method. First, in a complex multiproduct reaction it is necessary to label and radio-assay only the precursor rather than each of the products. For example, a reaction in which the precursor is labeled may yield five possible products. To determine the yield of each of these, it is necessary to prepare only one labeled compound, the precursor, and to make six radioactivity determinations. If, in the same reaction, the precursor is unlabeled, it would be necessary in the isotope-addition method to prepare the five possible products labeled with carbon-14 and to perform ten radioactivity determinations. Second, the carrier-addition method allows greater dilution than does the isotope-dilution method, the limit of dilution depending only on the level of the radioactivity of the reacting component. For the isotope-addition method, the effect of adding large amounts of the labeled compound is to magnify errors in the radioanalysis, since small differences between large numbers are measured. A striking example that illustrates the value of the carrier-addition method is to

be found in the study by Wolfgang, Anderson, and Dodson[7] of the bond rupture and nonrupture of doubly labeled (carbon-14) ethane. Their problem was to determine the amount of methylamine-^{14}C produced in a reaction for which the maximum amount of ethane was 80 μmole (2.4 mg) and the ratio of product to reactant was of the order of 10^{-5}. The amount of methylamine-^{14}C expected was therefore about 2×10^{-5} mg! Fifteen milligrams of carrier methylamine was added to scavenge the methylamine-^{14}C. The diluted methylamine was then isolated and converted to a suitable derivative, and the derivative was assayed for radioactivity.

Innumerable examples of carrier-addition techniques are given in publications by Benjamin, Collins, Raaen, and others.[8] A particularly lucid example is to be found in a study by Schaeffer and Collins[9] of the dehydration of isomeric 2-phenylcyclohex-anols. A condensation of the authors' description of the procedure follows.

The isolation of the olefins resulting from the dehydration-rearrangement reaction was accomplished by the following method: an accurately measured sample was removed from the volumetric flask and was diluted with a known weight of nonradioactive olefin. The mixture was then subjected to some preliminary purification, and the derivative was prepared. The calculation of the yields of the olefins may best be illustrated by a sample calculation for 1-phenylcyclohexene by means of Eq. 2-3 in the form

$$S(D + x) = S_0 x$$

where

S_0 = molar radioactivity of undiluted 1-phenylcyclohexene-1-^{14}C = molar radioactivity of initial reactant = 1.330 mc/mole

S = measured molar radioactivity of derivative = 0.3401 mc/mole

D = wt. of nonradioactive 1-phenylcyclo-hexene added = 0.6606 g

x = wt. of 1-phenylcyclohexene-1-^{14}C of molar radioactivity 1.330 mc/mole, g

Then

$(0.3401)(0.6606 + x) = 1.330(x)$

$$x = \frac{(0.3401)(0.6606)}{0.990}$$

= 0.227 g of 1-phenylcyclo-
hexene in 10% of the
reaction mixture or 2.27 g
in total reaction mixture

Theoretical yield of olefins = 2.59 g

$$\left(\frac{2.27}{2.59}\right) 100 = 87.7\% \text{ yield of}$$

1-phenylcyclohexene

One disadvantage of the carrier-addition method is the extra care needed to separate the greatly diluted labeled compound from highly radioactive contaminants (see Sec. 8-2). Several hypothetical examples that illustrate the ways in which this type of error might appear have been described by Ropp.[10] The test of purification to constant specific radioactivity must be rigorously applied. To ensure adequate purification, Wolfgang, Anderson, and Dodson[7] employed two solvent pairs, namely, methanol-water, which tends to retain polar impurities in solution, and benzene-hexane, which tends to retain nonpolar impurities in solution.

In dilution analyses of all kinds, prior knowledge of the composition of a mixture is assumed. Chromatographic analysis, especially thin-layer or paper chromatography, will give valuable accessory evidence of the presence of small amounts of unidentified radioactive impurities. Gas-liquid radiochromatography can be used to determine volatile radioactive impurities that might otherwise go undetected.

2-4 DOUBLE-CARRIER-DILUTION METHOD

There are instances in which neither the yield nor the specific radioactivity of a component in a chemical or biological system is known. For the simple carrier-dilution analysis, the measured specific radioactivity, S_1,

of the diluted compound is related to the yield, x, by the equation

$S_1(D_1 + x) = S_0 x$

where D_1 is the weight of diluent added and S_0 is the specific radioactivity of the undiluted compound. If the value of S_0 is not known from reaction precursors and cannot be determined directly, because the compound is resistant to purification, then the unknown values S_0 and x can be determined by performing a second dilution with a different weight, D_2, of carrier.[11,12] In the procedure of Bloch and Anker,[11] two identical aliquots of the mixture that contains the radioactive component to be determined are diluted separately with different amounts of inactive carrier. The two reisolated samples will then have different specific radioactivities, S_1 and S_2. If S_0 is the initial specific radioactivity, if D_1 and D_2 are the amounts of carrier added to the two aliquots, and if x is the amount of the radioactive product sought, then the following equations apply

$S_1(D_1 + x) = S_0 x$ (2-6)

$S_2(D_2 + x) = S_0 x$ (2-7)

These two equations may then be solved simultaneously for x and for S_0 to yield the following solutions

$$x = \frac{S_2 D_2 - S_1 D_1}{S_1 - S_2}$$

$$S_0 = \frac{S_1 S_2 (D_1 - D_2)}{S_1 D_1 - S_2 D_2}$$

Obviously, the accuracy of the double-carrier-dilution method is not as good as that of the simple carrier-dilution or isotope-addition method. The accuracy is improved by making D_1 as different from D_2 as the starting radioactivity will permit.

According to the procedure of Mayor and Collins,[12] a known fraction of the reaction mixture is diluted with an amount, D_1, of the inactive product. The diluted product is isolated, and a part of it is assayed for carbon-14. All the diluted product that remains is then diluted a second time with an amount, D_2, of inactive product. The specific radioactivity, S_2, after the second dilution is then related to S_1, the activity after the first dilution, by the equation

$$S_2(D_1 + D_2 + x - w_1) = S_1(D_1 + x - w_1) \quad (2\text{-}8)$$

where w_1 is the sum of the weights of samples taken for assay after the first dilution. The value for the yield, x, obtained from Eq. 2-8, is then substituted in Eq. 2-6 to obtain the specific radioactivity, S_0, for the undiluted product.

The procedure was validated by application in a synthesis of chrysene-5,6-^{14}C. The product of this reaction resisted purification and was used to test the double-dilution method, since its molar radioactivity was known from that of a precursor. The value 0.586 mc/mole for S_0 is close to the value 0.595 mc/mole determined by radioactivity assay of the reaction precursor. On the assumption that the least accurate data used result from the radioactivity assays, the value will be most accurate when $S_1 \gg S_2$ and $(D_1 - w_1)$ is as small as possible.

2-5 ISOTOPE-DERIVATIVE-DILUTION METHOD

Instances may arise in which it is difficult or impractical to prepare either the labeled precursor or its labeled products. The solution to this problem, as first suggested by Keston, Udenfriend, and Cannan,[13] lies in the conversion of the compound to be determined into a radioactive derivative by reaction with a radioactive reagent. By comparison with ordinary isotope-dilution analysis, the isotope-derivative-dilution method makes possible the determination of each of a whole class of compounds with one radioactive reagent. Often the derivative can be prepared in the pure state more easily than can the compound itself. Two requirements of the method are that the derivative-forming reaction be quantitative, or nearly so, and that throughout the isolation procedure the derivative remain

chemically stable and not subject to isotope exchange. Since excess labeled reagent must be used, it is desirable that the reagent not be labeled in the reacting position if isotope effects are to be avoided. For example, if acetic anhydride were chosen for the derivatization of amines, it would be preferable to prepare it from acetic acid labeled in the methyl group. However, the analyst has no choice when he prepares a reagent such as diazomethane!

Mathematically, the isotope-derivative-dilution method is identical with the carrier-addition method; it has the same advantages and disadvantages. In the isotope-derivative-dilution method, the formation of the radioactive derivative is followed by the addition of a weighed amount of the nonradioactive counterpart of the derivative. The amount of carrier derivative to be added depends on the amount of the unknown substance thought to be present in the mixture and on the techniques used for purification. After the carrier is added, the desired derivative is isolated. As in any preparation of derivatives for assay, the removal of radioactive contaminants is a strict requirement. The analyst may have to effect purification by the use of adsorbents (e.g., charcoal, alumina, or Florisil) and various solvents. It is always advisable to use as little carrier derivative as is practicable. A test of radiochemical purity even more sensitive than purification to constant activity is that suggested by Rapport and Lerner,[14] according to which the molar radioactivity of the derivative in the discarded portion should be equal to that of the purified residue. In the crystallization of benzoic-^{14}C acid from water, for example, there may be some question about the complete removal of other radioactive contaminants even after several recrystallizations. If a sample of the benzoic-^{14}C acid collected on the filter has the same specific radioactivity as that of the benzoic-^{14}C acid isolated from the filtrate, then this agreement is good evidence of the effectiveness of the purification; at its worst, this result indicates that no further purification can be achieved without the use of another solvent. It is also possible, if the contaminant is known, to add some of that contaminant in its nonradioactive form (holdback carrier) at some early stage in the purification so that chemical purity will be more indicative of radiochemical purity. The application of the holdback-carrier technique in the analysis of a mixture of several isotopically labeled compounds has been discussed at some length by DeWitt, Lester, and Ropp.[15] A similar "washing out" procedure is described by Radin[16] for obtaining only one labeled optical isomer at the end of a synthesis in which both enantiomers have been isotopically labeled.

A cursory examination of the literature on the qualitative analysis of organic compounds reveals few reagents that give products in reproducible yields of 95% or better. For most organic acids, the reagent of choice is diazomethane-^{14}C; it gives products in near-quantitative yields, and excess reagent can be removed by distillation at moderate temperatures. The anhydrides and chlorides of carboxylic acids can be converted to the toluides by reaction with p-toluidine-^{14}C labeled in the methyl or a ring position. Acids can be converted to acid chlorides and thence to the toluides. Sorensen[17] suggests the use of chlorine-36-labeled p-chloroaniline as a quantitative reagent for acid chlorides and anhydrides. He also describes a one-step reaction for the quantitative conversion of acids to the p-chloroanilides by treatment with a mixture of p-chlorophenyl-phosphazo-p-chloroanilide

$$Cl—C_6H_4—N=P—NH—C_6H_4—Cl$$

and p-chloroaniline. There is no reason for not substituting carbon-14 in the phosphazo compound, the use of which was first suggested by Grimmel, Guenther, and Morgan.[18] The reaction does not appear to be very general; it is not applicable to α-amino acids, and dicarboxylic acids cannot usually

be determined because of the formation of half-anilides or imides. Other references relative to the development of the method are given by Sorensen.[17]

Kibrick and Skupp[19] suggest that the p-bromo-α-haloacetophenones be used as reagents in the estimation of fatty acids by isotope-derivative dilution. The radioactive reagent (labeled with carbon-14 in the carbonyl group) was used to determine the yield of phenacyl ester obtained. In the case of the myristate, the yield averaged 60%. Once yields are established for decanoic, lauric, palmitic, stearic, oleic, linoleic, and linolenic acids, it is then presumed that a correction factor may be applied to determine these and other fatty acids by isotope-derivative-dilution analysis. Kibrick and Skupp[19] discuss the problems involved in the chromatographic separation of phenacyl esters.

Derivatives of hydroxy and amino compounds can be prepared by means of radioactive acid anhydrides or chlorides. The determination of submicrogram quantities of steroid alcohols with carbon-14-labeled acetic anhydride is described in detail by Hollander and Vinecour;[20] they discuss a procedure for the recovery of excess acetic anhydride when large numbers of analyses are contemplated. By a similar approach, Avivi and collaborators[21] used carbon-14-labeled acetic anhydride to estimate the number of hydroxyl groups in a small amount of a new hormone. They also estimated hydrocortisone by isotope-dilution analysis in which both carbon-14-labeled carrier and tritium-labeled acetic anhydride were used.

A variation of the isotope-derivative-dilution method requires the addition of a small amount of labeled derivative to the mixture that contains the unknown. The mixture is then treated with unlabeled reagent to form the derivative. The necessary separations are made to isolate the derivative; it is assayed for radioactivity, and the value is compared with the radioactivity of the originally added derivative. A good example of this technique is to be found in the method of Donia, Ott, and Drake[22] for the determination of stigmasterol in soy sterols. The procedure is:

1 Preparation of stigmasteryl acetate-^{14}C.

2 Determination of the molar radioactivity of stigmasteryl acetate-^{14}C.

3 Addition of stigmasteryl acetate-^{14}C to the sample of soy sterol.

4 Conversion of the entire mixture to the acetate by means of acetic anhydride.

5 Preparation and isolation of the sparingly soluble stigmasteryl acetate-^{14}C tetrabromide.

6 Determination of molar radioactivity of the diluted derivative.

As in the usual isotope-dilution procedure, the addition of amounts of labeled compound relatively small compared with the amount of compound sought would result in the diminution of error in the isotopic analysis. For this reason, Donia, Ott, and Drake restricted the amount of stigmasteryl acetate-^{14}C to 0.1 to 0.2 of the stigmasterol estimated to be present. It is wise in any dilution experiment that requires the addition of an isotopically labeled compound to restrict the amount of material added to an amount roughly equal to that sought.

Sorensen[23] has determined hydroxy and amino compounds by converting them to esters and amides with 3-chloroanisoyl chloride-^{36}Cl. The derivatives were then analyzed by means of an ordinary carrier-dilution method. The method of assay was applied to such typical hydroxy and amino compounds as phenol, pyrocatechol, methanol, ethylene glycol, aniline, and ethylenediamine. Because chlorine-36 is expensive and is of limited general application in organic chemical studies, it appears that this and other reagents would be more useful if prepared with a carbon-14 label.

The choice of reagents for aldehydes and ketones is more limited. Probably the most ideally suited reagent is 2,4-dinitrophenylhydrazine; its reactions with most aldehydes and many ketones are all nearly quantitative. The preparation of this reagent labeled with carbon-14 would be time-consuming and difficult—the labeled reagent is available from commercial suppliers of labeled compounds. In the absence of a suitable derivative, the carbonyl compound may be reduced with lithium aluminum hydride, and then it can be converted to a derivative with radioactive anhydrides or chlorides. Such a procedure can be used when it is difficult to isolate the pure compound in a normal dilution analysis or for compounds not readily converted to ordinary derivatives.[24]

Isotope-dilution analysis for both cyclic and linear dienes is facilitated[15,25,26] by the use of the carbon-14-labeled dienophile, maleic anhydride-1-^{14}C. The yields obtained with maleic anhydride in the Diels-Alder reaction are often very good; with cyclopentadiene the yield is 97%.[25]

2-6 DETERMINATIONS BY RELATED ANALYTICAL METHODS

2-6a OPTICAL ISOMERS

When a study involves optical isomers, the quantity of each isomer can be determined by either the isotope-addition or the carrier-addition method. If the compound that contains the optical isomers is radioactive, either the *d*- or *l*-form of its nonradioactive counterpart is added. A derivative of the diluted enantiomer is then formed by reaction with a second optically active compound. The diastereomeric derivative is isolated, purified, and assayed for radioactivity. The percentage of either *d*- or *l*-form present can then be determined by calculations analogous to those described above.

By a method similar to this one, Graff, Rittenberg, and Foster,[27] as long ago as 1940, made possible the determination of D- as well as L-amino acids in protein hydrolysates.

When isotopically labeled DL-glutamic acid is added to a solution of normal glutamic acid, the added isomers are diluted by their isomeric nonradioactive counterparts in the solution. To separate the (+)- or (−)-enantiomer from the optically impure glutamic acid, advantage is taken of the fact that the solubility of the hydrochloride of the DL-component is twice that of the D- or L-enantiomer. If carbon-14 is used (Graff, Rittenberg, and Foster used nitrogen-15) and if the simplest case is chosen as an illustration, that is, the case in which one fraction consists of pure DL-glutamic acid and the other of pure D(−)- or pure L(+)-glutamic acid, then the amounts of the isomers originally present in the mixture are, respectively,

$$x_{\mathrm{D}} = \frac{A}{2}\left(\frac{S_0}{S_{\mathrm{D}}} - 1\right)$$

and

$$x_{\mathrm{L}} = \frac{A}{2}\left(\frac{S_0}{S_{\mathrm{L}}} - 1\right)$$

where x_{D} is the amount of D-isomer and x_{L} is the amount of L-isomer, either of which may be present in the mixture to which A grams of labeled racemate has been added. The terms S_0, S_{D}, and S_{L} are the molar radioactivities of the added racemate, the isolated D isomer, and the L isomer, respectively. If the L isomer is in excess, then it it possible to calculate the molar radioactivity of the D isomer from the equation

$$S_{\mathrm{DL}} = \frac{S_{\mathrm{D}}}{2} + \frac{S_{\mathrm{L}}}{2}$$

where S_{DL} is the molar radioactivity of the reisolated racemate. The value for S_{D} obtained from this equation may be substituted for yield, x_{D}, in the earlier equation to give

$$x_{\mathrm{D}} = \frac{A}{2}\left(\frac{S_0}{2S_{\mathrm{DL}} - S_{\mathrm{L}}} - 1\right)$$

When there is no D-component present, the molar radioactivity of the isolated racemate will be half that of the added DL-component plus half that of the isolated L-component. The method for analyzing a complex mixture in which the D-enantiomer predominates or is the sole component is analogous. It may not be possible to obtain optically pure compounds, but with a knowledge, obtained from polarimeter readings, of the fractions present the same information can be obtained as in the more fortunate cases in which optically pure components could be isolated. The paper by Graff, Rittenberg, and Foster[27] should be consulted for details of the method.

A further simplification is available through the use of the washing-out technique described earlier. Thus, if one has a radioactive mixture of DL-glutamic acid and D-glutamic acid, it is often possible to discard the labeled D-isomer by several recrystallizations of the racemic mixture in the presence of large amounts of unlabeled D-isomer. After several such dilutions, the remaining DL-glutamic acid will have the label in the L-isomer only. The molar radioactivity of the L-isomer must then be twice that obtained by means of a radioassay of the DL-compound.

To ensure enantiomeric purity, it is often necessary to resolve a racemic compound by way of two or more diastereomeric derivatives. If the enantiomer recovered from each such path produces the same optical rotation, then it is reasonably certain that a limiting value has been obtained for the pure enantiomer. However, in practice it is often difficult to prepare one satisfactory diastereomeric salt, much less two or three! A technique for the nonpolarimetric determination of optical purity is described by Berson and Ben-Efraim.[28] A sample of weight B that is known to contain racemate and excess of one enantiomer only is mixed with A grams of racemic isotopic carrier having a known specific radioactivity, S_0. If B contains R grams of racemate and E grams of enantiomer, then $B = R + E$, and the percent optical purity equals $100E/B$. If it is assumed that the excess enantiomer is the (+)-enantiomer, then the specific radioactivities of the (+)-enantiomer, S_+, and of the (−)-enantiomer, S_-, are given by the equations

$$S_+ = \frac{AS_0/2}{E + (A + R)/2}$$

$$S_- = \frac{AS_0/2}{(A + R)/2}$$

As pointed out by Graff, Rittenberg, and Foster,[27] the racemic material in the mixture is a chemical racemate but not an isotopic racemate. The enantiomers, though present in equal amounts, will have different specific radioactivities. For this reason, the specific radioactivity of the racemate is given by a weighted average of the radioactivities of the enantiomers, the weighting factor being $\frac{1}{2}$.

$$S_\pm = \frac{S_+}{2} + \frac{S_-}{2} = \frac{1}{2}\left(\frac{AS_0/2}{E + (A + R)/2}\right)$$
$$+ \frac{1}{2}\left(\frac{AS_0/2}{(A + R)/2}\right)$$

By substituting $R = B - E$ in the above equation and solving for E, Berson and Ben-Efraim obtained the equation

$$E = [(A + B)^2 - (S_0/S_\pm)(A^2 + AB)]^{1/2}$$

With the information already given, it is necessary only to isolate the pure racemate and to assay it for radioactivity. Adequate purification of the racemate is indicated by zero optical rotation and a specific radioactivity that is not changed by further recrystallizations.

2-6b RADIOEQUIVALENT WEIGHT

In the preparation of a series of several radioactive compounds, the molar radioactivity of each compound should be identical with that of every other one of the series if there has been no dilution and if there has been no change in the number of labeled carbon positions. If the molar radioactivity of a single member of the series shows

considerable deviation from that of its precursors, then its purity is questionable.

If a compound of unknown structure is derived from a series of reactions that incorporate only one labeled position into the molecule, then a determination of its specific radioactivity can be used to calculate its molecular weight. Often the number · of labeled positions incorporated into a new molecule will not be known; in this case a determination of its specific radioactivity can be used to calculate its radioequivalent weight.[29] Thus, the *radioequivalent weight* of a product is defined as the weight of it in grams that possesses the radioactivity of one gram molecular weight of that product's precursor. If the number of labeled positions is unchanged from precursor to unknown, then obviously the molecular weight and the equivalent weight are identical. If compound formation occurs by dimerization or by incorporation of two or more labeled positions, the radioequivalent weight thus calculated, together with a crude determination of molecular weight, prvoides valuable evidence for the identification of an unknown compound.

2-6c NUMBER OF CARBON ATOMS IN A VOLATILE ORGANIC COMPOUND

A more absolute method for determining the number of carbon atoms is described[30] that permits comparison of the radioactivities when a carbon-14-labeled compound is counted in the form of vapor in an internally filled counter and, after combustion, as carbon dioxide. The method is limited to those compounds that have vapor pressures of at least 4 mm of mercury at the operating temperature. Thus, if a sample of ethyl acetate-^{14}C introduced into the counting tube at 15 mm pressure shows a radioactivity of 1000 counts/min, then combustion of the ethyl acetate-^{14}C, followed by isolation of the pure carbon-14 dioxide and introduction of it into the counting tube at 15 mm of mercury pressure will, if both gases behave ideally, give a radioactivity count of 250 counts/min. To minimize the effect of variations in ion-pair yield, a constant amount of ethyl alcohol vapor was introduced (14 mm partial pressure) into the counting chamber for each determination of carbon-14 dioxide. Likewise, a nearly constant amount of carrier carbon dioxide (about 46 mm partial pressure) was introduced into the chamber along with each organic compound that was counted. For compounds having high vapor pressure, the agreement between the total carbon atoms calculated and the total carbon atoms found by means of this method was very good.

2-6d MOLECULAR WEIGHT OF A POLYMER

Reactive end groups in synthetic polymers or in naturally occurring macro molecules can be determined accurately by means of radioactive reagents. Isbell[31] proposes the use of cyanide-^{14}C to react with the reducing aldehyde group. If the molar radioactivity of the cyanide-^{14}C is known, then the average molecular weight of a polysaccharide, for example, can be determined by radioassay of the cyanohydrin-^{14}C. A method has also been suggested[32] for carbon-14- or tritium-labeling of polysaccharides by micromethylation.

Rates and efficiencies of the polymerization of styrene monomer in benzene solution have been determined by use of azodiisobutyronitrile-^{14}C as initiator.[33] The efficiency was calculated from the amount of azodiisobutyronitrile-^{14}C incorporated in the polymer and also from the amount of side products formed from radicals not participating in the polymerization.

2-6e PURITY

A method mentioned earlier for assuring purity consists in equilibrating the non-radioactive component with its equivalent in labeled form and then radioassaying the homogeneous mixture. If, after further purification or conversion to derivatives, the molar radioactivity remains unchanged, this fact may often be accepted as evidence of the purity of the compound.

The addition of a carbon-14-labeled steroid to a purified tritium-labeled steroid[34] of the same species with or without the addition of unlabeled carrier has been used to evaluate purity. If the ratio of ^{3}H/^{14}C remains constant after a multistage purification, it is unlikely that either labeled or unlabeled impurities are present. The use of double labeling to reveal inhomogeneities in otherwise apparently homogeneous chromatograms is discussed in Sec. 12-5.

Carbon-14 can serve as a valuable auxiliary tracer for deuterium or tritium. Very often in tracer work involving hydrogen, the possibility of labilization of carbon-hydrogen bonds is of major concern. If a compound known to contain a certain percentage of deuterium is introduced in a reaction, it is expected that the unreacted fraction, as well as the derived product, should carry the same percentage of deuterium in the labeled position as does the starting material. If it does not, either unlabeled carrier has been produced in the reaction or labilization has occurred. To validate the use of deuterium as a tracer, the labeled reactant can be given a second label with carbon-14. Then, if the ratio ^{2}H/^{14}C is the same in both pure product and recovered reactant, the conclusion may be drawn that labilization of deuterium does not occur. Such a double-labeling procedure was used by Bloch and Rittenberg[35] to show that a metabolic acetylation reaction does not involve loss of carbon-bound deuterium. Isotopic acetate precursor was labeled both by carbon-bound deuterium in the methyl group and by carbon-13 in the carboxyl group. The ratio of deuterium to carbon-13 in the acetyl group of the acetylamino acid produced in the biological process was identical with that in the reactant.

2-6f EFFICIENCY OF A DISTILLATION COLUMN

There are many nonessential analytical uses for carbon-14 that facilitate research by simplifying problems of isolation, identification, or analysis. The technique of using labeled components in the determination of distillation column efficiencies[36] should continue to be of great value.

2-6g SOLUBILITY OF A SPARINGLY SOLUBLE COMPOUND

An application to the determination of physical properties is the determination of solubilities of sparingly soluble compounds, such as insecticides[37] and ion-exchange resins.

Eng, Meyer, and Bingham[38] use isotope dilution together with mass spectrometry to determine carbon in sodium metal. The amount of carbon present in a sample of reasonable size is so small (50 to 150 μg) that it is not practicable to use carbon-14 as a diluent; amorphous carbon enriched with carbon-13 is used instead. Carbon from the sample, as well as the added carbon-13, is oxidized to carbon dioxide, which is then analyzed mass spectrometrically for carbon-13. Knowledge of the approximate amount of carbon in the sample is needed if optimum sensitivity is to be attained. The carbon already present in the oxidizing reagent and in the diluent blank must be determined, and the necessary corrections must be made. However, purification and isolation of a derivative are not required—a distinct advantage over the use of carbon-14.

2-6h DISTRIBUTION COEFFICIENT

The determination of partition coefficients[39,40] is greatly facilitated by the use of labeled solutes, especially in cases where the solubility in one phase may differ by several orders of magnitude from the solubility in another. The use of labeled solutes also provides a sensitive method for determining the variation of distribution coefficients with great dilution, for example, the distribution coefficient of acetic acid in water was found to rise rapidly with dilution in the vicinity of 0.02 to 0.03 M.

Selectivity coefficients of ion-exchange resins have been described. One paper[41] reports a study of the exchange of carbon-14-labeled tetramethylammonium ion with sodium-24 ion in cross-linked polystyrene sulfonates. The use of labeled reagents made possible the determination of exchange capacity and exchange rate, as well as the determination of the equilibrium-selectivity coefficients.

2-6i ACTIVE HYDROGEN

Active hydrogen can be determined by reaction of the unknown with carbon-14-labeled methyl Grignard reagent, whereupon the labeled methane can be counted in an ion chamber. Naturally, all the shortcomings inherent in the conventional Zerewitinoff determination also apply here.

The water content of gases has been determined[42] by passing the gas over carbon-14-labeled calcium carbide to release acetylene-^{14}C.

2-6j TOTAL FUNCTIONAL GROUPS

Analysis for functional groups in a reaction mixture can be accomplished by means of one of the methods described for derivative-dilution analyses and the end-group analysis of polymers. Thus, total carboxyl group concentration can be determined by adding excess diazomethane-^{14}C, allowing sufficient time for the reaction to go to completion, distilling off the excess reagent, and then determining the radioactivity of a known fraction of the residue.

2-6k RATE OF A VERY SLOW REACTION

An obvious but uncommon use of carbon-14-labeled compounds is indicated for determining vapor pressures, equilibrium constants, etc. It is the ideal solution to the question of whether the rate of a reaction is indeterminably slow or has a very small equilibrium constant. Conway and Libby[43] have used carbon-14-labeling and low-level-counting techniques to determine reaction half-lives in the range from 0.1 to 10,000 y for the thermal decarboxylation of alanine over a range of temperatures. Their method also made possible the observation that oxygen reacts with alanine to release carboxyl carbon at a rate that corresponds to a half-life of about 20,000 y at room temperature. A serious limitation of the use of carbon-14 for the determination is that radiation-induced reactions could be confused with the reaction intended for measurement. This type of side reaction was found to be controlling below 100° and showed a half-life of about 100,000 y at room temperature for alanine having a radioactivity of 3 mc/mole. It was thought that radiation damage would not be objectionable in most applications. (For approximate calculation of the half-life radiation damage in such reactions, see Chap. 6.) Since the amount of radiation decomposition occurring is proportional to the level of radioactivity, it is obvious that low-level-counting techniques must be applied to systems having very slow reaction rates.

Rate studies are not necessarily limited to very slow reactions. If reactants are suitably labeled, they may combine in such a way as to yield a labeled gaseous product. Such reactions can be followed by use of continuous-flow-counting radiochemical techniques. Hyne and Wolfgang[44] describe a method for studying the kinetics of the hydrolysis of dimethyl-t-butylsulfonium iodide. Nitrogen was used as a carrier to sweep the hydrolysis product, dimethyl sulfide, through a proportional gas-flow counter. In the absence of an isotope effect, the count rate is directly proportional to the rate of appearance of product.

2-61 BIOLOGICAL PATHWAYS

Although it is important to know where a tracer element is fixed and how much of it is present in a given compound or system at any one time, it is even more important to know how the location and amount of a tracer vary with time. The majority of organic compounds of metabolic interest are ultimately degraded to carbon dioxide and urea. In metabolism studies, the technique of determining the amount and specific activity of carbon-14 dioxide from a suitably labeled substrate is known as radiorespirometry. The minimum equipment consists of an ionization chamber–vibrating-reed electrometer (in the "steady-deflection" or "high-resistance-leak" mode) (see Sec. 11-5c) and an infrared analyzer to determine total carbon dioxide.[45] Similar, but more sophisticated, equipment has been described;[46] it provides data in a form that permits direct processing in a high-speed computer. The adaptation of liquid-scintillation counters to flowing liquids and gases should be especially useful. Experimentation by use of such equipment is easy to perform and often provides important information about the occurrence and nature of a pathway in a particular biological system. However, the interpretation of results can be exceedingly difficult.

The applications of tracer techniques to biochemistry, especially to intermediary metabolism, is outside the scope of this book. Several comprehensive reviews already exist.[47–52] The use of carbon-14-labeled compounds in medical diagnosis has been relatively limited. Bayly[53] discusses the potentialities of isotopes (especially carbon-14) in medicine.

CITED REFERENCES

[1] G. Hevesy and E. Hofer, *Nature*, **134,** 879 (1934).
[2] F. Paneth, "Radio Elements as Indicators," p. 39, McGraw-Hill Book Company, Inc., New York, 1928.

[3] D. Rittenberg and G. L. Foster, *J. Biol. Chem.*, **133**, 737 (1940).

[4] H. Gest, M. D. Kamen, and J. M. Reiner, *Arch. Biochem.*, **12**, 273 (1947).

[5] K. A. Piez and H. Eagle, *J. Am. Chem. Soc.*, **78**, 5284 (1956).

[5a] L. M. Marshall and R. E. Cook, *J. Am. Chem. Soc.*, **84**, 2647 (1962).

[5b] N. S. Radin, *Nucleonics*, **1**(2), 48 (1947).

[6] V. Ya. Efremov, M. B. Neiman, and V. N. Panfilov, *Tr. Komis. po Analit. Khim., Akad. Nauk SSSR, Inst. Geokhim. i Analit. Khim.*, **9**, 361 (1958).

[7] R. L. Wolfgang, R. C. Anderson, and R. W. Dodson, *J. Chem. Phys.*, **24**, 16 (1956).

[8] See, for example, C. J. Collins and N. S. Bowman, *J. Am. Chem. Soc.*, **81**, 3614 (1959) and prior publications in this series.

[9] H. J. Schaeffer and C. J. Collins, *J. Am. Chem. Soc.*, **78**, 124 (1956).

[10] G. A. Ropp, *J. Chem. Educ.*, **34**, 60 (1957).

[11] K. Bloch and H. S. Anker, *Science*, **107**, 228 (1948).

[12] R. H. Mayor and C. J. Collins, *J. Am. Chem. Soc.*, **73**, 471 (1951).

[13] A. S. Keston, S. Udenfriend, and R. K. Cannan, *J. Am. Chem. Soc.*, **68**, 1390 (1946).

[14] M. M. Rapport and B. Lerner, *J. Biol. Chem.*, **232**, 63 (1958).

[15] E. J. DeWitt, C. T. Lester, and G. A. Ropp, *J. Am. Chem. Soc.*, **78**, 2101 (1956).

[16] N. S. Radin, *Nucleonics*, **2**(2), 33 (1948).

[17] P. Sorensen, *Anal. Chem.*, **28**, 1318 (1956).

[18] H. W. Grimmel, A. Guenther, and J. F. Morgan, *J. Am. Chem. Soc.*, **68**, 539 (1946).

[19] A. C. Kibrick and S. J. Skupp, *Anal. Chem.*, **31**, 2057 (1959).

[20] V. P. Hollander and J. Vinecour, *Anal. Chem.*, **30**, 1429 (1958).

[21] P. Avivi, S. A. Simpson, J. F. Tait, and J. K. Whitehead, *Proc. Radioisotope Conf., 2nd, Oxford, Engl.*, vol. I, "Med. and Physiol. Applications," pp. 313–324, Butterworth & Co. Ltd., London (1954).

[22] R. A. Donia, A. C. Ott, and N. Drake, *Anal. Chem.*, **29**, 464 (1957).

[23] P. Sorensen, *Anal. Chem.*, **27**, 388 (1955).

[24] V. F. Raaen and C. J. Collins, *J. Am. Chem. Soc.*, **80**, 1409 (1958).

[25] J. A. Berson and W. M. Jones, *J. Am. Chem. Soc.*, **78**, 6045 (1956).

[26] J. A. Berson, R. D. Reynolds, and W. M. Jones, *J. Am. Chem. Soc.*, **78**, 6049 (1956).

[27] S. Graff, D. Rittenberg, and G. L. Foster, *J. Biol. Chem.*, **133**, 745 (1940).

[28] J. A. Berson and D. A. Ben-Efraim, *J. Am. Chem. Soc.*, **81**, 4083(1959).

[29] V. F. Raaen and J. F. Eastham, *J. Am. Chem. Soc.*, **82**, 1349 (1960).

[30] I. A. Korshunov and N. F. Novotorov, *Zh. Obshch. Khim.*, **28**, 47 (1958).

[31] H. S. Isbell, *Science*, **113**, 532 (1951).

[32] H. S. Isbell, H. L. Frush, B. H. Bruckner, S. N. Kowlcabany, and S. Wampler, *Anal. Chem.*, **29**, 1523 (1957).

[33] J. C. Bevington, *Trans. Faraday Soc.*, **51**, 1392 (1955).

[34] R. E. Peterson, *Proc. Symp. Advan. Tracer Applications of Tritium*, p. 16, New England Nuclear Corp., Atomic Associates, Inc., and Packard Instrument Company, Inc., New York, 1958.

[35] K. Bloch and D. Rittenberg, *J. Biol. Chem.*, **159**, 45 (1945).

[36] H. E. Hughes and J. O. Maloney, *Chem. Eng. Progr.*, **48**, 192 (1952).

[37] F. H. Babers, *J. Am. Chem. Soc.*, **77**, 4666 (1955).

[38] K. Y. Eng, R. A. Meyer, and C. D. Bingham, *Anal. Chem.*, **36**, 1832 (1964).

[39] D. S. Goodman, *J. Am. Chem. Soc.*, **80**, 3887 (1958).

[40] Ya D. Zel'venskiĭ and V. A. Shalygin, *Zh. Fiz. Khim.*, **31**, 1501 (1957); *Chem. Abstr.*, **52**, 5938a (1958).

[41] A. Schwarz and G. E. Boyd, *J. Chem. Phys.*, **69**, 4268 (1965).

[42] J. L. Kalinsky, Jefferson, and T. A. Werkenthin, N. Y. Naval Shipyard Report USN-BY-1609.

[43] D. Conway and W. F. Libby, *J. Am. Chem. Soc.*, **80**, 1077 (1958).

[44] J. B. Hyne and R. Wolfgang, *J. Phys. Chem.*, **64**, 699 (1960).

[45] F. J. Dominques, K. J. Gildner, R. R. Baldwin, and J. R. Lowry, *Intern. J. Appl. Radiation Isotopes*, **7**, 77 (1959).

[46] G. V. LeRoy, G. T. Okita, E. C. Tocus, and D. Charleston, *Intern. J. Appl. Radiation Isotopes*, **7**, 273 (1960).

[47] S. Aronoff, "Techniques of Radiobiochemistry," Iowa State College Press, Ames, 1956.

[48] E. Broda, "Radioactive Isotopes in Biochemistry," English translation by P. Oesper, Elsevier Publishing Company, New York, 1960.

[49] G. E. Francis, W. Mulligan, and A. Wormall, "Isotopic Tracers," 2d ed., The Athlone Press, London, 1959.
[50] M. D. Kamen, "Isotopic Tracers in Biology," 3d ed., Academic Press Inc., New York, 1957.
[51] C. W. Sheppard, "Basic Principles of the Tracer Method," John Wiley and Sons, Inc., New York, 1962.
[52] C. H. Wang and D. L. Willis, "Radioactive Tracer Technique in Biology," Prentice-Hall International, Englewood Cliffs, N.J., and London, 1965.
[53] R. J. Bayly, *Nucleonics*, **24**(6), 46 (1966).

PROBLEMS

2-1. A 1.68-g (10-mmole) sample of diphenylmethane-^{14}C that had a molar radioactivity of 200 mc/mole was oxidized to carbonyl-labeled benzophenone (which, under the conditions of the reaction, may be partially oxidized further to carboxyl-labeled benzoic acid). To determine the yield of benzophenone, a $\frac{1}{100}$ aliquot of the reaction mixture was then added to and equilibrated with 1.82 g of unlabeled benzophenone. The 2,4-dinitrophenylhydrazone derivative was prepared, purified, and then assayed for radioactivity; the molar radioactivity was 1.00 mc/mole. (*a*) Calculate the percent yield of benzophenone. (*b*) Suppose that all the benzoic acid had not been removed from the benzophenone derivative and that the 10-mg sample taken for analysis contained 0.001 mg of benzoic-^{14}C acid. Calculate the percent error introduced by the high-level contaminant.

2-2. It was of interest to determine the amount of phenylacetonitrile formed by the reaction of triphenylacetonitrile with benzylmagnesium chloride. Immediately after the hydrolysis of the Grignard-reaction mixture, the ether extract was diluted to a known volume; a $\frac{1}{10}$ aliquot was taken for isotope-dilution analysis. On the basis of a 100% yield, this aliquot should have contained 10 mmoles of phenylacetonitrile. Five millimoles of phenylacetonitrile-^{14}C (0.586 g, 8.30 mc/mole) was added to the aliquot. The diluted phenylacetonitrile was isolated by fractional distillation and was then hydrolyzed to phenylacetic acid in order to obtain a compound that could be more readily purified. The pure phenylacetic acid was found to have a radioactivity of 5.02 mc/mole. Calculate the total yield of phenylacetonitrile in grams.

2-3. A solution contained a pure DL-amino acid and the corresponding pure D-amino acid. A 5-mmole sample of labeled racemate that had a molar radioactivity of 2.62 mc/mole was added to the solution. It was possible to isolate a small amount of the pure D-amino acid as its hydrochloride derivative. The optically active hydrochloride was found to have a molar radioactivity of 1.03 mc/mole. Calculate the number of millimoles of pure D-amino acid present in the original mixture.

2-4. The product of a series of reactions starting with carbon-14-labeled 2,6-dimethylbenzyl chloride (5.084 mc/mole) was a solid having the empirical formula $C_{10}H_{11}N$. Analysis of the product for radioactivity gave a specific activity of 0.0351 μc/mg. A crude determination of the molecular weight gave the value 320. Calculate (*a*) the radioequivalent weight and (*b*) the molecular weight of the product.

2-5. The average molecular weight of a linear polyester can be determined by end-group assay for either hydroxyl or carboxyl groups. In one such determination, a slight excess of a solution of diazomethane-^{14}C that had a radioactivity of 100 mc/mole was added in order to methylate all carboxyl groups. The excess diazomethane-^{14}C and solvent were removed by vacuum distillation. The carbon-14-labeled methylated polymer was then assayed for radioactivity; it contained 0.00430 μc of carbon-14 per milligram. Calculate the average molecular weight of the polymer.

2-6. A chemical reaction resulted in the formation of a known labeled compound whose yield and molar radioactivity were unknown. Two $\frac{1}{10}$ aliquots (*A* and *B*) of the compound were taken. To aliquot *A* was added 1 mmole of pure inactive carrier, and to aliquot *B* was added 6 mmoles of pure inactive carrier. After the additions of the carrier, it was possible to isolate the pure carrier-diluted compound from each aliquot. That from *A* was found to have a radioactivity of 2.28 mc/mole; that from *B*, 0.823 mc/mole. Calculate (*a*) the yield of the labeled compound in millimoles and (*b*) its molar radioactivity.

CHAPTER

3

LOCATION OF CARBON ATOMS

3-1 INTRODUCTION

An outstanding use of carbon-14 is to locate carbon atoms. This application is separate and distinct from the uses of this radionuclide in isotope dilution, isotope exchange, and isotope-effect studies. Carbon-13 has also been used for this purpose, but carbon-14 is now used far more extensively because of its greater practicality.

3-2 SOURCE OF A CARBON ATOM REMOVED FROM A MOLECULE

The results of studies[1,2] of the decarbonylation of benzoylformic acid show how the location of carbon atoms by simple methods can define the path of an organic reaction. Benzoylformic-1-^{14}C acid produces carbon-^{14}C monoxide having the same molar radioactivity, after the reaction has gone to completion, as the benzoylformic-1-^{14}C acid has initially.[1] The benzoic acid formed at the same time is not labeled.

$$\text{C}_6\text{H}_5-\overset{\text{O}}{\underset{\|}{\text{C}}}-^{14}\text{CO}_2\text{H} \xrightarrow{\text{H}_2\text{SO}_4} \text{C}_6\text{H}_5-\text{CO}_2\text{H} + {}^{14}\text{CO}$$

Quantitative decarbonylation of benzoylformic-2-^{14}C acid produces carbon monoxide having no carbon-14 activity.[2] The molar radioactivity of the benzoic-α-^{14}C acid formed is the same as that of the benzoylformic-2-^{14}C acid used initially.

$$\text{C}_6\text{H}_5-{}^{14}\overset{\text{O}}{\underset{\|}{\text{C}}}-\text{CO}_2\text{H} \xrightarrow{\text{H}_2\text{SO}_4} \text{C}_6\text{H}_5-{}^{14}\text{CO}_2\text{H} + \text{CO}$$

These results considered together prove unequivocally that the carboxyl group is the source of essentially all the carbon of the carbon monoxide formed in the decarbonylation of benzoylformic acid. The qualifying adverb "essentially" is necessary, because in this case, as in all quantitative tracer experiments, the conclusions drawn are limited by the accuracy of the determinations of carbon-14 or other isotopes. The carbon-14 determinations were sufficiently accurate to permit the conclusion that not more than a few tenths of one percent of the carbon monoxide can originate in the carbonyl group under the reaction conditions used. Probably no other type of simple experiments could give this information, which is obviously essential to an understanding of the mechanism of the decarbonylation reaction.

3-3 SOURCE OF A CARBON ATOM INTRODUCED INTO A MOLECULE

In some instances the source of a carbon atom introduced into a molecule during a chemical reaction can be demonstrated conveniently and positively by use of carbon-14. The action of alkaline aqueous formaldehyde on 9-formylfluorene to produce 9-fluorenylcarbinol and formic acid was demonstrated[3] to take place by displacement of the aldehyde group of 9-formylfluorene rather than by reduction of that aldehyde group and oxidation of the formaldehyde to formic acid. Carbon-14-labeled 9-formylfluorene and unlabeled formaldehyde were used. (See below.) The products 9-fluorenylcarbinol and formic-^{14}C acid were separated, purified, and radioassayed. Proof that all the carbon-14 was in the formic acid and none in the 9-fluorenylcarbinol established that the carbon of the hydroxymethyl group originates in the aldehyde group of the 9-formylfluorene. The nonoccurrence of carbon exchange between formaldehyde and sodium formate was also demonstrated. A reaction mechanism involving the intermediate shown just below in brackets is possible.

In the synthesis of Demerol

a hydrogen atom attached to a nitrogen atom of the piperidine nucleus is replaced by a methyl group; a mixture of formic acid and formaldehyde is used. The results of experiments[4] proved conclusively that the formaldehyde—not the formic acid—supplies the carbon of the N-methyl group. When only the formaldehyde is labeled with carbon-14, the Demerol is radioactive and has the same molar radioactivity as the formaldehyde. When only the formic acid is labeled, the Demerol is nonradioactive, and the carbon-14 appears only in the form of carbon dioxide, a by-product.

3-4 DETECTION OF SYMMETRICAL COMPOUNDS AND INTERMEDIATES

3-4a KETENE DIMERS

A clever application of carbon-14 was its use by Roberts and co-workers to study the structure of ketene dimers.[5] Of the several structures proposed for a ketene dimer, the following three have unequivalent carbon-to-oxygen bonding:

$CH_3COCH{=}C{=}O$
Acetylketene

$CH_3{-}C{=}CH$
| |
$O{-}C{=}O$
β-Crotonolactone

$CH_2{=}C{-}CH_2$
| |
$O{-}C{=}O$
Vinylaceto-β-lactone

Three other proposed structures are those of the symmetrical dimer (I), the monoenol (II), and the dienol (III)

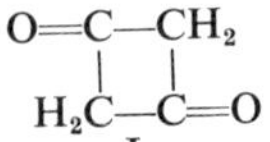

$$O=C-CH_2$$
$$H_2C-C=O$$
I

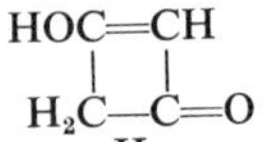

$$HOC=CH$$
$$H_2C-C=O$$
II

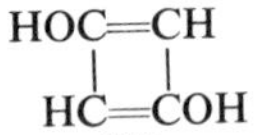

$$HOC=CH$$
$$HC=COH$$
III

Since ketonization of II and also of III would produce I, these three structures can be produced by symmetrical dimerization of the olefinic bonds in two molecules of ketene.

To elucidate the correct structures or structure of the aldoketene dimers in general, a mixed dimer was formed from methyl-ketene-1-^{14}C and hexylketene.[5] A symmetrical structure of the mixed dimer might be

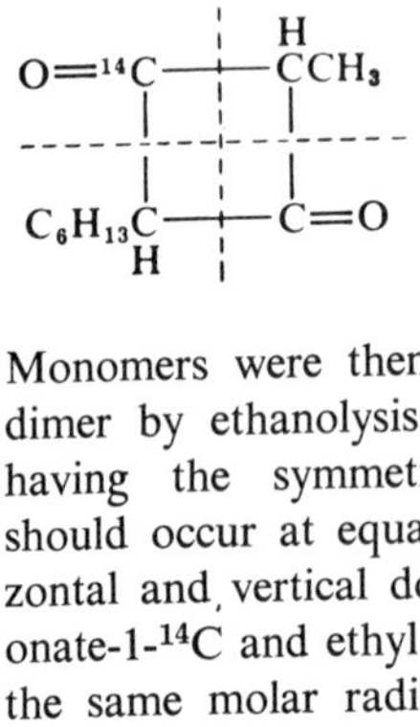

$$O=^{14}C \quad H$$
$$\phantom{O=^{14}C} CCH_3$$
$$C_6H_{13}C \quad C=O$$
$$\phantom{C_6H_{13}C} H$$

Monomers were then regenerated from the dimer by ethanolysis. Cleavage of a dimer having the symmetrical structure shown should occur at equal rates along the horizontal and vertical dotted lines; ethyl propionate-1-^{14}C and ethyl octanoate-1-^{14}C having the same molar radioactivity should result. Since radioassays showed that 98.5% of the carbon-14 of the dimer was in the ethyl propionate-1-^{14}C and only 1.5% in the ethyl octanoate-1-^{14}C, it was apparent that no appreciable part of the dimer has the symmetrical structure. The results of carbon-14 experiments and of studies of the physical properties of the dimer indicate that the dimer probably is made up of two unsymmetrical

structures in the percentages shown below, only one mode of cleavage occurring during the ethanolysis of each structure, as indicated by the dotted lines.

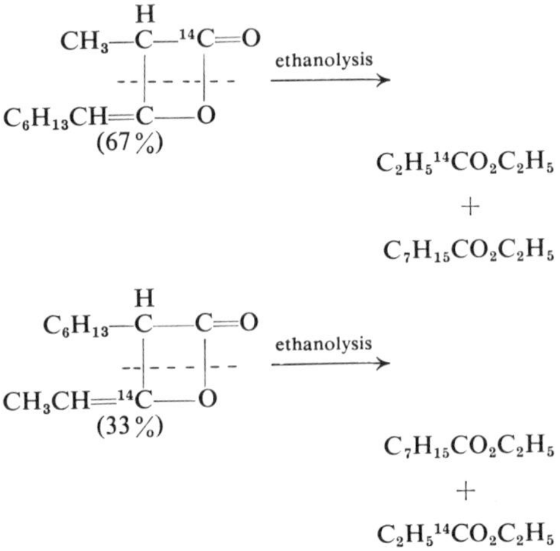

$$CH_3-C-^{14}C=O$$
$$H$$
$$C_6H_{13}CH=C-O$$
(67%)

ethanolysis →

$$C_2H_5{}^{14}CO_2C_2H_5$$
+
$$C_7H_{15}CO_2C_2H_5$$

$$C_6H_{13}-C-C=O$$
$$\phantom{C_6H_{13}-}H$$
$$CH_3CH=^{14}C-O$$
(33%)

ethanolysis →

$$C_7H_{15}CO_2C_2H_5$$
+
$$C_2H_5{}^{14}CO_2C_2H_5$$

3-4b FAVORSKI REARRANGEMENT

Symmetrical organic-reaction intermediates at concentrations too low to permit their isolation can sometimes be detected by use of carbon-14, as research of Loftfield[6] has shown. The Favorski rearrangement is the reaction of an α-haloketone in alkaline solution to produce an α,α-disubstituted ester, as in the example

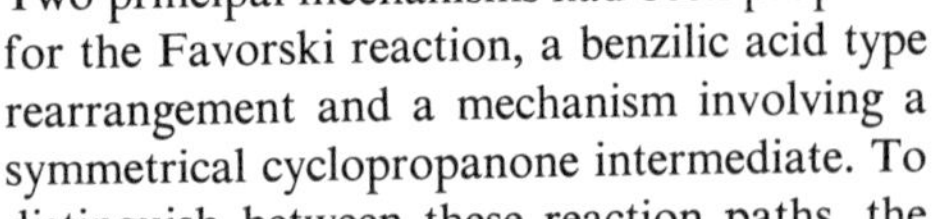

$$\text{(cyclohexanone ring)} =O \quad -Cl + NaOC_2H_5 \longrightarrow$$

$$\text{(cyclopentane ring)} -CO_2C_2H_5 + NaCl$$

Two principal mechanisms had been proposed for the Favorski reaction, a benzilic acid type rearrangement and a mechanism involving a symmetrical cyclopropanone intermediate. To distinguish between these reaction paths, the distribution of the carbon-14 label in the product was determined when 2-chlorocyclo-hexanone-1,2-$^{14}C_2$ was the reactant. The dispositions of carbon-14 that should accompany the two mechanisms are indicated in the equations below; the numbers in parentheses are percentages of the total carbon-14 content.

These equations show that if the mechanism is of the nature of a benzilic acid rearrangement, the product should have 50% of the original carbon-14 activity in the carboxyl group and 50% in position 1 of the cyclopentane ring. The cyclopropanone mechanism, by contrast, should lead to the appearance of 50% of the original carbon-14 activity in the carboxyl group, 25% in position 1 of the cyclopentane ring, and 25% in position 2. Since, after degradation of the carbon-14-labeled ethylcyclopentane carboxylate, the

latter distribution of carbon-14 activity was found, it was concluded that the Favorski rearrangement proceeds via a cyclopropanone intermediate.

3-4c SIMPLE STATISTICS OF DOUBLE-LABELING

In the foregoing discussion of the Favorski reaction, several structural formulas, each having two carbon-14 atoms in the same molecule, are shown in equations. These doubly labeled structures are used merely as convenient ways to illustrate the location of labeled positions; they should not be taken to mean that doubly labeled molecules occur in sufficiently high concentration to play an important

Benzilic Acid Type Mechanism

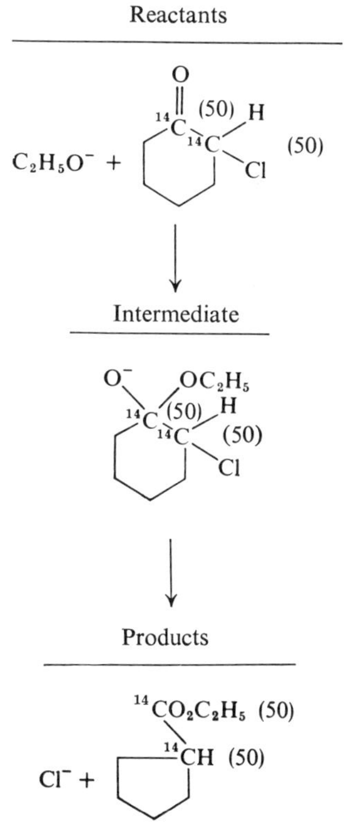

Reactants

Intermediate

Products

Cyclopropanone-intermediate Mechanism

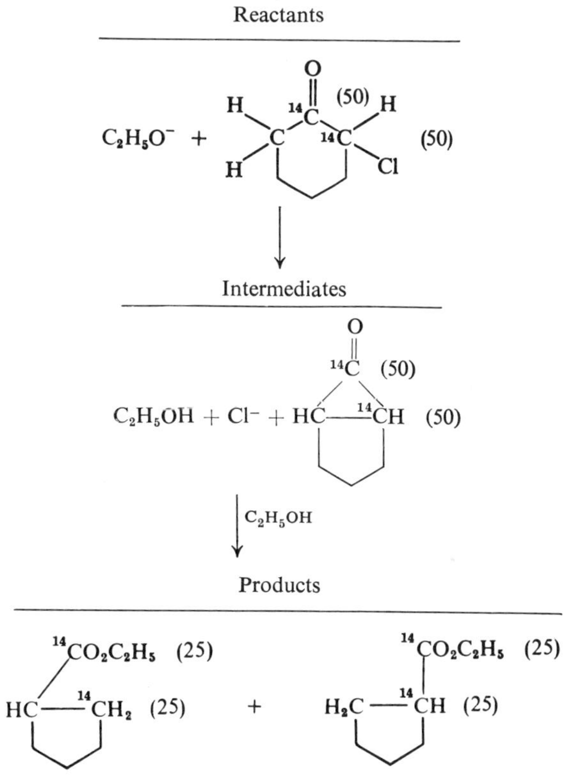

Reactants

Intermediates

Products

part in the reactions. For example, the structure

$$^{14}CO_2C_2H_5 \quad (50)$$

$$\underset{}{\overset{14}{C}H} \quad (50)$$

simply indicates that the following two species

$$^{14}CO_2C_2H_5 \qquad CO_2C_2H_5$$

$$\underset{}{CH} \quad \text{and} \quad \underset{}{\overset{14}{C}H}$$

are present in equal amounts. At the tracer level of carbon-14 at which the isotopic studies described in this section were made, only a negligibly small fraction of the carbon-14 atoms occurs in doubly labeled molecules. If f_1 is the fraction of molecules that contains carbon-14 in one position and f_2 is the fraction of molecules that contains carbon-14 in another position, then, according to simple statistics, the fraction of doubly labeled molecules is f_1f_2.

If carbon-14 is introduced into a symmetrical organic molecule such as dimethyl phthalate, the label can appear in each of two equivalent positions as shown in the equation

$$\underset{}{\overset{-CO_2H}{\underset{-CO_2H}{}}} + 2\ ^{14}CH_3OH \xrightarrow{H^+}$$

$$\underset{}{\overset{-CO_2{}^{14}CH_3}{\underset{-CO_2CH_3}{}}}$$

Each of the two methyl groups may contain the label. If the fraction of methanol molecules that contain carbon-14 is f, the fraction of dimethyl phthalate molecules that contain carbon-14 will be $2f$ when no isotope effect occurs in the ester formation (see Chap. 5). The fraction of doubly labeled dimethyl phthalate molecules will then be f^2. The fraction of carbon-14-containing molecules that are doubly labeled will be $f^2/2f$ or $0.5f$. Carbon-14 is often convenient to use at the

1-mc/mole level in tracer experiments. If the methanol-^{14}C referred to above contains carbon-14 at the 1-mc/mole level, the dimethyl phthalate will contain about 0.003% singly labeled molecules and about $2 \times 10^{-8}\%$ doubly labeled molecules. At this level, about $7 \times 10^{-4}\%$ of the labeled ester molecules will be doubly labeled.

These calculations based on simple statistics are only approximately correct, but they are adequate provided the carbon is at tracer level. It is quite clear that with carbon-14 at tracer level, the concentration of doubly labeled molecules is sufficiently small to be considered negligible for the purpose of most tracer studies. However, doubly labeled molecules can be significant in carbon-13 studies, because carbon-13 is not used below the natural 1% level. For some purposes carbon-13 is used well above the 50% level where 25% or more of the molecules may be doubly labeled (see Sec. 8-2).

3-5 STUDIES OF MOLECULAR REARRANGEMENTS

The term *molecular rearrangement* usually means an intramolecular process in which some of the atoms within a molecule change their positions relative to each other to produce a new structure. Compared with the total number of organic reactions, the number of molecular rearrangements is small. Molecular rearrangements appear to occur more frequently in complex biochemical processes and in high-energy systems, such as in the mass spectrometer, than they do under conditions ordinarily used in the organic chemistry laboratory. Nevertheless, it is recognized that a dozen or so molecular rearrangements do occur under mild conditions. Carbon-14 is an indispensable tool for the study of a number of these rearrangements. Generally, the study of a carbon-skeleton rearrangement consists in (a) the synthesis of the starting material that has carbon-14 in a specific position, (b) the rearrangement proper, and (c) the degradation of the product of the rearrangement in order to determine the new location or locations of carbon-14 atoms.

Carbon-13-enriched compounds can also be used in the study of rearrangements that involve movement of carbon atoms or carbon-containing groups. However, the precise determination of carbon-13 usually requires that a sample for introduction into a mass spectrometer be in the form of carbon dioxide or some other relatively simple compound of carbon. In many cases, this requirement is a serious obstacle to the use of carbon-13. As a rule it is far simpler to use carbon-14, because carbon-14 can be determined easily in almost any organic compound by relatively simple standard procedures, which are described in Chap. 11.

Tritium has also been suggested as an alternative nuclide for tracing the rearrangement path of a group, such as the methyl group, that contains both carbon and hydrogen atoms and that remains intact during a rearrangement. However, the high degree of mobility and the consequent ease of exchange of hydrogen and tritium atoms in organic compounds render this application of tritium a questionable one in the absence of subsidiary experiments to prove its validity (Sec. 1-5). Probably this use of tritium is justifiable in a biochemical study of a reaction of molecules which, because of their complexity, could be labeled with tritium but not with carbon-14. The validity of the conclusions reached in such an experiment would, however, rest upon the evidence for the absence of tritium-hydrogen exchange.

Unlike tritium, carbon-14 is a completely reliable tracer nuclide in the sense that, under ordinary chemical conditions, carbon atoms attached to other carbon atoms almost never undergo isotope-exchange reactions (see Sec. 4-1). Carbon atoms in the skeletons of organic compounds rarely change their relative locations except in the few well-understood and predictable molecular re-

arrangements mentioned above. Consequently, carefully planned and properly executed carbon-14 experiments designed to locate carbon atoms can lead to conclusions that are as firmly based as conclusions drawn from the most exacting chemical experiments of other types.

3-5a BENZILIC ACID REARRANGEMENT

The study of the Favorski reaction described above illustrates one type of study of a rearrangement in which carbon-14 was used to good advantage. The benzilic acid rearrangement has been studied with carbon-14 to equally good advantage but in a somewhat different way. The overall reaction in the case of the rearrangement of a *para*-substituted benzil is

$$(3\text{-}1)$$

The mechanism is thought to involve two principal steps, the reversible addition of hydroxyl ions to one of the carbonyl carbon atoms and the subsequent rate-controlling migration of the aryl group attached to that carbon atom. In the case of benzil itself, this mechanism may be shown as follows

In the case of the rearrangement of a *para*-substituted benzil represented by Eq. 3-1, one and the same product is formed regardless of whether the phenyl group migrates or the *para*-substituted phenyl group migrates. The decision as to which carbonyl group is attacked by the hydroxyl ion and which group moves can, however, be easily made by labeling one of the carbonyl groups with carbon-14 and determining the location of the carbon-14 in the *para*-substituted benzilic acid produced. Let us take as an example a case in which the carbon atom adjacent to the phenyl group is labeled in a *para*-substituted benzil and all the carbon-14 in the substituted benzilic acid formed is found in the *para*-substituted benzophenone produced when the acid is degraded by oxidation. It is clear, as the equations below show, that the hydroxyl ion attacks the unlabeled carbon atom and that the substituted phenyl group migrates.

R. If R is an electron-releasing group, migration of the phenyl group is favored; if R is electron-withdrawing, migration of the ring-substituted aryl group is favored. For example, the *p*-chlorophenyl group migrates 2.05 times as frequently as the phenyl group.[7] Such results are taken as evidence that the controlling factor is the relative stability of the two intermediate negative ions that are formed as a result of attack by the hydroxyl ions on either of the two carbonyl groups.[7,8]

Data from the study[7] of the rearrangement of 1-(*p*-chlorophenyl)-2-phenyl-1,2-ethanedione-2-^{14}C illustrate the simple calculations involved in this use of carbon-14 to locate carbon atoms. As is shown in Table 3-1, the original substituted benzil and the product, *p*-chlorobenzilic acid, have essentially the same molar radioactivities. The two degradation products of the *p*-chlorobenzilic acid, that is, *p*-chlorobenzophenone

In this hypothetical case, the molar radioactivities of the substituted benzil, the substituted benzilic acid, and the substituted benzophenone are all equal, and the carbon dioxide produced by the oxidation is not radioactive. Studies of the rearrangement of carbon-14-labeled substituted benzils[7,8] have shown that both the substituted and unsubstituted phenyl groups can move and that the relative amount of migration of each depends on the nature of the *para*-substituent,

and carbon dioxide, have still different molar radioactivities; however, the sum of their molar radioactivities is about equal to that of the *p*-chlorobenzilic acid or to that of the substituted benzil used initially. The percent of the reaction that proceeds by migration of the *p*-chlorophenyl group is approximately

$$100\left(\frac{0.835}{1.25}\right) = 67\%$$

The remainder of the reaction, 33%, proceeds

Table 3-1 Results of the study[7] of the rearrangement of 1-(p-chlorophenyl)-2-phenyl-1,2-ethanedione-2-^{14}C

^{14}C-labeled compound	Molar radioactivity, mc/mole
Reactant	
p-Substituted benzil	1.23
Products	
p-Chlorobenzilic acid	1.25
p-Chlorobenzophenone	0.835
Carbon dioxide	0.395

by phenyl migration. The ratio of the two migration rates is therefore

$$\frac{(\text{rate})_{p\text{-chlorophenyl}}}{(\text{rate})_{phenyl}} = \frac{67}{33} = 2.03$$

if the carbon-14 isotope effect (Chap. 5) is ignored.

In such experiments as the one just described, the synthesis of the specifically labeled starting material that is required may be tedious, but synthesis difficulties are rarely insurmountable. The carrying out of the reaction with the carbon-14-labeled compound is usually simple and straightforward. Techniques for radioassaying carbon-14 compounds have been developed thoroughly and are described in Chap. 11. Degradation, however, may prove to be most difficult. Sometimes the lack of a suitable method of degradation may render a particular experiment impossible. Hence, one of the first considerations in the planning of an experiment designed to locate carbon atoms should be that of providing a reliable degradation method. Chapter 10 discusses degradative methods.

3-5b   TEST FOR INTERMOLECULARITY

Knowledge as to whether a rearrangement proceeds by an *intramolecular* mechanism, an *intermolecular* mechanism, or both is essential to an understanding of the mechanism of the rearrangement. An isotopic test was applied to establish that no measurable part of a benzidine rearrangement is *intermolecular*.[9] The rearrangement of 2-methyl-^{14}C-hydrazobenzene,

and the rearrangement of 2,2′-dimethylhydrazobenzene,

which proceeds only three times faster, were carried out simultaneously in a mixture. Isolation of the 3,3′-dimethylbenzidine from the mixture and demonstration that it contained essentially no carbon-14 established definitely the *intramolecular* character of the benzidine rearrangement. An *intermolecular* process would have led to the formation of some carbon-14-labeled 3,3′-dimethylbenzidine. In a hypothetical intermolecular process, nitrogen-nitrogen bond cleavage within each of the two substituted hydrazobenzenes of a mixture of the two would lead to three fragments, I, II, and III

No account is taken of details of the mechanism, such as protonation of the nitrogen atoms. An *intermolecular* mechanism would lead to some product formed by combination of fragments I and III. Fragments I and III are chemically equivalent when small carbon-14 isotope effects are neglected.

3-6 BIOCHEMICAL APPLICATIONS

Most uses of carbon-14 in organic reactions to locate carbon atoms have been relative to biochemistry and closely related sciences. In the *Chemical Abstracts* 1947–56 *Decennial Index*, some 2700 entries appear under the subject-index heading, "Carbon, isotope of mass 14 as indicator." Of these, fewer than about 500 represent chemical and physical studies not directly connected with biochemical investigations. The more recent *Chemical Abstracts* indicate the same predominance of biochemical applications of carbon-14. In biochemical systems, many complex and little-understood processes and rearrangements of carbon skeletons occur that result in the redistribution of carbon atoms. Some of these changes cannot be detected except by the use of labeled carbon atoms. It is not surprising that ever since carbon-13 and carbon-14 became available they have been considered by biochemists to be indispensable tools.

The great usefulness of carbon-14 as a tracer to locate carbon atoms in biochemical systems is well illustrated by the extensive and highly significant investigations of photosynthesis by Calvin and co-workers.[10,11,12] The principles involved in such studies are much the same as those discussed earlier in this chapter and in other chapters of this volume. However, the extreme complexity of living systems frequently precludes the isolation of pure labeled compounds. This complexity often prevents attainment of the exactness in interpretation of experimental results that is sought and frequently achieved in tracer studies in physical and physical-organic chemistry.

The development of procedures for counting carbon-14 at levels near its natural abundance presents the possibility that carbon-14 compounds, introduced into the human body as tracers, can be used to study physiological processes. If such *in vivo* experimentation with carbon-14 in humans is practiced widely, invaluable information will undoubtedly result (see Sec. 7-2).

3-7 OTHER APPLICATIONS

A variety of practical uses of carbon-14 to locate carbon atoms are reported. For example, carbon-14-labeled methanol was useful in determining distillation data for the ternary system, water–methanol–ethyl alcohol.[13] Emmett and co-workers[14,15] used carbon-14 to advantage in their study of the commercially important Fischer-Tropsch process. Carbon-14-labeled organic compounds are convenient for use in quantitative studies of adsorption on activated carbon.[16] An autoradiographic method exists for detecting fingerprints by use of carbon-14 compounds.[17] Further applications of carbon-14 in the location of carbon atoms are discussed in Part IV of this volume.

CITED REFERENCES

[1] K. Banholzer and H. Schmid, *Helv. Chim. Acta*, **39**, 548 (1956).

[2] G. A. Ropp, *J. Am. Chem. Soc.*, **82**, 842 (1960).

[3] J. G. Burr, Jr., *J. Am. Chem. Soc.*, **73**, 823 (1951).

[4] W. Tarpey, H. Hauptmann, B. M. Tolbert, and H. Rapoport, *J. Am. Chem. Soc.*, **72**, 5126 (1950).

[5] J. D. Roberts, R. Armstrong, R. F. Trimble, Jr., and M. Burg, *J. Am. Chem. Soc.*, **71**, 843 (1949).

[6] R. B. Loftfield, *J. Am. Chem. Soc.*, **73**, 4707 (1951).

[7] M. T. Clark, E. C. Hendley, and O. K. Neville, *J. Am. Chem. Soc.*, **77**, 3280 (1955).

[8] J. D. Roberts, D. R. Smith, and C. C. Lee, *J. Am. Chem. Soc.*, **73**, 618 (1951).

⁹ D. H. Smith, J. R. Schwartz, and G. W. Wheland, *J. Am. Chem. Soc.*, **74**, 2282 (1952).

¹⁰ A. A. Benson, M. Calvin, V. A. Haas, S. Aronoff, A. G. Hall, J. A. Bassham, and J. W. Weigl, 'Carbon-14 in 'Photosynthesis', in J. Franck and W. E. Loomis, Eds., "Photosynthesis in Plants," p. 381, Iowa State College Press, Ames, Iowa, 1949.

¹¹ H. Gaffron, A. H. Brown, C. S. French, R. Livingston, E. I. Rabinowitch, B. L. Strehler, and N. E. Tolbert, Eds., "Gatlinburg Conference on Research in Photosynthesis," Gatlinburg, Tenn., Oct. 25–29, 1955, Interscience Publishers, New York, 1957.

¹² M. Calvin, *Science*, **135**, 879 (1962).

¹³ H. E. Hughes and J. O. Maloney, *Chem. Eng. Progr.*, **48**, 192 (1952).

¹⁴ P. H. Emmett and J. T. Kummer, *World Petrol. Congr., Proc.*, *3rd, The Hague, 1951*, sec. IV, 15–24; *Chem. Abstr.*, **49**, 4969i (1955).

¹⁵ R. J. Kokes, W. K. Hall, and P. H. Emmett, *J. Am. Chem. Soc.*, **79**, 2989 (1957).

¹⁶ A. S. Goldin, R. C. Kroner, A. A. Rosen, and M. B. Ettinger, paper 232 (U.S.A.). *Proc. Intern. Conf. Peaceful Uses At. Energy, 1st, Geneva, 1955*, **15**, 47 (1956).

¹⁷ T. Takeuchi, M. Sakaguchi, Y. Nakamoto, and S. Kadokura, paper 1342 (Japan). *Proc. Intern. Conf. Peaceful Uses At. Energy, 2nd, Geneva, 1958*, **20**, 166 (1958).

GENERAL REFERENCES

(a) M. Calvin, C. Heidelberger, J. C. Reid, B. M. Tolbert, and P. F. Yankwich, "Isotopic Carbon," John Wiley & Sons, Inc., New York, 1949.

(b) H. R. V. Arnstein and R. Bentley, *Nucleonics*, 6(6), 11 (1950).

(c) H. R. V. Arnstein and R. Bentley, *Quart. Rev. (London)*, **4**, 172 (1950).

(d) G. A. Ropp and O. K. Neville, *Nucleonics*, 9(2), 22 (1951).

(e) J. A. Bassham, A. A. Benson, and M. Calvin, *J. Chem. Educ.*, **30**, 274 (1953).

(f) D. A. Semenow and J. D. Roberts, *J. Chem. Educ.*, **33**, 1 (1956).

(g) V. N. Kondratyev, *Proc. Intern. Conf. Peaceful Uses At. Energy, 1st, Geneva, 1955*, **15**, 3 (1956).

(h) S. Aronoff, "Techniques of Radiobiochemistry," Iowa State College Press, Ames, Iowa, 1956.

(i) J. M. Gamboa, *Energia Nucl. (Madrid)*, **1**(3), 53 (1957).

(j) J. G. Burr, Jr., "Tracer Applications for the Study of Organic Reactions," Interscience Publishers, Inc., New York, 1957.

(k) M. D. Kamen, "Isotopic Tracers in Biology," Academic Press Inc., New York, 1957.

(l) A. Murray, III, and D. L. Williams, "Organic Syntheses with Isotopes," vol. I, Interscience Publishers, Inc., New York, 1958.

(m) H. Schmid, *Chimia (Aarau)*, **14**, 248 (1960).

(n) G. A. Ropp, *J. Am. Chem. Soc.*, **82**, 842 (1960).

(o) J. R. Catch, "Carbon-14 Compounds," Butterworth Inc., Washington, D.C., 1961.

(p) C. W. Sheppard, "Basic Principles of the Tracer Method," John Wiley & Sons, Inc., New York, 1962.

(q) G. M. Harris, *Rev. Pure Appl. Chem.*, **2**, 57 (1952).

(r) E. Havinga, *Chem. Weekblad*, **53**, 665 (1957); *Chem. Abstr.*, **52**, 15413e (1958).

(s) A. I. Brodskiĭ, "Isotopenchemie," chap. 8, Akademie-Verlag, Berlin, 1961.

(t) C. H. Wang and D. L. Willis, "Radiotracer Methodology in Biological Science," Prentice-Hall, Inc., Englewood Cliffs, N.J., 1964.

PROBLEMS

3-1. Acetone-1-¹⁴C that contained carbon-14 in the concentration 10 μc/mmole was condensed in sulfuric acid to form mesitylene-¹⁴C. The mesitylene-¹⁴C was strongly oxidized under such conditions that the trimesic-¹⁴C acid first formed was decarboxylated to yield benzoic-¹⁴C acid. Assuming no isotope effects, calculate (a) the molar radioactivity of the benzoic-¹⁴C acid, (b) the molar radioactivity of the carbon-14 dioxide released, and (c) the total radioactivity in the aromatic ring per gram of benzoic-¹⁴C acid.

3-2. Assuming that for carbon-14 $t_{1/2} = 5745$ y, what is the molar radioactivity of a sample of carbon-14 dioxide in which 1% of the carbon atoms are carbon-14 atoms?

3-3. Using the data given in Problems 3-1 and 3-2, estimate the percent of labeled molecules that are doubly labeled in the intermediate, trimesic-¹⁴C acid, referred to in Problem 3-1.

3-4. A sample of ethylbenzene-2-¹⁴C having a molar radioactivity of 6.25 mc was treated with a Friedel-Crafts catalyst for a prolonged period.

After the catalyst was quenched with water, the organic layer was extracted, dried, and fractionated. Recovered ethylbenzene-^{14}C was oxidized with nitric acid to p-nitrobenzoic-^{14}C acid that contained only 0.01 $\mu c/g$. A sample of the diethylbenzene-^{14}C fraction was oxidized to a mixture of phthalic-^{14}C acids from which pure terephthalic-^{14}C acid that contained 1.58 $\mu c/g$ was isolated. Calculate (a) the percent transfer of the *beta* carbon atom to the *alpha* position that had occurred in rearrangement of the ethylbenzene, and (b) the percent of the *alpha* carbon atoms of the ethyl groups of the diethylbenzene-^{14}C that originated in the *beta* position of ethylbenzene. (c) Suggest a tentative mechanism to account for the results calculated in (a) and (b).

3-5. Describe an additional tracer experiment that might help to determine whether the tentative mechanism suggested in Problem 3-4(c) may be correct.

CHAPTER

4

ISOTOPE
EXCHANGE

4-1a DEFINITION

An isotope-exchange reaction has been defined as "a chemical reaction in which the atoms of a given element interchange between two or more chemical forms of the element."[1] This definition would be more correctly applied to an "atom-exchange reaction," since the word "isotope" does not appear in the definition. Many such atom exchanges occur in chemical systems. For example, a number of alkyl iodides readily exchange their iodine atoms with iodide ions under the proper chemical conditions

$$RI + I^- \rightleftharpoons RI + I^-$$

Since the reactants and products are identical, the reaction cannot be detected without the use of isotopically labeled iodine atoms. However, if either the iodine of the alkyl iodide or that of the iodide ions is isotopically labeled, the exchange reaction is detectable and then can be described properly as an isotope-exchange reaction.

When either the iodine of the alkyl iodide or the iodine of the iodide ions initially contains some radioactive iodine atoms, the progress of the exchange reaction can be measured conveniently both by the appearance of radioactivity in the other reactant and by diminution of the radioactivity of the reactant that originally contained all the radioactivity. The equation for this isotope-exchange reaction is written either

$$RI^* + I^- \rightleftharpoons RI + I^{-*}$$

or

$$RI + I^{-*} \rightleftharpoons RI^* + I^-$$

depending on which reactant originally contained the radioactivity. If any equilibrium iodine isotope effect is ignored (see Sec. 5-6i), the iodine of the alkyl iodide and the iodine of the iodide ions will contain the same percentage of radioactive iodine atoms after sufficient time has elapsed to permit isotopic equilibrium to be established. Prior to the attainment of isotope equilibrium, measurement of the rate of change of the radioactivity of the alkyl iodide and/or of the iodide ions indicates the rate of the exchange reaction. The results of such isotopic studies of the rates of reactions in systems that are at chemical equilibrium are often highly valuable for elucidating reaction mechanisms.

4-1b   FUNCTION OF CARBON-14 IN ISOTOPE-EXCHANGE STUDIES

In the study of isotope-exchange reactions, the main function of carbon-14 is to indicate the exchange of carbon-containing groups, not of individual carbon atoms. A simple example is the ready exchange of a carbon-14-labeled ethyl group of ethyl alcohol with the ethyl group of many ethyl esters in the presence of acids or bases that catalyze the reaction. In the following equation, this exchange is illustrated with ethyl acetate

$$CH_3CO_2CH_2CH_3 + {}^{14}CH_3CH_2OH \rightleftharpoons$$
$$CH_3CO_2CH_2{}^{14}CH_3 + CH_3CH_2OH$$

Exchange of ethyl groups between the alcohol and the ester occurs, but there is no cleavage of bonds to the labeled carbon atom, for the ethyl groups remain intact and act as units in the exchange reaction.

Not many organic chemical reactions are known in which carbon-to-carbon bonds form and break reversibly. This is a fortunate condition in the sense that carbon skeletons of organic compounds can almost always be labeled with isotopic carbon at a specific position or positions without fear of removal or relocation of the label by an unpredicted carbon isotope-exchange reaction. A few exceptions to this rule are referred to in Sec. 4-3, but such exceptions are rare and occur only under special conditions. As has been mentioned elsewhere in this volume, deuterium and tritium labels are, in contrast with carbon-isotope labels, lost relatively easily by exchange from organic molecules.

Accordingly, carbon-13 and carbon-14 will always provide valuable means of tracing carbon atoms or carbon-containing groups in chemical reactions. The same degree of reliability can never be matched by deuterium or tritium, as has sometimes been proposed.

4-1c   ISOTOPE EXCHANGE AS A METHOD OF SYNTHESIZING LABELED COMPOUNDS

Exchange reactions of carbon-containing groups occasionally provide a rapid and convenient means for the synthesis of organic compounds labeled with carbon-13 or carbon-14 (see also Chap. 8). For example, acetic anhydride has been shown[2] to exchange rapidly with sodium acetate-2-^{14}C

$$\begin{array}{c} CH_3-C{=}O \\ \diagdown \\ O + {}^{14}CH_3CO_2Na \rightleftharpoons \\ \diagup \\ CH_3-C{=}O \end{array}$$

$$\begin{array}{c} {}^{14}CH_3-C{=}O \\ \diagdown \\ O + CH_3CO_2Na \\ \diagup \\ CH_3-C{=}O \end{array}$$

Acetic-2-^{14}C anhydride of tracer level, therefore, can be prepared very conveniently and quickly by distillation from a mixture that contains a very small weight of high-specific-activity sodium acetate-2-^{14}C and a relatively large weight of unlabeled pure acetic anhydride; the mole ratio of acetic anhydride to sodium acetate-2-^{14}C before distillation can be of the order of 100:1. As a result of this high mole ratio, about 99.5% of the carbon-14 activity has been transferred to the anhydride when isotopic equilibrium is reached. Therefore, a radiochemical yield (i.e., the percentage of the radioactivity used originally that is recovered in the form of the labeled compound desired) of about 99.5% is obtained by continuing the distillation to dryness and leaving only isotopically depleted sodium acetate in the still pot. If an additional amount of unlabeled pure acetic anhydride equal to the amount originally used is then added to the dry residue and the distillation to dryness is repeated, the total recovery of carbon-14 activity (as acetic-2-^{14}C anhydride) in the two distillates will be at least 99.99%. This technique, which has been applied in conjunction with extraction, distillation, and other laboratory operations, is known as the use of a "wash-out carrier." It leads to very high radiochemical yield which, however, is gained only at the price of correspondingly high isotope dilution of the labeled product. Since, for all practical purposes, isotope dilution of carbon-14-labeled compounds with carrier is an *irreversible* process, great care must be taken in planning syntheses that require the addition of carrier. If too much carrier is added, the labeled product may be too dilute isotopically to be useful in the tracer experiments for which it is intended. For most chemical applications of carbon-14, compounds having molar radioactivities of at least 1 μc/mmole are preferable. Sometimes, much higher molar radioactivities are required, particularly if an isotope dilution is to be made or if isotope dilution is unavoidable, as it often is in biochemical tracer experiments.

The experimenter should also bear in mind the fact that if a carbon-14-labeled compound can be prepared easily by exchanging an unlabeled group for a carbon-14-labeled group, the loss of the carbon-14 activity by the reverse exchange during a tracer study may be equally easy. Compounds that are labeled in relatively mobile groups must not be used in a tracer experiment in which loss of the label by exchange is rapid enough to invalidate the interpretation of the experimental results. As an extreme example, it would be very impractical to use 1 ml of methyl-^{14}C acetate in a tracer study if the solvent consisted of 100 ml of methanol that contained dissolved sodium methoxide. The loss by exchange of the labeled methyl group from the ester would undoubtedly proceed so rapidly that very little methyl-^{14}C acetate would remain after the first few minutes. Any calculations based on the original specific activity of the methyl-^{14}C acetate

would be meaningless, because the specific activity of the methyl-^{14}C acetate would change rapidly from the time the ester was added to the solvent.

In connection with the high isotope dilution ratios often used in the wash-out carrier technique and in other tracer-chemistry applications, it is necessary to emphasize that *radioactive impurities usually are not diluted isotopically when the products of a reaction are diluted.* A trace of undiluted impurity having a molar radioactivity of 100 μc/mmole in a product having a molar radioactivity of 1 μc/mmole may adversely affect the results of any isotopic tracer study in which the product is used. The effect of such an impurity is proportional to the percentage of the product radioactivity that it contains and not to the weight percentage of the impurity in the product. A detailed discussion of the effects of undiluted radiochemical impurities has been published.[3] The significance of radiochemical impurities is discussed further in Chap. 8. The synthesis of labeled compounds by isotope exchange is discussed in detail there.

4-2 RATES AND MECHANISMS OF ISOTOPE-EXCHANGE REACTIONS

Mathematical expressions for the instantaneous rate of change of the isotopic compositions of two chemical species undergoing a simple isotope exchange in a homogeneous system can be integrated to give logarithmic rate equations. Hughes and co-workers[4] and Hammett[5] indicate how such logarithmic rate expressions can be derived. A modification of their derivations follows.

If isotope effects (see Chap. 5) are ignored in the exchange of chlorine-36 between alkyl chloride and chloride ions, both reactions have the same specific rate constant, k, shown by Eq. 4-1

$$RCl + Cl^{-*} \overset{k}{\underset{k}{\rightleftharpoons}} RCl^{*} + Cl^{-} \qquad (4\text{-}1)$$

Since chlorine-36 has a very long half-life, its rate of decay need not be taken into account. Two differential equations may be written to define the rate of change of the concentration of the two isotopically labeled species; the equations are

$$\frac{d[RCl^*]}{dt} = k[RClC][l^{-*}] - k[RCl^*][Cl^-] \quad (4\text{-}2)$$

$$\frac{d[Cl^{-*}]}{dt} = k[RCl^*][Cl^-] - k[RCl][Cl^{-*}] \quad (4\text{-}3)$$

where

t = time elapsed since RCl and Cl^{-*} were mixed (usually expressed in seconds)

k = specific exchange rate constant, liters/mole-sec

bracketed terms = instantaneous concentrations at time t, moles/liter.

Additional terms are defined as follows

C_A = total concentration of alkyl chloride, moles/liter

C_I = total concentration of chloride ions, moles/liter

M_A = instantaneous molar radioactivity of the alkyl chloride, radioactivity units/mole

M_I = instantaneous molar radioactivity of the chloride ions, radioactivity units/mole

P = proportionality constant

r = experimentally measurable ratio of the instantaneous molar radioactivity of the alkyl chloride to that of the chloride ions

R = rate constant of exchange, moles/liter/sec (this constant equals kC_AC_I for a bimolecular process)

Therefore

$$M_A = \frac{P[RCl^*]}{C_A}$$

$$M_I = \frac{P[Cl^{-*}]}{C_I}$$

$$r = \frac{M_A}{M_I} = \frac{[RCl^*]/C_A}{[Cl^{-*}]/C_I} \quad (4\text{-}4)$$

Because consistent units were used, the proportionality constant cancels and does not appear in Eq. 4-4. Combining Eqs. 4-2, 4-3, and 4-4 gives a new differential equation

$$\left(\frac{1}{k}\right)\left(\frac{dr}{dt}\right) = C_I + (C_A + C_I)r - C_A r^2 \quad (4\text{-}5)$$

Integration of Eq. 4-5 gives the useful equation[4,5]

$$Rt = \left(\frac{C_A C_I}{C_A + C_I}\right) \ln\left(\frac{1 + r(C_A/C_I)}{1 - r}\right) \quad (4\text{-}6)$$

Use of Eq. 4-6 is limited to the special case of isotope exchange in which all the radioactivity is originally present in one chemical species, the chloride ion.

In exchange-rate studies, the exchanging chloride ions and alkyl chloride are separated at the exact time t. The molar radioactivities, M_A and M_I, are measured individually. The ratio r is calculated and, together with t and the values C_A and C_I, is substituted into Eq. 4-6, which is then solved for R. In cases where the exchanging species are separated at different times, t, and radioassayed, it is often convenient to plot values of the logarithmic term of Eq. 4-6 versus t on semilogarithmic paper and to calculate R from the slope.

For some isotope-exchange experiments in which not one but both chemical species originally contain radioactivity, a more generally applicable equation[1] is

$$-Rt = \left(\frac{C_A C_I}{C_A + C_I}\right) \ln(1 - F) \quad (4\text{-}7)$$

The term F is the fraction of exchange,[1] which is defined in terms of the instantaneous molar radioactivities of the exchanging species as follows

$$F = \frac{M_A - M_{A_0}}{M_{A_\infty} - M_{A_0}} = \frac{M_I - M_{I_0}}{M_{I_\infty} - M_{I_0}} \quad (4\text{-}8)$$

Subscripts 0 and ∞ refer, respectively, to values of the instantaneous molar radioactivities before exchange has begun ($t = 0$) and after isotopic equilibrium is reached ($t = \infty$). Since F is the fraction of exchange that is complete at time t, the term $(1 - F)$ of Eq. 4-7 may be thought of as the "fraction unexchanged" or the "distance from isotopic equilibrium." In this sense, Eq. 4-7 states— and it is convenient to remember—that if the logarithm of the "fraction unexchanged" is plotted against the elapsed time, a constant that represents the rate of exchange can be calculated from the slope.

The application of Eqs. 4-6 and 4-7 is described best with an example. Methyl cyanide exchanges slowly with carbon-14-labeled cyanide ions in basic solution at elevated temperatures. Under a particular set of chemical and physical conditions, one mole of methyl cyanide and one mole of sodium cyanide that contained 100 μc of carbon-14 were mixed in a liter of solution. After 100 hr the ionic cyanide was caused to precipitate as silver cyanide in order to separate it from the organically bound cyanide. The silver cyanide-^{14}C was found by radioassay to contain a total of 80 μc of carbon-14 activity. It was desired to calculate the constant rate of exchange. By use first of Eq. 4-6, C_A and C_I each have a value of unity, and t has the value 100 hr. At this value of t, $r = 20/80 = 0.25$, and

$$100R = \tfrac{1}{2}\ln\left(\frac{1 + 0.25}{1 - 0.25}\right)$$

$$R = 2.56 \times 10^{-3} \text{ moles/liter-hr}$$

The use of Eqs. 4-7 and 4-8 must yield the same answer.

$$F = \frac{M_I - M_{I_0}}{M_{I_\infty} - M_{I_0}} = \frac{80 - 100}{50 - 100}$$

$$F = \frac{-20}{-50} = 0.4$$

Substitution into Eq. 4-7 of 0.4 for F along with the values for C_A, C_I, and t gives

$$-R = \frac{1}{100}[\tfrac{1}{2}\ln(1 - 0.4)]$$

$$+R = \frac{2.303}{200}(\log 1.67)$$

$$R = 2.56 \times 10^{-3} \text{ moles/liter-hr}$$

In both calculations for this particular example, total activities could be used directly in place of molar or specific activities, because the total molar concentrations of the cyanide ions and of the methyl cyanide were equal.

The half-time of exchange, $t_{1/2}$, is frequently used to state the rate of isotope exchange. For a simple bimolecular-exchange mechanism, $t_{1/2}$ can be calculated either from the specific exchange rate constant, k, or from the constant rate of exchange, R, by use of the equation

$$t_{1/2} = \frac{0.693}{k(C_A + C_I)} = \frac{0.693(C_A C_I)}{R(C_A + C_I)} \tag{4-9}$$

For the methyl cyanide–cyanide ion exchange described above, Eq. 4-9 gives

$$t_{1/2} = \frac{0.693}{(2.56 \times 10^{-3})(1 + 1)} = 135 \text{ hr}$$

The foregoing discussion applies to *simple* exchange reactions in homogeneous systems; however, the exchange rate could be complicated by such effects as surface-induced exchange, side reactions that might alter the concentration of one or both exchanging entities, or the unsuspected presence of a third substance capable of exchanging with either of the first two substances. Deviation from the linear relationship of t to $\ln(1 - F)$, as defined by Eq. 4-7, could then be expected.

Occasionally, an organic substance that is undergoing isotope exchange with a second substance contains two or more exchangeable atoms or groups. For example, methylene cyanide contains two cyano groups that should exchange with cyanide-^{14}C ions in water solution according to the equation

$$\underset{\diagdown\!CN}{\overset{CN\diagup}{CH_2}} + {}^{14}CN^- \rightleftharpoons \underset{\diagdown\!CN}{\overset{{}^{14}CN\diagup}{CH_2}} + CN^-$$

Because the two cyano groups in methylene cyanide are chemically equivalent, they exchange with labeled cyanide ions at the same rate and, barring unforeseen complications, no deviation from a simple logarithmic expression like Eq. 4-6 or Eq. 4-7 is expected. If, however, the two cyano groups were not chemically equivalent, they would exchange at different rates with labeled cyanide ions, and the simple rate laws of Eqs. 4-6 and 4-7 would no longer apply.[1] The latter type complex exchange reaction would probably occur in the exchange of unsymmetrical propanedinitrile with cyanide-^{14}C ions in aqueous solution. The two cyano groups in unsymmetrical propanedinitrile are not in chemically equivalent positions

$$2CH_3CHCNCH_2CN + 2\,^{14}CN^- \rightleftharpoons$$
$$CH_3CH^{14}CNCH_2CN$$
$$+ CH_3CHCNCH_2{}^{14}CN + 2CN^-$$

The exchange rate constant would be different for the two cyano groups. As a result, the simple exchange-rate expression represented by Eqs. 4-6 and 4-7 would not apply. A plot of $\ln(1 - F)$ vs. t would not be a straight line. In general, if such a plot does give a straight line, equivalence of two exchangeable groups in a molecule is indicated.

In the case of a compound that has two nonequivalent exchangeable groups, *intramolecular* isotope exchange may be possible. For example, in unsymmetrical propanedinitrile an *intramolecular* isotope exchange might occur according to the following equation if all the carbon-14 were originally in the terminal cyano group

$$CH_3CHCNCH_2{}^{14}CN \rightleftharpoons CH_3CH^{14}CNCH_2CN$$

However, it seems very likely that such an apparent *intramolecular* exchange in aqueous solution would occur only through the intermediary of a small amount of cyanide ions. In such a case, the apparent *intramolecular* isotope exchange would actually be due to the *intermolecular* processes shown in the following sequence of equations

$$CH_3CHCNCH_2{}^{14}CN + CN^- \rightleftharpoons$$
$$CH_3CHCNCH_2CN + {}^{14}CN^-$$
$$CH_3CHCNCH_2CN + {}^{14}CN^- \rightleftharpoons$$
$$CH_3CH^{14}CNCH_2CN + CN^-$$

Complex exchange reactions have been discussed in some detail by Myers and Prestwood.[1]

Evaluation of k, R, or $t_{1/2}$ for isotope exchange of atoms or groups in organic molecules may serve to indicate the ease of dissociation of the particular atoms or groups from the organic molecules. Thus, the exchange of most organic cyanides with carbon-14-labeled cyanide ions is slow, as might be expected, since a carbon-carbon bond is broken during the exchange. For phenyl cyanide the value for $t_{1/2}$ at 75° under one set of chemical conditions is greater than 700 hr.[6]

In some isotope-exchange reactions in which a bond or bonds to the isotopically labeled atom are broken and are formed again during the exchange, equilibrium isotope effects (see Sec. 5-6i) occur. Equilibrium isotope effects are indicated by a measurable difference between the molar radioactivities or molar isotopic concentrations of two exchanging compounds even after isotopic equilibrium has been reached. In the case of carbon-14 isotope-exchange reactions, the equilibrium isotope effects are usually about 5% or less. This is to say that the carbon-14 molar radioactivities of two compounds at isotopic equilibrium may differ by as much as about 5%. Carbon-13 equilibrium isotope effects are normally about one-half as large as the corresponding carbon-14 equilibrium isotope effects. These small equilibrium carbon-isotope effects can usually be ignored in kinetic studies. However, carbon equilibrium isotope effects are important in the field of isotope separation.[7] They are also significant in the study of organic reaction mechanisms[8,9,10] and must be taken into account in interpreting carbon-13 and carbon-14 kinetic isotope effects.[11,12,13]

Although exchange of individual carbon atoms, as distinguished from exchange of carbon-containing groups, is relatively rare in organic chemistry, exchange of carbon atoms into molecules can be forced to occur in high-energy processes. For example, Lemmon and co-workers[14] used a mass spectrometer to bombard frozen benzene with positive ions of mass 14, including the ion $[^{14}C]^+$ (see also

Sec. 8-4c). Benzene-^{14}C was formed, apparently by displacement of a carbon-12 atom by a carbon-14 atom. Broadly speaking, this displacement reaction may be termed an isotope-exchange reaction.

Myers and Prestwood[1] have tabulated rate data for a number of exchange reactions of carbon isotopes. Roginsky[15] has published a volume that includes a very thorough general treatment of the subject of isotope-exchange reactions.

4-3 ISOTOPE-EXCHANGE REACTIONS IN THE STUDY OF REACTION MECHANISMS

Several applications of isotope-exchange reactions in the study of organic reaction mechanisms are discussed in this section, and examples are given.

4-3a TEST FOR REVERSIBILITY

A very simple and highly useful test for the reversibility of a bimolecular organic reaction consists in mixing a sample of pure unlabeled reaction product with a sample of a pure isotopically labeled reactant and subjecting the mixture to the conditions necessary to bring about the forward reaction. The product is recovered from the mixture and is purified. If the pure recovered product is radioactive, some reversibility of the reaction is indicated. This technique was applied in a study[16] of a Diels-Alder reaction

$$C_6H_5CH{=}CHNO_2$$
$$+ CH_2{=}C(CH_3)C(CH_3){=}CH_2 \rightarrow$$

An equimolar mixture of β-nitrostyrene-α-^{14}C and the unlabeled adduct formed by the reaction of β-nitrostyrene and 2,3-dimethylbutadiene was equilibrated as a melt for 24 hr at 130°. The adduct was then separated from the mixture and was carefully purified

by recrystallization. The fact that the pure recovered adduct showed only background radioactivity indicated that essentially none of the adduct had dissociated reversibly to β-nitrostyrene and 2,3-dimethylbutadiene under conditions like those used for the Diels-Alder reaction.

Two other results might have been obtained. The adduct recovered after the isotope experiment might have had one-half the original molar radioactivity of the β-nitrostyrene-α-^{14}C. This result would have proved that the adduct dissociates rather rapidly into diene and dienophile under the conditions used to effect the Diels-Alder reaction. The rapidity of the occurrence of the dissociation might have been determined by repeating the same isotope experiment but for shorter periods of time. Alternatively, the recovered adduct might have contained some carbon-14 activity but less than one-half the molar radioactivity of the β-nitrostyrene-α-^{14}C used. This latter result would have indicated that the Diels-Alder reaction was reversible, but that the reverse reaction was slower than the forward reaction. The relative rates of the forward and reverse reactions could then have been determined by comparing the absolute rate of the Diels-Alder reaction with the rate of the isotope exchange between β-nitrostyrene-α-^{14}C and the unlabeled adduct.

In an interesting study by Bothner-By[17] in which carbon-14 was used, the quinhydrone complexes formed from duroquinone and durohydroquinone were proved not to be symmetrical resonance hybrids. In one experiment, duroquinhydrone-^{14}C was prepared from durohydroquinone-α-^{14}C and unlabeled duroquinone. After thermal dissociation of the duroquinhydrone-^{14}C, the carbon-14 was again found mainly in the durohydroquinone-α-^{14}C. In a symmetrical resonance hybrid, the quinone and hydroquinone forms would have lost their separate identities, and isotope equilibration between the durohydroquinone-α-^{14}C and the duroquinone would have resulted. This application of carbon-14 is very similar to that discussed in Sec. 3-4.

4-3b COMPARISON OF ISOTOPE EXCHANGE RATES WITH RATES OF OTHER CONCURRENT PROCESSES

The highly ingenious experiments of Hughes and co-workers[4,18,19] deserve emphasis here, although no carbon isotopes were used. Their research clearly demonstrates the value of a few carefully planned isotope-exchange experiments in leading to an incontrovertible conclusion about a reaction mechanism. In the first of the reactions investigated by Hughes and co-workers,[4] the exchange of radioactive iodide ions with *sec*-octyl iodide in the solvent acetone was studied

$$C_6H_{13}-\underset{\underset{CH_3}{|}}{\overset{\overset{H}{|}}{C}}-I + I^{*-} \rightleftharpoons C_6H_{13}-\underset{\underset{CH_3}{|}}{\overset{\overset{H}{|}}{C}}-I^{*} + I^{-}$$

One stereoisomer of *sec*-octyl iodide was used, and both the rate constant for racemization, k_r, and the specific isotope-exchange rate constant, k_E, were determined. The nearly identical values obtained for these two rate constants, 1.31×10^{-3} and 1.36×10^{-3}, respectively, show that every individual act of displacement of a normal iodine atom by a radioactive iodine atom is accompanied by inversion of the asymmetric carbon atom to which the iodine is bound. It was therefore concluded that the displacement of the iodine atom on carbon and the inversion or racemization of the carbon atom are effected by one and the same process, namely, backside attack on the asymmetric carbon atom. The original iodine atom is lost from *sec*-octyl iodide as an iodide ion at the same time the carbon tetrahedron turns "inside out" to meet the incoming radioactive iodide ion. This is the well-known Walden inversion.

Hughes and co-workers obtained similar results using α-phenylethyl bromide[18] and α-bromopropionic acid.[19] These experiments have been used as models for more recent

studies, some of which involve exchange of carbon-14-labeled groups in organic molecules. Such studies are based on a very simple principle: *two processes that occur simultaneously, in the same environment, and at the same rate most probably take place via the same mechanism or via closely related mechanisms.*

4-3c OTHER EXAMPLES

Although the reversible making and breaking of carbon-to-carbon bonds occurs only infrequently in organic reactions, isotope-exchange studies should provide useful information about such processes when they do occur. Friedel-Crafts type alkylations of aromatic nuclei and base-catalyzed condensations of aldehydes and ketones are typical examples of reactions in which reversible making and breaking of carbon-to-carbon bonds can be expected. The interesting exchange of the carbon of carbon monoxide with 2-methyl-2-ethylbutyric-1-^{14}C acid in concentrated sulfuric acid is another example that was described by Lundeen.[20] Nazarova[21] has reported the use of isotope-exchange studies to measure the tendency of carbon-14-labeled *t*-butyl groups to move. Ferric chloride and aluminum chloride catalyzed isotope exchanges between *t*-butyl chloride and aromatic compounds that contain *t*-butyl groups were studied at 120° in sealed ampoules. The conclusion reached is that exchange takes place by an ionic mechanism.

Carbon isotopes have been used occasionally as indicators in the study of deuterium exchange reactions. For example, Wagner and co-authors[22] found that for the catalyzed exchange

$$(CH_3)_3C-D + (CH_3)_2(^{13}CH_3)C-H \rightleftharpoons$$
$$(CH_3)_3C-H + (CH_3)_2(^{13}CH_3)C-D$$

the half-time of exchange, $t_{1/2}$, at 25° is less than 2 min. The presence of carbon-13 permitted the exchange to be followed by use of a mass spectrometer.

Creak and co-workers[23] used carbon-14 as a tracer to study the kinetics of the following exchange reaction, which involves radicals,

$$\cdot CD_3 + CD_4 \rightleftharpoons CD_4 + \cdot CD_3$$

Carbon-14 has also been used in a similar way to study deuterium kinetic isotope effects in reactions[24] of formic-d acid. This latter technique is possible only because the deuterium atom in formic-d acid is tightly bound to carbon. The loss of deuterium by exchange is too slow to be of importance under the conditions at which the deuterium kinetic isotope effect was studied. Because carbon-14 can be determined very accurately, even small secondary deuterium isotope effects can be measured.[25] This method requires that the isotope effects contributed by carbon-14 be known unless the carbon-14 label is far removed from the reaction site.

CITED REFERENCES

1 O. E. Myers and R. J. Prestwood in A. C. Wahl and N. A. Bonner, Eds., "Radioactivity Applied to Chemistry," chap. 1, John Wiley & Sons, Inc., New York, 1951.
2 S. Ruben, M. B. Allen, and P. Nahinsky, *J. Am. Chem. Soc.*, **64**, 3050 (1942).
3 G. A. Ropp, *J. Chem. Educ.*, **34**, 60 (1957).
4 E. D. Hughes, F. Juliusburger, E. Masterman, B. Topley, and J. Weiss, *J. Chem. Soc.*, 1525 (1935).
5 L. P. Hammett, "Physical Organic Chemistry," pp. 164–165, McGraw-Hill Book Company, Inc., New York, 1940.
6 L. Tsai and M. Kamen, *J. Chem. Phys.*, **17**, 585 (1949).
7 H. C. Urey, *J. Chem. Soc.*, 562 (1947).
8 G. A. Ropp and O. K. Neville, *Nucleonics*, **9**, 22 (1951).
9 G. A. Ropp, *Nucleonics*, **10**, 22 (1952).
10 D. R. Stranks, *J. Chem. Phys.*, **21**, 2232 (1953).
11 P. E. Yankwich and H. S. Weber, *J. Am. Chem. Soc.*, **78**, 564 (1956).
12 A. Fry and M. Calvin, *J. Phys. Chem.*, **56**, 897 (1952).
13 C. C. Lee and J. W. T. Spinks, *Can. J. Chem.*, **32**, 327 (1954).
14 R. M. Lemmon, F. Mazzetti, F. L. Reynolds, and M. Calvin, *J. Am. Chem. Soc.*, **78**, 6414 (1956).
15 S. Z. Roginsky, "Theoretical Principles of Isotope Methods of Investigating Chemical Reactions," chaps. I, II, III, and V, Academy of Sciences, USSR Press, Moscow, 1956; AEC-TR-2873, Office of Technical Services, Washington 25, D.C.
16 G. A. Ropp, V. F. Raaen, and A. J. Weinberger, *J. Am. Chem. Soc.*, **75**, 3694 (1953).
17 A. Bothner-By, *J. Am. Chem. Soc.*, **73**, 4228 (1951).
18 E. D. Hughes, F. Juliusburger, A. D. Scott, B. Topley, and J. Weiss, *J. Chem. Soc.*, 1173 (1936).
19 W. A. Cowdrey, E. D. Hughes, T. P. Nevell, and C. L. Wilson, *J. Chem. Soc.*, 209 (1938).
20 A. Lundeen, *J. Am. Chem. Soc.*, **82**, 3228 (1960).
21 L. M. Nazarova, *Zh. Obshch. Khim.*, **26**, 1640 (1956); *Chem. Abstr.*, **51**, 1711 (1957).
22 C. D. Wagner, O. Beeck, J. W. Ötvös, and D. P. Stevenson, *J. Chem. Phys.*, **17**, 419 (1949).
23 G. A. Creak, F. S. Dainton, and K. J. Ivin, *Trans. Faraday Soc.*, **58**, 326 (1962).
24 G. A. Ropp in "Radioisotopes in the Physical Sciences and Industry," p. 235, vol. III, International Atomic Energy Agency, Vienna, 1962.
25 V. F. Raaen and C. J. Collins, *Pure Appl. Chem.*, **8**, 347 (1964).

GENERAL REFERENCES

(a) A. C. Wahl and N. A. Bonner, "Radioactivity Applied to Chemistry," John Wiley & Sons, Inc., New York, 1951.
(b) S. Z. Roginsky, "Theoretical Principles of Isotope Methods for Investigating Chemical Reactions," Academy of Sciences, USSR Press, Moscow, 1956; AEC-TR-2873, Office of Technical Services, Washington 25, D.C.
(c) R. T. Overman and H. M. Clark, "Radioisotope Techniques," McGraw-Hill Book Company, Inc., New York, 1960.
(d) G. M. Harris, "Kinetics of Isotope Exchange Reactions," *Trans. Faraday Soc.*, **47**, 716 (1951).
(e) C. A. Bunton, D. P. Craig, and A. E. Halevi, "Kinetics of Isotope Exchange Reactions," *Trans. Faraday Soc.*, **51**, 196 (1955).

(*f*) M. Haissinsky, "La Chimie Nucléaire et Ses Applications," Masson et Cie Editeurs, Paris, 1957; also English translation by D. G. Tuck, "Nuclear Chemistry and Its Applications," Addison-Wesley, Reading, Mass., 1964.

PROBLEMS

4-1. Potassium cyanide-^{14}C has been shown to exchange carbon-14 with potassium selenocyanide in aqueous solution. One gram of potassium cyanide-^{14}C that contained 50 μc total radioactivity was warmed in 100 ml of an aqueous solution of potassium selenocyanide until ample time had elapsed for isotopic equilibrium to be reached. A small sample of the potassium selenocyanide was again separated from the solution and purified. Carbon-14 assay of the purified potassium selenocyanide indicated that it contained 0.35 μc/100 mg. Calculate the weight of potassium selenocyanide that was originally in the 100 ml of solution.

4-2. Acetone-2-^{14}C was found to exchange carbon-14 with aluminum isopropoxide in dry toluene solution at 50°. An exchange mechanism similar to the mechanism of the Meerwein-Ponndorf reduction was assumed. The exchange rate was followed by determining the molar radioactivity of the acetone-2-^{14}C precipitated as the 2,4-dinitrophenylhydrazone from aliquots of the toluene solution taken at measured time intervals after the exchange reaction began. The isotope exchange reaction was rapid at first but slowed down and stopped before the calculated isotopic equilibrium was reached. Suggest a reason for the apparent slowing down of the isotope exchange (see Sec. 4-2).

4-3. A 50-mg sample of methanol-^{14}C having 5.0 μc total radioactivity was heated 1 hr with 0.2 mg of sodium methoxide and 100 mg of an ester that had been prepared by completely methylating a polybasic organic acid with diazomethane. At the end of the hour, a sample of the methanol-^{14}C that was recovered by cold distillation under high vacuum was radioassayed and found to have a molar radioactivity of 1.93 mc. The molecular weight of the original acid was independently determined and found to be 166. Suggest a possible identity of the original acid.

4-4. In a warm furnace, the value $t_{1/2} = 20$ hr was found for the gas-phase exchange of carbon between carbon monoxide and carbon dioxide. A liter (S.T.P.) of carbon-14 dioxide that contained 100 μc of radioactivity was added to a liter (S.T.P.) of carbon monoxide, and the mixture was cycled through the furnace. Calculate (*a*) the molar radioactivity of the carbon-^{14}C monoxide after 10 hr, (*b*) the radioactivity per gram of pure barium carbonate-^{14}C precipitated by adding saturated barium hydroxide solution to the gas after 25 hr, and (*c*) the ratio of the molar radioactivity of the carbon-14 monoxide to that of the carbon-14 dioxide after 10 hr and (*d*) after 16 hr.

4-5. How else could the isotope-exchange test for reversibility of the Diels-Alder reaction of β-nitrostyrene and 2,3-dimethylbutadiene described in Sec. 4-3a have been performed? Does either way of performing the test for reversibility have any advantage over the other?

CHAPTER
5
KINETIC
ISOTOPE EFFECTS

5-1 INTRODUCTION TO KINETIC ISOTOPE EFFECTS

A brief introduction to the field of kinetic isotope effects is presented in this Sec. 5-1. Several of the topics discussed briefly are considered in more detail in later sections of this chapter or in other chapters.

5-1a DEFINITIONS

When the reaction rate constant of a chemical reaction is changed by the substitution of an isotope in a reacting molecule, the change is called a *kinetic or rate isotope effect*. For example, if both hydrogen atoms in a water molecule are replaced by deuterium atoms, the rates of some of the reactions of the water molecule are reduced by 50% or more. The substitution of carbon isotopes in organic molecules may also alter the rates of chemical reactions of the organic molecules. However, the substitution of carbon isotopes causes a much smaller isotope effect than does the substitution of hydrogen isotopes. This smaller effect is to be expected since the masses of carbon-12 and carbon-14 differ by less than 17%, whereas the mass of a deuterium atom is twice that of a hydrogen atom. Rate isotope effects are expressed conveniently as ratios of specific reaction rate constants. The ratio most often used is k/k^*, in which k is the reaction rate constant of the normal molecules, and k^* is that of the isotopically substituted molecules. Occasionally it is more convenient to use the inverse ratio, k^*/k. Isotope effects may also be expressed in percent. A 10% isotope effect ordinarily means

$$100\left(\frac{k}{k^*} - 1\right) = 10$$

In addition to kinetic isotope effects, *equilibrium isotope effects* also occur. These are usually expressed as K/K^*, that is, the ratio of the equilibrium constants for reversible reactions of normal and of isotopically substituted molecules. Equilibrium isotope effects are of particular interest relative to practical methods of separating isotopes. They are also of significance in some studies of complex reaction mechanisms.

In any discussion of kinetic isotope effects of carbon isotopes, it is essential to distinguish clearly between *intermolecular* and *intramolecular rate isotope effects*. In *intermolecular rate isotope effects*, which occur the more frequently, labeled and unlabeled molecules compete. This type of effect is exemplified by the competition between ethyl benzoate-α-^{14}C molecules and unlabeled ethyl benzoate molecules when these two kinds of molecules undergo saponification in the same solution by hydroxyl ions. The competing reactions and their rate constants can be written

$$C_6H_5CO_2C_2H_5 + OH^- \xrightarrow{k_{12}}$$
$$C_6H_5CO_2^- + C_2H_5OH$$

and

$$C_6H_5{}^{14}CO_2C_2H_5 + OH^- \xrightarrow{k_{14}}$$
$$C_6H_5{}^{14}CO_2^- + C_2H_5OH$$

The intermolecular rate isotope effect for carbon-14 is expressed as the ratio k_{12}/k_{14}, which has a value of about 1.08 for this reaction at 25°.[1] *Intramolecular rate isotope effects* occur in the reactions of labeled symmetrical molecules. The classic example is the isotope effect that accompanies the decarboxylation of malonic-1-^{14}C acid[2]

$$CH_2 \begin{cases} CO_2H \xrightarrow{k_{12}} CH_3{}^{14}CO_2H + CO_2\uparrow \\ {}^{14}CO_2H \xrightarrow{k_{14}} CH_3CO_2H + {}^{14}CO_2\uparrow \end{cases} \quad (5\text{-}1)$$

The *intramolecular* isotope effect, $k_{12}/k_{14} \cong 1.05$, in this reaction[3] is an expression of the greater frequency of rupture of a $^{12}C-^{12}C$ bond than of a $^{12}C-^{14}C$ bond *within the same molecule*.

Intermolecular and *intramolecular isotope effects* have significantly different characteristics. *Intermolecular isotope effects* can be observed only in partially completed reactions,

whereas *intramolecular isotope effects* can be observed as differences between the isotopic compositions of the products even after the reaction of the starting material is complete. The two types of effects may have different significance in terms of reaction rate theory,[4,5] but the theory of *intramolecular* isotope effects awaits further clarification.

5-1b HISTORY

Much of the earliest work on isotope effects in chemical reactions was concerned with the separation of hydrogen isotopes by means of equilibrium processes. Urey and Rittenberg[6] showed by calculations based on theoretical principles that the equilibrium constant of the reaction between hydrogen and hydrogen halides should be altered appreciably by the substitution of deuterium for the hydrogen. Farkas and Farkas[7] discussed the separation of hydrogen and deuterium from the standpoint of the equilibria among water, hydrogen, and deuterium. Urey and Greiff[8] calculated from spectroscopic data the equilibrium constants and enrichment factors of several exchange reactions involving the stable isotopes of lithium, carbon, nitrogen, oxygen, chlorine, and bromine. The publications that resulted from these early studies, and which appeared in the early nineteen thirties, indicated clearly the relatively large differences to be expected between the chemical properties of hydrogen compounds and the corresponding deuterium compounds. The expected large deuterium and tritium equilibrium isotope effects, as well as the predicted[8] smaller, but definite, equilibrium isotope effects due to isotopic substitution of other light elements including carbon, have been observed repeatedly during the past years.

The kinetic isotope effect that occurs during the electrolysis of water was one of the earliest studied.[9] The liquid phase was found to be enriched in deuterium. Subsequently, deuterium rate isotope effects were used widely in the study of reaction mechanisms. Deuterium isotope effects and their applications are discussed in a comprehensive review by Wiberg.[10]

Kinetic isotope effects caused by the substitution of carbon-13 or carbon-14 for carbon-12 were first studied by Beeck and co-workers,[11] Stevenson and co-workers,[12] and Yankwich and Calvin.[2] Interest in kinetic isotope effects that result both from the isotopic substitution of hydrogen and from isotopic substitution of light elements other than hydrogen has spread rapidly during the past fifteen years. Much of the credit for this rapid development belongs to Bigeleisen[13] and co-workers, who developed a theory of kinetic isotope effects and from it developed equations that are useful in the interpretation of experimentally measured isotope-effect ratios.

5-1c SIGNIFICANCE OF KINETIC ISOTOPE EFFECTS IN CHEMICAL RESEARCH

Rate isotope effects have been studied intensively for three reasons. First, they may cause errors in the results of experiments in which isotopic tracers are used. The magnitude of such errors is determined by the extent to which the labeled compound reacts at a rate that differs from the reaction rate of the corresponding unlabeled compound. For example, in an organic-reaction yield measured by means of an isotope-dilution technique, an error could result from the alteration of the isotope concentration of the labeled product if isotope fractionation accompanied the reaction. In Chaps. 9 and 10, the possibility of errors due to isotope fractionation during derivative formation and degradation is discussed. Although it is possible for hydrogen isotope effects to cause large errors in experiments with isotope tracers, errors that are caused by carbon isotope effects are usually small enough to be neglected in all except the most demanding experimentation.

The second reason for studying rate

isotope effects is that a measured isotope-effect ratio often gives useful information about the mechanism of the reaction in which the isotope effect occurs. Generally, the occurrence of an *intermolecular* isotope effect during the reaction of a compound labeled in a specific position is considered to be evidence that a bond, or bonds, to the labeled position is altered during the rate-controlling step. A simple example of such an application of isotope-effect measurements is the study of the decarbonylation of formic acid[14,30] in 96% sulfuric acid at 25°

$$HCO_2H \xrightarrow{H_2SO_4} CO\uparrow + H_2O$$

When the formic acid was labeled with carbon-14, an isotope effect of about 9% was observed (i.e., $k_{12}/k_{14} \cong 1.09$). This large carbon-14 rate isotope effect indicated clearly that a bond, or bonds, to carbon is altered during the rate-controlling step of the decarbonylation reaction. When formic-d acid, DCO_2H, was used, the reaction rate was lowered only about 33% ($k_H/k_D \cong 1.5$). Since deuterium-isotope-effect ratios, k_H/k_D, of 2 to 7 are commonly observed in rate processes, the relatively small deuterium isotope effect observed in this case indicated that cleavage of the carbon-to-hydrogen bond is likely not the rate-determining step. Since the carbon in formic acid is bonded only to one hydrogen atom and two oxygen atoms, it follows that a carbon-to-oxygen bond must be the bond that is altered in the rate-determining step of the decarbonylation reaction. The small rate isotope effect of deuterium may be a secondary effect of deuterium on the rate of cleavage of the carbon-to-oxygen bond.

The use of isotope-effect studies to identify the rate-determining step in a reaction scheme is based on ideas that are more or less self-evident. For the sake of completeness, these ideas are listed here. They are: (a) to change the rate of a reaction, it is necessary to change the rate of the rate-controlling step; (b) the rate-controlling process in a sequence of processes is the slowest process; (c) for isotope substitution to alter the rate of the rate-controlling step, the position in the reacting molecule of the isotopically substituted atom must be such that bonds to that atom are altered during the rate-controlling step; and (d) in case of isotope substitution of an atom that is at least one position removed from the reaction center, no *primary* kinetic isotope effect can be expected, because bonds to that atom will be altered far less during the rate-controlling step than would have been the case if that isotopically substituted atom had been at the reaction center. *Secondary* kinetic isotope effects (Sec. 5-4f), which are generally of much smaller magnitude than primary kinetic isotope effects, can occur in cases where the isotopically substituted atom is not at the reaction center but near (i.e., one or two atoms away) the reaction center. When the isotopically substituted atom is far removed from the reaction center, isotopic substitution usually will have no measurable effect on the reaction rate. This condition is especially true for isotopic substitution of elements other than hydrogen.

The carbon-14 isotope effects to be expected during decarboxylation of cinnamic acid

$$\text{C}_6\text{H}_5\text{CH}=\text{CHCO}_2\text{H} \xrightarrow{\Delta}$$
$$\text{C}_6\text{H}_5\text{CH}=\text{CH}_2 + \text{CO}_2\uparrow$$

illustrate the dependency of the magnitude of the kinetic isotope effect on the location of the isotopically substituted atom. With cinnamic-1-^{14}C acid and with cinnamic-2-^{14}C acid, *primary* carbon-14 isotope effects can be expected. With cinnamic-3-^{14}C acid, a secondary carbon-14 isotope effect might be observed if the method of detection is sufficiently sensitive. With ring-labeled cinnamic acid, it is doubtful that any measurable carbon-14 isotope effect would occur.

The third reason for studying kinetic isotope effects is that they provide experimental checks on the validity of some phases of reaction-rate theory. As most theoretical estimates of kinetic-isotope-effect ratios have been based on absolute reaction-rate theory,[13,15] agreement between these theoretically estimated ratios and experimentally measured ratios tends to increase confidence in absolute reaction-rate theory.

5-1d DIRECTION AND MAGNITUDE OF KINETIC ISOTOPE EFFECTS

Kinetic isotope effects almost always occur in such a direction that the lighter of two isotopic species has the greater specific rate constant. A few exceptions that have been observed are discussed in a later section of this chapter. The theoretical maximum values for ratios of isotopic rate constants have been estimated.[16] However, these theoretical maxima have rarely, if ever, been observed experimentally. The maximum values for *intermolecular* isotope effects actually observed are given in Table 5-1. Certain high values that have been reported but not verified are not included in this table.

Kinetic isotope effects are a function of the atomic masses of the isotopes involved. The difference between the atomic mass of carbon-14 and that of carbon-12 is two parts in twelve. Percentagewise, this is a larger difference than the maximum difference between any of the useful isotopes of any other element except hydrogen. In reactions in which the mass of the labeled carbon atom can exert its maximum effect, carbon-14 substitution accordingly results in larger isotope effects than those effects caused by isotopic substitution of any element other than hydrogen. As might be expected, the carbon-14 isotope effect is about twice as large as the carbon-13 isotope effect for the same reaction under the same conditions.

5-1e EXPERIMENTAL METHODS

Of the tracer nuclides used thus far in organic studies, only deuterium has been obtained

Table 5-1   Maximum experimental values of intermolecular *kinetic isotope effects*

Species	Tracer isotope	T, °C	$k/k*$	Reference
^{1}H	^{2}H	24.88	24.2	17
	^{3}H		63	18
^{12}C	^{13}C	43	1.074	19
	^{14}C	25	1.14	20
^{14}N	^{15}N	180	1.014[a]	21
^{16}O	^{18}O	25	1.07	22
^{32}S	^{34}S	25	1.003	23
	^{34}S	25	$K/K* = 1.021$[b]	24
^{35}Cl	^{37}Cl	20	1.008	25

[a] Intramolecular isotope effect. This is the largest nitrogen-15 isotope effect that has been observed at this temperature.

[b] Equilibrium isotope effect. This is the largest isotope effect that has been observed for any sulfur isotope.

carrier-free in large quantities. Consequently, only in the case of deuterium can the isotope effect be evaluated by measuring first the rate of reaction of the isotopically pure labeled compound, then the rate of reaction of the corresponding unlabeled compound, and calculating the quotient of the two specific rate constants.

Carbon isotope effects, like the isotope effects that result from the substitution of isotopes of nitrogen, phosphorus, oxygen, sulfur, and chlorine, must be evaluated by other methods. These other methods involve competition between two isotopic species reacting simultaneously in the same environment. The specific rate constants for the reactions of the two species need not be determined individually, because their ratio can be estimated by measurement of the concentrations of the competing isotopic species in a labeled product or in the unreacted labeled starting material at a known percent reaction. The percent reaction and the ratio of the isotope concentration of this product or of residual starting material to the isotope concentration of the original starting material can then be used (Sec. 5-2) to compute the ratio of isotopic rate constants, $k/k*$.

5-1f   THEORETICAL INTERPRETATION OF KINETIC ISOTOPE EFFECTS

A very elementary theoretical interpretation[26,27] of kinetic isotope effects is presented in this section. Emphasis is on those isotope effects that result from the isotopic substitution of one of the light elements other than hydrogen. A very simple example is a reaction in which the rate-controlling process is the cleavage of a ^{14}C—O bond. *Intermolecular* isotope fractionation can occur, the competing elementary processes being

$$^{12}C-O \xrightarrow{k_{12}} {}^{12}C + O$$

and

$$^{14}C-O \xrightarrow{k_{14}} {}^{14}C + O$$

To simplify the presentation as much as possible, all bonds except the bonds being broken are excluded from these equations.

According to reaction-rate theory, most bond-dissociation processes proceed through an activated state whose energy level is located at the top of the hump in a potential-energy profile as shown in Fig. 5-1. The rate of the dissociation is determined largely by the activation energy, E, which is the difference between the average energy of the

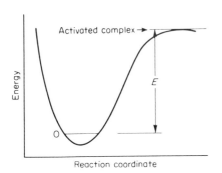

FIG. 5-1 Activation energy in a dissociation process.

molecules in the energy well and the energy at the top of the hump. The smaller the activation energy, the faster is the reaction rate, since the specific rate constant, k, is related logarithmically to the activation energy

$$k \propto e^{-E/RT}$$

where

e = base of natural logarithms
R = molar gas constant = 1.987 cal/deg
T = temperature, $^\circ$K

The question is: how does substitution of a carbon-14 atom for a carbon-12 atom in the carbon-to-oxygen bond increase the activation energy and thereby decrease the specific reaction rate? One answer is: not by changing the shape of the potential-energy curve shown as Fig. 5-1, because it is known from spectroscopic data that isotopic substitution of light elements other than hydrogen has no appreciable effect on the force constants of molecular vibrations. The correct answer is: by lowering the average vibrational-energy level of molecules in the energy well; this energy level is indicated in Fig. 5-1 by the line designated 0. Substitution of the heavier carbon-14 lowers the 0-point vibrational frequency and thereby lowers the 0-point vibrational energy. For a harmonic oscillator, the fundamental frequency, v,

is given by the expression[28]

$$v = \frac{1}{2\pi}\left(\frac{f}{M}\right)^{\frac{1}{2}} \tag{5-2}$$

where

v = vibrational frequency, sec^{-1}
f = force constant of vibration, dynes/cm
M = reduced mass of the two vibrating masses

If the vibrational frequency, v_{12}, of the ^{12}C—O bond is known, then the frequency of the ^{14}C—O bond can be estimated, since substitution of carbon-14 for carbon-12 alters only the value of M in Eq. 5-2. The ratio of the vibrational frequency of the ^{12}C—O bond to that of the ^{14}C—O bond, v_{14}, is therefore

$$\frac{v_{12}}{v_{14}} = \left(\frac{M_{14}}{M_{12}}\right)^{\frac{1}{2}} = \left[\frac{(14 \times 16)/(14 + 16)}{(12 \times 16)/(12 + 16)}\right]^{\frac{1}{2}}$$
$$= 1.044$$

The 0-point vibrational energy of an oscillator is $(\frac{1}{2})Nhv$
where

N = Avogadro number = 6.02 $\times$ 10^{23}
h = Planck constant = 6.624 $\times$ 10^{-27} erg sec

Therefore, the difference in 0-point vibrational energy per mole that results from the isotopic shift in the vibrational frequency is

$$\frac{1}{2}Nh(v_{12} - v_{14}) = \frac{1}{2}Nhv_{12}\left(1 - \frac{1}{1.044}\right)$$

If the stretching frequency, v_{12}, of the ^{12}C—O bond is taken to be 1093 cm^{-1} or 3.28 $\times$ 10^{13} sec^{-1},[29] the 0-point energy difference due to the carbon isotopic substitution is

$$\left[\frac{(6.02 \times 10^{23})(6.62 \times 10^{-27})}{2}\right](3.28 \times 10^{13})$$
$$\times \left(1 - \frac{1}{1.044}\right) = 2.74 \times 10^9 \text{ ergs/mole}$$

This 0-point energy difference, which is equal to 65 cal/mole, is taken to be $(E_{14} - E_{12})$, the difference between the activation energies for reaction of the two isotopic species,

^{14}CO and ^{12}CO. This relationship between the activation energies and the 0-point energies of carbon-12 and carbon-14 is illustrated graphically in Fig. 5-2. From the previously

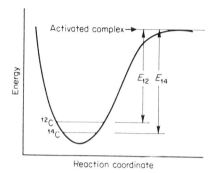

FIG. 5-2   Relationship between the isotopic 0-point vibrational energy levels and the activation energies of labeled and unlabeled species.

stated logarithmic relationship between the specific reaction rate constant and the activation energy, it is seen that the ratio of the two isotopic rate constants is

$$\frac{k_{12}}{k_{14}} = \frac{\exp{(-E_{12}/RT)}}{\exp{(-E_{14}/RT)}} = \exp{[(E_{14} - E_{12})/RT]}$$

The substituting of the value of $(E_{14} - E_{12})$ at a temperature of 298°K gives the rate-constant ratio

$$\frac{k_{12}}{k_{14}} = 1.116$$

In view of the oversimplified approach taken, it is rather surprising, and is probably merely fortuitous, that the 11.6% isotope effect calculated agrees well with a ratio calculated by somewhat more refined methods.[15] It also agrees reasonably well with the experimentally observed carbon-14 isotope effect ($k_{12}/k_{14} \simeq 1.09$ at 25°) in the decarbonylation of formic acid[14,30] (Sec. 5-1c) in which carbon-to-oxygen bond cleavage controls the reaction rate.

In the interest of simplicity, a number of

significant factors were omitted from the above discussion of the theoretical interpretation of kinetic isotope effects. Some of these factors will be mentioned later in this chapter. Part of the above discussion is rather loose, because concepts from both classical reaction rate theory and transition state theory are referred to. Strictly speaking, the mixing of concepts from the two theories is not permissible.

5-2   GENERAL METHODS OF EVALUATING KINETIC ISOTOPE EFFECTS

5-2a   METHODS FOR *INTER-MOLECULAR* EFFECTS

Intermolecular kinetic-isotope-effect ratios for carbon-14, that is, k_{12}/k_{14} or k_{14}/k_{12}, are usually evaluated by means of one of the four general methods described below. These methods can also be used to evaluate kinetic-isotope-effect ratios for carbon-13, nitrogen-15, oxygen-18, and other isotopes. Various researchers have altered these methods somewhat to suit their own needs, but the basic concepts of all methods of evaluating intermolecular carbon-isotope effects are summarized here.

For simplicity the following discussion is limited to isotope effects in reactions in which a labeled reactant produces only a single labeled product. If two labeled products are formed, as occurs in some reactions, this fact must be taken into account in calculating $k*/k$. The four methods of isotope-effect evaluation are designated by Numbers I through IV.

I. The molar radioactivity of the reaction product accumulated up to a measured percent reaction—preferably a small percent reaction—is compared with the molar radioactivity of the labeled reactant or with the molar radioactivity of the labeled product accumulated at 100% reaction. A simple relationship exists[31] between the ratio of the isotopic rate constants, $k*/k$, the fraction of the reaction that

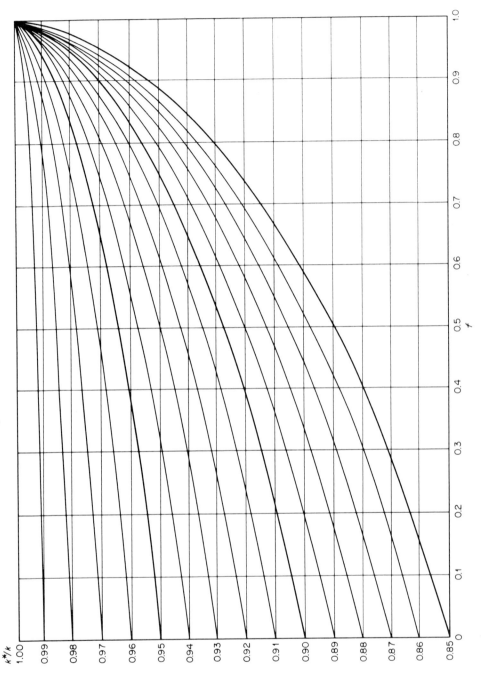

FIG. 5-3 Plot of $k*/k$ values as a function of r and f.

has been completed, f, and the ratio of the molar radioactivity of the labeled product of partial reaction to the molar radioactivity of the labeled reactant, r, as follows

$$\frac{k^*}{k} = \frac{\log (1 - rf)}{\log (1 - f)} \qquad (5\text{-}3)$$

Figure 5-3 shows the values for r at different values of f for the k^*/k ratios of 0.85 to 1.00; the values were calculated by means of Eq. 5-3. At values of f that approach 0, r becomes essentially equal to k^*/k. If f is unity, r is unity for any value of k^*/k. This relationship is necessarily true for an *intermolecular* isotope effect, although not for an *intramolecular* isotope effect. Figure 5-3 is useful for the rapid estimation of k^*/k values from isotopic data. It is used in the following way. Experimentally measured values of r and f determine a point on the graph through which a curve is drawn, the position of the curve being established by interpolation between the nearest given curves. The k^*/k value sought is the value for the intersection of the drawn curve with the ordinate axis.

Since the molar radioactivity of *accumulated* product at 100% reaction is equal to the molar radioactivity of the starting material, r can also be computed as the ratio of the specific (or molar) radioactivity of the product of partial reaction to the specific (or molar) radioactivity of the product of 100% reaction. Indeed, the computation of r in this manner is often preferred. Certain types of carbon-14 assay errors, for example, assay errors that are due to incomplete combustion of the labeled compounds to carbon-14 dioxide (Sec. 11-5), may not affect the ratio of the specific radioactivities of two samples of the *same labeled organic compound*. By contrast, it is much less likely that the effect of such carbon-14 assay errors will cancel in the calculation of the ratio of the *molar* radioactivities of two *different labeled organic compounds*.

In the foregoing discussion, the tacit assumption was made that no side reactions

occurred to complicate the calculation of values of k^*/k. However, many organic reactions cannot be carried to completion without the occurrence of side reactions. The extent of any error introduced into a calculated value of k^*/k as a result of a side reaction depends on whether or not the side reaction proceeds at a rate comparable with that of the main reaction and whether or not the side reaction proceeds with its own isotope effect.

The use of Fig. 5-3 is illustrated by the study of the isotope fractionation in the formation of the 2,4-dinitrophenylhydrazone of acetophenone-α-^{14}C at 78°

The specific radioactivity of the 2,4-dinitrophenylhydrazone formed by conversion of 30% of a sample of the labeled ketone was 0.00867 μc/mg. The specific radioactivity of the 2,4-dinitrophenylhydrazone formed by 100% conversion of another sample of the same labeled ketone was 0.00897 μc/mg. Therefore,

$$r = \frac{0.00867}{0.00897} = 0.967$$

and

$$f = 0.30$$

These values for r and f locate a point on Fig. 5-3. A curve drawn through this point and located by reference to the line that represents $k^*/k = 0.96$ intersects the ordinate axis at 0.959. Hence the ratio, k_{14}/k_{12}, is 0.959 at 78°. Alternatively, r could have been calculated as the ratio of the *molar* radioactivity of the 2,4-dinitrophenylhydrazone formed at 30% conversion of the acetophenone-α-^{14}C to the *molar* radioactivity of the acetophenone-α-^{14}C. Figure 5-3 would be used in the same way, and the answer arrived at should be the same. However, for the reason indicated above, it is preferable to calculate r as the ratio of the specific radioactivities of two samples of the *same* labeled compound whenever this is practical.

Figure 5-3 also has other uses. Suppose, for example, that an experimenter needs to know the molar radioactivity of the 2,4-dinitrophenylhydrazone produced by 50% conversion of a sample of *m*-nitroacetophenone-α-^{14}C of specific radioactivity 0.0120 μc/mg to the derivative at 25°. The literature[1] indicates that in this case $r = 0.962$ at $f = 0.10$. These values locate a point on Fig. 5-3 which happens to fall on the line that represents $k^*/k = 0.960$. This line has an ordinate value of 0.971 at $f = 0.50$. Therefore,

$$r = 0.971 = \frac{S_{50}}{0.0120}$$

where

S_{50} = specific activity of the derivative formed at 50% conversion of the *m*-nitro-acetophenone-α-^{14}C, μc/mg

From this simple equation, S_{50} is calculated to be 0.01165 μc/mg.

II. *The molar radioactivity of product formed at a very small percent reaction is compared with the molar radioactivity of labeled reactant or with the molar radioactivity of labeled product at 100% reaction.* This method is merely a special case of method I; in this special case the percent reaction is very small and need not be measured. The method has been referred to as the "low-conversion approximation."[32] The expression used to calculate the isotope effect is simply

$$\frac{k^*}{k} = r \tag{5-4}$$

Equation 5-4 is sufficiently accurate for use in estimating carbon-14 isotope effects if the

percent reaction is kept to about 3% or lower. At this low percent conversion, the error in the value for k_{14}/k_{12} that is introduced by the use of the low-conversion approximation is of about the same magnitude as the error in carbon-14 assays.

Method II is sometimes of particular value in estimating the ratio of two isotope effects, since some of the error may cancel in the calculation of the ratio.[1] For example, the ratio of the carbon-14 isotope effects for the same reaction at two temperatures can be estimated by means of Eq. 5-5

$$\frac{(k_{12}/k_{14})_{T_1}}{(k_{12}/k_{14})_{T_2}} = \frac{(S_3/S_{100})_{T_1}}{(S_3/S_{100})_{T_2}} = \frac{(S_3)_{T_1}}{(S_3)_{T_2}} \tag{5-5}$$

where

S_3 = specific (or molar) radioactivity of product at 3% reaction

S_{100} = specific (or molar) radioactivity of product at 100% reaction

If portions of the same carbon-14-labeled reactant are used for the reactions at the two temperatures, the values for S_{100} are identical; therefore, they cancel and need not be measured. Furthermore, if the reactions at the two temperatures are both carried to the same percent reaction (e.g., 3%), most of the error inherent in the low-conversion approximation also cancels in the calculation of the ratio of the two isotope effects. However, the method must be used with caution, because isotopically labeled impurities sometimes concentrate in the product of the first few percent of reaction. A serious error might thereby be introduced in the value for S_3. For specific examples of the use of this method, the reader is referred to the original literature.[1]

III. *The molar radioactivity of labeled reactant remaining after a measured percent reaction—preferably a high percent reaction—is compared with the molar radioactivity of the initial labeled reactant or with the molar radioactivity of labeled product accumulated at 100% reaction.* From the Stevens-Attree equation,[31] the relationship between the ratio of the isotopic rate constants, k^*/k, the fraction of the reaction that has been completed, f, and the ratio of the molar radioactivity of residual reactant to the molar radioactivity of the labeled reactant, r', can be shown to be

$$\frac{k^*}{k} = \frac{\log r'}{\log (1 - f)} + 1 \qquad (5\text{-}6)$$

For use in the rapid estimation of values of k^*/k from isotopic data, two graphs are given that are based on Eq. 5-6 and that show the relationship between r' and $(1 - f)$ for fifteen values of k^*/k. Figure 5-4 is for the reaction range 0 to 90%; Fig. 5-5 is for the range 90 to 99%. In practice, experimentally determined values for r' and for $(1 - f)$ locate a point on one of the two graphs. The

FIG. 5-4   Log-log plot of k^*/k values as a function of r' and $(1 - f)$ from 0 to 90% reaction.

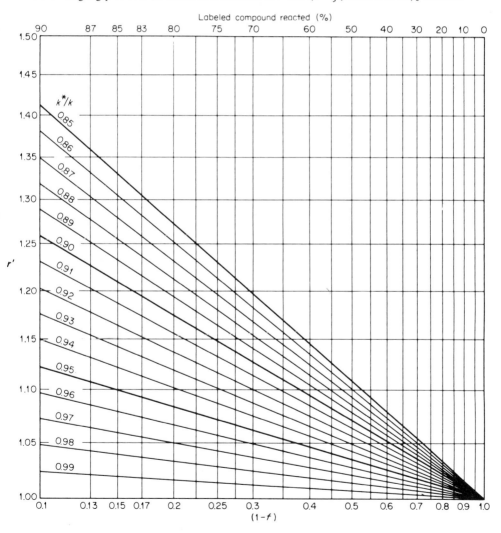

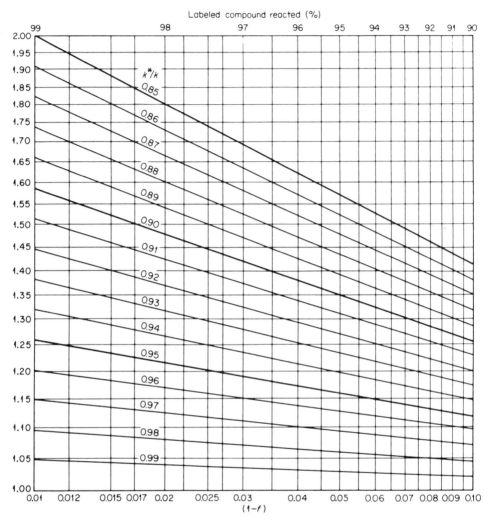

FIG. 5-5   Log-log plot of k^*/k values as a function of r' and $(1-f)$ from 90 to 99% reaction.

corresponding k^*/k ratio is estimated by interpolation between the nearest diagonal lines. Figures 5-4 and 5-5 indicate that the correct use of this method requires the accurate measurement of the percent reaction. Furthermore, for this method to be really effective, the percent reaction should be not less than 50%—preferably greater than 90%. At such high percent conversion, side reactions may interfere with the method. However, the method can be very effective in the estimation of isotope-effect ratios in clean reactions that are fast enough to be carried to more than 90% completion in a reasonable time.

A typical example of the application of Figs. 5-4 and 5-5 is taken from a study of the photochemical oxidation of gaseous formic-^{13}C acid with chlorine.[33] The *intermolecular* isotope fractionation involves the competition of two isotopic species for chlorine

$$Cl_2 + H^{12}CO_2H \xrightarrow{k_{12}} 2\,HCl + {}^{12}CO_2\uparrow$$

and

$$Cl_2 + H^{13}CO_2H \xrightarrow{k_{13}} 2\,HCl + {}^{13}CO_2\uparrow$$

In one experiment, the ratio k_{13}/k_{12} was evaluated by comparing the percent carbon-13 in the carbon dioxide produced during the last 16% of the reaction with the percent carbon-13 in the carbon dioxide accumulated during total (100%) reaction of another portion of the same formic-^{13}C acid. The carbon dioxide samples were analyzed by mass spectrometry. If the symbol P is used to represent the percent carbon-13 and if the subscripts indicate the percent of the reaction during which the carbon dioxide was collected, then

$$r' = \frac{P_{16}}{P_{100}} = 1.017 \quad \text{at} \quad (1-f) = 0.16$$

These values for r' and $(1-f)$ locate a point on Fig. 5-4 just below the line that represents $k^*/k - 0.99$. The point lies about 10% of the way between the lines representing $k^*/k = 0.99$ and $k^*/k = 1.00$. The ratio of isotopic rate constants for the two species (i.e., k_{13}/k_{12}) is therefore estimated to be 0.991. A more accurate estimate could be obtained by actually substituting the values for r' and $(1-f)$ in Eq. 5-6 and solving for k^*/k.

IV. The specific activity of small product increments is studied as a function of percent reaction. Only a few applications of this method have been found so far, because it is usually impractical to collect a small increment of product at a known percent reaction. However, the method can be useful in studies of some reactions in which the product is evolved as a gas, is separated as a precipitate, or is extracted as rapidly as it forms. Downes[34] discusses this method of studying kinetic isotope effects. A relationship between k^*/k, f, and r'' (the ratio of the molar radioactivity of the increment of product to the molar radioactivity of the labeled reactant) has been derived[34,35]

$$\ln r'' = \left(\frac{k^*}{k} - 1\right)[\ln(1-f)] + \ln\left(\frac{k^*}{k}\right) \quad (5\text{-}7)$$

where

f = fraction of reaction at the end of which the product increment was collected. In some cases Eq. 5-7 can be used conveniently to evaluate $[(k^*/k) - 1]$ as the slope of the line obtained by plotting $\log r''$ vs $\log(1-f)$.

The effect of the value for k^*/k on the variation of r'' with f (the fraction of reaction at which an increment of product was collected) is shown in Figs. 5-6 and 5-7. Figure 5-6 is for the reaction range 0 to 90%; Fig. 5-7 is for the range 90 to 99%.

An application of Figs. 5-6 and 5-7 is illustrated by the decarbonylation of formic-^{14}C acid in concentrated sulfuric acid[30] at room temperature; the reaction produces carbon-^{14}C monoxide, which bubbles out of solution as rapidly as it forms if the solution is stirred vigorously. Small samples of carbon-^{14}C monoxide can be collected at any stage of the reaction. It is desired to estimate the specific radioactivity of the increment of carbon-^{14}C monoxide produced just at the instant when 80% of a sample of formic-^{14}C acid has decomposed at 25°. A sample of carbon-^{14}C monoxide produced by quantitative decarbonylation of a portion of the original formic-^{14}C acid had a specific radioactivity of 0.10 μc/mg. The value for k_{14}/k_{12} is reported to be 0.914 at 25°.[30] Figure 5-6 is used. Interpolation between the lines representing $k^*/k = 0.91$ and $k^*/k = 0.92$ shows that $r'' = 1.05$ at $f = 0.80$. Therefore, by solution of the simple equation

$$r'' = 1.05 = \frac{S_{80}}{0.10}$$

where

S_{80} = instantaneous specific radioactivity of ^{14}CO at 80% reaction, μc/mg

the value for S_{80} is found to be 0.105 μc/mg.

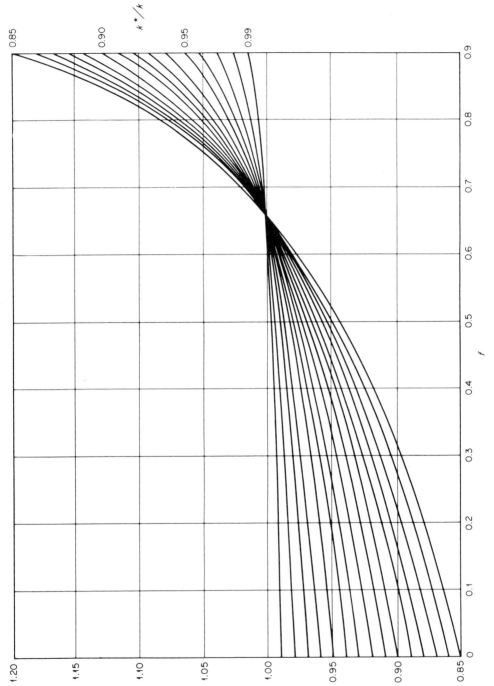

FIG. 5-6 Plot of $k*/k$ values as a function of r'' and f from 0 to 90% reaction.

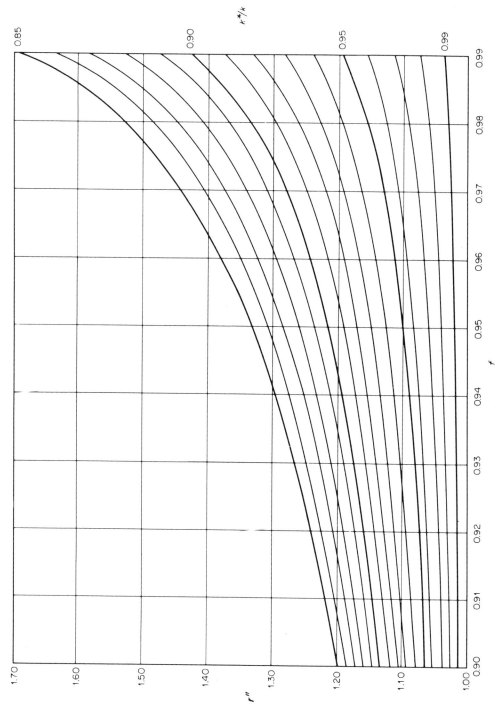

FIG. 5-7 Plot of k^*/k values as a function of r'' and f from 90 to 99% reaction.

Raaen and co-workers[35a,35b] used closely related techniques to study various isotope effects in the formation of the 2,4-dinitro-phenylhydrazone of acetophenone. In the study of hydrazone formation, the data were programmed for an IBM computer through a generalized least squares program written by Lietzke.[35c] The program includes a sub-routine to perform all matrix operations and to furnish the main calling program with the coefficients, standard errors in the coefficients, variance of fit, and a complete error analysis.

For secondary isotope effects, small differences between large numbers are measured; consequently, it is necessary to be very cautious in evaluating the data. Erroneous kinetic methods are used, in some instances, to investigate small isotope effects. These considerations are discussed in a review by Collins.[35d]

The relationship between the specific radioactivity of a very small increment of product and the time of collection of the product increment has also been derived for a first-order reaction of a carbon-14-labeled compound[30]

$$\ln S = C + t(k_{12} - k_{14}) \qquad (5\text{-}8)$$

where

S = specific radioactivity
C = constant
t = time

By use of Eq. 5-8, the value for $(k_{12} - k_{14})$ is measured as the slope of a plot of $\ln S$ versus t. If k_{12}, the first-order rate constant, can also be measured, the ratio of isotopic rate constants can be calculated by means of the simple expression

$$\frac{k_{12} - k_{14}}{k_{12}} = 1 - \frac{k_{14}}{k_{12}}$$

For a more rigorous treatment of variations of specific radioactivity during reactions that exhibit isotope fractionation, the reader is referred to the works of Bigeleisen

and co-workers[16,32] and to other independent work.[35e] The expected error in the calculated values of isotope-effect ratios that arises from errors in the determination of specific radioactivities and of the percent reaction has also been discussed.[36,37]

5-2b METHODS FOR *INTRA-MOLECULAR* EFFECTS

The methods used to evaluate *intramolecular* isotope effects can be illustrated best by reference to the decarboxylation of malonic-1-^{14}C acid (Eq. 5-1). After any fraction of the malonic-1-^{14}C acid has decarboxylated, a simple relationship holds

$$\left(\frac{k_{14}}{k_{12}}\right)_{\text{intra}} = \frac{S_{CO_2}}{S_{CH_3CO_2H}} \qquad (5\text{-}9)$$

where

S_{CO_2} = molar radioactivity of the accumulated carbon-14 dioxide, mc/mole
$S_{CH_3CO_2H}$ = molar radioactivity of the accumulated acetic-1-^{14}C acid, mc/mole

Alternately, after complete reaction[38]

$$\left(\frac{k_{14}}{k_{12}}\right)_{\text{intra}} = \frac{S_{CO_2}}{S_M^0 - S_{CO_2}}$$
$$= \frac{S_M^0 - S_{CH_3CO_2H}}{S_{CH_3CO_2H}} \qquad (5\text{-}10)$$

where

S_M^0 = molar radioactivity of malonic-1-^{14}C acid used in the reaction, mc/mole

During the course of the reaction, the *intra-molecular* isotope effect is superimposed on an *intermolecular* isotope effect. As a result, the relationships between S_M^0 and S_{CO_2} and those between S_M^0 and $S_{CH_3CO_2H}$ are more complex than the relationships expressed in Eq. 5-10 if the decarboxylation is less than 100% complete (Sec. 15-5a). The *intra-molecular* isotope effect in other reactions can, of course, be calculated by use of expressions analogous to Eqs. 5-9 and 5-10 (Sec. 15-5a).

5-2c RELATIVE MERITS OF CARBON-13 AND CARBON-14 IN ISOTOPE-EFFECT STUDIES

In some applications of carbon isotope effects to the study of reaction mechanisms, the measurement of either k_{12}/k_{14} or k_{12}/k_{13} gives the same information. The study of the mechanism of the decarbonylation of formic acid (Sec. 5-1c) is an illustration. The decarbonylation reaction could as well have been investigated by using formic-^{13}C acid and evaluating k_{12}/k_{13}. The conclusions reached would have been the same, although the carbon-13 kinetic isotope effect, which has also been determined,[39] is only about one-half as great as the measured carbon-14 kinetic isotope effect under the same reaction conditions. Since an experimenter may sometimes have to choose between carbon-14 and carbon-13 for an isotope-effect study, the advantages and limitations of each isotope are discussed at this point.

The use of carbon-13 offers two advantages. First, carbon-13 isotope effects can be studied by use of naturally occurring carbon-13, which exists in amounts of about 1% in ordinary carbon-containing reagents. This advantage is a distinct one over carbon-14, the compounds of which must be synthesized and in some cases are very difficult to obtain or very expensive. Second, carbon-13 compounds can be isotopically assayed with greater precision and accuracy by use of a ratio mass spectrometer than carbon-14 compounds can by radiochemical methods. The precision and accuracy of carbon-14 assays are discussed in Sec. 11-7. Although mass spectrometric assay of carbon-14 compounds is possible, this has not been done except in a few cases, because most compounds that contain the necessary 0.1 to 1.0% of the carbon-14-labeled species are costly.

The use of carbon-13 also has disadvantages; these can be discussed most easily by means of an example. The study of the isotope fractionation in the saponification of carbonyl-labeled ethyl benzoate is a relatively

simple matter if the label is carbon-14 (Sec. 5-1a). By contrast, a precise study of the carbon-13 isotope fractionation in the corresponding saponification of ethyl benzoate that contained carbon-13 at the natural level of abundance could be very difficult. The reason is that the percent carbon-13 in the *alpha* position of the ester or in the *alpha* position of the product, benzoic acid, would have to be determined by mass spectrometric analysis of the carbon dioxide derived solely *from the carboxyl group*. The degradation process (Chap. 10) used to isolate the carboxyl-group carbon atom as carbon dioxide would need either to be free of any isotope effect of its own or otherwise to be completely quantitative. For further discussion of these requirements, see Sec. 10-2c. Their stringency explains why carbon-13 isotope effects can seldom be measured precisely in chemical reactions of compounds that contain more than one carbon atom.

Carbon-14 is, for the reason just stated, more generally applicable than is carbon-13 as a tracer isotope in isotope-fractionation studies. Furthermore, carbon-14 isotope effects are about twice as large as carbon-13 effects. The greater magnitude of carbon-14 isotope effects partly offsets the fact that carbon-14 radioassays are less precise than carbon-13 mass spectrometric assays.

5-3 THEORETICAL EVALUATION OF CARBON ISOTOPE EFFECTS

Although a rigorous treatment of the theory of kinetic isotope effects would be out of place in this volume, it is worthwhile to expand somewhat the rather sketchy introduction given in Sec. 5-1f. Several examples are included to illustrate how theoretical values for kinetic carbon isotope effects have been estimated. A number of assumptions that underlie these estimates are discussed briefly. References to detailed treatments of isotope-effect theory are given in this chapter. The interested reader of the works referred to will soon realize that isotope-effect theory is still in the development stage and that for some reactions of labeled compounds there is no general agreement as to how theoretical values should be computed. Part of this difficulty arises because the overall reaction mechanism has a controlling influence on the magnitude of the isotope effect to be expected for a given reaction (see Sec. 5-4). Melander describes broadly the theoretical treatment of carbon isotope effects, as well as isotope effects in general, in a volume[39a] that should help provide perspective for organic chemists who apply isotopes in their research.

5-3a INTERMOLECULAR KINETIC ISOTOPE EFFECTS

In the simplified treatment of the carbon-14 isotope effect in carbon-to-oxygen bond cleavage (Sec. 5-1f), several significant factors were ignored. The assumptions implied there can be explained best by using as an example the rate-controlling carbon-to-oxygen cleavage in the decarbonylation of formic-^{14}C acid (Sec. 5-1c).

First, the use of a diatomic model is only a crude approximation, because the vibrational frequencies in a real molecule such as formic acid are interrelated and cannot properly be treated as if they were independent. Therefore, calculation of a vibrational-frequency shift by considering only a carbon-to-oxygen bond and treating it as a harmonic oscillator will introduce some error in the calculation of the carbon-14 isotope effect. In a few cases, it is possible to measure experimentally the shifts in vibrational frequencies that result from isotopic substitution in a reactant. Otherwise, the methods described by Herzberg[40] may be useful. For predicting carbon-isotope-effect ratios in reactions of complex labeled molecules, frequency shifts based on the simple diatomic model have been used occasionally; in these cases, the justification is that the error introduced is not excessive in comparison with the errors that arise from

other unavoidable assumptions or approximations.

Second, it was assumed in Sec. 5-1f that only one bond in the formic acid molecule (i.e., a carbon-to-oxygen bond) is altered in proceeding from the ground state to the activated state. The observed secondary deuterium isotope effect referred to in Sec. 5-1c indicates that this is a false assumption. A logical interpretation of this secondary deuterium isotope effect is that the carbon-to-hydrogen bond is also altered in proceeding from the ground state to the transition state. It is probable that the second carbon-to-oxygen bond is also altered to some degree during the activation process, but the degree of its alteration cannot be measured.

Third, not all the formic acid molecules are in their lowest vibrational-energy level. The population of higher vibrational-energy levels can modify the simple picture of the effect of isotope substitution on the 0-point energy shown in Fig. 5-2.

Fourth, in the simple interpretation of carbon-to-oxygen bond cleavage presented in Sec. 5-1f, the carbon-to-oxygen bond was assumed to have no residual strength in the transition state at the top of the hump shown in Fig. 5-2. There is no assurance that this is a correct assumption, since work with hydrogen isotopes has shown that an activated complex can have some of the properties of a real molecule including a 0-point energy.[41] The effect of residual carbon-to-oxygen bonding in the activated complex is to decrease the difference in activation energy between the two isotopic species, $(E_{14} - E_{12})$, as shown in Fig. 5-8. As the spread of isotopic 0-point energy levels in the activated state approaches the spread of isotopic 0-point energy levels of molecules in the energy well to the left, E_{12} approaches E_{14}, and the isotope effect due to carbon-14 substitution diminishes.

Also ignored was quantum-mechanical tunneling[42] through the energy barrier. However, there seems to be little reason to

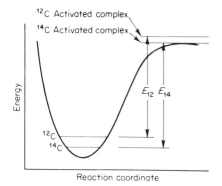

FIG. 5-8 Reduction of $(E_{14} - E_{12})$ by residual bonding in the activated complex.

expect the tunnel effect to exert an appreciable influence on carbon-14 isotope fractionation, although Bell, Fendley, and Hulett[42] report evidence for quantum-mechanical tunneling in a series of deuterium isotope effects in organic reactions involving transfer of protons. Bigeleisen and Wolfsberg take the tunnel effect into account in predicting carbon isotope effects by Eq. 5-15, which is given later in this section.

Bigeleisen,[13,43] Eyring and Cagle,[15] Melander,[27,39a] and others who used a similar approach have considered the problem of calculation of kinetic-isotope-effect ratios in the light of the theory of absolute reaction rates.[44] Bigeleisen devised an equation based on earlier work with Mayer;[45] this equation (Eq. 5-11) is useful in predicting kinetic-isotope-effect ratios that result from isotope substitution of light elements including carbon. Equation 5-11 is not applicable to the calculation of kinetic isotope effects caused by substitution of deuterium or tritium for hydrogen. Equation 5-11,

$$\frac{k}{k^*} = \left(\frac{\mu^*}{\mu}\right)^{1/2}\left[1 + \sum_{i}^{3N-6} G(u_i)\,\Delta u_i\right.$$
$$\left. - \sum_{j}^{3N-7} G(u_j^{\ddagger})\,\Delta u_j^{\ddagger}\right]   (5-11)$$

and most of the concepts in Sec. 5-3, are applicable to bimolecular reactions and to

reactions of higher orders, but they are applicable to unimolecular reactions at high pressures only. In Eq. 5-11

μ = reduced mass associated with the atoms separating in the reaction coordinate

μ^* = corresponding reduced mass for the labeled or heavy molecule

N = number of atoms in molecule

$$G(u) = \text{a function of } u = \frac{1}{2} - \frac{1}{u} + \frac{1}{e^u - 1}$$
$$u = \frac{hc\omega}{kT}$$

where

h = Planck constant = 6.624×10^{-27} erg sec

c = velocity of light = 2.998×10^{10} cm/sec

ω = vibrational frequency, cm^{-1}

$k = 1.381 \times 10^{-16}$ erg/deg

T = temperature, $^\circ$K

$$\Delta u = \frac{hc\,\Delta\omega}{kT}$$

where

$\Delta\omega$ = change in the vibrational or other frequency as a result of isotopic substitution Starred terms refer to the activated complex. To keep Eq. 5-11 as simple as possible, symmetry numbers have been left out. They are small whole numbers and ordinarily have no net effect on the calculated value of k/k^* for an *intermolecular* isotope effect.

The term $(\mu^*/\mu)^{1/2}$ in Eq. 5-11 has been called the "temperature-independent factor" or simply the "reduced-mass factor." The bracketed term is sometimes called the "0-point energy factor," although it actually includes more than the simple 0-point energy effect described in Sec. 5-1f. It is also called the "temperature-dependent factor." Its numerical value approaches unity as the reaction temperature is raised. The value for k/k^* therefore should approach the temperature-independent factor as a lower limit at high temperatures. Numerous experiments have demonstrated that isotope effects actually do decrease as the temperature is increased.

Other things being equal, the bracketed term, and therefore the value for k/k^*, is greatest when

$$\sum_{j}^{3N-7} G(u_j{}^{\ddagger}) \, \Delta u_j{}^{\ddagger} = 0 \qquad (5\text{-}12)$$

Equation 5-12 is a quantitative statement of the conclusion reached above by inspection of Fig. 5-8, namely, the predicted isotope effect should become greater as the residual bonding to the labeled atoms in the transition state becomes weaker. Unfortunately, the properties of the activated complex in a real reaction are never known, and therein lies one of the greatest drawbacks to applying Eq. 5-11: the calculated value of k/k^* must always be the result of an "educated guess" as to the degree of residual bonding to the labeled atom in the activated complex.

The terms

$$\sum_{i}^{3N-6} G(u_i) \, \Delta u_i$$

and

$$\sum_{j}^{3N-7} G(u_j{}^{\ddagger}) \Delta u_j{}^{\ddagger}$$

are summations that take into account the effects of isotopic substitution on *all* the vibrational frequencies in the molecule and in the activated state. Thus, the calculated value of k/k^* is not based merely on the effect of isotope substitution on the vibrational frequency of the one bond being broken, as was the case in the simple model described in Sec. 5-1f. Clearly, a better estimate of k/k^* should be obtained by use of Eq. 5-11 than by use of the simpler calculation of Sec. 5-1f. However, since the bracketed expression in Eq. 5-11 consists of a net total of terms for the normal molecules and for the activated complex, only frequencies that are affected by isotopic substitution and that change in proceeding from normal molecules to the activated state need be considered in applying Eq. 5-11. Accordingly, frequencies of bonds that are remote from the labeled position and remote from the reaction center

do not appear in calculations based on Eq. 5-11.

Many years ago Pitzer[46] demonstrated the use of Eq. 5-11 in a study of intermolecular isotope effects. His application of this equation to the decarboxylation of carboxyl-labeled acids is given in detail here

$$\text{R--}{}^{14}\text{C} \overset{\displaystyle \diagup \text{OH}}{\underset{\displaystyle \diagdown \text{O}}{}} \;\; \to \text{RH} + {}^{14}\text{CO}_2 \qquad (5\text{-}13)$$

The activated complex is assumed to be

$$\text{R---C} \overset{\displaystyle \diagup \text{OH}}{\underset{\displaystyle \diagdown \text{O}}{}}$$

with the force constant of the R---C bond taken to be about zero. The activated complex is left with only two frequencies, a C—O stretching frequency and a C=O stretching frequency. Table 5-2 lists values for $G(u) \, \Delta u$ given by Pitzer[46] for the decarboxylation of a carboxyl-^{14}C acid at 400°K. The values for

Table 5-2   Values for $G(u) \, \Delta u$ for the decarboxylation of a carboxyl-^{14}C acid at 400°K^a

$(\omega)_{12_C}$	$(\omega)_{14_C}$	$\Delta\omega$	$G(u)$	$G(u) \, \Delta u$
Normal acid molecule				
1800	1713	87	0.343	0.107
837	834	3	0.219	0.002
493	490	3	0.140	0.002
1423	1346	77	0.301	0.083
483	481	2	0.138	0.001
700	659	41	0.180	0.029
			Total =	0.224
Activated complex				
1711	1633	78	0.332	0.093
1088	1053	35	0.260	0.032
			Total =	0.125

^{a} From K. S. Pitzer, *J. Chem. Phys.*, **17**, 1341 (1949), with permission of the *Journal of Chemical Physics* and the author.

the stretching or bending frequencies of the bonds in such an acid are given in the first column of the table; other terms required in the calculation of the $G(u) \Delta u$ values are also given. The two carbon-to-oxygen stretching frequencies for the activated complex are listed at the bottom of the first column. The values for $(\omega)_{14C}$ are estimated by methods described by Herzberg,[40] and the $\Delta \omega$ values are the differences between corresponding listings for $(\omega)_{12C}$ and $(\omega)_{14C}$. The values for $G(u)$ and $G(u) \Delta u$ are calculated from formulas given above. All frequencies of the acid molecule that are omitted from the list are assumed to be unchanged by the isotopic substitution. Therefore,

$$\frac{k_{12}}{k_{14}} = \left[\frac{(12 \times 14)/(12 + 14)}{(12 \times 12)/(12 + 12)} \right]^{1/2}$$
$$\times (1 + 0.224 - 0.125) = 1.141$$

The calculations that lead to this value for k_{12}/k_{14} are taken from Pitzer.[46] The temperature-independent factor, $(\mu^*/\mu)^{1/2}$, is based simply on the reduced masses of the carbon atoms joined by the bond that breaks in the decarboxylation reaction (Eq. 5-13). It is apparent that the calculated value for the carbon-14 isotope effect, 14.1%, is highly dependent on the values assumed for the frequencies in the normal molecules and in the activated complex. Few, if any, observed carbon-14 isotope effects are as large as 14% at 130°.

In the study of reaction mechanisms, it is sometimes helpful to estimate roughly the isotope effect to be expected for cleavage of bonds of various types. Table 5-3 was compiled for this purpose. As stretching frequencies usually contribute much more to the isotope effect than do other frequencies, typical stretching frequencies[47,48] are tabulated for various bonds to carbon. The corresponding values of $(\mu^*/\mu)^{1/2}$, the temperature-independent factor based on the listed frequencies, are also tabulated for each bond type. For the sake of evaluating $G(u) \Delta u$

Table 5-3 Typical stretching frequencies and reduced-mass factors for carbon-14 substitution in various bonds to carbon

Bond	Stretching frequency (ω), cm^{-1}	Reduced-mass factor $\left(\dfrac{\mu^*}{\mu} \right)^{1/2}$
C—H	3000	1.0056
C—C	830	
C=C	1625	1.038
C≡C	2175	
C—N	900	
C=N	1600	1.041
C≡N	2150	
C—O	850	
C=O	1730	1.044
C≡O	2160	
C—F	1070	1.047
C—Cl	650	1.059
C—Br	550	1.069
C—I	500	1.073
C—SH	650	
C=S	1520	1.056

in the normal molecule, the assumption is made that $(\mu^*/\mu)^{1/2}$ can also be used to estimate $\Delta \omega$ according to the expression

$$\Delta \omega = \omega \left(1 - \frac{1}{(\mu^*/\mu)^{1/2}} \right) \qquad (5\text{-}14)$$

This use of $(\mu^*/\mu)^{1/2}$ in Eq. 5-14 to evaluate $\Delta \omega$, and thence the bracketed term of Eq. 5-11, is the same approximation as that referred to in Sec. 5-1f.

The values for $G(u) \Delta u$ for carbon-14 substitution in the various types of bonds to carbon are plotted against temperature in Figs. 5-9, 5-10, and 5-11. Two examples of the use of these figures and of Table 5-3 follow.

First, let us suppose that we need to know the approximate value of k_{12}/k_{14} to be

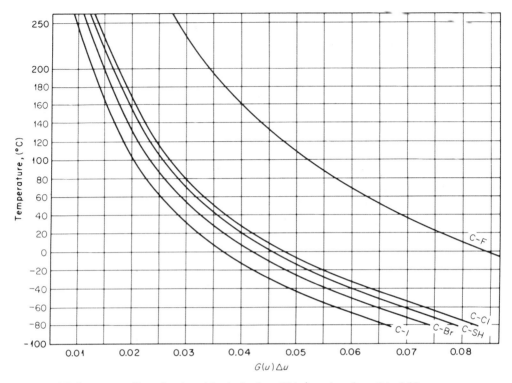

FIG. 5-9 0-Point energy effect of carbon-14 substitution. $G(u) \, \Delta u$ values from 0 to 0.08.

expected in the cleavage of a carbon-to-nitrogen single bond in a reaction of a carbon-14-labeled molecule at 50°. The value given in Table 5-3 for $(\mu^*/\mu)^{1/2}$ for carbon-to-nitrogen bonds is 1.041. The value for $G(u) \, \Delta u$ for the carbon-to-nitrogen single bond at 50° is indicated in Fig. 5-10 to be 0.043. If it is assumed that there is no residual bonding to the labeled carbon in the activated complex, then

$$\frac{k_{12}}{k_{14}} = 1.041(1 + 0.043 - 0) = 1.086$$

Obviously, the calculated value of the carbon-14 isotope effect, 8.6%, must not be used without consideration of the many assumptions on which it is based.

Table 5-3 and Figs. 5-9, 5-10, and 5-11 are also helpful in indicating the *relative*

carbon-14 isotope effects to be expected for cleavage of various types of bonds under the same reaction conditions. For example, we may estimate the relative carbon-14 isotope effects in the cleavage of a carbon-to-fluorine bond and a carbon-to-chlorine bond at 100° as follows if no residual bonding in the activated complex in either reaction is assumed

$$\frac{[(k_{12}/k_{14}) - 1]_{\text{F}}}{[(k_{12}/k_{14}) - 1]_{\text{Cl}}} = \frac{1.047(1 + 0.052 - 0) - 1}{1.059(1 + 0.027 - 0) - 1}$$

$$= 1.16$$

If it is assumed that the mechanisms for the carbon-to-fluorine cleavage and the carbon-to-chlorine cleavage are the same, the calculation indicates that a one-sixth larger carbon-14 isotope effect should be expected for the former than for the latter cleavage reaction at 100°.

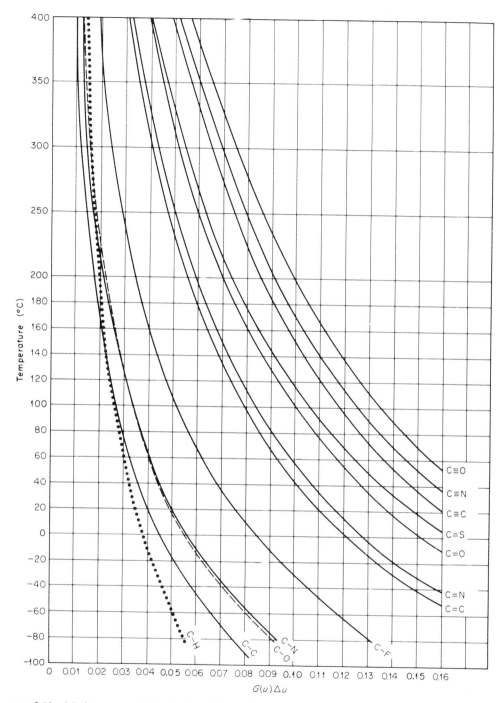

FIG. 5-10 0-Point energy effect of carbon-14 substitution. $G(u)$ Δu values from 0 to 0.15.

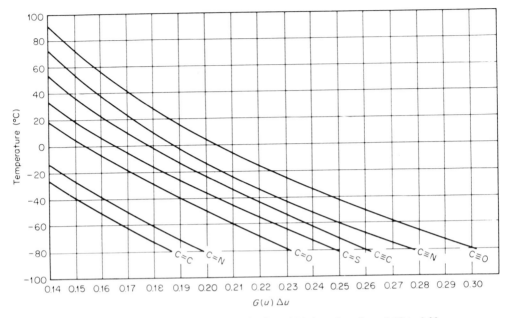

FIG. 5-11   0-Point energy effect of carbon-14 substitution. $G(u) \, \Delta u$ values from 0.15 to 0.30.

Estimates of carbon-14 isotope effects based on Table 5-3 and Figs. 5-9, 5-10, and 5-11 as just described are first approximations only. The justification for such estimates is that they can be made very quickly.

Carbon-13 isotope effects, being about one-half as great as carbon-14 isotope effects, can be estimated by using Table 5-3 and Figs. 5-9, 5-10, and 5-11 and dividing the resulting value for $[(k_{12}/k_{14}) - 1]$ by 2.

Other equations related to Eq. 5-11 have been derived by Bigeleisen and Wolfsberg.[48a] Among these are Eq. 5-15, which is copied here without the symmetry numbers for simplicity. Equation 5-15, like Eq. 5-11, is limited to isotope effects other than those due to substitution of deuterium and tritium for hydrogen. Equation 5-15 was derived for small values of u (as defined for Eq. 5-11). It includes a correction for the influence of the tunnel effect on the isotope effect; it also provides a convenient alternative to the use of Eq. 5-11 for some purposes. In Eq. 5-15

$$\frac{k_1}{k_2} = (\nu_{1L}^{\ddagger}/\nu_{2L}^{\ddagger}) \left[1 + \frac{\bar{\nu}}{24} \left(\frac{hc}{kT} \right) \sum_i^{3N} \left(\frac{1}{m_{1i}} - \frac{1}{m_{2i}} \right) \right.$$
$$\left. \times (a_{ii} - a_{ii}^{\ddagger}) \right] \quad (5\text{-}15)$$

k_1, k_2 = rate constants for light and heavy species, respectively

$\nu_{1L}^{\ddagger}$, $\nu_{2L}^{\ddagger}$ = frequencies along the path of decomposition of the light and heavy species, respectively

$\bar{\nu}$ = estimated average value of 12 $G(u_i)/u_i$ for the chemical reaction involved

m_{1i}, m_{2i} = masses (atomic mass units) of light and heavy nuclides, respectively

a_{ii}, $a_{ii}^{\ddagger}$ = diagonal cartesian force constants (md · A^{-1}) for the bond in the reactant and in the transition state, respectively[48b]

All other symbols were defined in connection with Eq. 5-11. Bigeleisen and co-workers[48b] applied Eq. 5-15 in a study of the temperature dependence of the carbon-13 and carbon-14 isotope effects in the decarbonylation of formic acid. This equation has also been used to study the influence of solvents on the isotope effect (Sec. 5-6e).

Like Eq. 5-11, Eq. 5-15 expresses the isotopic-rate-constant ratio as a product of a temperature-independent factor (in parentheses) and a temperature-dependent factor [in brackets]. The temperature-independent factor in Eq. 5-15 is expressed in general terms only, but Eq. 5-11 provides for a specific calculation of the temperature-independent factor from reduced masses. Three methods for the evaluation of $\nu_{1L}{}^{\ddagger}/\nu_{2L}{}^{\ddagger}$ are discussed briefly in Sec. 5-6h.

5-3b INTRAMOLECULAR KINETIC ISOTOPE EFFECTS

Intramolecular isotope effects can occur only in the reactions of molecules whose reacting groups are chemically equivalent. Accordingly, such effects are not of major interest to the student of reaction mechanisms simply because most chemical reactions are not reactions of molecules that have such symmetry. However, because many of the basic studies of kinetic isotope effects have been studies of *intramolecular* isotope effects, the theoretical basis of *intramolecular* isotope fractionation is considered very briefly at this point.

It was believed at one time that the 0-point energy effect should not enter into the calculation of the *intramolecular* isotope effect in the decarboxylation of carboxyl-^{14}C malonic acid (Eq. 5-1) and that the *intramolecular* fractionation factor was simply the temperature-independent factor of Eq. 5-11

$$\left(\frac{k}{k^*}\right)_{intra} = \left(\frac{\mu^*}{\mu}\right)^{1/2} \qquad (5\text{-}16)$$

However, the simple relationship expressed in Eq. 5-16 cannot explain a number of experimental values[48c] of *intramolecular* isotope effects and, in particular, their temperature coefficients.[48d] Equations like Eqs. 5-11 and 5-15 with symmetry numbers included[48a]

are necessary for prediction of the isotope effects to be expected in cases of *intramolecular* isotope fractionation. Table 5-5 supplies references to a number of *intramolecular* isotope-effect studies.

5-4 RELATION OF KINETIC CARBON ISOTOPE EFFECTS REACTION MECHANISMS

The estimation of expected values for k/k^* from theoretical considerations as discussed in Sec. 5-3 presupposes a reaction mechanism in which the reaction velocity is controlled by the rate of cleavage of a bond to a labeled carbon atom. The overall reaction mechanism must always be considered when such estimates of k/k^* are made. Often, as in the case of the bromodecarboxylation of 3,5-dibromo-4-hydroxybenzoic acid (Sec. 5-4g), the dependence of k/k^* on the reaction mechanism is rather intricate. It is the fact that k/k^* is intimately related to the overall reaction scheme that makes determination of isotope effects a useful tool for the study of reaction mechanisms.

The mere observation of a *primary* carbon-13 or carbon-14 isotope effect provides helpful information about the reaction scheme in some cases such as that discussed in Sec. 5-1c.[14,35] In these cases, a broad view of the mechanism can be obtained without either measuring k/k^* accurately or comparing quantitatively a measured ratio with a value to be expected from theoretical considerations.

In the following sections, the isotope effects probable in several types of reaction schemes are discussed briefly.

5-4a DIFFUSION-CONTROLLED REACTIONS

We may consider a bimolecular process for which the reactions of the unlabeled and labeled species are, respectively,

$$A + B \xrightarrow{k} \text{products}$$

$$A^* + B \xrightarrow{k^*} \text{labeled products} + \text{other products}$$

If the reaction rate is diffusion-controlled and if reaction occurs at every collision of A and B or A* and B, it is apparent that the only difference between k and $k*$ will be due to a difference between the relative collision frequencies of A with B and of A* with B. Therefore, the considerations discussed in Sec. 5-3 do not apply. Instead, a calculation of the approximate relative collision frequencies leads to the simple relation

$$\frac{k}{k*} = \left(\frac{M_{A*}}{M_A}\right)^{1/2} \qquad (5\text{-}17)$$

where

M_A and M_{A*} = molecular weights

A more accurate expression[33] of the relative collision frequency takes M_B into account also, but Eq. 5-17 is sufficiently accurate for the purpose of the present discussion. If the value of M_A is 100 and if A* is labeled with carbon-14, then

$$\frac{k}{k*} = \left(\frac{102}{100}\right)^{1/2} = 1.01$$

The point illustrated is that carbon-14 isotope effects will *usually* be small in a diffusion-controlled reaction, particularly if the reaction occurs in solution where the molecular weights may well be enlarged by solvation of the molecules. Possibly the only large carbon-14 isotope effect in a diffusion-controlled reaction would occur in some gas-phase reactions of methane-^{14}C. The carbon-14 isotope effect might in that case approach

$$\frac{k}{k*} = \left(\frac{18}{16}\right)^{1/2} = 1.06$$

5-4b ACTIVATION-CONTROLLED REACTIONS

The calculations of Sec. 5-3 apply to activation-controlled processes in which a bond, or bonds, to an isotopically labeled position is altered in proceeding from the reactant

to the transition state. However, as was indicated in Sec. 5-3, isotope effects having a range of values may be observed in an activation-controlled process depending on the degree to which the bond, or bonds, to the labeled position is altered in proceeding from the reactant to the transition state. Hammond[49] discusses this point in detail with reference to an observation made by Melander.[50] Melander did not find a measurable tritium isotope effect in the nitration or bromination of aromatic rings with tritium substituted for the hydrogen attached to the ring carbon at which electrophilic substitution occurs. The reactions are

and

The principle, which is brought out in Hammond's discussion[49] and which is also applicable to reactions involving isotopes of carbon, may be stated as follows: *the observation of a primary isotope effect demonstrates unequivocally that the labeled atom is critically involved in the rate-controlling step, but the observed absence of a primary isotope effect can have either of two meanings. The two possible meanings are (a) that the labeled atom is not directly involved in the rate-controlling step and (b) that the critical bond which becomes the reaction coordinate changes very little in proceeding from the reactant to the transition state.* According to Hammond, meaning (b) is most likely to be applicable to highly exothermic reactions that have low activation energies.

The dependence of the magnitude of carbon isotope effects on aspects of a reaction mechanism is illustrated by the example that is discussed in detail in Sec. 5-4g.

5-4c REACTION MECHANISMS THAT MAY LEAD TO UNEXPECTED ISOTOPE EFFECTS

The possibility that large cumulative isotope effects might be found in systems of successive reactions, particularly in complex biochemical reactions, has been mentioned in the chemical literature from time to time. One example of an unexpectedly large carbon-13 isotope effect is that which Rosenfeld and Silverman[50a] found in the anaerobic conversion of methanol to methane. Little or no research has been done to determine the cause of such unexpectedly large effects, chiefly because too little is as yet known about how the net experimental value of k/k^* is related to the reaction mechanism even in relatively simple chemical systems for which the kinetics have been studied.

One mechanistic combination that appears to occur frequently in organic reactions is that in which a rate-limiting step is preceded by a rapid reversible equilibrium. The application of such a combination to a reaction in which one reactant is isotopically labeled is shown in Eqs. 5-18 and 5-19

$$A + R \underset{}{\overset{\text{fast}}{\rightleftharpoons}} I \tag{5-18}$$

$$I \overset{\text{slow}}{\longrightarrow} P + B \tag{5-19}$$

where

R = labeled reactant
I = labeled intermediate
P = labeled product
A, B = unlabeled molecules

The overall carbon-14 isotope effect in such a system would usually be measured (Sec. 5-1e) by studying the molar radioactivity of R, of P, or of both R and P as a function of percent reaction. However, the expected value of k/k^* would be the resultant of the equilibrium isotope effect in Eq. 5-18 and the kinetic isotope effect in Eq. 5-19 if both reactions involved the carbon-14-labeled reaction center. The resultant isotope effect, that is, the expected experimentally observable value for k/k^*, would depend on various factors. In some instances, the experimentally

observed isotope effect might be unexpectedly large because of the mechanism. In other cases, an apparent *inverse* rate isotope effect (see Sec. 5-6c) might result. The latter possibility is of particular interest and therefore is discussed briefly here.

Let us assume an example in which reaction 5-19 involved no measurable isotope fractionation for some reason that we need not specify. If, then, reaction 5-18 caused enrichment of the heavy isotope in the intermediate, I, the experimental data might be interpreted as evidence for an *inverse* kinetic isotope effect, that is, the initially formed product, P, would be enriched in the heavy isotope, because P would have the same isotopic composition as I.

An apparent inverse rate isotope effect may also be indicated in a system of competing rate processes, such as that represented by the equations

$$A + R \begin{cases} \overset{k_1}{\nearrow} P_1 + B \quad\quad (5\text{-}20) \\ \underset{k_2}{\searrow} P_2 + C \quad\quad (5\text{-}21) \end{cases}$$

where

R = labeled reactant
P_1, P_2 = labeled products
k_1, k_2 = specific rate constants
A, B, C = unlabeled molecules

We shall assume that the reaction represented by Eq. 5-20 is being examined for the presence of a carbon-14 rate isotope effect, but that the reaction is not in fact accompanied by carbon-14 isotope fractionation. The isotope effect is studied by permitting 40% of R to react and by comparing the molar radioactivity of the P_1 (after purification) formed with the molar radioactivity of R before the reaction began. If it is arbitrarily assumed that $k_2 \cong \frac{1}{2} k_1$ and that the true value of k_{14}/k_{12} for reaction 5-21 is 0.88, about one-third the labeled product at 40% reaction will be P_2, and reaction 5-21 will have proceeded to the extent of about 14%. From

Fig. 5-4, $r' \cong 1.02$ at $1 - f = 0.86$ for $k^*/k = 0.88$. Therefore, R will have been enriched in the heavy isotope by about 2% during the reaction, with the result that the sample of purified P_1 recovered and assayed will also be enriched, perhaps by as much as 0.5 to 1% above the level of heavy isotope in the initial sample of R used. Although these calculations are only approximately correct, they suffice to demonstrate how a competing reaction might cause an enrichment of heavy isotope in the initial product formed and give the appearance of a small *inverse* kinetic isotope effect.

The above discussions of apparent *inverse* isotope effects should not be interpreted as a suggestion that all observed *inverse* carbon isotope effects are only apparent effects caused by such "depletion" processes. Section 5-6c treats further the subject of *inverse* carbon isotope effects.

For an indication of how reaction mechanisms can affect isotopic concen-

trations of labeled entities during complex biochemical processes, the reader is referred to biochemical literature.[51]

5-4d CARBON ISOTOPE DISCRIMINATION IN ENZYMATIC REACTIONS AS A RESULT OF STERIC RELATIONSHIPS

Aronoff[51] and Racusen and Aronoff[52] discuss a special type of isotope discrimination[53,54] which could result entirely from the steric relationship of a labeled atom or labeled group to the remainder of the asymmetric molecule that contains the labeled atom or group.

Reactions involving enzymes are usually stereospecific. Ogston[53] first indicated how an enzymatic reaction can be accompanied by isotope discrimination between two chemically identical groups, one of which is isotopically labeled, in a symmetrical molecule. The mechanism is indicated in Fig. 5-12. Reaction requires attachment of a definite face of the tetrahedron to sites X, Y, and Z.

FIG. 5-12 Isotope selectivity in a reaction at an enzyme surface.

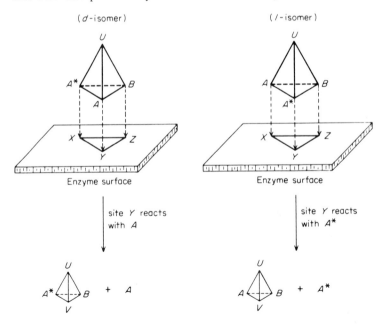

In the extreme case pictured in Fig. 5-12, which causes complete isotope selectivity, only site Y is active enough to bring about the reaction of group A (or its labeled counterpart, $A*$) and the consequent conversion of group A (or $A*$) to group V. Consequently, in the reaction of the pure d-isomer only group A is converted to group V, and none of the isotopic label is lost from the molecule. In the reaction of the pure l-isomer, only group $A*$ is converted, and all the isotopic label is lost from the molecule. If, as is more probable in any real case, both sites X and Y can cause conversion of group A or group $A*$, partial isotope selectivity can still occur provided either of the sites X or Y on the enzyme surface is more active than the other.

Clearly, the mass of the nuclide used as a label has nothing to do with the isotope selectivity in such a system. The degree of isotope selectivity is therefore independent of whether the label is carbon-14, tritium, or some other isotopic species.

5-4e PSEUDO CARBON ISOTOPE EFFECTS

Pseudo carbon isotope effects are illustrated by the apparent isotope selectivity in the oxidation of carbon-14-labeled xanthydrol ureide.[55] In this reaction, partial oxidation produces carbon-14 dioxide of molar radioactivity different from that expected in view of the number of carbon atoms in the compound oxidized. A simple explanation is that the molecule contains carbon atoms which are not structurally equivalent and are therefore converted to carbon dioxide at different rates. The labeled carbon atom appears to be at a position where it is converted to carbon dioxide more slowly than certain other carbon atoms in the molecule;[55] the carbon-14 dioxide initially collected therefore has a lower molar radioactivity than is expected. No actual isotope fractionation that results because the mass of carbon-14 is greater than that of carbon-12 need be assumed to explain the experimental results.

However, there is no reason to rule out the possibility that both a pseudo isotope effect and a true isotope effect could occur simultaneously during partial oxidation of some labeled organic compounds.

5-4f SECONDARY ISOTOPE EFFECTS

Secondary isotope effects that are about an order of magnitude smaller than *primary* isotope effects have been observed with deuterium-labeled organic compounds. Two studies[35a,35b] of isotope fractionation in a carbonyl-group reaction of acetophenone labeled with carbon-14 one atom away from the carbonyl group have been performed with great care. The observed values for these *secondary* isotope effects, 0.85% and 0.38%, indicate that with carbon-14 also, *secondary* isotope effects are about an order of magnitude smaller than *primary* isotope effects. It is interesting that both these *secondary* isotope effects are *inverse* isotope effects. The significance of *secondary inverse* isotope effects is discussed in Sec. 5-6c.

Secondary carbon isotope effects are both difficult to measure accurately and difficult to interpret because of their small magnitude. When the source of a small *secondary* carbon isotope effect is considered, even the possibility of a contribution made by a small collision-frequency isotope effect (Sec. 5-4a) cannot be dismissed hastily.

5-4g ILLUSTRATION OF THE USE OF CARBON ISOTOPE EFFECTS TO STUDY A REACTION MECHANISM

Although in the study[55a] described in this section carbon-13 isotope effects were used to test a reaction mechanism, the principles discussed are equally applicable in the use of carbon-14.

The bromodecarboxylation of 3,5-dibromo-4-hydroxybenzoic acid proceeds quantitatively in acetic acid at 20° according to the

equation

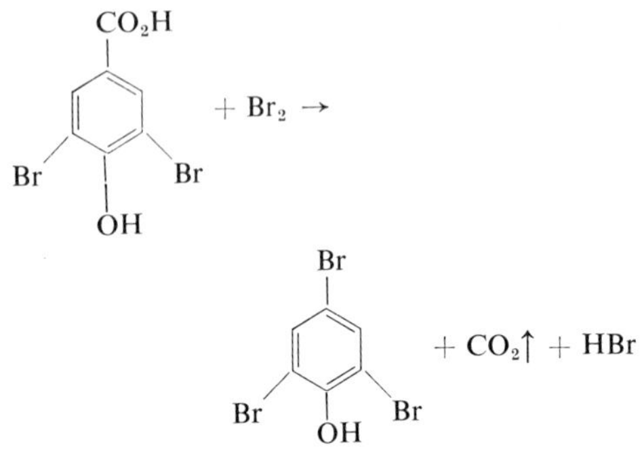

$$+ \; Br_2 \; \rightarrow$$

$$+ \; CO_2\uparrow \; + \; HBr$$

Results of earlier kinetic studies of the bromo-decarboxylation reaction[55b] could be explained by one of the two mechanisms shown in Figs. 5-13 and 5-14.

In Mechanism I, Step 1 simply indicates ionization of the original 3,5-dibromo-4-hydroxybenzoic acid. Steps 2 and 3 show how the postulated cyclohexadienone intermediate, A, may be formed by reaction of bromine with either the original acid or with its anion. Step 4 designates ionization of the postulated intermediate, A. Step 5 represents the breakup of the ionized form of this intermediate to release the products, carbon dioxide and the anion of *sym*-tribromophenol.

In Mechanism II, Step 1 shows the formation of protonated hypobromous acid, and Step 2 represents double ionization of 3,5-dibromo-4-hydroxybenzoic acid. Step 3 indicates the reaction of the doubly ionized 3,5-dibromo-4-hydroxybenzoic acid with

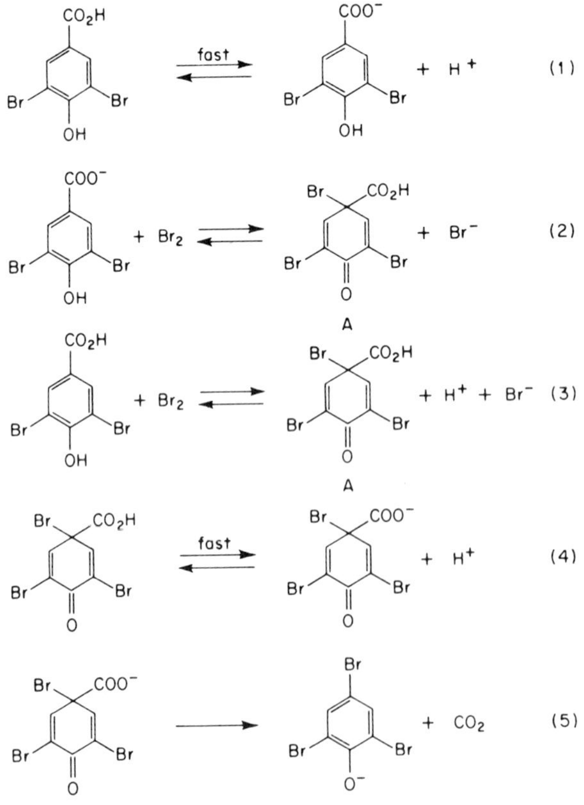

FIG. 5-13 Mechanism I for the bromodecarboxylation of 3,5-dibromo-4-hydroxybenzoic acid.

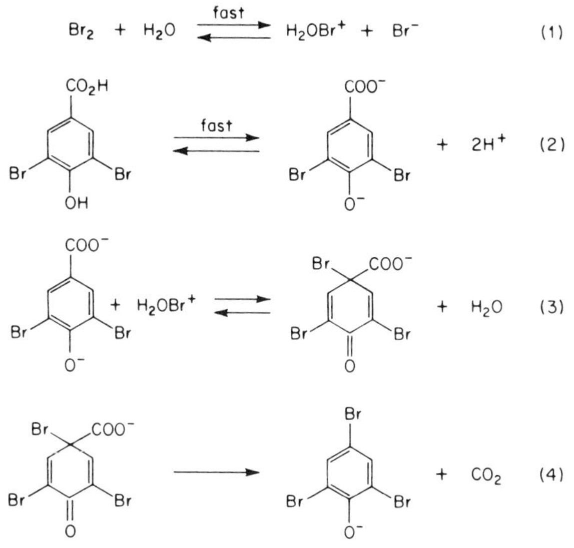

$$Br_2 + H_2O \underset{\longleftarrow}{\overset{fast}{\longrightarrow}} H_2OBr^+ + Br^- \quad (1)$$

FIG. 5-14 Mechanism II for the bromodecarboxylation of 3,5-dibromo-4-hydroxybenzoic acid.

protonated hypobromous acid to yield the ionized form of the intermediate A. Step 4 is identical with Step 5 of Mechanism I.

To distinguish between these two mechanisms, carbon-13 isotope effects under several sets of reaction conditions were measured by mass spectrometric analysis of the carbon dioxide released. The 3,5-dibromo-4-hydroxybenzoic acid contained only the natural 1.1% carbon-13. In each case, the isotope effect was measured by determining the carbon-13 content of the carbon dioxide as a function of percent reaction (Sec. 5-2). By this technique, the only isotope fractionation that was observed was among the carbon atoms of the carboxyl groups; therefore the carboxyl-group carbon atom may be referred to as the "labeled" atom.

The logic behind this use of carbon-13 isotope effects is as follows:

(a) For Mechanism II, only Step 4 involves breaking a bond to the "labeled" carbon atom (the carboxyl-group carbon atom). Hence, if Mechanism II were the

correct mechanism and if Step 4 were its rate-controlling step, a primary carbon-13 isotope effect should be observed, and its magnitude should not vary with the concentration of bromide ions added to the solution. Further, if Mechanism II were correct and Step 3 were rate-controlling, no *primary* isotope effect should be observed; the *secondary* isotope effect, if any, to be expected if Step 3 were rate-controlling would be very small and probably not detectable.

(b) For Mechanism I, in the absence of added bromide ions little or no reversal of Steps 2 and 3 should occur, and these steps should become rate-controlling. Under these conditions, essentially every molecule of the intermediate A should decompose to products by the reaction designated as Step 5 as rapidly as it forms, and there would be no accumulation of intermediate A. Thus, there would be no chance for isotope fractionation to occur in Step 5. Since Step 5 is the only step of Mechanism I in which a bond to the "labeled" carbon atom is broken, it would be predicted from Mechanism I that there should be no primary isotope effect in the absence of added bromide ions.

(c) However, according to Mechanism I the addition of bromide ions in high concentration would permit reversion of the intermediate A to reactants by reversal of Steps 2 and 3. In the extreme case, the intermediate would be in rapid reversible equilibrium with the reactants, and Step 5 would be rate-determining. Therefore, Mechanism I would predict a full primary carbon-13 isotope effect at very high concentrations of added bromide ions, because Step 5 involves cleavage of a bond to the "labeled" carbon atom.

(d) If Mechanism I is operative, carbon-13 isotope effects ranging in magnitude from no isotope effect to a maximum primary isotope effect (maximum predicted by use of Table 5-3 and Fig. 5-10: $k_{12}/k_{13} = 1.04$ at 20°) should be observed if the amount of added bromide ions is gradually increased. Furthermore, since bromide ions are a product of the reaction, the observed isotope effect could increase steadily during the course of the reaction from no isotope effect at the beginning to some definite value near 100% reaction that could presumably be computed in advance if enough were known about the rates of the various steps in the mechanism.

Table 5-4 lists the values for the measured isotope effects. Data grouped together in the third and fourth columns of the table were taken from the same experiment. *The*

Table 5-4 Carbon-13 isotope effects measured for the bromodecarboxylation of 3,5-dibromo-4-hydroxybenzoic acid in 80% acetic acid at 20.5 ± 0.5°

Reagent added	Concentration of added reagent, M	Range of percent reaction represented	k_{12}/k_{13}	Mean k_{12}/k_{13}
None	—	12.5–25	1.000	
		75–100	1.005	
		13–26	1.000	
		13–26	1.004	
		75–100	1.002	1.002 ± 0.003
HBr	0.300	0–10.5	1.045	
		10.5–23	1.044	
		23–37	1.044	
		0–10	1.046	
		10–23.5	1.045	
		23.5–37	1.045	
		37–47.5	1.044	1.045 ± 0.001
HClO₄	0.300	0–9.0	1.005	
		9–20	1.006	
		20–50	1.012	
		79–100	1.019	1.011 ± 0.007

data clearly support Mechanism I and not Mechanism II, because essentially no carbon-13 isotope effect is observed in the absence of any additive and because a full primary *isotope effect is observed in the presence of a high concentration of added hydrobromic acid.* The experiment in which perchloric acid was used serves mainly as a control to prove that the effect of added hydrobromic acid is not due merely to the increased concentration of protons.

It is interesting that, when perchloric acid is added, the influence on the isotope effect of bromide ions produced during the reaction is enhanced. In the absence of added perchloric acid, the trend toward a measurable isotope effect caused by bromide ions produced during the reaction is hardly noticeable. However, in the presence of 0.300 M perchloric acid, there is a noticeable trend toward higher isotope effects as the reaction proceeds and produces more bromide ions. This enhancement by added perchloric acid of the ability of increasing amounts of bromide ions to increase the isotope effect is in accord with Mechanism I, because both protons and bromide ions should promote reversal of Step 3 of that mechanism.

The exact structure of intermediates can, of course, not be shown either by isotope-effect studies or overall kinetic measurements. However, on the basis of general evidence,[55b] the structure of the intermediate A shown above was considered to be probable.

5-5 CARBON ISOTOPE EFFECTS IN PROCESSES OTHER THAN SIMPLE CHEMICAL REACTIONS

Carbon isotope fractionation has been reported for various processes that are in some degree physical rather than chemical in nature. These include distillation,[56,57] gaseous diffusion,[58] dissociation on electron impact,[59] ion exchange,[60] and thermal-cracking reactions.[12] Effects of carbon-13 substitution on vapor pressure have been calculated.[60a]

5-6 INVESTIGATION OF THE NATURE OF CARBON ISOTOPE EFFECTS

Numerous studies of various aspects of carbon isotope fractionation not already presented in this chapter are described in the chemical literature. A brief outline of some of the principal areas of investigation is given here.

5-6a DECARBOXYLATION REACTIONS

Many of the studies made to elucidate the nature of carbon isotope effects have involved decarboxylation of organic acids. Perhaps the decarboxylation of malonic-1-^{13}C acid and malonic-1-^{14}C acid has received as much attention as any other single reaction of a labeled organic compound. Some readers may well ask why this is so. There are several reasons. The earlier carbon-isotope-effect studies were studies of *intramolecular* isotope fractionation, and a reaction that was suited for *intramolecular* isotope fractionation studies was needed. The decarboxylation of malonic acid (Eq. 5-1) met this requirement, because malonic acid is a symmetrical molecule and its decarboxylation at moderate temperatures proceeds quantitatively to the half-way point and no further. Also, decarboxylation produces carbon dioxide as one of the products. Samples of carbon-13 dioxide formed by decarboxylation of malonic-1-^{13}C acid can be introduced directly into the mass spectrometer for isotopic assay. Similarly, carbon-14 dioxide formed by decarboxylation of malonic-1-^{14}C acid is already in a form convenient for radioassaying. For details of various isotope-effect studies of the decarboxylation of malonic acid and of other acids, the reader is referred to the numerous publications by Yankwich and co-workers and by Bigeleisen and co-workers listed in Table 5-5.

5-6b RATIO OF CARBON-14-ISOTOPE EFFECTS TO CARBON-13-ISOTOPE EFFECTS

One important conclusion drawn from the work of Bigeleisen on the theory of kinetic isotope effects is that the magnitude of carbon-14 kinetic isotope effects should be about twice that of carbon-13 isotope effects[43] under the same conditions. This conclusion has been thoroughly tested experimentally. The most recent experimental investigations of the relative isotope effects in the decarboxylation of malonic-1-^{14}C acid and malonic-1-^{13}C acid indicate that the two isotope fractionation factors are indeed in about a 2-to-1 ratio.[61] This experimental work was done with samples of malonic acid that contained about 1 % each of malonic-1-^{14}C and malonic-1-^{13}C acid. The mass spectrometer was used to analyze for both carbon-14 and carbon-13 in the same product samples. In this way, the possibility of certain errors that might otherwise have cast doubt on the results was eliminated.

5-6c INVERSE CARBON-14 ISOTOPE EFFECTS

An early report[61a] of an *inverse primary* isotope effect (*intramolecular*) in the iodoform reaction of acetone-1-^{14}C could not be verified, although several very careful efforts were made to repeat the original work in a second laboratory.[62] Another report[62a] of an *inverse primary* isotope effect (*intermolecular*), in this case in the conversion of *o*-benzoylbenzoic acid-^{14}C (carboxyl-labeled) to anthraquinone-9-^{14}C, was also refuted.[63] In the second case, it was shown[63] that impurities of high specific radioactivity in the labeled reactant could have caused the *apparent inverse* carbon-14 isotope effect and that the reaction was actually accompanied by an isotope effect of about 3 % in the *normal* direction. Although other *inverse primary* carbon-14 isotope effects[64,64a] have been reported, evidently none has ever been substantiated by independent work in a second laboratory.[64b] However, as was indicated in Sec. 5-4f, *inverse secondary* carbon-14 isotope effects of small magnitude have been proved to occur in carefully performed experiments.[35a,35b] It is probable

that numerous small, *secondary* carbon-14 isotope effects, both *inverse* and *normal* in direction, could be detected in a variety of reactions if sufficient research effort were expended. On the other hand, for reasons presented below, it is very doubtful that any large *primary inverse* carbon-14 isotope effects will be proved to exist.

The conditions necessary for the occurrence of an *inverse* isotope effect have been discussed[48a] in terms of Eq. 5-11; these are described briefly here. The temperature-independent factor in Eq. 5-11 always has a value equal to or greater than unity. Therefore, one condition for an *inverse* isotope effect (i.e., for $k/k^* < 1$) is that stated in Eq. 5-22

$$\sum_{j}^{3N-7} G(u_j^{\ddagger}) \, \Delta u_j^{\ddagger} > \sum_{i}^{3N-6} G(u_i) \, \Delta u_i \qquad (5\text{-}22)$$

Further, the difference between the first and second summations in Eq. 5-22 must be enough less than unity to override the temperature-independent factor. Under these circumstances, the product of the temperature-independent factor and the temperature-dependent factor would have a value less than unity, and k/k^* would necessarily also have a value less than unity according to Eq. 5-11.

These stated requirements for an *inverse* isotope effect mean, in general, that the labeled atom must be more tightly bonded in the transition state than in the labeled reactant. Therefore it has been suggested[48a]— and logically so—that measurable *inverse* isotope effects should be found in the association of atoms (or radicals) to form molecules if they are to be found at all. Hammond,[49] however, argues that, for the association of highly active species, such as radicals and ions, the transition state is reached early—long before the new bond being formed has acquired any real strength. *It would appear, therefore, that there is no theoretical basis for expecting large* inverse primary *carbon isotope effects*. On the other hand, *inverse secondary* isotope effects would be somewhat more likely to occur than *inverse primary* isotope effects. The reason is that the temperature-independent factor, which tends to preclude or to diminish *inverse primary* isotope effects as indicated above, is essentially equal to unity for secondary isotope effects.[48a] However, there is no reason to expect large *inverse secondary* isotope effects. The upper limit for *inverse secondary* carbon-14 isotope effects has been estimated to be about 3% ($1 - k/k^* = 0.032$ at $25°$) by Bigeleisen and Wolfsberg.[48a] Since the largest kinetic carbon-14 isotope effect actually observed (see Table 5-1) is less than one-third the calculated upper limit[48a] of 50% ($k/k^* - 1 = 0.5$ at $25°$), it might be more realistic to expect *inverse secondary* carbon-14 isotope effects to have values no greater than 1% ($1 - k/k^* = 0.01$ at $25°$).

5-6d TEMPERATURE COEFFICIENTS OF CARBON ISOTOPE EFFECTS

As expected from theoretical considerations (Secs. 5-1f and 5-3), kinetic isotope effects decrease in magnitude as the temperature is raised. From carbon isotope effects determined experimentally at two or more temperatures, ($E_{14} - E_{12}$), the difference between the Arrhenius activation energies for reaction of the labeled and unlabeled species can be estimated.[30] This simple calculation requires the assumption that A_{14}/A_{12}, the ratio of the isotopic pre-exponential factors, be temperature-independent over the range of temperatures used. The value for ($E_{14} - E_{12}$) so computed is often about 50 cal/mole. A much higher value is reported for the isotope effect in the decarbonylation of formic-^{14}C acid.[30,39a] An unexpectedly high temperature coefficient of the carbon-13 isotope effect in that reaction has also been observed.[48b] Temperature-coefficient studies of a number of other *intermolecular* carbon isotope ef-

fects[65,66,67] and of *intramolecular* carbon isotope effects[48c,48d,68] have been made. In many of these studies, efforts were made to correlate quantitatively the observed temperature coefficient of an isotope effect with that predicted from theoretical considerations. Although some success has been achieved in this objective, temperature coefficients of carbon isotope effects are usually very small, and their accurate evaluation requires extreme care.

5-6e INFLUENCE OF SOLVENT AND OF CONCENTRATION AND STRUCTURE OF THE LABELED MOLECULE ON THE CARBON ISOTOPE EFFECT

Yankwich and co-workers have studied the effect of the choice of solvent or medium on the carbon-13 isotope effects in malonic-1-^{13}C acid decarboxylation. References are given in Table 5-5. Solvent, concentration, and structural influences have also been measured in carbon-14 isotope effect studies.[1,68a]

5-6f EFFECT OF ACTIVATION ENERGY ON THE MAGNITUDE OF ISOTOPE EFFECTS

In several studies of series of isotope effects, larger isotope effects were found for reactions with high activation energy than for reactions with low activation energy.[1,33,69] Wiberg[10] gives a reasonable explanation of this tendency. His views are much like those of Hammond,[49] but in some instances there may be no correlation between activation energy and magnitude of isotope effect.[49a]

5-6g USE OF ISOTOPE EFFECTS IN THE STUDY OF THE CHARACTER OF THE ACTIVATED COMPLEX

As discussed in Sec. 5-3, the magnitude of a kinetic isotope effect should depend on the character of the bonds in the activated complex. For this reason, the experimental value of k/k^* has been used in attempts to select a reasonable model for the activated complex. Such models were chosen on the basis of values of carbon isotope effects measured experimentally by Johnston, Bonner, and Wilson[70] and by Weston.[71]

5-6h THE TEMPERATURE-INDEPENDENT FACTOR (TIF) IN CALCULATIONS OF CARBON ISOTOPE EFFECTS

Evaluation of the temperature-independent factor (TIF), which is the factor immediately preceding the square-bracketed term in Eqs. 5-11 and 5-15, has been the subject of a number of investigations. As indicated earlier, the value for the TIF can be only unity or greater. This limitation is stated concisely in general terms in Eq. 5-23

$$\nu_{1L}^{\ddagger}/\nu_{2L}^{\ddagger} \geqq 1 \tag{5-23}$$

The uncertainty in making a presumptive assignment of a value to the TIF is one of the difficulties in using equations such as Eqs. 5-11 and 5-15 to predict isotope effects.

Three types of computation of $\nu_{1L}^{\ddagger}/\nu_{2L}^{\ddagger}$ have been used. The first was explicitly indicated in Eq. 5-11 as

$$\frac{\nu_{1L}^{\ddagger}}{\nu_{2L}^{\ddagger}} = \left(\frac{\mu^*}{\mu}\right)^{1/2} \tag{5-24}$$

The use of Eq. 5-24 to compute the TIF is described in Sec. 5-3.

More recently,[48a,48b] a reduced mass based on the masses of the molecular fragments separating in the reaction coordinate has also been used to compute $\nu_{1L}^{\ddagger}/\nu_{2L}^{\ddagger}$. This use is illustrated by the calculation of the TIF for the carbon-14 isotope effect in the decarbonylation of formic acid (Sec. 5-1c). The rate-controlling step is the cleavage of the carbon-oxygen bond in the protonated acid[35]

$$\overset{H}{HCOOH^+} \rightarrow HCO^+ + H_2O$$

For the unlabeled species, the separating fragments have mass numbers of 18 and 29.

For the carbon-14-labeled species, the separating fragments have mass numbers of 18 and 31. The TIF is therefore calculated as follows

$$\frac{\nu_{1L}^{\ddagger}}{\nu_{2L}^{\ddagger}} = \left[\frac{1/18+1/29}{1/18+1/31}\right]^{1/2} = 1.012$$

For comparison, the TIF computed by the first method is 1.044 (Table 5-3). Obviously, these two methods of computing the TIF will lead to very different predicted values for k/k^*.

A third method has been employed for computing the TIF in three-center[72,73] and four-center[74] reactions. The displacement reaction (three-center reaction) occurs frequently in organic chemistry, and any special method that is useful in predicting isotope effects in displacement reactions is therefore of some importance. The general pattern of the displacement reaction is indicated in Eq. 5-25

$$A + BC \rightarrow \{A\text{-}\text{-}\text{-}B\text{-}\text{-}\text{-}C\} \rightarrow AB + C \tag{5-25}$$
$$\text{transition state}$$

Displacement reactions are characterized by the fact that the A—B bond and the B—C bond have considerable strengths—though not necessarily equal strengths—in the transition state. The transition state shown in Eq. 5-25 is linear, but—depending on the geometry of the potential energy surface—the transition state may be triangular

$$\begin{bmatrix} & B & \\ A & & C \end{bmatrix}$$

The value of $\nu_{1L}^{\ddagger}/\nu_{2L}^{\ddagger}$ is decided by the distances A---B and B---C along the reaction coordinate. Bigeleisen and Wolfsberg[72,73] show how the TIF can be estimated for several types of transition states.

5-6i EQUILIBRIUM CARBON ISOTOPE EFFECTS

Although equilibrium carbon-14 isotope effects are not considered in detail in this chapter, a large amount of .work in this area has been done by Harris and co-workers[75,76,77] and by Stranks.[78,79,80] Table 5-5 refers to additional studies of equilibrium isotope effects. These effects are also treated very briefly in Sec. 4-2. The treatise by Roginsky[81] contains a thorough discussion of equilibrium isotope effects, as well as a chapter on isotope effects in chemical kinetics.

5-7 TABULATION OF CARBON-ISOTOPE-EFFECT STUDIES

In this chapter only a few examples of carbon isotope effects are discussed in detail; the theoretical aspects of carbon-isotope-effect studies receive only a rudimentary treatment. Therefore, Table 5-5 has been compiled as a guide to the literature of isotope effects. This table should also be a help in locating information about the carbon isotope effects reported for particular reactions or processes.

Table 5-5 is a reasonably complete list of the studies of carbon isotope effects made during the period that ends approximately with the references included in the June 1962 Subject Index of *Chemical Abstracts;* some more recent studies are also included. Entries are grouped according to the type of reaction or process in which the isotope effect was observed.

Since both carbon-13 and carbon-14 isotope effects are listed, the second column of the table indicates which isotope was involved in the study.

The third column tells the position of the labeled carbon atom in the labeled molecule. In many carbon-13 isotope effect studies, compounds that contain the normal abundance of the carbon-13 isotope (about 1%) were used. In these cases, the carbon atom is listed that was involved in the carbon isotope effect studied. If monocarbon compounds were used or if the location of the labeled atom is apparent, the third column is left blank.

In the fourth column the type of isotope-effect study is described. The abbreviations "Inter." and "Intra." indicate *intermolecular* and *intramolecular* isotope-effect studies, respectively, and "Inter.-Intra." means both types.

Unless designated as an equilibrium isotope effect by "Equil.," entries are relative to kinetic carbon isotope effects only. The abbreviation "Mech." indicates study of a reaction mechanism. The word "Theory" designates that a theoretical interpretation of a specific carbon isotope effect or of isotope effects in general was studied. If a carbon isotope effect was evaluated experimentally and its value was compared with an isotope effect calculated from theory, the symbol "Comp." appears. The expression "T. Coeff." refers to the determination of a temperature coefficient of a carbon isotope effect.

The designation "Ratio 14/13" indicates that the ratio of the carbon-14 isotope effect to the carbon-13 isotope effect in the same reaction was measured. In almost all the entries the carbon kinetic isotope effects referred to are in the normal direction, that is, the lighter molecules react faster. For publications concerned with inverse kinetic isotope effects, the words "Inverse Effect" are written. Similarly, most of the entries refer to primary isotope effects, that is, isotope effects in which the carbon-13 or carbon-14 atom involved is at the reaction center.

For those entries that emphasize a secondary carbon isotope effect—an isotope effect in which the carbon-13 or carbon-14 atom concerned is not at the reaction center— the words "Secondary Effect" are written. For some entries, other self-explanatory descriptive phrases are used to assist in locating a particular type of carbon-isotope-effect study.

The permission of A. Fry to use the bibliography on kinetic isotope effects (general reference *q*) in the preparation of Table 5-5 is gratefully acknowledged.

Table 5-5 Descriptive list of carbon-isotope-effect studies

Labeled reactant	Carbon isotope	Labeled position	Description of study	Ref.
Addition to multiple carbon-carbon bonds				
Diphenylacetylene	^{14}C	α-C	Intra.	38
Methyl cinnamate	^{14}C	α-C, β-C	Inter., no effect found in bromine addition	112
Styrene	^{14}C	α-C, β-C	Inter., no effect found in bromine addition	112
Biochemical processes				
Carbon dioxide	^{14}C	—	Inter., uptake of CO_2 by barley seedlings	141, 142
			Inter., no unusual effect due to high sp. act. $^{14}CO_2$	69
			Inter. (photosynthesis)	127
	^{13}C		Inter. (during illumination)	5
			Inter. effect under various conditions	93
Methane	$^{14}C, ^{13}C$		Inter., inverse effect in uptake of ^{14}C by snail shells	35
	^{13}C		Inter., t. coeff.	116
			Degrees of ^{12}C enrichment in 105 plants	144
Brominative decarboxylation				
3,5-Dibromo-4-hydroxybenzoic acid	^{13}C	Carboxyl group	Inter., mech.	62
Cannizzaro reaction				
Benzaldehyde	^{14}C	Carbonyl group	Inter.	130
Formaldehyde	^{14}C	—	Inter.	47
Carbonyl group reactions				
Acetophenone	^{14}C	Methyl group	Inter., secondary effect of 0.8 to 0.9%	97
		Carbonyl group	Inter., t. coeff. in formation of keto-group derivatives	112
Acetophenone (ring-substituted)	^{14}C	Carbonyl group	Inter., t. coeff., theory, influence of solvent and concentration on isotope effects	113
Benzoic anhydride	^{14}C	Carboxyl group	Intra., t. coeff., in reactions with ethyl alcohol and p-toluidine	96
Benzophenone	^{14}C	Carbonyl group		112
			Inter.	34

Table 5-5 (Continued)

Labeled reactant	Carbon isotope	Labeled position	Description of study	Ref.
Carbonyl group reactions (cont'd.)				
Diethyl phenylene-diacetate	^{14}C	1-C, 2-C	Inter., intra.	40
Ethyl benzoates (ring-substituted)	^{14}C	Carboxyl group	Inter., t. coeff., theory, influence of solvent and concentration on isotope effects	113
Formaldehyde	^{14}C	—	Inter.	46
			Inter., mech.	76
Cyclization				
o-Benzoylbenzoic acid	^{14}C	Carboxyl group	Inter., inverse effect, mech.	131
			Inter., equil., mech., refutes claims of Stevens and Crowder[131] that there is an inverse isotope effect	103
Decarbonylation				
Benzoylformic acid	^{14}C	Keto group	Inter., mech.	104
		Carboxyl group	Inter., mech.	52
Formic acid	^{14}C	—	Inter., t. coeff.	115
			Inter., mech.	106
	^{13}C		Inter., isotope enrichment	16
			T. coeff., mech., comp.	64
			Inter., t. coeff.	152
Triphenylacetic acid	^{14}C	2-C	Inter., mech.	104, 106
Decarboxylation				
Acetic anhydride	^{14}C	1-C	Inter., intra., mech.	125
Anisoyl peroxide	^{14}C	α-C	Inter., mech.	7
Anthranilic acid	^{13}C	Carboxyl group	Inter., mech.	133
Barium adipate	^{13}C	α-C	Inter., mech.	28
Bromomalonic acid	^{14}C	Carboxyl group	Intra., very large effect (40%)	150
			Intra.	61
	$^{14}C, ^{13}C$		Intra., ratio 14/13	157
o-Chlorophenylacetic anhydride	^{14}C	1-C	Inter., intra., mech.	125
2,4-Dihydroxybenzoic acid	^{13}C	Carboxyl group	Inter., mech.	80
Malonic acid	^{14}C	Carboxyl group	Intra.	102, 150
			Inter., intra. (patent)	39

Table 5-5   (Continued)

Labeled reactant	Carbon isotope	Labeled position	Description of study	Ref.
Decarboxylation (cont'd.)				
Malonic acid (cont'd.)	^{14}C	Carboxyl group	Intra., comp.	61
		1-C	Intra., theory, comp.	18
		1-C, 2-C	Inter., comp., effect of location of label on the isotope effect	110
	^{14}C, ^{13}C	Carboxyl group	Intra., ratio 14/13	156, 157, 158
		1-C, 2-C	Theory	23
	^{13}C	Carboxyl group	Intra.	155
			Inter., t. coeff.	78
			Inter., intra., mech.	28
			Inter., t. coeff., comp.	148
			Intra., t. coeff., comp. in quinoline	147
			Inter., t. coeff., mech. in dioxane	153
			Inter., t. coeff., mech., equil. in quinoline	146
			Inter., intra., t. coeff., comp., equil.	70
			Inter., intra., influence of the source of the malonic acid on the isotope effect	77
		1-C, 2-C	Inter., intra., comp., theory	21
Malonic acid mono-anion	^{13}C	Carboxyl group	Intra. effect in quinoline	160
			Intra., t. coeff., comparison of intra. and inter. effects in quinoline	161
Mesitoic acid	^{13}C	Carboxyl group	Inter., comp.	27
	^{14}C, ^{13}C		Inter., ratio 14/13	132
Methyl acetylsalicylate	^{14}C	Acetyl group	Inter., mech.	140
α-Naphthylmalonic acid	^{14}C	Carboxyl group	Intra., comp.	58
Oxalacetic acid	^{13}C	1-C	Inter., mech., for metal-catalyzed and enzymatic reactions	123
Metal salts of oxalacetic acid	^{13}C	Carboxyl group	Inter., magnetic effect of certain cations on isotope effect is proposed	59
Phenylmalonic acid	^{14}C	Carboxyl group	Intra., comp.	58
Trichloroacetic acid anion	^{13}C	1-C	Inter.	19
n-Valeric acid	^{14}C	Carboxyl group	Inter.	87

Table 5-5   (Continued)

Labeled reactant	Carbon isotope	Labeled position	Description of study	Ref.
Decarboxylation-decarbonylation				
Oxalic acid	^{13}C	—	Intra.	79
			Intra., t. coeff., ratio 14/13	57
Diels-Alder reactions				
β-Nitrostyrene	^{14}C	α-C	Inter., no effect found in reaction (reaction with 2,3-dimethyl-butadiene)	112
Displacement reactions				
1-Bromo-1-phenylethane	^{13}C	1-C	Inter., comp. (solvolysis in CH_3OH, C_2H_5OH)	136
Methyl iodide	^{14}C	—	Inter., mech. (reaction with tert. amines)	12, 36
			Inter., mech., comp. (reaction with bases and Ag^+)	13
	^{13}C		Inter., t. coeff., theory (reaction with H_2O)	81
Methyl halides	^{14}C	—	Inter., t. coeff., theory (reaction with CN^-)	82, 83
Potassium cyanide	^{14}C	—	Inter. comp. (isotope effects in SN1 and SN2 mechanisms; reaction with benzyl chloride)	89
Sodium cyanide	^{13}C	—	Inter., t. coeff., theory (reaction with CH_3I)	81
Distillation				
Benzene	^{13}C	—	Inter., inverse effect, theory	6
Carbon tetrachloride	^{13}C	—	Inter., inverse effect, theory	6
Chloroform	^{13}C	—	Inter., inverse effect, theory	6
Hydrocyanic acid	^{13}C	—	Equil., comp. (vapor vs solution)	8
Methane	^{13}C	—	Vapor pressures	41
Methanol	^{13}C	—	Inter., inverse effect, theory	6
Friedel-Crafts reaction				
Ethylene	^{14}C	—	Inter., mech., no isotope effect found	68
Gas adsorption				
Carbon dioxide	^{14}C	—	Inter., no isotope effect in adsorption in benzyl amine	112
	^{13}C		Inter.	4

Table 5-5   (Continued)

Labeled reactant	Carbon isotope	Labeled position	Description of study	Ref.
Hydrogenation				
Benzophenone	^{14}C	Keto group	Inter., comparison of isotope effects in hydrogenation and chemical reduction	26
Stilbene	^{14}C	α-C	Inter.	26
Hydrolysis				
2-Chloro-2-methylpropane	^{14}C	2-C	Inter., comp., mech.	11
sym-Dimethylurea	^{13}C	—		85
sym-Diphenylurea	^{13}C	—		85
Methyl iodide	^{13}C	—	Inter., t. coeff., theory	81
Phenylurea	^{13}C	—		85
Urea	^{14}C	—	Hydrolysis by urease, inverse effect	88
	$^{14}C, ^{13}C$	—	Inter., comp., ratio 14/13	121, 122
	^{13}C	Carbonyl group	Inter., theory	85
	—		Inter., comp., t. coeff. in acid hydrolysis	159
Iodoform reaction				
Acetone	^{14}C	1-C	Intra., inverse effect	100
			Inter., intra., refute earlier claims of Roe and Albenesius$^{(100)}$ that these reactions exhibit inverse isotope effects	107
Ion exchange				
System: OH-HCN-HCl on Dowex 2	^{14}C	—	Equil. achievement of ^{14}C enrichment	43
Isotope effect on ionization constant				
D-Arabinose	^{14}C	1-C	Physical effect	86
Triphenylcarbinol	^{13}C	α-C	Equil.	75
Isotope-exchange reactions				
Bicarbonate ions and their complexes	^{14}C	—	Equil., t. coeff., large equilibrium isotope effect	138
Carbon monoxide	^{14}C	—	Inter., equil.	49
			Equil., t. coeff.	137
Carbonate-bicarbonate ions and carbonate-*bis*-ethylenediamine-cobalt	^{13}C	—	Inter., equil.	154

Table 5-5 (Continued)

Labeled reactant	Carbon isotope	Labeled position	Description of study	Ref.
Isotope-exchange reactions (cont'd.)				
Carbonate and carbonatotetramine-cobaltic complex	^{14}C	—	Not strictly an isotope-effect study (exchange rate study)	63
Cyanide ion and cyanogen iodide	^{14}C	—	Equil.	72
Various molecules	^{14}C	—	Equil., t. coeff., tabulation of Q_{14}/Q_{12} for molecules at 0°, 20°, and 40°C for rapid evaluation of ^{14}C equilibrium isotope effects	139
	$^{14}C, {}^{13}C$	—	Technological study of isotope enrichment	124
Mass spectrometry				
Butanes	^{13}C	1-C, 2-C	Inter., intra., theory	134
Carbon dioxide	^{13}C	—	Inter.	128
			Inter., theory	44, 45, 119, 120
Carbon dioxide	^{13}C	—	Inter., comp., theory	118
Carbon monoxide	^{13}C	—	Inter., theory	44, 45
			Inter., comp., theory	118
Propane	^{13}C	1-C	Inter., intra., theory	17
			Inter. and intra., secondary effect also	9
		1-C, 2-C	Inter., intra., theory	134
Meerwein reaction				
Butadiene	^{14}C	1-C	Intra., mech.; no isotope effect detected	114
Oxidation				
Acetic acid	^{14}C	Carboxyl group	Inter.	50
Acetone	^{14}C	1-C	Inter., mech.	109
Benzyl alcohol	^{14}C	Methylene carbon	Inter., mech.	109
Carbon monoxide	$^{14}C, {}^{13}C$	—	Inter., theory, ratio 14/13, effect of heterogeneity on magnitude of isotope effect	2
	^{13}C		Inter., t. coeff., theory	73
Formic acid	^{13}C		Inter., effect of absolute reaction rate on isotope effects	108
Isopropyl alcohol	^{14}C	2-C	Inter., mech.	109
Mannitol	^{14}C	2-C	Inter., biochemical process	56

Table 5-5 (Continued)

Labeled reactant	Carbon isotope	Labeled position	Description of study	Ref.
Oxidation (cont'd.)				
D-Mannitol	[14]C	1-C, 2-C 3-C	Inter., mech.	126
Oxalic acid	[13]C	—		37
2-Phenyl-1-acenaphthenol	[14]C	1-C	Inter., mech., possible inverse isotope effect	24
Urea nitrate	[14]C	—	Inter.	1
Xanthydrol ureide	[14]C	—	Pseudo isotope effect due to incomplete oxidation	1
Ozonization				
Stilbene	[14]C	α-C	Inter. (probably), mech.	25
Photochemical processes				
Ethyl bromide	[13]C	1-C, 2-C	Inter.	60
			Inter., t. coeff.	55
Methyl bromide	[13]C	1-C, 2-C	Inter.	60
Oxalic acid	[13]C	—	Inverse effect in photolysis in presence of uranyl nitrate	149
Polymerization				
Ethylene	[14]C	Vinyl group	Inter., mech.	92
Propylene	[14]C	Vinyl group	Inter., mech.	92
Styrene	[14]C	Vinyl group	Inter.	71
			Inter., mech.	92
Vinyl chloride	[14]C	1-C, 2-C	Inter.	71
Rearrangements				
Benzil	[14]C	Carbonyl group	Intra.	130
Phenanthraquinone; also 2- and 7-chlorophenanthraquinone	[14]C	9-C	Inter., mech.	91
Cyclopropane	[13]C	—	Inter., mech.	143
Halobenzenes	[14]C	1-C	Intra., mech.	99
1-(1-Naphthyl)-3-diazo-2-propanone	[14]C	1-C, 3-C	Inter.	98

Table 5-5   (Continued)

Labeled reactant	Carbon isotope	Labeled position	Description of study	Ref.
Rearrangements (cont'd.)				
Pinacol	^{14}C	1-C, 2-C	Inter., intra., t. coeff.	48
			Inter.; refutes earlier results reported by Duncan and Lynn[48]	95
Saponification				
Ethyl benzoate	^{14}C	Carboxyl group	Inter., derivation of relation of percent reaction to product specific activity	129
Ring-substituted ethyl benzoates	^{14}C	Carboxyl group	Inter.	111, 113
Schmidt reaction				
Acetone	^{14}C	1-C	Inter., intra.; refute earlier claims of Roe and Albenesius[100] that these reactions exhibit inverse isotope effects	107
Thermal decomposition				
Barium acetate	^{13}C	Carboxyl group	Inter. (acetaldehyde formation)	10
Barium adipate	^{13}C	Carboxyl, α-C	Inter., mech.	20
Dimethyl mercury	^{13}C	—	Inter., mech., isotope effect depends on total pressure	117
Ethane	^{14}C	—	Intra., theory	31
			Inter., anomalously large isotope effect	32
		1-C, also doubly labeled	Inter.	33
Ethyl bromide	^{13}C	1-C, 2-C	Inter., intra., mech.	54
			Inter., intra., mech., t. coeff.	53
			Mech., radical-chain mechanism proposed	84
Lead oxalate	^{13}C	—	Intra., t. coeff., theory	151
Lithium acetate	^{14}C	Carboxyl group	Inter.	101
Malonic acid	^{13}C	1-C, 2-C	Isotope enrichment, inter., intra.	14
Mercurous formate	^{14}C	—	Inter.	112
Methyl iodide	^{13}C	—	Inter., t. coeff. (in methane formation)	74
S-Methyl-*trans*-2-methyl-1-indanyl xanthate	^{13}C	Carbonyl group	Inter., mech.	3

Table 5-5 (Continued)

Labeled reactant	Carbon isotope	Labeled position	Description of study	Ref.
Thermal decomposition (cont'd.)				
Nickel carbonyl	^{13}C	—	Isotope enrichment, inter., intra.	14
Nickel carbonyl	^{13}C	—	Inter., intra., t. coeff., comp., theory	15
Oxazolidine-2,5-dione	^{13}C	2-C	Inter., mech.	65, 67
	(^{18}O)	Carbonyl group	Relation of oxygen and carbon isotope effects, mech.	66
Propane	^{13}C	1-C	Intra.	135
Sodium acetate	^{14}C	2-C	Inter., theory	162
General information				
—	—	—	Limestones are enriched in ^{13}C; plants are enriched in ^{12}C	90
—	—	—	Broad discussion of rate isotope effects in isomerization, decarboxylation, and photosynthesis	145
			Theory	22
—	^{14}C	—	Reliability of assay techniques in isotope-effect studies	42
			Methods of calculating isotope effects	29, 30
			Specific activity–percent reaction relations for carbon and other similar isotope effects	105
Acetic acid	^{14}C	Carboxyl group	Theory; comp. for oxidation	51
Formic acid	^{14}C	—	Theory; comp. for decarbonylation	51
Malonic acid	^{14}C	Carboxyl group	Theory	94

References for Table 5-5

¹ W. D. Armstrong, L. Singer, S. H. Zbarsky, and B. Dunshee, "Errors of Combustion of Compounds for Carbon¹⁴ Analysis," *Science*, **112**, 531 (1950); *Chem. Abstr.*, **45**, 2819a (1951).

² R. W. Attree, F. Brown, G. E. Dunn, and M. Lounsbury, "Isotope Effects in the Combustion of Carbon Monoxide," *Can. J. Chem.*, **32**, 921 (1954); *Chem. Abstr.*, **49**, 7936c (1955).

³ R. F. W. Bader and A. N. Bourns, "A Kinetic Isotope Effect Study of the Chugaev Reaction," *Can. J. Chem.*, **39**, 348 (1961); *Chem. Abstr.*, **55**, 11374f (1961).

⁴ P. Baertschi, "The Fractionation of the Isotopes of Carbon during the Absorption of Carbon Dioxide," *Helv. Chim. Acta*, **35**, 1030 (1952); *Chem. Abstr.*, **46**, 8204b (1952).

⁵ P. Baertschi, "Fractionation of Naturally Occurring Isotopes in Carbon Dioxide Exchange in Green Plants," *Helv. Chim. Acta*, **36**, 773 (1953); *Chem. Abstr.*, **47**, 10638d (1953).

⁶ P. Baertschi, W. Kuhn, and H. Kuhn, "Fractionation of Isotopes by Distillation of Some Organic Substances," *Nature*, **171**, 1018 (1953); *Chem. Abstr.*, **49**, 15554b (1955).

⁷ T. H. Bates and J. C. Bevington, "Carbon Isotope Effect in the Decarboxylation of the Anisoyloxy Radical," *Nature*, **197**, 1294 (1963); *Chem. Abstr.*, **59**, 404g (1963).

[8] E. W. Becker and W. Vogell, "Shift of Isotopic Abundances in the Solution Equilibrium: Hydrogen Cyanide—Glacial Acetic Acid," *Z. Physik*, **130**, 129 (1951); *Chem. Abstr.*, **45**, 10091e (1951).

[9] O. Beeck, J. W. Otvos, D. P. Stevenson, and C. D. Wagner, "The Isomerization of Propane with C^{13} in One End Position," *J. Chem. Phys.*, **16**, 255 (1948); *Chem. Abstr.*, **42**, 4054d (1948).

[10] J. Bell and R. I. Reed, "Isotopic Tracer Studies of Pyrolytic Reactions. I. The Formation of Acetaldehyde," *J. Chem. Soc.*, 1383 (1952); *Chem. Abstr.*, **46**, 10100e (1952).

[11] M. L. Bender and G. J. Buist, "Carbon-14 Kinetic Isotope Effects. III. The Hydrolysis of 2-Chloro-2-methylpropane-2-C^{14}," *J. Am. Chem. Soc.*, **80**, 4304 (1958); *Chem. Abstr.*, **53**, 6051f (1959).

[12] M. L. Bender and D. F. Hoeg, "Carbon-14 Kinetic Isotope Effect in the Nucleophilic Displacement Reaction of Methyl-C^{14} Iodide and Triethylamine," *Chem. Ind. (London)*, 463 (1957); *Chem. Abstr.*, **51**, 12867d (1957).

[13] M. L. Bender and D. F. Hoeg, "Carbon-14 Kinetic Isotope Effects in Nucleophilic Substitution Reactions," *J. Am. Chem. Soc.*, **79**, 5649 (1957); *Chem. Abstr.*, **52**, 1738b (1958).

[14] R. B. Bernstein, "Enrichment of Isotopes by Difference in Rate for Isotopic Reactions," *J. Phys. Chem.*, **56**, 893 (1952); *Chem. Abstr.*, **47**, 2053e (1953).

[15] R. B. Bernstein, "Carbon-13 Isotope Effect in the Thermodecomposition of Nickel Carbonyl," *J. Chem. Phys.*, **22**, 710 (1954); *Chem. Abstr.*, **48**, 9132f (1954).

[16] R. B. Bernstein, "Simple Laboratory Method for Producing Enriched Carbon-13," *Science*, **126**, 119 (1957); *Chem. Abstr.*, **51**, 16130b (1957).

[17] J. Bigeleisen, "Isotope Effect in the Rupture of Carbon-Carbon Bonds in Propane-1-C^{13}," *J. Chem. Phys.*, **17**, 344 (1949); *Chem. Abstr.*, **43**, 5299b (1949).

[18] J. Bigeleisen, "Isotope Effect in the Decarboxylation of Labelled Malonic Acids," *J. Chem. Phys.*, **17**, 425 (1949); *Chem. Abstr.*, **43**, 7333a (1949).

[19] J. Bigeleisen and T. L. Allen, "Fractionation of the Carbon Isotopes in Decarboxylation Reactions. IV. The Relative Rates of Decomposition of 1-C^{12} and 1-C^{13} Trichloroacetate," *J. Chem. Phys.*, **19**, 760 (1951); *Chem. Abstr.*, **46**, 364d (1952).

[20] J. Bigeleisen, A. A. Bothner-By, and L. Friedman, "Fractionation of Carbon Isotopes in Decarboxylation Reactions. V. Mechanisms of the Pyrolysis of Barium Adipate," *J. Am. Chem. Soc.*, **75**, 2908 (1953); *Chem. Abstr.*, **47**, 12034b (1953).

[21] J. Bigeleisen and L. Friedman, "C^{13} Isotope Effect in the Decarboxylation of Malonic Acid," *J. Chem. Phys.*, **17**, 998 (1949); *Chem. Abstr.*, **44**, 3340e (1950).

[22] J. Bigeleisen and M. Wolfsberg, "Temperature Independent Factor in the Relative Rates of Isotopic Three Center Reactions," *J. Chem. Phys.*, **21**, 1972 (1953); *Chem. Abstr.*, **48**, 1848i and 12570c (1954).

[23] J. Bigeleisen and M. Wolfsberg, "Fractionation of the Carbon Isotopes in Decarboxylation Reactions. VI. Comparison of the Intermolecular Isotope Effects of a Pair of Isotopic Isomers," *J. Chem. Phys.*, **21**, 2120 (1953); *Chem. Abstr.*, **48**, 4944e (1954).

[24] W. A. Bonner and C. J. Collins, "An Isotope Effect in the Oxidation of a Secondary Carbinol," *J. Am. Chem. Soc.*, **75**, 2308 (1953); *Chem. Abstr.*, **48**, 5842a (1954).

[25] W. A. Bonner and C. J. Collins, "An Isotope Effect During Ozonization," *J. Am. Chem. Soc.*, **75**, 3693 (1953); *Chem. Abstr.*, **48**, 12048i (1954).

[26] W. A. Bonner and C. J. Collins, "Isotope Effects during Catalytic Hydrogenations," *J. Am. Chem. Soc.*, **75**, 4516 (1953); *Chem. Abstr.*, **48**, 12047f (1954).

[27] A. A. Bothner-By and J. Bigeleisen, "Fractionation of the Carbon Isotopes in Decarboxylation Reactions. III. The Relative Rates of Decomposition of Carboxyl-C^{12} and -C^{13} Mesitoic Acids," *J. Chem. Phys.*, **19**, 755 (1951); *Chem. Abstr.*, **46**, 364c (1952).

[28] A. A. Bothner-By, L. Friedman, and J. Bigeleisen, "Isotope Effects in the Decarboxylation of Dibasic Acids," *Brookhaven Conf. Rept.*, *Chem. Conf.*, No. **4**, 39 (Jan., 1950); *Chem. Abstr.*, **45**, 3807a (1951).

[29] A. I. Brodskii, "Connection Between Kinetics of the Isotope Effect and Change of an Isotope Content in Process of Reaction," *Probl. Kinetiki i Kataliza, Akad. Nauk SSSR*, **9**, 360 (1956) (see reference 30).

[30] A. I. Brodskii, "Calculation of the Kinetic Isotope Effect from Experimental Data," *Ukr. Khim. Zh.*, **22**, 417 (1956) (in Russian); *Chem. Abstr.*, **51**, 3249g (1957).

[31] A. M. Brodskii, R. A. Kalinenko, and K. P. Lavrovskii, "Kinetic Isotope Effect in Cracking," *Intern. J. Appl. Radiation Isotopes*, **7**, 118 (1959); *Chem. Abstr.*, **54**, 6273f (1960).

[32] A. M. Brodskii, R. A. Kalinenko, and K. P. Lavrovskii, "Isotope Effect in the Cracking of Ethane," *Dokl. Akad. Nauk SSSR*, **124**, 340 (1959); *Chem. Abstr.*, **55**, 9848c (1961).

[33] A. M. Brodskii, R. A. Kalinenko, and K. P. Lavrovskii, "Relation Between Kinetic Isotope Effect in C^{12}—C^{14} and C^{14}—C^{14} Bond Rupture," *Dokl. Akad. Nauk SSSR*, **126**, 1293 (1959); *Chem. Abstr.*, **55**, 22999h (1961).

[34] F. Brown and D. A. Holland, "Isotope Effects: Reaction at the Carbonyl Group," *Can. J. Chem.*, **30**, 438 (1952); *Chem. Abstr.*, **47**, 2149h (1953).

[35] D. L. Buchanan, A. Nakao, and G. Edwards, "Carbon-Isotope Effects in Biological Systems," *Science*, **117**, 541 (1953); *Chem. Abstr.*, **47**, 10567b (1953).

[36] G. J. Buist and M. L. Bender, "Carbon-14 Kinetic Isotope Effects. IV. The Effect of Activation Energy on Some Carbon-14 Kinetic Isotope Effects," *J. Am. Chem. Soc.*, **80**, 4308 (1958); *Chem. Abstr.*, **53**, 6051h (1959).

[37] C. A. Bunton and D. R. Llewellyn, "Isotope Effects in the Oxidation of Oxalic Acid," *Research (London)*, **5**, 443 (1952).

[38] J. G. Burr, Jr., "The Addition of Water to Diphenylacetylene-1,2-C^{14}," *J. Am. Chem. Soc.*, **75**, 1990 (1953); *Chem. Abstr.*, **49**, 12309a (1955).

[39] M. Calvin and P. E. Yankwich, "Chemical Method for Concentrating Isotopes of Carbon," U. S. Patent 2,511,667, June 13, 1950; *Chem. Abstr.*, **44**, 8796c (1950).

[40] W. L. Carrick and A. Fry, "A Carbon-14 Isotope Effect Study of the Dieckmann Condensation of Diethyl Phenylenediacetate," *J. Am. Chem. Soc.*, **77**, 4381 (1955); *Chem. Abstr.*, **50**, 5574a (1956).

[41] K. Clusius, F. Endtinger, and K. Schleich, "Results of Low-Temperature Research. XXX. Vapor Pressure Difference of $C^{12}H_4$ and $C^{13}H_4$ Between the Melting and Boiling Point," *Helv. Chim. Acta*, **43**, 1267 (1960); *Chem. Abstr.*, **55**, 3141i (1961).

[42] C. J. Collins and G. A. Ropp, "A Study of the Accuracy Obtained in Van Slyke Combustion and Radioassay of Carbon-14 Compounds," *J. Am. Chem. Soc.*, **77**, 4160 (1955); *Chem. Abstr.*, **50**, 4871i (1956).

[43] C. N. Davidson, C. K. Mann, and R. K. Sheline, "The Isotopic Separation of Carbon by Ion Exchange," *J. Am. Chem. Soc.*, **83**, 2389 (1961); *Chem. Abstr.*, **56**, 4320e (1962).

[44] V. H. Dibeler, F. L. Mohler, E. J. Wells, Jr., and R. M. Reese, "Mass Spectra of Some Simple Isotopic Molecules," *J. Res. Natl. Bur. Std.*, **45**, 288 (1950); *Chem. Abstr.*, **45**, 2765i (1951).

[45] V. H. Dibeler, E. J. Wells, Jr., and R. M. Reese, "Mass Spectra of $C^{13}O_2$ and $C^{13}O$," *Phys. Rev.*, **79**, 223 (1950); *Chem. Abstr.*, **46**, 6944e (1952).

[46] A. M. Downes, "Isotope Effect in the Reaction of C^{14}-Formaldehyde with Dimedon," *Australian J. Sci. Research* (now *Australian J. Chem.*), **5A**, 521 (1952); *Chem. Abstr.*, **47**, 1475d (1953).

[47] A. M. Downes and G. M. Harris, "Isotope Effect in the Cannizzaro Reaction of Carbon-14-labeled Formaldehyde," *J. Chem. Phys.*, **20**, 196 (1952); *Chem. Abstr.*, **46**, 6966a (1952).

[48] J. F. Duncan and K. R. Lynn, "Mechanism of the Pinacol-Pinacolone Rearrangement. V. Carbon Isotope Effects," *Australian J. Chem.*, **10**, 7 (1957); *Chem. Abstr.*, **51**, 1037g (1957).

[49] R. P. Eischens, "Isotopic Exchange Rates as Criteria of Surface Heterogeneity," *J. Am. Chem. Soc.*, **74**, 6167 (1952); *Chem. Abstr.*, **47**, 3668g (1953).

[50] E. A. Evans and J. L. Huston, "Isotope Effect in the Oxidation of Carboxyl-C^{14} Acetic Acid," *J. Chem. Phys.*, **19**, 1214 (1951); *Chem. Abstr.*, **45**, 10091h (1951).

[51] H. Eyring and T. W. Cagle, Jr., "Significance of Isotopic Reactions in Rate Theory," *J. Phys. Chem.*, **56**, 885 (1952); *Chem. Abstr.*, **47**, 2021g (1953).

[52] B. Fingerman and R. M. Lemmon, "The Isotope Effect in the Decarbonylation of Benzoylformic Acid," U.S. Atomic Energy Commission Report UCRL-8731 (April, 1959); *Chem. Abstr.*, **54**, 1403c (1960).

[53] H. L. Friedman, R. B. Bernstein, and H. E. Gunning, "Carbon-13 Isotope Effect in the Thermodecomposition of Ethyl Bromide," *J. Chem. Phys.*, **23**, 109 (1955); *Chem. Abstr.*, **49**, 5939a (1955).

[54] H. L. Friedman, R. B. Bernstein, and H. E. Gunning, "Comments on the Carbon-13 Isotope Effect in the Thermodecomposition of Ethyl Bromide," *J. Chem. Phys.*, **23**, 1722 (1955); *Chem. Abstr.*, **50**, 656i (1956).

[55] H. L. Friedman, R. B. Bernstein, and H. E. Gunning, "Carbon-13 Isotope Effect in the Photolysis of Ethyl Bromide," *J. Chem. Phys.*, **26**, 528 (1957); *Chem. Abstr.*, **51**, 9332d (1957).

[56] H. L. Frush and L. J. Tregoning, "Isotope Effect in Oxidation of D-Mannitol-2-C^{14} by Acetobacter Suboxydans," *Science*, **128**, 597 (1958); *Chem. Abstr.*, **53**, 5401e (1959).

[57] A. Fry and M. Calvin, "Isotope Effect in the Decomposition of Oxalic Acid," *J. Phys. Chem.*, **56**, 897 (1952); *Chem. Abstr.*, **47**, 20553 (1953).

[58] A. Fry and M. Calvin, "The Carbon^{14} Isotope Effect in the Decarboxylation of 1-Naphthyl- and Phenylmalonic Acids," *J. Phys. Chem.*, **56**, 901 (1952); *Chem. Abstr.*, **47**, 8653f (1953).

[59] E. Gelles and R. I. Reed, "Carbon-13 Isotope Effects in the Decarboxylation of Some Oxalo-acetates," *Nature*, **176**, 1262 (1955); *Chem. Abstr.*, **50**, 6934b (1956).

[60] A. A. Gordus and R. B. Bernstein, "Carbon-13 and Deuterium Isotope Effects in the Photolysis of Methyl and Ethyl Bromide," *J. Chem. Phys.*, **30**, 973 (1959); *Chem. Abstr.*, **53**, 15788b (1959).

[61] E. C. M. Grigg, "Carbon-14 Intramolecular Isotope Effects of Malonic and Bromomalonic Acids," *Australian J. Chem.*, **9**, 252 (1956); *Chem. Abstr.*, **50**, 11780c (1956).

[62] E. Grovenstein, Jr., and G. A. Ropp, "Carbon-13 Isotope Fractionation as a Criterion of the Mechanism of Bromodecarboxylation of 3,5-Dibromo-4-hydroxybenzoic Acid," *J. Am. Chem. Soc.*, **78**, 2560 (1956); *Chem. Abstr.*, **51**, 1089f (1957).

[63] G. M. Harris and D. R. Stranks, "Kinetics of Isotopic Exchange Reactions. Exchange Between Free Carbonate Ion and Carbonatotetraminecobaltic Complex Ion," *Trans. Faraday Soc.*, **48**, 137 (1952); *Chem. Abstr.*, **46**, 7854b (1952).

[64] R. H. Haschemeyer, "Carbon Isotope Effect Studies of the Decarbonylation of Formic Acid," *Dissertation Abstr.*, **18**, 419 (1958); *Chem. Abstr.*, **52**, 7828a (1958).

[65] K. Heyns and R. Brockmann, "The Thermal Decomposition of Leuchs' Compound to Give Polyglycine," *Z. Naturforsch.*, **9b**, 21 (1954); *Chem. Abstr.*, **49**, 1706f (1955).

[66] K. Heyns and H. Schultze, "The Isotope Effect. III. Mechanism of Polymerization of 2,5-Oxazo-lidinediones," *Ann. Chem.*, **611**, 40 (1958); *Chem. Abstr.*, **52**, 12764d (1958).

[67] K. Heyns, H. Schultze, and R. Brockmann, "The Isotope Effect. II. Mechanism of Polymerization of 2,5-Oxazolidinediones," *Ann. Chem.*, **611**, 33 (1958); *Chem. Abstr.*, **52**, 12764c (1958).

[68] E. M. Hodnett and C. F. Feldman, Jr., "Kinetics of the Friedel-Crafts Ethylation of Benzene with Ethylene and with Ethylene-C^{14}," *J. Am. Chem. Soc.*, **81**, 1638 (1959); *Chem. Abstr.*, **53**, 19927g (1959).

[69] O. Holm-Hansen, V. Moses, C. F. Van Sumere, and M. Calvin, "Effect of Radiocarbon on the Rate of Carbon Dioxide Utilization During Photosynthesis," *Biochem. Biophys. Acta*, **28**, 587 (1958); *Chem. Abstr.*, **52**, 17420f (1958).

[70] R. M. Ikeda, "Carbon Isotope Effects: Malonic Acid Decarboxylation," *Dissertation Abstr.*, **19**, 2491 (1959); *Chem. Abstr.*, **53**, 14934f (1959).

[71] F. L. Ingley and A. F. Roche, "Polymerization of Radioactive Monomers," Abstracts of 121st American Chemical Society Meeting, Division of Paint, Varnish, and Plastic Chemistry, Mar. 30–Apr. 3, 1952, Milwaukee, Wis.

[72] F. E. Jenkins and G. M. Harris, "An Unusual Isotope Fractionation Effect," *J. Am. Chem. Soc.*, **77**, 4439 (1955); *Chem. Abstr.*, **50**, 1488g (1956).

[73] H. S. Johnston, W. A. Bonner, and D. J. Wilson, "Carbon-Isotope Effect During Oxidation of Carbon Monoxide with Nitrogen Dioxide," *J. Chem. Phys.*, **26**, 1002 (1957); *Chem. Abstr.*, **41**, 13531g (1957).

[74] R. F. Klemm and R. B. Bernstein, "Kinetics of the Reaction of Methyl Iodide with Toluene," *J. Am. Chem. Soc.*, **82**, 5987 (1960); *Chem. Abstr.*, **55**, 8325f (1961).

[75] A. J. Kresge, N. N. Lichtin, and K. N. Rao, "An Inverse Carbon Isotope Effect on the Ionization of Triphenylmethyl Chloride, Kinetic Isotope Effects on SN1 and SN2 Reactions," *J. Am. Chem. Soc.*, **85**, 1210 (1963); *Chem. Abstr.*, **59**, 404d (1963).

[76] C. C. Lee and J. W. T. Spinks, "The Isotope Effect in the Synthesis of 3,3'-Methylene-C[14]-*bis*(4-hydroxycoumarin)," *Can. J. Chem.*, **32**, 327 (1954); *Chem. Abstr.*, **49**, 8932f (1955).

[77] J. G. Lindsay, A. N. Bourns, and H. G. Thode, "Carbon[13] Isotope Effect in the Decarboxylation of Normal Malonic Acid," *Can. J. Chem.*, **29**, 192 (1951); *Chem. Abstr.*, **45**, 7420c (1951).

[78] J. G. Lindsay, A. N. Bourns, and H. G. Thode, "Influence of Temperature on the Intermolecular Carbon[13] Isotope Effect in the Decarboxylation of Normal Malonic Acid," *Can. J. Chem.*, **30**, 163 (1952); *Chem. Abstr.*, **46**, 8481e (1952).

[79] J. G. Lindsay, D. E. McElcheran, and H. G. Thode, "The Isotope Effect in the Decomposition of Oxalic Acid," *J. Chem. Phys.*, **17**, 589 (1949); *Chem. Abstr.*, **43**, 8859d (1949).

[80] K. R. Lynn and A. N. Bourns, "Carbon-13 Kinetic Isotope Effects and the Mechanism of Decarboxylation of 2,4-Dihydroxybenzoic Acid," *Chem. Ind.* (*London*), **19**, 782 (1963); *Chem. Abstr.*, **59**, 3743b (1963).

[81] K. R. Lynn and P. E. Yankwich, "Cyanide Carbon Isotope Fractionation in the Reaction of Cyanide Ion and Methyl Iodide. Carbon Isotope Effect in the Hydrolysis of Methyl Iodide," *J. Am. Chem. Soc.*, **83**, 53 (1961); *Chem. Abstr.*, **55**, 17168d (1961).

[82] K. R. Lynn and P. E. Yankwich, "High Concentration-Ratio Experiments: Isotope Fractionation at the Methyl Carbon in the Reaction of Cyanide Ion and Methyl Iodide. Isotope Effect Under Conditions of Equal Reagent Concentrations," *J. Am. Chem. Soc.*, **83**, 790 (1961); *Chem. Abstr.*, **55**, 15073b (1961).

[83] K. R. Lynn and P. E. Yankwich, "Isotope Fractionation at the Methyl Carbon in the Reactions of Cyanide Ion with Methyl Chloride and Methyl Bromide," *J. Am. Chem. Soc.*, **83**, 3220 (1961); *Chem. Abstr.*, **56**, 302d (1962).

[84] A. Maccoll and P. J. Thomas, "Mechanism of the Pyrolysis of Ethyl Bromide. A Note on a Paper by Friedman, Bernstein and Gunning," *J. Chem. Phys.*, **23**, 1722 (1955); *Chem. Abstr.*, **50**, 41e (1956).

[85] E. M. Magee and F. Daniels, "Kinetics and C[13] Isotope Effect in the Decomposition of Substituted Ureas," *J. Am. Chem. Soc.*, **79**, 829 (1957); *Chem. Abstr.*, **51**, 7116e (1957).

[86] L. W. Marshall and R. E. Cook, "Isotope Effect During the Countercurrent Distribution of D-Arabinose-1-C[14]," *J. Am. Chem. Soc.*, **84**, 2647 (1962); *Chem. Abstr.*, **57**, 11287g (1962).

[87] N. I. Mitskevich, I. I. Uskov, and V. A. Lashitskii, "Change in the Degree of Decarboxylation with Depth of Autoxidation of Mixtures of Isopropylbenzene with Fatty Acids," *Dokl. Akad. Nauk Belorussk. SSR*, **6**, 706 (1962); *Chem. Abstr.*, **59**, 403h (1963).

[88] A. L. Myerson and F. Daniels, "Relative Rates of Hydrolysis of Urea Containing C[12] and C[14]," *Science*, **108**, 676 (1948).

[89] P. M. Nair, "Kinetic and Isotope Effect Study of a Borderline Case in Nucleophilic Substitution: Reaction Between Benzyl Chloride and Potassium Cyanide in Eighty Per Cent Ethanol," *Dissertation Abstr.*, **17**, 1469 (1957); *Chem. Abstr.*, **51**, 14575i (1957).

[90] A. O. Nier and E. A. Gulbransen, "Variations in the Relative Abundance of the Carbon Isotopes," *J. Am. Chem. Soc.*, **61**, 697 (1939); *Chem. Abstr.*, **33**, 81099 (1939).

[91] D. G. Ott and G. G. Smith, "A Carbon-14 Tracer Study of the Alkaline Rearrangement of Chlorophenanthraquinones," *J. Am. Chem. Soc.*, **77**, 2325 (1955); *Chem. Abstr.*, **50**, 3372a (1956).

[92] G. Pajaro and V. Desio, "Isotopic Effects in the Polymerization of Carbon-14-labeled Ethylene, Propylene, and Styrene," *Gazz. Chim. Ital.*, **91**, 880 (1961); *Chem. Abstr.*, **56**, 7485e (1962).

[93] R. Park and S. Epstein, "Carbon Isotope Fractionation During Photosynthesis," *Geochim. Cosmochim. Acta*, **21**, 110 (1960); *Chem. Abstr.*, **55**, 10592f (1961).

[94] K. S. Pitzer, "Carbon Isotope Effect on Reaction Rates," *J. Chem. Phys.*, **17**, 1341 (1949); *Chem. Abstr.*, **44**, 5198g (1950).

[95] V. F. Raaen and C. J. Collins, "Carbon Isotope Effect in the Pinacol-Pinacolone Rearrangement: A Reinvestigation," *J. Am. Chem. Soc.*, **80**, 4432 (1958); *Chem. Abstr.*, **53**, 7003h (1959).

[96] V. F. Raaen and G. A. Ropp, "Intramolecular Isotope Effects in the Reactions of Benzoic-α-C[14] Anhydride," *J. Chem. Phys.*, **21**, 1902 (1953); *Chem. Abstr.*, **48**, 1171a (1954).

[97] V. F. Raaen, A. K. Tsiomis, and C. J. Collins, "A Secondary Isotope Effect in the Formation of a Derivative of Acetophenone-β-C[14]," *J. Am. Chem. Soc.*, **82**, 5502 (1960); *Chem. Abstr.*, **55**, 10369c (1961).

[98] D. B. Richardson, "Isotope Effect Study of the Mechanism of the Wolff Rearrangement," *Dissertation Abstr.*, **16**, 1345 (1956); *Chem. Abstr.*, **50**, 16665g (1956).

[99] J. D. Roberts, D. A. Semenow, H. E. Simmons, Jr., and L. A. Carlsmith, "Mechanism of Aminations of Halobenzenes," *J. Am. Chem. Soc.*, **78**, 601 (1956); *Chem. Abstr.*, **50**, 12860f (1956).

[100] A. Roe and E. L. Albenesius, "Isotope Effect. III. Reaction of Acetone-1-C^{14} with Alkaline-hypoiodite," *J. Am. Chem. Soc.*, **74**, 2402 (1952); *Chem. Abstr.*, **48**, 7533i (1954).

[101] A. Roe and J. B. Finlay, "Isotope Effect. II. Pyrolysis of Lithium Acetate-1-C^{14}," *J. Am. Chem. Soc.*, **74**, 2442 (1952); *Chem. Abstr.*, **48**, 30b (1954).

[102] A. Roe and M. Hellmann, "Determination of an Isotope Effect in the Decarboxylation of Malonic-1-C^{14} Acid," *J. Chem. Phys.*, **19**, 660 (1951); *Chem. Abstr.*, **45**, 7891h (1951).

[103] G. A. Ropp, "Examination of the Isotope Effect in the Condensation of *o*-Benzoylbenzoic Acid-Carboxyl-C^{14} to Anthraquinone-9-C^{14}," *J. Chem. Phys.*, **23**, 2196 (1955); *Chem. Abstr.*, **50**, 8578d (1956).

[104] G. A. Ropp, "Isotopic Evidence for the Mechanisms of Decarbonylation of Three Carboxylic Acids in Sulfuric Acid," *J. Am. Chem. Soc.*, **80**, 6691 (1958); *Chem. Abstr.*, **53**, 8064h (1959).

[105] G. A. Ropp, "Curves for Computation of Kinetic Isotope Effects," U.S. Atomic Energy Commission Report ORNL-CF-59-12-4 (Dec. 8, 1959).

[106] G. A. Ropp, "Studies Involving Isotopically Labeled Formic Acid and its Derivatives. V. Decarbonylation of Formic, Benzoylformic and Triphenylacetic Acids," *J. Am. Chem. Soc.*, **82**, 842 (1960).

[107] G. A. Ropp, W. A. Bonner, M. T. Clark, and V. F. Raaen, "Examination of the Iodoform and Schmidt Reactions of Acetone-1-C^{14} for Isotope Effects," *J. Am. Chem. Soc,*. **76**, 1710 (1954); *Chem. Abstr.*, **49**, 8794d (1955).

[108] G. A. Ropp, C. J. Danby, and D. A. Dominey, "Isotopically Labeled Formic Acid and its Derivatives. II. Relation of the Absolute Reaction Rates to the Magnitudes of the Isotope Effects in the Oxidation of Formic-C^{13} Acid by Halogen Atoms," *J. Am. Chem. Soc.*, **79**, 4944 (1957); *Chem. Abstr.*, **52**, 4482e (1958).

[109] G. A. Ropp and E. M. Hodnett, "Isotope Fractionation Studies of Reactions with Cleavage of a Carbon-14 to Hydrogen Bond in the Rate-Determining Step," *J. Chem. Phys.*, **25**, 587 (1956); *Chem. Abstr.*, **51**, 819c (1957).

[110] G. A. Ropp and V. F. Raaen, "A Comparison of the Magnitudes of the Isotope Intermolecular Effects in the Decarboxylations of Malonic-1-C^{14} and Malonic-2-C^{14} Acids at 154°," *J. Am. Chem. Soc.*, **74**, 4992 (1952); *Chem. Abstr.*, **47**, 1476d (1953).

[111] G. A. Ropp and V. F. Raaen, "Effect of Nuclear Substituents on the Carbon-14 Isotope Effect in the Saponification of Carboxyl-labeled Ethyl Benzoates at 25°C," *J. Chem. Phys.*, **20**, 1823 (1952); *Chem. Abstr.*, **48**, 1311e (1954).

[112] G. A. Ropp, V. F. Raaen, and A. J. Weinberger, "Some Carbon-14 Isotope Effects in Organic Chemistry," *J. Am. Chem. Soc.*, **75**, 3694 (1953); *Chem. Abstr.*, **48**, 13611h (1954).

[113] G. A. Ropp and V. F. Raaen, "The Effect of Ring Substituents on the Isotope Effects in Reactions of Carbonyl-C^{14} Esters and Ketones," *J. Chem. Phys.*, **22**, 1223 (1954); *Chem. Abstr.*, **49**, 8858c (1955).

[114] G. A. Ropp and V. F. Raaen, "Examination of a Meerwein Reaction for an Intramolecular Isotope Effect with Carbon-14," *J. Am. Chem. Soc.*, **76**, 4484 (1954); *Chem. Abstr.*, **49**, 12328a (1955).

[115] G. A. Ropp, A. J. Weinberger, and O. K. Neville, "Determination of the Isotope Effect and its Variation with Temperature in the Dehydration of Formic-C^{14} Acid," *J. Am. Chem. Soc.*, **73**, 5573 (1951); *Chem. Abstr.*, **46**, 2424c (1952).

[116] W. D. Rosenfeld and S. R. Silverman, "Carbon Isotope Fractionation in Bacterial Production of Methane," *Science*, **130**, 1658 (1959); *Chem. Abstr.*, **54**, 7827b (1960).

[117] M. E. Russel, "Kinetics and Carbon-13 Isotope Effect in the Thermal Decomposition of Dimethylmercury," *Dissertation Abstr.*, **19**, 3150 (1959); *Chem. Abstr.*, **53**, 16939e (1959).

[118] O. A. Schaeffer, "Effect of Isotopic Substitution on Mass Spectra of Molecules," *J. Chem. Phys.*, **18**, 1501 (1950); *Chem. Abstr.*, **45**, 3707a (1951).

[119] O. A. Schaeffer, "Effect of Isotopic Substitution on the Mass Spectra of Molecules. III. Carbon Dioxide, Theoretical Interpretation," *J. Chem. Phys.*, **23**, 1309 (1955); *Chem. Abstr.*, **49**, 14472c (1955).

[120] O. A. Schaeffer and H. R. Owen, "Effect of Isotopic Substitution on the Mass Spectra of Molecules. II. Oxygen and Carbon Dioxide, Experimental," *J. Chem. Phys.*, **23**, 1305 (1955); *Chem. Abstr.*, **49**, 14471i (1955).

[121] J. A. Schmitt and F. Daniels, "The Carbon-Isotope Effect in the Acid Hydrolysis of Urea," *J. Am. Chem. Soc.*, **75**, 3564 (1953); *Chem. Abstr.*, **48**, 1125d (1954).

[122] J. A. Schmitt, A. A. Myerson, and F. Daniels, "Relative Rates of Hydrolysis of Urea Containing Carbon[14], Carbon[13] and Carbon[12]," *J. Phys. Chem.*, **56**, 917 (1952); *Chem. Abstr.*, **47**, 2024g (1953).

[123] S. Seltzer, G. A. Hamilton, and F. H. Westheimer, "Isotope Effects in the Enzymatic Decarboxylation of Oxalacetic Acid," *J. Am. Chem. Soc.*, **81**, 4018 (1959); *Chem. Abstr.*, **53**, 22154h (1958).

[124] Y. K. Shaposhnikov, "The Concentration of the Heavy Isotopes of Carbon by a Chemical Method," *Zh. Fiz. Khim.*, **32**, 869 (1958); available as Translation No. JPRS-2528 from Office of Technical Services.

[125] G. G. Smith and D. M. Fahey, "Mechanism of Base-Catalyzed Acylative Decarboxylation," *J. Am. Chem. Soc.*, **81**, 3391 (1959); *Chem. Abstr.*, **54**, 105a (1960).

[126] L. J. Tregoning Sniegoski, "Isotope Effects in the Oxidation of Carbon-14 and Tritium-Labeled D-Mannitols," *Dissertation Abstr.*, **22**, 1832 (1961); *Chem. Abstr.*, **56**, 8824c (1962).

[127] Y. I. Sorokin, "Determination of the Isotope Effect on Photosynthesis in Scenedesmus Quadricauda Cultures," *Byul. Inst. Biol. Vodokhranilishch, Akad. Nauk SSSR*, No. 4, 7 (1959); *Chem. Abstr.*, **55**, 7561g (1961).

[128] F. S. Stein, "Mass Spectra of Isotopic Carbon Dioxide Molecules," *Phys. Rev.*, **87**, 236 (1952); *Chem. Abstr.*, **48**, 8025c (1954).

[129] W. H. Stevens and R. W. Attree, "Effect on Reaction Rates Caused by the Substitution of C^{14} for C^{12}. I. Alkaline Hydrolysis of Carboxyl-labeled Ethyl Benzoate," *Can. J. Research*, **27B**, 807 (1949); *Chem. Abstr.*, **44**, 6244d (1950).

[130] W. H. Stevens and R. W. Attree, "The Effect on Reaction Rates Caused by the Substitution of Carbon-14 for Carbon-12," *J. Chem. Phys.*, **18**, 574 (1950); *Chem. Abstr.*, **44**, 5688h (1950).

[131] W. H. Stevens and D. A. Crowder, "The C^{14} Isotope Effect in the Condensation of Benzoylbenzoic Acid-Carboxyl-C^{14} to Anthraquinone-9-C^{14}," *Can. J. Chem.*, **32**, 792 (1954); *Chem. Abstr.*, **49**, 11610f (1955).

[132] W. H. Stevens, J. M. Pepper, and M. Lounsbury, "Relative Isotope Effects of Carbon[13] and Carbon[14]," *J. Chem. Phys.*, **20**, 192 (1952); *Chem. Abstr.*, **46**, 6965g (1952).

[133] W. H. Stevens, J. M. Pepper, and M. Lounsbury, "Decarboxylation of Anthranilic Acid," *Can. J. Chem.*, **30**, 529 (1952); *Chem. Abstr.*, **46**, 9958a (1952).

[134] D. P. Stevenson, "The Mass Spectra of Propanes and Butanes Containing Carbon[13]," *J. Chem. Phys.*, **19**, 17 (1951); *Chem. Abstr.*, **45**, 6479f (1951).

[135] D. P. Stevenson, C. D. Wagner, O. Beeck, and J. W. Otvos, "Isotope Effect in the Thermal Cracking of Propane-1-C^{13}," *J. Chem. Phys.*, **16**, 993 (1948); *Chem. Abstr.*, **42**, 8627a (1948).

[136] J. B. Stothers and A. N. Bourns, "Carbon-13 Kinetic Isotope Effects in the Solvolysis of 1-Bromo-1-phenylethane," *Can. J. Chem.*, **38**, 923 (1960); *Chem. Abstr.*, **55**, 81g (1961).

[137] D. R. Stranks, "Carbon-14 Isotope Effect in the Exchange Reaction between Carbon Monoxide and Phosgene," *J. Chem. Phys.*, **21**, 2232 (1953); *Chem. Abstr.*, **48**, 4296b (1954).

[138] D. R. Stranks and G. M. Harris, "Isotope Effect in Some Reactions of Carbon-14-Labeled Carbonatotetramine Cobaltic Complex Ion," *J. Phys. Chem.*, **56**, 906 (1952); *Chem. Abstr.*, **47**, 2079a (1953).

[139] D. R. Stranks and G. M. Harris, "Predicted Isotopic Enrichment Effects in Some Isotopic Exchange Equilibria Involving Carbon-14," *J. Am. Chem. Soc.*, **75**, 2015 (1953); *Chem. Abstr.*, **47**, 2079a (1953).

[140] V. G. Vasil'ev and E. N. Kharlamova, "Thermal Decarboxylation of Methyl Acetylsalicylate Labeled with Carbon-14," *Zh. Obshch. Khim.*, **29**, 1973 (1959); *Chem. Abstr.*, **54**, 9831d (1960).

[141] J. W. Weigel and M. Calvin, "An Isotope Effect in Photosynthesis," *J. Chem. Phys.*, **17**, 210 (1949); *Chem. Abstr.*, **43**, 4730c (1949).

[142] J. W. Weigel, P. M. Warrington, and M. Calvin, "The Relation of Photosynthesis to Respiration," *J. Am. Chem. Soc.*, **73**, 5058 (1951); *Chem. Abstr.*, **46**, 8726d (1952).

[143] R. E. Weston, Jr., "Effect of Pressure on the Isotope Effect in a Unimolecular Gaseous Reaction: Tritium and Carbon-13 Effects in the Isomerization of Cyclopropane," *J. Chem. Phys.*, **26**, 975 (1957); *Chem. Abstr.*, **51**, 13531b (1957).

[144] F. E. Wickman, "Variations in the Relative Abundance of the Carbon Isotopes in Plants," *Geochim. Cosmochim. Acta*, **2**, 243 (1952); *Chem. Abstr.*, **46**, 9167c (1952).

[145] P. E. Yankwich, "Isotope Effects in Some Simple Chemical Processes," *Brookhaven Conf. Rept., Isotopic Exchange Reactions and Chem. Kinetics, Chem. Conf.*, No. 2, 44 (1948); *Chem. Abstr.*, **46**, 364a (1952).

[146] P. E. Yankwich and R. L. Belford, "Intermolecular Carbon Isotope Effect in the Decarboxylation of Normal Malonic Acid in Quinoline Solution," *J. Am. Chem. Soc.*, **75**, 4178 (1953); *Chem. Abstr.*, **47**, 11923f (1953).

[147] P. E. Yankwich and R. L. Belford, "Intramolecular Carbon-Isotope Effect in the Decarboxylation of Normal Malonic Acid in Quinoline Solution," *J. Am. Chem. Soc.*, **76**, 3067 (1954); *Chem. Abstr.*, **48**, 10411g (1954).

[148] P. E. Yankwich, R. L. Belford, and G. Fraenkel, "Temperature Coefficient of the Intermolecular Carbon Isotope Effect in the Decarboxylation of Normal Malonic Acid," *J. Am. Chem. Soc.*, **75**, 832 (1953); *Chem. Abstr.*, **47**, 5816d (1953).

[149] P. E. Yankwich and R. W. Buddemeier, "Large Reverse Carbon Isotope Effect," *J. Chem. Phys.*, **30**, 861 (1959); *Chem. Abstr.*, **53**, 14717c (1959).

[150] P. E. Yankwich and M. Calvin, "An Effect of Isotopic Mass on the Rate of a Reaction Involving the Carbon-Carbon Bond," *J. Chem. Phys.*, **17**, 109 (1949); *Chem. Abstr.*, **43**, 2862d (1949).

[151] P. E. Yankwich and J. L. Copeland, "Pyrolysis of Lead Oxalate; Isotope Effects and Product Composition," *J. Am. Chem. Soc.*, **79**, 2081 (1957); *Chem. Abstr.*, **51**, 12616i (1957).

[152] P. E. Yankwich and R. H. Haschemeyer, "Temperature Dependence of the Carbon Isotope Effect in the Decarbonylation of Formic Acid," *J. Phys. Chem.*, **67**, 694 (1963); *Chem. Abstr.*, **58**, 8438b (1963).

[153] P. E. Yankwich and R. M. Ikeda, "Intermolecular Carbon Isotope Effect in the Decarboxylation of Malonic Acid in Dioxane Solution," *J. Am. Chem. Soc.*, **81**, 5054 (1959); *Chem. Abstr.*, **54**, 5458e (1960).

[154] P. E. Yankwich and J. E. McNamara, "Isotope Effects in the Exchange Reaction Between Uncomplexed Carbonate-Bicarbonate Ions and Carbonate-*Bis*-Ethylenediamine-Cobalt(III) Ion," *J. Chem. Phys.*, **20**, 1325 (1952); *Chem. Abstr.*, **46**, 11004a (1952).

[155] P. E. Yankwich and A. L. Promislow, "Intramolecular Carbon-Isotope Effect in the Decarboxylation of Liquid Malonic Acid near the Melting Point," *J. Am. Chem. Soc.*, **76**, 4648 (1954); *Chem. Abstr.*, **49**, 2161g (1955).

[156] P. E. Yankwich, A. L. Promislow, and R. F. Nystrom, "Carbon-14 and Carbon-13 Intramolecular Isotope Effects in the Decarboxylation of Liquid Malonic Acid at 140.5°," *J. Am. Chem. Soc.*, **76**, 5893 (1954); *Chem. Abstr.*, **49**, 10023h (1955).

[157] P. E. Yankwich and E. C. Stivers, "Intramolecular Carbon Isotope Effects in the Decarboxylation of Malonic Acid and Bromomalonic Acid," *J. Chem. Phys.*, **21**, 61 (1953); *Chem. Abstr.*, **47**, 10975c (1953).

[158] P. E. Yankwich, E. C. Stivers, and R. F. Nystrom, "Intramolecular Isotope Effects in the Decarboxylation of Malonic Acid," *J. Chem. Phys.*, **20**, 344 (1952); *Chem. Abstr.*, **46**, 6966c (1952).

[159] P. E. Yankwich and A. E. Veazie, "Temperature Dependence of the Carbon-Isotope Effect in the Acid Hydrolysis of Urea," *J. Am. Chem. Soc.*, **80**, 1835 (1958); *Chem. Abstr.*, **52**, 15210c (1958).

[160] P. E. Yankwich and H. S. Weber, "Intramolecular Carbon Isotope Effect in the Decarboxylation of the Mono-Anion of Malonic Acid in Quinoline Solution," *J. Am. Chem. Soc.*, **77**, 4513 (1955); *Chem. Abstr.*, **49**, 15405h (1955).

[161] P. E. Yankwich and H. S. Weber, "Intramolecular Carbon Isotope Effect in the Decarboxylation of the Mono-Anion of Malonic Acid in Quinoline Solution," *J. Am. Chem. Soc.*, **78**, 564 (1956); *Chem. Abstr.*, **50**, 7550c (1956).

[162] I. Zlotowski and M. Zielinski, "Isotope Effect in the Pyrolysis of Sodium Acetate," *Nukleonika*, **5**, 27 (1960); *Chem. Abstr.*, **55**, 6110b (1961).

CITED REFERENCES

[1] G. A. Ropp and V. F. Raaen, *J. Chem. Phys.*, **22**, 1223 (1954).

[2] P. E. Yankwich and M. Calvin, *J. Chem. Phys.*, **17**, 109 (1949).

[3] P. E. Yankwich, A. L. Promislow, and R. F. Nystrom, *J. Am. Chem. Soc.*, **76**, 5893 (1954).

[4] J. Bigeleisen, *J. Chem. Phys.*, **17**, 344 (1949).

[5] J. Bigeleisen, *J. Chem. Phys.*, **17**, 425 (1949).

[6] H. C. Urey and D. Rittenberg, *J. Chem. Phys.*, **1**, 137 (1933).

[7] A. Farkas and L. Farkas, *J. Chem. Phys.*, **2**, 468 (1934).

[8] H. C. Urey and L. J. Greiff, *J. Am. Chem. Soc.*, **57**, 321 (1935).

[9] E. R. Washburn and H. C. Urey, *Proc. Nat. Acad. Sci. U.S.*, **18**, 496 (1932).

[10] K. Wiberg, *Chem. Rev.*, **55**, 713 (1955).

[11] O. Beeck, J. W. Otvos, D. P. Stevenson, and C. D. Wagner, *J. Chem. Phys.*, **16**, 255 (1948).

[12] D. P. Stevenson, C. D. Wagner, O. Beeck, and J. W. Otvos, *J. Chem. Phys.*, **16**, 993 (1948).

[13] J. Bigeleisen, *J. Chem. Phys.*, **17**, 675 (1949).

[14] G. A. Ropp, *J. Am. Chem. Soc.*, **80**, 6691 (1958).

[15] H. Eyring and F. W. Cagle, Jr., *J. Phys. Chem.*, **56**, 889 (1952).

[16] J. Bigeleisen, *Science*, **110**, 14 (1949).

[17] L. Funderburk and E. S. Lewis, *J. Am. Chem. Soc.*, **86**, 2531 (1964).

[18] J. R. Jones, *Trans. Faraday Soc.*, **61**, 95 (1965).

[19] K. R. Lynn and P. E. Yankwich, *J. Am. Chem. Soc.*, **83**, 790 (1961).

[20] M. L. Bender and D. F. Hoeg, *J. Am. Chem. Soc.*, **59**, 5649 (1957).

[21] F. W. Stacey, J. G. Lindsay, and A. N. Bourns, *Can. J. Chem.*, **30**, 135 (1952).

[22] A. E. Cahill and H. Taube, *J. Am. Chem. Soc.*, **74**, 2312 (1952).

[23] W. A. Sheppard, R. F. W. Bader, and A. N. Bourns, *Can. J. Chem.*, **32**, 345 (1954).

[24] W. A. Sheppard and A. N. Bourns, *Can. J. Chem.*, **32**, 4 (1954).

[25] R. M. Bartholomew, F. Brown, and M. Lounsbury, *Can. J. Chem.*, **32**, 979 (1954); *Nature*, **174**, 133 (1954).

[26] F. Daniels, "Chemical Kinetics," p. 249, Cornell University Press, Ithaca, N.Y., 1937.

[27] L. Melander, "The Use of Nuclides in the Determination of Organic Reaction Mechanisms," pp. 34–48, University of Notre Dame Press, Notre Dame, Indiana, 1955.

[28] S. Glasstone, "Textbook of Physical Chemistry," 2d ed., p. 569, D. Van Nostrand Company, Inc., New York, 1946.

[29] L. G. Bonner and R. Hofstadter, *J. Chem. Phys.*, **6**, 531 (1938).

[30] G. A. Ropp, A. J. Weinberger, and O. K. Neville, *J. Am. Chem. Soc.*, **73**, 5573 (1951).

[31] W. H. Stevens and R. Attree, *Can. J. Chem.*, **B27**, 807 (1949).

[32] J. Bigeleisen and M. Wolfsberg, 'Theoretical and Experimental Aspects of Isotope Effects in Chemical Kinetics,' chapter from "Advances in Chemical Physics," vol. I, p. 15, Interscience Publishers, New York, 1958.

[33] G. A. Ropp, C. J. Danby, and D. A. Dominey, *J. Am. Chem. Soc.*, **79**, 4944 (1957).

[34] A. M. Downes, *Australian J. Chem.*, **A5**, 521 (1952).

[35] G. A. Ropp, *J. Am. Chem. Soc.*, **82**, 842 (1960).

[35a] V. F. Raaen, A. K. Tsiomis, and C. J. Collins, *J. Am. Chem. Soc.*, **82**, 5502 (1960).

[35b] V. F. Raaen, T. K. Dunham, D. D. Thompson, and C. J. Collins, *J. Am. Chem. Soc.*, **85**, 3497 (1963).

[35c] M. H. Lietzke, United States Atomic Energy Commission Report ORNL-3259, March 21, 1962.

[35d] C. J. Collins in V. Gold, Ed., "Advances in Physical Organic Chemistry," vol. 2, pp. 60–91, Academic Press, New York, 1964.

[35e] A. I. Brodskii, *Ukr. Khim. Zh.*, **22**, 417 (1956).

[36] J. Bigeleisen and T. L. Allen, *J. Chem. Phys.*, **19**, 760 (1951).

[37] W. M. Jones, *J. Chem. Phys.*, **19**, 78 (1951).

[38] A. Fry and M. Calvin, *J. Phys. Chem.*, **56**, 80 (1952).

[39] R. B. Bernstein, *Science*, **126**, 119 (1957).

[39a] L. Melander, "Isotope Effect on Reaction Rates," Ronald Press, New York, 1960.

[40] G. Herzberg, "Infrared and Raman Spectra," p. 227, D. Van Nostrand Company, Inc., New York, 1947.

[41] A. Farkas and L. Farkas, *Proc. Roy. Soc. (London)*, **A152**, 124 (1935).

[42] R. P. Bell, J. A. Fendley, and J. R. Hulett, *Proc. Roy. Soc. (London)*, **A235**, 453 (1956).

[43] J. Bigeleisen, *J. Phys. Chem.*, **56**, 823 (1952).

[44] S. Glasstone, K. J. Laidler, and H. Eyring, "The Theory of Rate Processes," McGraw-Hill Book Company, Inc., New York, 1941.

[45] J. Bigeleisen and M. Maycr, *J. Chem. Phys.*, **15**, 261 (1947).
[46] K. S. Pitzer, *J. Chem. Phys.*, **17**, 1341 (1949).
[47] S. Glasstone, "Textbook of Physical Chemistry," 2d ed., pp. 578–579, D. Van Nostrand Company, Inc., New York, 1946.
[48] G. Branch and M. Calvin, "The Theory of Organic Chemistry," p. 153, Prentice-Hall, Inc., New York, 1941.
[48a] J. Bigeleisen and M. Wolfsberg in I. Prigogine, Ed., "Advances in Chemical Physics," vol. 1, p. 15, Interscience Publishers, Inc., New York, 1958.
[48b] J. Bigeleisen, R. H. Haschemeyer, M. Wolfsberg, and P. E. Yankwich, *J. Am. Chem. Soc.*, **84**, 1813 (1962).
[48c] V. F. Raaen and G. A. Ropp, *J. Chem. Phys.*, **21**, 1902 (1953).
[48d] P. E. Yankwich and H. S. Weber, *J. Am. Chem. Soc.*, **78**, 564 (1956).
[49] G. S. Hammond, *J. Am. Chem. Soc.*, **77**, 337 (1955).
[49a] K. Wiberg, *Tetrahedron*, **19**, 2009 (1963).
[50] L. Melander, *Arkiv Kemi*, **2**, 213 (1950).
[50a] W. D. Rosenfeld and S. R. Silverman, *Science*, **130**, 1658 (1959).
[51] S. Aronoff, "Techniques of Radiobiochemistry," chaps. 1 and 5, The Iowa State College Press, Ames, Iowa, 1956.
[52] D. W. Racusen and S. Aronoff, *Arch. Biochem. Biophys.*, **34**, 218 (1951).
[53] A. G. Ogston, *Nature*, **162**, 963 (1948).
[54] R. Altschul, P. Bernstein, and S. Cohen, *J. Am. Chem. Soc.*, **78**, 509 (1956).
[55] W. D. Armstrong, L. Singer, S. H. Zbarsky, and B. Dunshee, *Science*, **112**, 531 (1950).
[55a] E. Grovenstein, Jr., and G. A. Ropp, *J. Am. Chem. Soc.*, **78**, 2560 (1956).
[55b] E. Grovenstein, Jr., and U. V. Henderson, *J. Am. Chem. Soc.*, **78**, 569 (1956).
[56] P. Baertschi, W. Kuhn, and H. Kuhn, *Nature*, **171**, 1018 (1953).
[57] D. C. Bradley, *Nature*, **173**, 260 (1954).
[58] D. E. Wooldridge and F. A. Jenkins, *Phys. Rev.*, **49**, 404 (1936).
[59] F. H. Field and J. L. Franklin, "Electron Impact Phenomena," p. 204, Academic Press, Inc., New York, 1957.
[60] K. A. Piez and H. Eagle, *J. Am. Chem. Soc.*, **78**, 5284 (1956).
[60a] G. G. Devyatykh, *Zh. Fiz. Khim.*, **31**, 1445 (1957).
[61] P. E. Yankwich, A. L. Promislow, and R. F. Nystrom, *J. Am. Chem. Soc.*, **76**, 5893 (1954).
[61a] A. Roe and E. L. Albenesius, *J. Am. Chem. Soc.*, **74**, 2402 (1952).
[62] G. A. Ropp, W. A. Bonner, M. T. Clark, and V. F. Raaen, *J. Am. Chem. Soc.*, **76**, 1710 (1954).
[62a] W. H. Stevens and D. A. Crowder, *Can. J. Chem.*, **32**, 792 (1954).
[63] G. A. Ropp, *J. Chem. Phys.*, **23**, 2196 (1955).
[64] P. E. Yankwich and R. W. Buddemeier, *J. Chem. Phys.*, **27**, 861 (1959).
[64a] Y. Yukawa and M. Kawakami, *Chem. Ind. (London)*, 1401 (1961).
[64b] I. T. Glover and V. F. Raaen, *J. Org. Chem.*, **31**, 1987 (1966).
[65] P. E. Yankwich and H. S. Weber, *J. Am. Chem. Soc.*, **77**, 4513 (1955).
[66] P. E. Yankwich and A. E. Veazie, *J. Am. Chem. Soc.*, **80**, 1835 (1958).
[67] P. E. Yankwich and R. M. Ikeda, *J. Am. Chem. Soc.*, **81**, 5054 (1959).
[68] P. E. Yankwich and R. M. Ikeda, *J. Am. Chem. Soc.*, **82**, 1891 (1960).
[68a] P. Riesz and J. Bigeleisen, *J. Am. Chem. Soc.*, **81**, 6187 (1959).
[69] G. J. Buist and M. L. Bender, *J. Am. Chem. Soc.*, **80**, 4308 (1958).
[70] H. S. Johnston, W. A. Bonner, and D. J. Wilson, *J. Chem. Phys.*, **26**, 1002 (1957).
[71] R. E. Weston, Jr., *J. Chem. Phys.*, **26**, 975 (1957).
[72] J. Bigeleisen and M. Wolfsberg, *J. Chem. Phys.*, **21**, 1972 (1953).
[73] J. Bigeleisen and M. Wolfsberg, *J. Chem. Phys.*, **22**, 1264 (1954).
[74] P. E. Yankwich and R. M. Ikeda, *J. Am. Chem. Soc.*, **81**, 1532 (1959).
[75] D. R. Stranks and G. M. Harris, *J. Phys. Chem.*, **56**, 906 (1952).
[76] D. R. Stranks and G. M. Harris, *J. Am. Chem. Soc.*, **75**, 2015 (1953).
[77] F. E. Jenkins and G. M. Harris, *J. Am. Chem. Soc.*, **79**, 276 (1957).
[78] D. R. Stranks, *J. Chem. Phys.*, **21**, 2232 (1953).
[79] D. R. Stranks, *Trans. Faraday Soc.*, **51**, 492 (1955).
[80] D. R. Stranks, *Trans. Faraday Soc.*, **51**, 499 (1955).

[81] S. Z. Roginsky, "Theoretical Principles of Isotope Methods for Investigating Chemical Reactions," chaps. I and IV, Academy of Sciences, U.S.S.R. Press, Moscow, 1956; AEC-tr-2873, available from Office of Technical Services, Dept. of Commerce, Washington 25, D.C.

GENERAL REFERENCES

LIST OF REVIEWS AND COMPENDIA THAT INCLUDE CARBON ISOTOPE EFFECTS

(a) G. A. Ropp and O. K. Neville, *Nucleonics*, **9**, 31 (1951).
(b) J. Bigeleisen in G. K. Rollefson and R. E. Powell, Eds., "Annual Review of Physical Chemistry," vol. 3, pp. 39–56, Annual Reviews, Inc., Stanford, California, 1952.
(c) J. Bigeleisen, *J. Phys. Chem.*, **56**, 823 (1952).
(d) H. Eyring and F. W. Cagle, Jr., *J. Phys. Chem.*, **56**, 889 (1952).
(e) G. A. Ropp, *Nucleonics*, **10**, 22 (1952).
(f) P. E. Yankwich in J. G. Beckerley, M. D. Kamen, D. F. Mastick, and L. I. Schiff, Eds., "Annual Review of Nuclear Science," vol. 3, pp. 235–248, Annual Reviews, Inc., Stanford, California, 1953.
(g) H. G. Thode in G. K. Rollefson and R. E. Powell, Eds., "Annual Review of Physical Chemistry," vol. 4, pp. 95–118, Annual Reviews, Inc., Stanford, California, 1953.
(h) W. M. Jones in G. K. Rollefson and R. E. Powell, Eds., "Annual Review of Physical Chemistry," vol. 5, pp. 91–118, Annual Reviews, Inc., Stanford, California, 1954.
(i) H. Craig and G. Boato in G. K. Rollefson and R. E. Powell, Eds., "Annual Review of Physical Chemistry," vol. 6, pp. 403–432, Annual Reviews, Inc., Stanford, California, 1955.
(j) L. Melander, "The Use of Nuclides in the Determination of Organic Reaction Mechanisms," University of Notre Dame Press, Notre Dame, Indiana, 1955.
(k) J. Silverman and K. Cohen in H. Eyring, C. J. Christensen, and H. S. Johnston, Eds., "Annual Review of Physical Chemistry," vol. 7, pp. 335–358, Annual Reviews, Inc., Palo Alto, Stanford, California, 1956.
(l) S. Aronoff, "Techniques of Radiobiochemistry," chap. I, The Iowa State College Press, Ames, Iowa, 1956.
(m) D. Semenow and J. D. Roberts, *J. Chem. Educ.*, **33**, 2 (1956).
(n) S. Z. Roginsky, "Theoretical Principles of Isotope Methods for Investigating Chemical Reactions," chaps. I and IV, Academy of Sciences, U.S.S.R. Press, Moscow, 1956; AEC-tr-2873, available from Office of Technical Services, Washington 25, D.C.
(o) J. Bigeleisen and M. Wolfsberg, in I. Prigogine, Ed., "Advances in Chemical Physics," vol. I, chap. 2, Interscience Publishers, New York, 1958.
(p) L. Melander, "Isotope Effect on Reaction Rates," The Ronald Press, New York, 1960.
(q) A. Fry, J. C. Wright, J. M. Hill, and M. M. Bufalini, "A Bibliography of Research on Kinetic Isotope Effects," United States Atomic Energy Commission Report ORO-252, 1960, Technical Information Service, Washington 25, D.C.
(r) H. Schmid, "Anwendung radioaktiver Isotope zum Studium von Reactionmechanismen in der Organischen chimie," *Chimia (Aarau)*, **14**, 248 (1960).
(s) J. Bigeleisen, "Chemistry of Isotopes," *Science*, **147**, 463 (1965).
(t) E. M. Hodnett, "The Isotope Effect in the Study of Chemical Reactions," Final Report, January 16, 1964–May 31, 1965 of the Research Foundation, Oklahoma State University, Stillwater, Okla., United States Atomic Energy Commission Document TID-22251, UC-4-4.
(u) K. J. Laidler, "Chemical Kinetics," 2d ed., pp. 90–98, McGraw-Hill Book Company, Inc., New York, 1965.
(v) C. J. Collins in V. Gold, Ed., "Advances in Physical Organic Chemistry," vol. 2, pp. 1–91, Academic Press, Inc., New York (1964).

PROBLEMS

5-1. A sample of mesitoic acid of natural isotope composition (1.11% carbon-13) is decarboxylated to the extent of only 3% after it is heated in a bath at 92° and the reaction is quenched with ice. If the value for k_{12}/k_{13} for the decarboxylation is 1.032 at 92°, what is the approximate percent carbon-13 in the carbon atoms of the carbon dioxide that is released?

5-2. If the decarboxylation referred to in Question 5-1 is performed by heating the same mesitoic acid in a bath at 110° until 3% decarboxylation has occurred, what then is the approximate percent carbon-13 in the carbon atoms of the carbon dioxide released?

5-3. A sample of the same mesitoic acid is decarboxylated at 92° to the extent of 60%. Estimate (a) the percent carbon-13 in the carbon atoms of the carbon dioxide accumulated (after the gas sample is mixed thoroughly) and (b) the percent carbon-13 in the carbon atoms of the carboxyl group of the residual mesitoic acid.

5-4. How can the answer to Question 5-3(a) be checked for consistency with the answer to Question 5-3(b)?

5-5. A sample of formic-^{14}C acid having a specific radioactivity of 20 μc/g is mixed with excess 95% sulfuric acid, and decarbonylation (Sec. 5-1c) is permitted to proceed to 96% completion at 0°. A sample of carbon-14 monoxide is collected between 96 and 97% reaction. Assume that $k_{14}/k_{12} = 0.889$ at 0°, and by means of Eq.

5-6 calculate the specific radioactivity of the carbon-14 monoxide collected.

5-6. Estimate the specific radioactivity of the sample of carbon monoxide referred to in Question 5-5 by using Fig. 5-7 and assuming that the mean value for f for the sample collected is 0.965.

5-7. Of two nucleophilic substitutions on a carbon-14-labeled carbon atom in an organic molecule, would an SN1 or an SN2 reaction be expected to be accompanied by the larger carbon-14 isotope effect?

5-8. Considered in the light of Eq. 5-11, would a small carbon-14 kinetic isotope effect be expected in an oxidation of methane-^{14}C that had carbon-hydrogen bond cleavage as its rate-limiting step?

5-9. Kinetic or unidirectional isotope effects are generally as large as, or larger than, isotope effects in equilibrium or two-directional systems. Why then are equilibrium isotope effects ordinarily preferred as the basis of practical systems for chemical isotope separation processes?

CHAPTER
6
RADIATION CHEMISTRY AND NUCLEAR EFFECTS

6-1 EFFECTS OF IONIZING RADIATION ON MATTER

The ability of ionizing radiation (including radiations from radioactive nuclei, high-energy charged particles, and energetic electromagnetic radiation) to penetrate matter has been considered from two complementary points of view, namely, the effect of matter on the radiation and the effect of the radiation on matter. The high-speed particle was the tool used by Thomson and Rutherford in their exploration of the inner structure of matter. Refinements and variations of their technique are being used to study the individual collisions of high-speed particles of greater and greater energy with atoms or molecules. The effects of massive amounts of ionizing radiations on aggregates of matter, by contrast, were studied only in a cursory way until nuclear technology made ionizing radiation plentifully available. X-ray generators are now much larger; high-voltage electrical machines that generate two million volts or more provide ionizing radiation at much lower cost than do radiation sources from nuclear reactors. Particle accelerators can produce radiations that are both more intense and more energetic than are those normally available from radioisotope sources. Particle accelerators have the advantage that the source can be switched on or off; once turned off, there is no radiation hazard from the source. However, access to the cave of a particle accelerator is frequently allowed only after minutes or hours because of background radiation. Many chemists expected the availability of nuclear energy sources to lead to the development of a new chemical technology based on routes to syntheses not attainable by the use of catalysts, heat, or pressure. However, the industrial use of ionizing radiation has thus far been extremely limited, because the same results can almost always be accomplished by less costly techniques. As radiation chemistry is better understood and as still cheaper sources of radiation become available, it is possible that radiation processes will have many industrial applications. For the organic chemist using carbon-14 solely as a tracer in the study of reactions having extremely long half-time or in applications requiring high levels of radioactivity, the effect of radiation is largely a nuisance.

The primary effect of energetic electromagnetic waves or charged particles on atoms or molecules is the removal of electrons. The consequences of ionization vary, but they are often most significant for molecules that are involved in the structure and function of living matter. The effect of ionization is of less significance in many inorganic solids. For example, in metals the electrons in the conduction band are not bound to any one atom but are shared by all atoms; as soon as a positive hole is left by ionization, it is rapidly filled. As a result, in the permanently ionized metals the only significant effect of radiation is the displacement of atoms from their position in the crystal. Such displacement is most commonly produced by energetic heavy particles (protons, deuterons, α-particles, etc.).

The extent to which each type of radiation will interact with matter depends on the mass and charge of the radiation, as well as on its energy. Gamma and x rays and neutrons have great penetrating power, because they have no charge. Because they *have* a charge, electrons, protons, deuterons, and alpha particles cause intense and devastating effects along their relatively short paths. Under the influence of ionizing radiation, organic compounds undergo chemical changes that result in isomerization, fragmentation, and polymerization. The radiation of a single compound may produce a great number of products.[1,2,3,4]

In their interaction with matter, the various types of ionizing radiation produce the same ultimate effects, the most conspicuous effect being the ionization of atoms or molecules as a result of ejection of orbital electrons. Thus, most of the chemical effects

of high-energy radiation are produced through the same medium—secondary electrons. The quantitative difference between the result produced when a gamma ray interacts with matter and that produced when an energetic alpha particle or electron interacts with matter depends on the energy transfer per unit distance of penetration. It is possible to predict the energy loss per unit distance of penetration; this property is referred to as linear energy-transfer (sometimes indicated by the letter designation LET). It is proportional to the square of the charge on the particle and approximately proportional to the inverse square of the speed. Thus, at the very end of an electron track in a cloud chamber, the density of ions approximates that for an alpha-particle track, although the LET of an alpha particle is hundreds of times greater than that of an energetic electron. Positive and negative particles are equally proficient in causing ionization.

In a system being subjected to radiation, the events are thought to occur in a three-stage sequence[5,6] within a period in the range from less than 1 μsec to (rarely) several days.

In the first stage, the ionizing radiation and associated secondary electrons cause excitation and ionization along the path of the ray, producing electrons together with ionized and excited atoms and molecules. This stage, which is purely physical in nature, requires only 10^{-15} sec in an aqueous medium.

In the second stage, the "physico-chemical" stage, the primary products undergo secondary reactions. Excited molecules may decompose by fragmentation; ions may combine with unexcited molecules or with free electrons to yield many new molecules. At the end of this stage, which requires about 10^{-11} sec, the only unstable chemical species remaining are the free radicals. If the excited molecule is benzene or any one of a number of aromatic compounds, it is thought[7] that the radiation energy is absorbed by electronic excitation in nonlocalized pi orbitals. The energy is then converted to rotational or vibrational energy, which is transferred to other molecules and is eventually radiated as photons of light or as heat. This ability to degrade radiation is the mark of a radiation-resistant compound.

In the final "chemical" stage, the free radicals react with stable molecules (old and new), with each other, and with the solvent. These reactions may be extremely rapid or they may persist for days, depending partly on the nature of the solvent and partly on the presence of oxygen, which reacts with the free radicals to enhance the decomposition. The use of water as a solvent in radiation studies results in the production of hydrogen peroxide and peroxide radicals, which then react further with the organic compounds present. The various concepts developed to clarify the primary processes in the radiation chemistry of water have been reviewed briefly by Burton[8] and more extensively by Hochanadel,[9] Allen,[10] Swallow,[7] Hart and Platzman,[11] and by Spinks and Woods.[12]

6-2 SELF-DECOMPOSITION OF LABELED ORGANIC COMPOUNDS

Many of the difficulties that arise in the storage and use of high-level radioactive compounds are a direct result of the minute quantities involved. If pure tritium is admitted into a vacuum line, several hundred millicuries of it may be lost easily as a result of exchange with moisture and stopcock grease and of adsorption. For example, 0.1 mmole of a substance having a radioactivity of 10 mc/mmole is much more subject to oxidation and volatilization than is 1 mole of a substance whose radioactivity is 0.001 mc/mmole. Very small samples of sodium acetate-1-^{14}C kept in a humid atmosphere that contained carbon dioxide lost some activity as a result of hydrolysis and the subsequent liberation of acetic acid; samples larger than 0.5 mg did not lose activity when stored below $0°C$.[13]

The actual molecular consequences of radioactive decay of carbon-14-labeled compounds have not been studied in many instances.

Two experimental methods are in use to study the chemical changes that occur in β-decay processes: (1) the mass spectrometry of the fragments formed, and (2) the radiochemical study of the ultimate products of the radioactive transformation, usually through the use of double labeling and isotope-dilution analysis.

Mass spectrometry is very useful for determining the initial distribution of the fragments with respect to mass and charge. By this method it is possible to study the consequences of radioactive decay in isolated atoms and molecules; the daughter atoms need not be radioactive. Snell and Pleasonton[14] have found that pure beta emission in molecules frequently fails to cause dissociation; examples are $^{14}CO_2$ and TH for which atoms remain bound as $(NO_2)^+$ and $(^3HeH)^+$ following 81 and 93%, respectively, of the decays. The dissociation of $(NO_2)^+$ then yields $(NO)^+$, O^+, and N^+ from 8.4, 5.9, and 3.6%, respectively, of the decays. In addition to $(NO_2)^+$, about 0.6% of the nitrogen is bound in the form of $(NO_2)^{2+}$. The formation of $(NO_2)^{2+}$ is thought to be due to the "shaking"[15] undergone by the electrons as a result of the sudden change in the charge of the nucleus; this phenomenon leads to the removal of one orbital electron without further dissociation of the ion.

The radiochemical method for studying the chemical consequences of β-decay can be extremely useful. The method depends on the feasibility of double labeling and requires that the fragment containing the daughter atom be radioactive and not subject to isotopic exchange. The present low cost and high specific activity (occasionally greater than 90 atom percent) of carbon-14 have greatly increased the practicability of synthesizing compounds that contain a high percentage of doubly labeled molecules. Isotope-dilution methods have been used for the determination of the identity and quantity of the molecules that contain the daughter element, but such methods are good only for determining products whose presence can be inferred by the investigator. No doubt, combined chromatography-radioactivity measurement (Chap. 12) will be a helpful adjunct to the use of carriers. The first study of the effect of decay on a molecule slightly more complicated than carbon dioxide was made by Wolfgang, Anderson, and Dodson.[16] They prepared ethane-1,2-^{14}C in which both carbons in a substantial percentage of the molecules were labeled. The decay of one carbon-14 atom then resulted in the reaction

$$^{14}CH_3{}^{14}CH_3 \rightarrow \rightarrow {}^{14}CH_3NH_2$$

Those molecules that were labeled in only one position would yield nonradioactive methylamine. By the addition of a calculated amount of inactive methylamine, it was possible by isotope-dilution analysis to determine the yield of labeled methylamine. The amounts of methylamine produced under various conditions were all about 50% of the amount that would be found if every decay produced a stable methylamine molecule.

In addition to organic systems that contain carbon-14, systems that contain tritium, bromine-82, and the heavy metals have also been studied. For a review of the studies made on chemical changes during β-decay processes, the excellent review by Nefedov, Zaitsev, and Toropova[15] should be consulted.

After 1946 to 1947, when carbon-14 became generally available, hundreds of millicuries of labeled organic compounds were prepared at the Oak Ridge National Laboratory, the University of California Radiation Laboratory, and elsewhere. At the time, very little thought was given to radiation damage. Since some of the compounds, for example, methanol-^{14}C, were to be used later to synthesize large quantities of other intermediates, it was convenient to store them in high-level (multimillicurie) lots. The number

of publications in 1953 on the subject of radiation decomposition indicates that four to six years passed before the effects of radiation damage were noticed. In some instances the change was obvious, as in the case of carbon-14-labeled methyl iodide, which became red during storage.[17] Assuming that an ion pair is formed for every 32.5 ev of energy expended, Wagner and Guinn[17] calculated that the carbon-14 beta particle of average energy destroys 1570 molecules of methyl iodide in addition to the molecule that contains the disintegrating carbon-14 atom. The effects of self-radiation on a large number of other compounds have been discussed in the literature.[1–4,18–25b] The excellent review by Bayly and Evans[25b] summarizes the present knowledge concerned with decomposition by self-irradiation of compounds labeled with carbon-14, as well as with many other common radioisotopes. Rochlin[25a] describes the methods that have been used to calculate the absorbed dose, percentage decomposition, and G($-$M) values for carbon-14-labeled compounds.

In describing the susceptibility of a compound to radiation damage, it is convenient to use the term radiation destruction coefficient or G-value.[22] A G-value, frequently designated G($-M$), is defined as the number of molecules of a substance that are permanently altered or decomposed per 100 ev of energy absorbed. G-values can be expressed specifically to indicate the number of molecules, atoms, or radicals produced for 100 ev of absorbed energy (e.g., G(H$_2$) for the number of molecules of hydrogen produced, G(CH$_4$) for the number of molecules of methane produced, etc.). G-values may range from less than one to 2000 or more. A summary made by Tolbert[22] of radiation destruction coefficients is given in Table 6-1. The values apply to pure compounds irradiated *in vacuo*. The radiation susceptibility of hydroxylamines, nitriles, quinones, and nitroso or nitro compounds is not known. Large numbers of compounds have radiation

Table 6-1   *Radiation destruction coefficients and radiation yields*[a]

Compounds	Destruction coefficients, molecules/100 ev	Radiation yields, molecules/100 ev	Radiation-induced reactions
Saturated hydrocarbons	6–9	H_2, 1–7	Fragmentation, dimerization
Unsaturated hydrocarbons	14–2000	H_2, 1	Polymerization
Aromatic hydrocarbons	1	H_2, 0.3	Polymerization
Alcohols	4–12	H_2, 1–3	Fragmentation, dimerization
Ethers	7[b]	H_2, 2–3	Fragmentation, dimerization
Ketones	7[b]	H_2, 1–5; CO, 1–3	Fragmentation at CO
Carboxylic acids	5[b]	H_2, 1; CO_2, 1–4; CO, 0.1–0.5	
Esters	4[b]	H_2, 2–3	Fragmentation at ester group
Organic halides	4	HX or $\frac{1}{2}X_2$, 2–5	
Quaternary ammonium salts	5–2000	Amines and aldehydes	
Amino acids	2–30	Ammonia, amines, CO_2	

[a] From B. M. Tolbert, *Nucleonics*, **18**(8), 74 (1960), with permission.
[b] Estimated values.

destruction coefficients in the range from 5 to 7; others, such as a few quaternary ammonium salts and unsaturated hydrocarbons, are more unstable toward irradiation. The unsaturated hydrocarbons readily undergo polymerization and cross-linking reactions. The reason for the enhanced stability of aromatic compounds was mentioned earlier in this chapter. The use of benzene as an energy converter to protect less stable molecules was validated by an extensive study made on the benzene-cyclohexane system by Manion and Burton.[26] Earlier, Schoepfle and Fellows[27] found that when a cyclohexane-benzene system is bombarded with cathode rays, it behaves, as far as the production of gaseous products is concerned, more like benzene than like a noninteracting mixture of the two. The radiation yield, $G(H_2)$, of molecular hydrogen from the irradiation of cyclohexane only, of benzene only, and of

mixtures of these compounds is shown in Fig. 6-1. It is believed that the transfer of energy from cyclohexane to benzene leads to a pronounced protection of cyclohexane and a slight sensitization of benzene.[28] Iodine and alkyl iodides apparently afford similar protection except that they show a different concentration dependence.[28] In the studies of protection mechanisms, the data have been interpreted on the basis of yields of gases, for example, hydrogen, methane, acetylene, and ethylene, without necessarily the secure event of a material balance that included nonvolatile products. However, the data accumulated (both direct and indirect) on the effects of a variety of additives on the radiolysis of a number of compounds indicate that the protective effect is genuine.

A serious problem in the storage of organic compounds labeled with carbon-14 is the decomposition induced by radiation

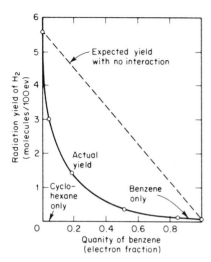

FIG. 6-1   The protection of cyclohexane by benzene. (*From J. P. Manion and M. Burton, J. Phys. Chem.*, **56**, 560 (1952), *with permission*.)

from the carbon-14 nuclide. The requirements for purity in the labeled compound will determine whether it will be necessary to repurify the labeled compound after several months or several years. The rate at which self-destruction occurs will depend on the following factors, which were summarized by Tolbert:[22]

1   specific radioactivity of the sample
2   average energy, $\bar{E}$, of the radiation
3   fraction of $\bar{E}$ absorbed by the organic compound
4   *G*-values of the system
5   half-life of the radionuclide

The first of these factors, specific radioactivity (see Sec. 11-1), should be expressed in terms of disintegrations per gram. The average energy, $\bar{E}$, for carbon-14 is 45,000 ev.[29] The fraction of $\bar{E}$ absorbed by the organic compound depends on the geometry and mass of the sample; it will approach one for samples whose dimensions are large compared with the path length of the radiation.

This condition will be met readily for the weak-beta emitters, such as tritium and carbon-14, and less often for emitters of more-energetic beta particles (e.g., phosphorus-32) and for gamma emitters in general. For the most energetic (156 kev) beta particle from carbon-14, the maximum range as found from a chart that shows a range-energy relationship[30] is approximately 28 mg/cm². For the carbon-14 beta particle of average energy (45 kev), the range decreases to a little more than 3 mg/cm². For most organic substances, the range of the 45-kev beta particle is therefore only 0.03 to 0.04 mm. The *G*-value, already defined, is a quantitative measure of the effectiveness of a radiation-chemical effect. The great variation in *G*-values for different classes of organic compounds is evident from the data of Table 6-1. The half-life factor will not normally apply for studies made with carbon-14.

A method for the estimation of the magnitude of the radiation decomposition in a simple hypothetical system has been described by Hentz.[31] The calculation of absorbed radiation energy was given in detail by Rossi and Ellis.[32] The radiation dose is calculated in terms of rads, one rad being defined as the absorption of 100 ergs of ionizing radiation by one gram of a substance. For carbon-14, the self-radiation dose can be determined from the formula

$$\text{radiation dose, rads} = \frac{N\bar{E}F}{100\ W} \qquad (6\text{-}1)$$

where

N = number of beta particles from carbon-14

$\bar{E}$ = average energy of beta particles from carbon-14, ev = 45,000

F = conversion factor, ergs/ev = 1.602 × 10⁻¹²

W = weight of substance irradiated, g

This formula has been used by Tolbert[22,23] to calculate self-radiation doses for a series of organic compounds having various specific radioactivities and, by comparison, for a

Table 6-2   Self-radiation for a hypothetical carbon-14- or tritium-labeled compound[a]

| Specific activity | Self-radiation dose, rads | | | |
| | In 1 day | | In 1 year | |
	^{14}C	^3H	^{14}C	^3H
1 mc/g	2.3×10^3	2.9×10^2	8.3×10^5	1.1×10^4
10 mc/g	2.3×10^4	2.9×10^3	8.3×10^6	1.1×10^5
100 mc/g	2.3×10^5	2.9×10^4	8.3×10^7	1.1×10^6
1000 mc/g	2.3×10^6	2.9×10^5	8.3×10^8	1.1×10^7
1 mc/mmole[b]	1.8×10^4	2.3×10^3	6.8×10^6	8.3×10^6

[a] Adapted from B. M. Tolbert, *Nucleonics*, **18**(8), 74 (1960), with permission.
[b] For a compound of molecular weight 125.

hypothetical organic compound of molecular weight 125 and radioactivity of 1 mc/mmole. The data that pertain to carbon-14 and tritium, which were tabulated by Tolbert,[22] are given in Table 6-2. The formula as given above implies that all the radiant energy is absorbed in the sample. However, a factor of 0.93 must be used to obtain the values given in Table 6-2.[25a]

Tolbert has used the typical self-radiation-dose values given in Table 6-2 to calculate the percent decomposition of a hypothetical organic compound having a molecular weight of 125 and one of three different *G*-values. His percent decomposition values are given in Table 6-3.[22] It is apparent from these data that radiation doses become very important at a magnitude of about 10^7 rads for many compounds. By extrapolation, it is evident that such doses are intolerable for those unsaturated hydrocarbons and quaternary ammonium salts that have *G*-values of the order of 2000. One such compound, carbon-14-labeled choline chloride, which has a *G*-value of about 1000, was studied by Lemmon, Parsons, and Chin.[24] They found that approximately 300 choline ions are decomposed by the energy normally required to ionize a single molecule, for example, of

an alcohol or ester. They presumed that a radical-chain mechanism, initiated by a single choline ion, continued through about 300 ions before the chain terminated. The chain reaction would not proceed at liquid-nitrogen temperature. In some types of tracer experiments, self-radiation values of the order of 10 rads/day may become important. Conway and Libby,[33] in their measurement of the rate of decarboxylation of alanine, found that a radiation-induced side reaction is controlling below 373°K and that this reaction has a half-time of about 10^5 years

Table 6-3   Percent decomposition of organic compounds as a function of radiation dose and G-value[a]

| Dose, rads | Percent decomposition[b] | | |
	$G = -5$	$G = -10$	$G = -20$
10^6	0.06	0.12	0.24
10^7	0.59	1.19	2.38
10^8	5.8	11.3	21.4
10^9	45.0	70.2	90.9

[a] Adapted from B. M. Tolbert, *Nucleonics*, **18**(8), 74 (1960).
[b] Calculated for a molecular weight of 125.

at room temperature. This ordinarily negligible side reaction is important in this case, because the reaction half-times studied varied from 0.1 to 10^4 years.

Lemmon[18] and also Tolbert[22] have suggested a number of ways to reduce self-decomposition of labeled organic compounds. To appreciate their suggestions, it is only necessary to review the factors, discussed above, that influence self-radiation damage in carbon-14-labeled organic compounds.

When vacuum-line techniques are used to prepare labeled compounds, products usually have high molar radioactivities. For the manufacturer of labeled compounds, this procedure also effects economies in storage and shipping. Unlike the biochemist, the organic chemist who uses carbon-14 for such purposes as mechanism studies and dilution analysis rarely requires that the labeled compound have a molar radioactivity greater than 10 mc/mole. Such a level of activity usually will warrant neither vacuum-line techniques nor special precautions for guarding against radiation decomposition, even for periods of several years. However, the continued bench-top use of carbon-14 at the 1- to 10-mc/mole level will soon preclude the use of that area for very low-level studies.

For those instances in which high-level labeling is necessary, it is not possible to dilute with the inactive carrier; therefore, recourse must be had to other diluents. For example, the compound can be intimately mixed with a finely divided solid such as powdered glass. If such a heterogeneous diluent is to be effective, the state of subdivision must be such that the average particle size of the organic compound will be much less than the average carbon-14 β-particle range (about 30 μ in most organic substances). More thought must be given to the inertness of a solid diluent than would normally be given to a storage container. For example, the dicyanohydrin of benzil, if stored in a glass bottle, would be reasonably stable

over a period of several months. If the same compound (labeled or unlabeled) were mixed thoroughly with powdered glass (a basic reagent), the dicyanohydrin would, in a few days, be completely converted to hydrogen cyanide and benzil.

Labeled compounds can be dissolved in benzene, in other radiation-resistant aromatic compounds, or in an unreactive ester or ketone. Water is a suitable diluent in some instances[25b] but should be used with caution until proved satisfactory for the compound to be stored.

If it is desirable to avoid the dilution, it is possible to spread the compound on glass in a layer that is an order of magnitude less thick than the average penetration of the beta particles. A small amount of the compound can be left on a developed paper chromatogram or developed column of solid adsorbent to be eluted whenever the labeled compound is needed. The artificial zeolites, "molecular sieves," now commercially available[34] are very useful for absorbing a large number of compounds whose greatest molecular dimensions lie below 13 A. The absorbed material is released by heating the molecular sieve at reduced pressure. The use of Type 4A sieve for collecting atmospheric carbon dioxide (for carbon-14 measurement) is described by Fergusson.[35]

The protection afforded cyclohexane by benzene, iodine, and alkyl iodides, discussed above, indicates that radiation-sensitive compounds can be converted to derivatives that contain radiation-resistant groups. Thus, the iodide, bromide, and acetate of choline are more radiation resistant than is choline chloride. It has been suggested that iodides, benzoates, phenolates, and acetates should be good derivatives of radiation-sensitive compounds.[22]

Oxygen as well as water almost always increases the amount of radiation destruction; it is therefore advisable to store compounds *in vacuo* or in an inert atmosphere. It is always possible that unknown contaminants in a radiochemical preparation may hasten self-decomposition. This is true in the storage of glucose-^{14}C of high specific activity.[19] Bayly and Weigel[36] have reported the results of numerous procedures for storing high-specific-activity sucrose-^{14}C and glucose-^{14}C. A compound such as a labeled sulfonate may be pure when it is first stored, but subsequent radiation decomposition may release a sulfonic acid that is capable of destroying much of the remaining pure compound. Radiation changes induced in pure compounds are therefore meaningful only by extrapolation to zero radiation time. Finally, some degree of protection can be achieved by keeping the sensitive labeled compound cold, preferably by storage in a food freezer. Methanol-^{14}C (10 c/mole) from the same lot used by Skraba, Burr, and Hess[2] to study its deterioration was repackaged in 1-mc lots in break-seal tubes and was stored for seven years in a household refrigerator at 5°C. It was observed that, after the storage, 20% of the labeled methanol had been destroyed. It is apparent that 3 to 4 μl of liquid in a break-off tip provides good geometry for radiation decomposition and that under these conditions a storage temperature much lower than 5°C is desirable.

In an investigation of the purities of a number of commercially available carbon-14-labeled hydrocarbons, it was found[37] that all the compounds tested had satisfactory chemical purity (>99%) but very poor radiochemical purity (0 to 50%). It was suggested that an analysis for impurities should involve (1) gas-liquid radiochromatography (Sec. 12-1b) to determine volatile radioactive impurities and (2) a total-activity balance between the injected and the eluted material for an estimation of nonvolatile radiochemical impurities.

It is necessary to conclude with the caution that users of labeled compounds should always check the purity of all high-specific-activity compounds before using them, manufacturers' claims notwithstanding.

CITED REFERENCES

[1] B. M. Tolbert and R. M. Lemmon, *Radiation Res.*, **3**, 52 (1955).

[2] W. J. Skraba, J. G. Burr, Jr., and D. N. Hess, *J. Chem. Phys.*, **21**, 1296 (1953).

[3] E. Collinson and A. J. Swallow, *Chem. Rev.*, **56**, 571 (1956).

[4] P. Rochlin, *Chem. Rev.*, **65**, 685 (1965).

[5] R. L. Platzman, *Sci. Am.*, **201**, 74 (1959).

[6] A. P. Wolf, "Annual Review of Nuclear Science," E. Segrè, Ed., pp. 259–290, vol. 10, Annual Reviews, Inc., Palo Alto, Calif., 1960.

[7] A. J. Swallow, "Radiation Chemistry of Organic Compounds," chap. V, Pergamon Press, New York, 1960.

[8] M. Burton, *J. Chem. Educ.*, **36**, 273 (1959).

[9] C. J. Hochanadel, 'Radiation Chemistry of Water,' chap. 8 in M. Burton, J. S. Kirby-Smith, and J. L. Magee, Eds. "Comparative Effects of Radiation," John Wiley & Sons, Inc., New York, 1960.

[10] A. O. Allen, "The Radiation Chemistry of Water and Aqueous Solutions," D. Van Nostrand Company, Inc., New York, 1961.

[11] E. J. Hart and R. L. Platzman in M. Errera and A. Forssberg, Eds. "Mechanisms in Radiobiology," Academic Press, Inc., New York, 1961.

[12] J. W. T. Spinks and R. J. Woods, "An Introduction to Radiation Chemistry," John Wiley & Sons, Inc., New York, 1964.

[13] A. Babicky, *Chem. Listy*, **53**, 844 (1959).

[14] A. H. Snell and F. Pleasonton, *J. Phys. Chem.*, **62**, 1377 (1958).

[15] V. D. Nefedov, V. M. Zaitsev, and M. A. Toropova, *Russ. Chem. Rev. (English Transl.)*, **32**, 604 (1963); *Usp. Khim.*, **32**, 1367 (1963); *Chem. Abstr.*, **60**, 6389d (1964).

[16] R. L. Wolfgang, R. C. Anderson, and R. W. Dodson, *J. Chem. Phys.*, **24**, 16 (1956).

[17] C. D. Wagner and V. P. Guinn, *J. Am. Chem. Soc.*, **75**, 4861 (1953).

[18] R. M. Lemmon, *Nucleonics*, **11**(10), 44 (1953).

[19] N. Baker, A. P. Gibbons, and R. A. Shipley, *Biochim. Biophys. Acta*, **28**, 579 (1958).

[20] R. J. Woods and J. D. Taylor, *Can. J. Chem.*, **35**, 941 (1957).

[21] B. M. Tolbert, P. T. Adams, E. L. Bennett, A. M. Hughes, M. R. Kirk, R. M. Lemmon, R. M. Noller, R. Ostwald, and M. Calvin, *J. Am. Chem. Soc.*, **75**, 1867 (1953).

[22] B. M. Tolbert, *Nucleonics*, **18**(8), 74 (1960).

[23] B. M. Tolbert, *Atomlight*, p. 1 (Feb., 1960).

[24] R. M. Lemmon, M. A. Parsons, and D. M. Chin, *J. Am. Chem. Soc.*, **77**, 4139 (1955).

[25] F. A. Bovey, "Effects of Ionizing Radiation on Natural and Synthetic Polymers," Interscience Publishers, Inc., New York, N.Y., 1958.

[25a] P. Rochlin, *Chem. Rev.*, **65**, 685 (1965).

[25b] R. J. Bayly and E. A. Evans, *J. Labelled Com.*, **2**(1), 1 (1966).

[26] J. P. Manion and M. Burton, *J. Phys. Chem.*, **56**, 560 (1952).

[27] C. S. Schoepfle and C. H. Fellows, *Ind. Eng. Chem.*, **23**, 1396 (1931).

[28] M. Burton and S. Lipsky, *J. Phys. Chem.*, **61**, 1461 (1957).

[29] G. H. Jenks and F. H. Sweeton, *Phys. Rev.*, **86**, 803 (1952).

[30] G. Friedlander and J. W. Kennedy, "Nuclear and Radiochemistry," 2d ed., p. 202, John Wiley & Sons, Inc., New York, 1955.

[31] R. R. Hentz, *J. Chem. Educ.*, **35**, 625 (1958).

[32] H. H. Rossi and R. H. Ellis, Jr., *Nucleonics*, **7**(1), 18 (1950).

[33] D. Conway and W. F. Libby, *J. Am. Chem. Soc.*, **80**, 1077 (1958).

[34] Linde Company, Tonawanda, New York.

[35] G. J. Fergusson, *Rev. Sci. Instr.*, **34**, 403 (1963).

[36] R. J. Bayly and H. Weigel, *Nature*, **188**, 384 (1960).

[37] M. A. Muhs, E. L. Bastin, and B. E. Gordon, *Intern. J. Appl. Radiation Isotopes*, **16**, 537 (1965).

CHAPTER
7
RADIATION HAZARDS
AND PROTECTION

In work with any radioisotope, it is imperative to understand the hazards of radiation and to protect against them. Comprehensive references exist on radiation hazards and protection.[1-9] Much of the information given in these is applicable to carbon-14. Tolbert and Siri[10] discuss the radiation hazards and protection from the soft-beta emitters (including carbon-14) used in organic chemistry. Precautions specific to carbon-14 are described by Catch.[11]

7-1 DANGEROUS PROPERTIES OF CARBON-14

Carbon-14 emits weak (0.156-Mev) beta radiation and transmutes to nitrogen-14 via the reaction $^{14}C \rightarrow {}^{14}N + \beta$; its half-life is relatively long (5745 ± 50 y). These properties necessitate caution in the use of carbon-14, especially because carbon is the most important element in the chemical composition of living matter. The hazards of carbon-14 are negligible compared with those of most other radioisotopes, and the precautions required are few. However, there is *no* limit of radioactivity, or of transmutation of an element contained in living tissue, below which danger is considered to be impossible. Exposure to such effects should therefore be avoided whenever possible.

7-2 BIOLOGICAL SIGNIFICANCE OF CARBON-14

Biological data on carbon-14 are of particular interest in considering the type and magnitude of the hazard of this radioisotope. About 18% of the total body weight is carbon. In the "standard man" (70 kg),[12] the amount of carbon-14 acquired from natural sources is of the order of 0.1 μc; it is taken up from food and water and from atmospheric material that enters the respiratory tract during inhalation.[13] The average dose rate of internal irradiation received from this natural carbon-14 is 1.06 mrem/year throughout the human body (average carbon content,

18%), 0.71 mrem/year to soft tissue (carbon content, 12%), and 1.64 mrem/year to bone (carbon content, 27.8%).[13a] These values for dose rate are based on the following: specific disintegration rate of carbon-14, 14 dpm/g; average beta energy of carbon-14, 50 kev; a 70-kg body; and the relative biological effectiveness (RBE) for carbon-14, 1.[13a] Radioisotopes of biological interest are divided into four "radiotoxicity" classes according to the potential hazard from ingestion; carbon-14 is in class 4, the group of low potential danger.[14] It has an ~35-d "effective half-life," that is, the time taken for the radioactivity of carbon-14 incorporated as carbon dioxide to decrease by one half; this approximate value takes into account excretion as well as negligible radioactive decay and will vary considerably with the chemical form of the carbon-14.[14] Its "effective energy dose" is 0.053 Mev, which is the energy imparted to the critical organ per disintegration of carbon-14 incorporated in that tissue.[14] Incorporated carbon-14 results in greatest irradiation damage to fat, the so-called "critical" organ.[14] The whole-body burden for carbon-14 is 260 μc, that is, the amount of it which, when ingested by a 70-kg man, will result in the maximum permissible dose rate to the critical organ (0.3 rem/week for all organs except the whole body or gonads; 0.1 rem/week for these organs).[14]

The biological hazards to man of carbon-14 are discussed by a number of writers.[4,15-18] The effect of fallout of carbon-14 from nuclear weapons tests has received special attention.[13,19-26]

Some hazard of carbon-14 exists from external exposure to the soft-beta radiation (see Sec. 7-4a). The greatest potential hazard, however, is from internal exposure; both the emitted radiation and the transmutation process can affect living cells. It is possible that the transmutation to nitrogen-14 of a carbon-14 atom, contained in a molecule of the genetic material deoxyribonucleic acid

(DNA), can produce a chemical change in a chromosome, since all DNA is contained in the chromosomes. Such a change might either cause mutations or prevent duplication of the DNA and thus kill the cell in which transmutation occurs; the transmutation effect could lead to about the same number of genetic mutations as the radiation effect.[17] Thus, the 50-rem "doubling dose," which is the amount of irradiation required to double the natural or spontaneous mutation rate, for carbon-14 may be high by a factor of 2.[20] Because of the very long half-life of carbon-14, the genetic effects on future generations of exposure of the present population to carbon-14 may be significant.[16,17,19,20] Much more information is needed before such effects can be assessed critically. On the assumption that nuclear test explosions were discontinued from November, 1958, estimates have been made of the internal carbon-14 doses that will be received by the gonads over 30-year periods; they are (in mrad): beginning 1954, 10; beginning 1960, 10; and beginning 1984, ~5.[4]

Two reports exist[26a,26b] that document measurements of atmospheric carbon-14 initiated in 1953.

The somatic effects (effects limited to one generation) of carbon-14 that have been considered are leukemia,· bone cancer, and diseases resulting from radiation damage to tissues other than bone tissue and bone marrow.[16,27,28] Of the radioisotopes tested in one study, carbon-14 was the least carcinogenic; its relatively small hazard in spite of its long half-life is believed to be due to its rapid elimination from the tissues and relatively small retention in the bones.[15]

Purdom[18] concludes that estimates of biological hazards from carbon-14 are negligible when viewed on a short-term basis or on a restricted sample of individuals—and also on a long-term basis when compared with hazards from natural radiations or from infections. He suggests that the man-made nature of carbon-14 from fallout, together with other radiations from fallout, raises philosophical or emotional problems and that man obviously should not wantonly expose himself to risks.

In the United States, administration of carbon-14 compounds to humans requires a special license. An application for a license is carefully reviewed and appraised by the Advisory Committee on Medical Uses of Isotopes of the Division of Licensing and Regulation of the Atomic Energy Commission (A.E.C.). If the Advisory Committee approves the application, the license is issued by the Division. The information required by the Advisory Committee in order to make the necessary judgments is enumerated and discussed in a most informative article by LeRoy.[29] The relatively nonhazardous nature of carbon-14 is attested to by the fact that the administration of readily metabolized carbon-14 compounds in tracer doses up to 0.5 to 1.0 mc to adult human subjects is not considered to be unethical or to violate accepted standards of maximum permissible dose;[29,30] Catch[30] cites several references regarding such use of carbon-14. The danger from improper preparation and administration of the dosage form of carbon-14 is possibly far greater than the danger from the radioisotope itself. The nonapparent pitfalls to be avoided in the formulation of parenteral dosage forms of radiochemical compounds are discussed by Briner[31] in a very interesting article. Among the dangers are contamination with pyrogens; improper preparation of glassware and equipment; lack of adequate control of formulation (for example, lack of purity of chemicals and radiochemicals, use of improper additives, and the presence of particulate or suspended foreign matter); inadequate sterilization; improper packaging; and inadequate biological control testing. Briner suggests ways of ensuring against these dangers. In this connection, it is of interest to know that some reagent chemicals in general use can be expected to have a carbon-14 concentration of 15 dpm/g, but

that those of coal or petroleum origin will be free of carbon-14.[32]

A simple nomogram that permits direct reading of the dose rate for numerous isotopes of biological and medical interest, including carbon-14, was developed by Bertinchamps and Cotzias.[33] One of the assumptions made in constructing the nomogram is that the radioisotope is immediately and homogeneously dispersed; thus, no account is taken of the chemical form of the radioisotope. In view of the increasing importance of the problem of irradiation from internally located radioisotopes and the need to know, in either tracer or radiobiological experiments, whether a radioisotope is a weak or a substantial source of energy, the nomogram should be useful.

7-3 MAXIMUM PERMISSIBLE LEVELS OF CARBON-14

Recommended maximum permissible levels of carbon-14 are summarized in Table 7-1; the values given are taken from the U.S. National Bureau of Standards Handbook 69,[34] which contains the recommendations of the National Committee on Radiation Protection (NCRP). This publication should be consulted for further detailed information regarding the assumptions and factors used in the derivation of the recommended maximum permissible values and the restrictions essential to the proper interpretation and use of the values. The recommended maximum permissible values are such that, from present knowledge, occupational exposure for the working life of an individual at these levels is not expected to entail appreciable risk to the individual or to present a hazard more severe than those commonly accepted in present-day industries.

The NCRP has also formulated basic rules and recommendations concerning exposure to ionizing radiation; these are applicable to carbon-14, and the limits given in Table 7-1 are in keeping with them. The basic rules are summarized in Table 7-2.

Table 7-1 *Maximum permissible body burdens and maximum permissible concentrations of carbon-14 in air and in water for occupational exposure*[a]

Organ of reference	Maximum permissible burden in total body (q), μc	Maximum permissible concentration (MPC), μc/cc			
		For 40-hr week		For 168-hr week	
		Water	Air	Water	Air
Soluble CO_2					
Fat[b]	300	**0.02**	**4 × 10⁻⁶**	**8 × 10⁻³**	**10⁻⁶**
Total body	400	0.03	5×10^{-6}	0.01	2×10^{-6}
Bone	400	0.04	6×10^{-6}	0.01	2×10^{-6}
Immersion (in air containing $^{14}CO_2$)	**Total body**[b]		**5 × 10⁻⁵**		**10⁻⁵**

[a] Based on intake to the "standard man" by ingestion and inhalation only.

[b] Critical organ; values given for other organs are for reference only and are not, by themselves, permissible levels.

Table 7-2 *Summary of NCRP basic rules on exposure to ionizing radiation*

Type of dose	Maximum permissible dose (MPD), rem[a]
Accumulated	
External exposure	
Critical organs	
Whole body, head and trunk, active blood-forming organs, eyes, or gonads	$5(N - 18)$[b]; ≯3 in 13 consecutive weeks
Other organs	
Skin of whole body	$10(N - 18)$[b]; ≯6 in 13 consecutive weeks
Hands and forearms; feet and ankles	75 per year; ≯25 in 13 consecutive weeks
Internal exposure	(Specified by means of MPC values)
Accidental or emergency	25 per lifetime to whole body
From neighborhood of a controlled area	0.5 per year
Medical	(Not included in estimation of radiation exposure of an individual)

[a] Absorbed dose of ionizing radiation that has the same biological effectiveness as 1 rad of x radiation. A rad is a unit of absorbed dose of ionizing radiation equal to an energy of 100 ergs per gram of irradiated material.

[b] N = age of individual in years and >18.

More detailed discussions of maximum permissible levels of carbon-14 are included in several other references.[35–39] Barnes and Taylor[39] give a tabulation of the fraction of carbon uptake going to the critical organ (fat) from ingestion, inhalation, and the bloodstream; they also discuss interestingly the fate of inhaled particulates.

7-4 MONITORING FOR CARBON-14

7-4a PERSONNEL MONITORING

At the level of radioactivity at which most laboratory work with carbon-14 is done (0.1 to 5 mc), the carbon-14 compounds can be handled safely with rubber gloves. The principal hazard is from the radioactive material getting into the body through open wounds and abrasions, by inhalation, by ingestion, or directly through the skin—the probability of the hazard decreasing in that order. Morgan[40] states that beta emitters with energy less than 70 kev do not cause body damage when kept outside the body, because radiation from them has a range less than 0.07 mm of skin, the thickness of the epidermal layer ranging from 0.07 to 0.12 mm on most of the body to 0.8 mm on the palm of the hands and 1.4 mm on the soles of the feet.

Monitors of the type that can be worn conveniently by a person (photographic film meters, pocket ionization chambers, and quartz-fiber or chemical pocket dosimeters) are not sufficiently sensitive to detect the weak beta radiation from carbon-14. Since no adequately sensitive personnel monitor exists, it is especially important to prevent body contamination by using care in handling carbon-14 compounds and by exercising personal cleanliness. If there are open cuts or abrasions on the body, work with carbon-14 should not be done unless the wounds are protected adequately with watertight bandages.

Personal cleanliness can be maintained by washing the hands frequently—always before eating, smoking, and after a work period. Pipetting with the mouth, eating, and smoking should never be permitted in the laboratory.

The presence of carbon-14 on the surface of the body can be detected by surveying the skin with a thin-window (window thickness 2 mg/cm^2 or less) Geiger-Müller counter. The maximum permissible level of such contamination is 0.1 mrep/hr (<100 counts/min).[41] The sensitivity of a thin-window Geiger-Müller tube is such that it will respond to every beta particle that enters it provided the particles do not follow one another more rapidly in time than the recovery time of the tube.[42]

Carbon-14 absorbed in the body cannot be measured by a simple urine analysis, even when the body burden of carbon-14 exceeds the maximum permissible level; perhaps one of the best ways to estimate the quantity of carbon-14 in the body is to analyze the exhaled air.[43] One company provides a routine service[44] of breath analysis for carbon-14 by scintillation counting. The method is reported to be sufficiently sensitive to measure exhalation rates as low as 0.16 μc of carbon-14 per day, which corresponds to 5 μμc per millimole of carbon dioxide if it is assumed that 32,000 mmoles of carbon dioxide are exhaled per day; less than 4% of body tolerance can thereby be detected.[44]

A special apparatus is shown by von Schuching and Abt[44a] for collecting exhaled air in a Douglas bag. The exhaled air is subsequently analyzed by ionization-chamber counting or with a liquid-scintillation counter.

In their study of the degradation of carbon-14-labeled thymidine and its halogenated analogs in man, Kriss, Shaw, and Edmunds[44b] used the Metabolic Gas Analyzer,[44c] an apparatus that continuously monitors and records the carbon dioxide content and the activity of carbon-14 in the breath expired directly from the individual into the apparatus.

A method of measuring carbon-14 in breath is described by Cook and Dancer.[44d] The carbon dioxide is extracted from a breath sample into sodium hydroxide solution, from which it can be released, when required, by the addition of an excess of lactic acid. The released carbon dioxide is used as the "filling" of a proportional counter. The limit of sensitivity is stated to be 3×10^{-8} μc of carbon-14 per milliliter of carbon dioxide. The results of measurements on persons who work in the Organic Chemistry Laboratory at the Radiochemical Centre, Amersham, England, are given. That laboratory handles hundreds of millicuries of carbon-14 daily, almost entirely by vacuum techniques. As the results show, the material is handled safely in standard fume cabinets with low air flow rates at the openings without the complete containment typical of most radioactive operations of similar scale.

A case in point perhaps illustrates most vividly the extent of the hazard of skin contamination with carbon-14. Dancer, Morgan, and Hutchinson[44e] have taken the pains to describe in the literature a case of skin contamination with carbon-14-labeled chloroacetic acid; the corrosiveness of chloroacetic acid to the skin increased the potential hazard. A worker spilled about 0.3 ml (60 to 70 mc of activity) of the hot acid on his fingers. Measurements were made of the skin contamination in the blistered areas; the dose to the skin was estimated to have been 200 to 1600 rad, depending on the depth of penetration. Also, carbon-14 was determined in samples of his breath, whole blood, red blood cells, blood plasma, and urine. It is reported that no sign of skin erythema or other radiation damage was observed and that the wound healed in the normal time. Determination of carbon-14 in urine by liquid-scintillation counting is suggested as a valuable supplement to breath measurements

where people are exposed to contamination with carbon-14-labeled compounds.

7-4b ENVIRONMENT MONITORING

The end-window Geiger-Müller counter provided with a thin (≤ 2 mg/cm^2) mica window is both the most suitable and most versatile instrument for monitoring carbon-14 in the environment. The performance and use of a Geiger-Müller counter are discussed in Sec. 11-2. This inexpensive counter can be either a fixed or portable detector and can be arranged so as to register response on meters, mechanical counters, indicator lights, and speakers. When the Geiger-Müller tube is mounted in a probe attached by way of a cord to the unit that receives the electrical response, it becomes especially useful for monitoring surfaces such as laboratory bench tops, apparatus, the skin, and clothing. Filters or impingers from collectors on which particulates are deposited from air samples are easily scanned with a Geiger-Müller counter; residues obtained by evaporating water samples likewise are. The N.B.S. Handbook 92[45] gives much helpful information on monitors for beta emitters and refers to previous N.B.S. handbooks that are pertinent.

7-5 SAFE WORKING AREA

Ways of providing a safe area for work with radioactive materials and the features of proper laboratory design and construction materials are discussed in N.B.S. Handbook 92.[45] Low-level amounts of carbon-14 can be handled safely if reasonable precautions are taken and if the work area is provided with only a minimum of special facilities. The most important safeguard is adequate containment of the carbon-14 compounds. Other safeguards to be considered include monitors, protective clothing, shielding, adequate ventilation, and proper storage facilities. Personnel and environment monitors are discussed above.

The usual laboratory work with carbon-14 compounds requires no protective clothing other than rubber gloves and eye protection (safety glasses or goggles). Gloves are needed only in work with solids and liquids when there is a chance of spillage on the hands. The sense of touch is less keen through rubber gloves; therefore, they may even slightly increase the danger of spillage. However, if it should occur, they prevent having to decontaminate the hands. Eye protection should always be required.

The beta radiation from carbon-14 (0.156 Mev maximum energy) is readily absorbed by many materials of low density, such as transparent plastics and glass. N.B.S. Handbook 92[46] gives a plot of beta energy (Mev) vs maximum range (cm), which shows the ability of beta radiation to penetrate air, water, glass, aluminum, and iron. A glove box provides adequate shielding and a completely enclosed container for work with high levels of carbon-14. The chemical laboratory type fume hood, having an easily decontaminated surface and provided with adequate air flow in a direction away from the worker, is a suitable place for most work. If such measures are justified, the hood can be equipped with containment trays, strippable finishes, air filters, and the like to restrict the dissemination of carbon-14. Blotting paper placed in trays is a good surface over which to work. The weak beta radiation from carbon-14 produces some but not appreciable amounts of bremsstrahlung (x rays). Therefore, only low-atomic-number materials should be used for shielding against carbon-14. At the millicurie level of carbon-14, bremsstrahlung production is of no concern. The design of hoods, glove boxes, and exhaust systems that ensure adequate containment and ventilation is discussed in N.B.S. Handbook 92.

The storage of carbon-14 compounds for use in the research laboratory is no great safety problem. The level of radioactivity is so low that the containers themselves give sufficient shielding. The problem is one of reducing self-irradiation decomposition of the carbon-14 compounds[47,48] (see also Chap. 6) rather than of protecting against beta radiation. The compounds are often stored in refrigerators or freezers (sometimes at temperatures as low as $-80°C$, the case at the Centre d'Études Nucléaires de Saclay, France), which themselves provide considerable shielding. Only refrigerators that have no internal spark source, such as an open thermostat, should be used. Also, every attempt should be made to store carbon-14 compounds in a fireproofed area.

7-6 DISPOSAL OF CARBON-14 WASTES

It is unnecessary to give here any detailed information about the proper way to dispose of carbon-14 wastes, because this subject is adequately covered in the inexpensive and easily secured N.B.S. Handbook 53.[49] This handbook should be available in any laboratory where work with carbon-14 compounds is done. General considerations and bases for the recommendations are discussed in the handbook; the recommendations are summarized in Handbook 53 as follows:

1 Isotopic Dilution Carbon-14 may be disposed of in any manner provided it is intimately mixed with stable carbon, *in the same chemical form*, in a ratio that never exceeds 1 μc of C^{14} for every 10 g of stable carbon.

2 Sewers Carbon-14 may be discharged to sewers in amounts that do not exceed 1 mc/100 gal of sewage based on the sewage flow available to the disposer within his own institution.

3 Incineration Combustible material containing C^{14} may be incinerated if the *maximum* concentration does not exceed 5 μc per gram of carbon. (In animal carcasses, this requirement would usually be met by an *average* concentration not exceeding 0.2 μc/g of tissue.) Sufficient fuel should be employed to make sure there is not more than 5 μc of C^{14} per pound of total combustible material.

4 Atmospheric Dilution $C^{14}O_2$ from carbonates may be discharged in the exhaust system of a standard chemical laboratory hood that has a linear air flow of at least 50 ft/min, at a rate not to exceed 100 $\mu c/hr/ft^2$ of air intake area in the face of the hood as operated.

5 Garbage Carbon-14 may be disposed of with garbage in amounts that do not exceed 1 $\mu c/lb$ of garbage available to the disposer within his own institution.

Approximate equivalents of the above requirement are stated below for convenience.

1 $\mu c/lb$ of garbage = 20 μc per 10-gal garbage can (allowing for 50 percent voids), 800 $\mu c/yd^3$ of garbage, or 0.5 $\mu c/day$ per person contributing garbage.

6 Burial Carbon-14-containing material may be buried provided it is covered with at least 4 ft of well compacted earth and does not exceed the following limits.

(*a*) The maximum permissible concentration of C^{14} in biological material (plant or animal) for burial shall not exceed 5 $\mu c/g$.

(*b*) The maximum permissible amount of C^{14} in chemical compounds mixed with 1 ft^3 of soil shall not exceed 10 mc.

Some of the A.E.C. and state-enacted regulations regarding the use and disposal of radioactive materials differ from the Handbook 53 recommendations. For example, the A.E.C. regulations do not cover garbage that contains carbon-14, differ somewhat regarding the burial of carbon-14 compounds, and prohibit incineration of carbon-14 compounds without specific approval of the Licensing Branch of the A.E.C. for By-product Materials. The Code of Federal Regulations, Title 10, Section 20 (see Sec. 7-8), although not specifically for carbon-14 and revised frequently, should also be available, as well as Handbook 53.

7-7 DECONTAMINATION

Decontamination is seldom necessary if care and good housekeeping are exercised. The N.B.S. Handbook 48[41] gives very practical and thorough information about the control and removal of radioactive contamination in laboratories. The contents of

this handbook includes discussions of contamination and decontamination of the skin, clothing and bedding, laboratory tools and glassware, and specific materials. Ways of preventing emergency situations and procedures to be followed when they occur are described. Suitable decontaminating detergents and wetting agents are listed. In view of the low cost (15¢), availability, and thoroughness of Handbook 48, it is not necessary to say more here than that this handbook should be secured as a reference.

7-8 LICENSING REQUIREMENTS FOR PROCUREMENT OF CARBON-14 COMPOUNDS

The legal aspects of radiation control are aptly discussed by Blatz[50] and more briefly by Shilling;[51] these references are commended to the reader. In the United States, the A.E.C. is empowered to license, regulate, and inspect activities in which atomic energy is used. These activities include the use of carbon-14 compounds. The principal regulations are published in the Code of Federal Regulations (CFR) in the section designated Title 10, which is subdivided into Parts; of particular interest to those working with radioisotopes are Parts 20, 30, 40, 50, 55, and 70.[52] Part 30 (10CFR30), titled "Licensing of By-product Materials," defines the established policies of the A.E.C. with respect to the licensing of radioisotopes. The most recent issue of the entire Title 10 should be reviewed by anyone about to begin work with carbon-14, because Title 10 is amended frequently. A very concise summary of the licensing regulations regarding carbon-14 compounds follows.

It is permissible to purchase without a *specific* license as many as ten packages, each containing 0.05 mc of carbon-14. For amounts in excess of this exempt amount, a By-product Material License (A.E.C. Form 374) or a state agreement form is required; the latter is provided if the A.E.C. has transferred its regulatory jurisdiction to the state. This license or agreement authorizes the holder to possess particular radioactive materials in specified amounts. Request for a license is made on A.E.C. Form 313, which is available from the Division of Licensing and Regulation, U.S. Atomic Energy Commission, Washington 25, D.C., and also from commercial suppliers of carbon-14 compounds. The license is valid for two years; the number of the license must accompany a purchase order. A specific license is issued only if reasonable assurance has been given that the carbon-14 compounds will be used safely and properly.

If carbon-14 compounds are to be applied to humans, an additional application form must be reviewed and approved by the Advisory Committee on Medical Uses of Isotopes of the Division of Licensing and Regulation of the A.E.C. The A.E.C. licensing of radioisotopes for clinical research is discussed by LeRoy.[29]

A *general* license is available that does not require the filing of A.E.C. Form 313. It permits the purchase and use of microcurie amounts of certain nonhazardous materials; the up-to-date list that gives the identities and exact quantities of these materials is available from the A.E.C. or the *Federal Register*.

7-9 TRANSPORTATION OF CARBON-14 COMPOUNDS

The transfer of carbon-14 compounds beyond the area in which they are produced or used requires conformity with certain specific regulations, even though the quantity of radioactivity moved may be very small. It is possible that international, federal, state, and local regulations must be met. These regulations are comprehensive and complex, they are described completely in existing publications, and they are subject to change. For these reasons, only the sources of information about them rather than the regulations themselves are given here.

Recommended regulations to govern the international transport of radioactive materials[53] have been published by the International Atomic Energy Agency (I.A.E.A.) and discussed further in a supplementary I.A.E.A. publication.[54]

Portions of the federal regulations are included in an A.E.C. handbook,[55] which gives references to the complete federal regulations. The federal regulations are established by the Interstate Commerce Commission, Civil Aeronautics Board, U.S. Coast Guard, and Post Office. Also, the Bureau of Explosives regulations must be met. Handbook 92[9] includes a very brief discussion of on-site transfers, off-site transportation, and transportation containers.

General information about the shipping of radioisotopes from the Oak Ridge National Laboratory is given in an isotopes catalog.[56] All regulations pertaining to the shipment of radioactive material by land, sea, and air have been abstracted and collected into one convenient reference[57] that is in use in the Isotopes Division of the Oak Ridge National Laboratory.

Regulations on the transport of radioactive materials in Great Britain are discussed briefly by Barnes and Taylor.[58]

According to the Interstate Commerce Commission classification of radioactive materials, carbon-14 compounds are in Class D Poison, Group III. In many instances they fulfill the conditions for exemption from prescribed packing, marking, and labeling requirements; the conditions as defined in the federal regulations[55] are as follows:

1) The package must be such that there can be no leakage of radioactive material under conditions normally incident to transportation.

2) The package must contain not more than 0.1 millicuries of radium, or polonium, or that amount of strontium 89, strontium 90, or barium 140 which disintegrates at a rate of more than 5 million atoms per second; or that amount of any other radioactive substance which disintegrates at a rate of more than 50 million atoms per second.

That amount of material which disintegrates at the rate of 5 million atoms per second is 0.135 millicuries; and that which disintegrates at the rate of 50 million atoms per second is 1.35 millicuries.

3) The package must be such that no significant alpha, beta, or neutron radiation is emitted from the exterior of the package and the gamma radiation at any surface of the package must be less than 10 milliroentgens for 24 hours.

It is often thus possible to ship carbon-14 compounds by mail.

The discussion in this chapter[59] is an attempt to convey accurate information about the radiation hazards of carbon-14 and the protection required against them. The health physics status of carbon-14 is likely to change from time to time. This change will undoubtedly be reflected in revisions to many of the references cited, for example, the N.B.S. and I.A.E.A. publications. The possibility that more recent editions of these references exist should be considered.

CITED REFERENCES

1 "Radiological Health Handbook," Division of Radiological Health, U.S. Department of Health, Education, and Welfare, Washington, D.C., Sept., 1960.

2 G. J. Appleton and P. N. Krishnamoorthy, "Safe Handling of Radioisotopes. Health Physics Addendum," Safety Series No. 2, International Atomic Energy Agency, Kärntner Ring 11, Vienna 1, Austria, 1960.

3 C. W. Shilling, "Radiation Use and Control in Industrial Application," Grune & Stratton, New York, 1960.

4 "The Hazards to Man of Nuclear and Allied Radiations. A Second Report to the Medical Research Council," Her Majesty's Stationery Office, London, Dec., 1960.

5 B. M. Zlobinskii, "Safety Rules for Working with Radioactive Materials," 2d suppl'd. ed., State Scientific Technical Publishing House of Literature on Ferrous and Nonferrous Metallurgy, Moscow, 1961; U.S. Atomic Energy Commission, Division of Technical Information, Translation Series, AEC-tr-5445.

6 D. E. Barnes and D. Taylor, "Radiation Hazards and Protection," 2d ed., George Newnes Ltd., London, 1963.

7 "Radiation Effects on Man" (a special report), Nucleonics, 21(3), 45–60 (1963).

8 H. Blatz, "Introduction to Radiological Health," McGraw-Hill Book Company, New York, 1964.

9 "Safe Handling of Radioactive Isotopes," U.S. Department of Commerce, National Bureau of Standards Handbook 92, March 9, 1964, Superintendent of Documents, U.S. Government Printing Office, Washington 25, D.C.; also others in the N.B.S. Handbook series, which is revised from time to time.

10 B. M. Tolbert and W. E. Siri in A. Weissberger, Ed., "Physical Methods of Organic Chemistry," pt. IV, 3d ed., pp. 3341–3345, Interscience Publishers, Inc., New York, 1960.

11 J. R. Catch, "Carbon-14 Compounds," chap. 8, Butterworth Inc., Washington, D.C., 1961.

12 D. E. Barnes and D. Taylor, "Radiation Hazards and Protection," 2d ed., chap. 6, George Newnes Ltd., London, 1963.

13 "Report of the United Nations Scientific Committee on the Effects of Atomic Radiation," pp. 56–58, General Assembly Official Records: Thirteenth Session, Suppl. 17 (A/3838), United Nations, New York, 1958.

13a "Report of the United Nations Scientific Committee on the Effects of Atomic Radiation," pp. 216–217, General Assembly Official Records: Seventeenth Session, Suppl. 16 (A/5216), United Nations, New York, 1962.

14 G. E. Francis, W. Mulligan, and A. Wormall, "Isotopic Tracers," apx. II, 2d ed., Essential Books Division, Oxford University Press Inc., New York, 1959.

15 A. M. Brues and D. L. Buchanan, "Summary of Conference on the Toxicity of Carbon-14," Argonne National Laboratory Report ANL-4787, March, 1952.

16 L. Pauling, Science, 128(3333), 1183 (1958).

17 J. R. Totter, M. R. Zelle, and H. Hollister, Science, 128(3337), 1490 (1958).

18 C. E. Purdom, New Scientist, 15(298), 255 (1962).

19 Anon., "Science and the Citizen," Sci. Am., 200(1), 62 (1959).

20 G. M. Wiederholt, "The Nature and Effects of Worldwide Fallout from Nuclear Weapons," General Electric Company Report R59TMP-66, pp. viii, xiii–xv, and 41–55 (Nov. 20, 1959).

[21] W. S. Broecker and A. Walton, *Science*, **130**(3371), 309 (1959).

[22] "Preliminary Report on Radiocarbon from Nuclear Tests," United Nations. Secretariat. A/AC.82/R.77.

[23] H. Tauber, *Science*, **131**(3404), 921 (1960).

[24] W. S. Broecker and E. A. Olson, *Science*, **132**(3429), 712 (1960).

[25] F. Heřcík, *Jaderna Energie*, **6**, 181 (1960) (In Czech.); *Nucl. Sci. Abstr.*, 17680.

[26] R. K. Appleyard in R. S. Caldecott and L. A. Snyder, Eds., "A Symposium on Radioisotopes in the Biosphere," pp. 227–239, University of Minnesota, Minneapolis, 1960.

[26a] F. T. Hagemann, J. Gray, Jr., and L. Machta, "Carbon-14 Measurements in the Atmosphere—1953 to 1964," U.S. Atomic Energy Commission Report HASL-159, April 1, 1965.

[26b] Anon., "Carbon-14 Measurements in the Atmosphere," U.S. Atomic Energy Commission Report HASL-166, January 1, 1966.

[27] J. Furth and J. L. Tullis, *Cancer Res.*, **16**, 5 (1956).

[28] E. Browning, "Harmful Effects of Ionising Radiations," Elsevier Publishing Co., New York, 1959.

[29] G. V. LeRoy, *Atomlight*, no. 26, 1 (1963).

[30] J. R. Catch, "Carbon-14 Compounds," p. 112, Butterworth Inc., Washington, D.C., 1961.

[31] W. H. Briner, *Atomlight*, no. 34, 1, Dec., 1963.

[32] "Radioactivity. Recommendations of the International Commission on Radiological Units and Measurements (1962) (ICRU) Report 10c," U.S. Department of Commerce, National Bureau of Standards Handbook 86, Nov. 29, 1963, Superintendent of Documents, U.S. Government Printing Office, Washington 25, D.C.

[33] A. J. Bertinchamps and G. C. Cotzias, *Science*, **128**, 988 (1958).

[34] "Maximum Permissible Body Burdens and Maximum Permissible Concentrations of Radionuclides in Air and in Water for Occupational Exposure," U.S. Department of Commerce, National Bureau of Standards Handbook 69, June 5, 1959, Superintendent of Documents, U.S. Government Printing Office, Washington 25, D.C.

[35] "Permissible Dose from External Sources of Ionizing Radiation," U.S. Department of Commerce, National Bureau of Standards Handbook 59, Sept. 24, 1954, Superintendent of Documents, U.S. Government Printing Office, Washington 25, D.C.

[36] C. W. Shilling, "Radiation Use and Control in Industrial Application," chap. 10, Grune & Stratton, New York, 1960.

[37] J. R. Catch, "Carbon-14 Compounds," pp. 107–110, Butterworth Inc., Washington, D.C., 1961.

[38] "Basic Safety Standards for Radiation Protection," Safety Series No. 9, International Atomic Energy Agency, Kärntner Ring 11, Vienna 1, Austria, 1962.

[39] D. E. Barnes and D. Taylor, "Radiation Hazards and Protection," 2d ed., chaps. 6 and 7, George Newnes Ltd., London, 1963.

[40] K. Z. Morgan in A. H. Snell, Ed., "Nuclear Instruments and Their Uses," p. 397, John Wiley & Sons, Inc., New York, 1962.

[41] "Control and Removal of Radioactive Contamination in Laboratories," U.S. Department of Commerce, National Bureau of Standards Handbook 48, Dec. 15, 1951, Superintendent of Documents, U.S. Government Printing Office, Washington 25, D.C.

[42] D. E. Barnes and D. Taylor, "Radiation Hazards and Protection," 2d ed., p. 58, George Newnes Ltd., London, 1963.

[43] K. Z. Morgan in A. H. Snell, Ed., "Nuclear Instruments and Their Uses," p. 442, John Wiley & Sons, Inc., New York, 1962.

[44] Described in a six-page brochure available from New England Nuclear Assay Corporation, 575 Albany Street, Boston 18, Mass.

[44a] S. L. von Schuching and A. F. Abt, 'Carbon-14 Fat Oxidation Test: A New Method for Measuring Fat Utilization in the Human,' in S. Rothchild, Ed., "Advances in Tracer Methodology," vol. 2, p. 293, Plenum Press, New York, 1963.

[44b] J. P. Kriss, R. K. Shaw, and N. A. Edmunds, *Atomlight*, no. 47, 1 (September, 1965).

[44c] General Measurements Corp., Garnerville, N.Y.

[44d] D. A. Cook and G. H. C. Dancer, "Measurements of the Specific Activity of Respired Carbon-14 Dioxide as a Method of Health Physics Control," United Kingdom Atomic Energy Authority Report RCC-R178, The Radiochemical Centre, Amersham, Buckinghamshire, England, 1965.

44e G. H. Dancer, A. Morgan, and W. P. Hutchinson, *Health Phys.*, **11**, 1055 (1965).

45 "Safe Handling of Radioactive Materials," U.S. Department of Commerce, National Bureau of Standards Handbook 92, March 9, 1964 (esp. chap. 6); Superintendent of Documents, U.S. Government Printing Office, Washington 25, D.C.

46 *Ibid.*, p. 26.

47 J. R. Catch, "Carbon-14 Compounds," pp. 68–72, Butterworth Inc., Washington, D.C., 1961.

48 J. Sirchis, Ed., "Methods of Preparing and Storing Marked Molecules," Proceedings of the International Symposium Held in Brussels, Belgium, Nov. 13–16, 1963, Presses Académiques Européennes, Brussels, 1964.

49 "Recommendations for the Disposal of Carbon-14 Wastes," U.S. Department of Commerce, National Bureau of Standards Handbook 53, Superintendent of Documents, U.S. Government Printing Office, Washington 25, D.C., Oct. 26, 1953.

50 H. Blatz, "Introduction to Radiological Health," chap. 10, McGraw-Hill Book Company, New York, 1964.

51 C. W. Shilling, "Radiation Use and Control in Industrial Application," pp. 86–90, Grune & Stratton, New York, 1960.

52 Available on request from the Division of Licensing and Regulation, U.S. Atomic Energy Commission, Washington 25, D.C.

53 "Regulations for the Safe Transport of Radioactive Materials," Safety Series No. 6, International Atomic Energy Agency, Kaerntnerring, Vienna I, Austria, 1961. (Published in English, French, Russian, and Spanish.)

54 "Regulations for the Safe Transport of Radioactive Materials. Notes on Certain Aspects of the Regulations," Safety Series No. 7, International Atomic Energy Agency, Karntner Ring 11, Vienna 1, Austria, 1961. (Published in English, French, Russian, and Spanish.)

55 "Handbook of Federal Regulations Applying to Transportation of Radioactive Materials," U.S. Atomic Energy Commission, Division of Construction and Supply, Traffic Management Section, Washington, D.C., May 1958; Superintendent of Documents, U.S. Government Printing Office, Washington 25, D.C.

56 "Oak Ridge National Laboratory Catalog Radio and Stable Isotopes," Isotopes Development Center, Oak Ridge National Laboratory, P.O. Box X, Oak Ridge, Tenn., 4th Revision, April, 1963, pp. 10–15.

57 F. V. Williams, Jr., "Abstract of Radioactive Material Shipping Regulations," listing: T. C. George's Tariff No. 15 Publishing Interstate Commerce Commission Regulations, International Air Transport Regulations, Federal Aviation Regulations, Air Transport Board Tariff No. 6-C Supplement No. 4, and Code of Federal Regulations Title 46—Shipping Parts 146–149; Isotopes Division, Oak Ridge National Laboratory, P.O. Box X, Oak Ridge, Tenn.

58 D. E. Barnes and D. Taylor, "Radiation Hazards and Protection," George Newnes Ltd., London, pp. 193–195, 1963.

59 The authors are grateful to D. M. Davis and T. J. Burnett of the Health Physics Division of the Oak Ridge National Laboratory for reviewing this chapter, especially with respect to its adequacy in the area of health physics, and for offering helpful suggestions.

CHAPTER

8

SYNTHESIS OF CARBON-14-LABELED COMPOUNDS

8-1 INTRODUCTION

The approach to the synthesis of carbon-14-labeled organic compounds has changed greatly since the late 1940's. At that time production facilities in the United States were limited to those established in laboratories operated by the United States Atomic Energy Commission. Eventually this function was taken over by private commercial producers, who supply more than 1000 compounds of general and particular interest. Some of the more unusual labeled compounds, such as vitamins, natural and synthetic drugs, and hormones, are being made available as the demand develops. At least one company offers a custom-synthesis service. A list of companies producing carbon-14-labeled compounds is provided in Apx. II.

The advisability of synthesis versus purchase of the more common compounds is largely a question of economics. A pharmaceutical laboratory needing only a millicurie or two of a labeled amino acid would find the purchase of it advantageous. For the commercial product, a guarantee of purity would be provided, as well as the value for its specific or molar radioactivity. On the other hand, if 50 mc of carboxyl-labeled benzoic acid were required, the synthesis would probably be more economical than the direct purchase. As universities develop programs in radiochemistry, they will undoubtedly offer courses in the synthesis of radiochemicals that parallel the courses in organic and inorganic preparations which they now offer. In such work, barium carbonate-^{14}C most likely will be the starting material for the synthesis of carbon-14-labeled organic compounds.

There are three methods for converting barium carbonate-^{14}C and its simple derivatives into more complex labeled compounds: chemical synthesis, isotope exchange, and biological synthesis. Of these, chemical synthesis is the most generally used. Isotope-exchange methods are convenient but are limited in applicability; they are discussed in

Chap. 4. In the "hot atom" or recoil method (not very practical) of preparing carbon-14-labeled compounds, labeled starting materials are not required; most frequently compounds that contain one or more nitrogen atoms are used. Biological and recoil methods permit very little control of the product, usually do not ensure either indiscriminate or specific labeling, often provide only low-to-moderate levels of activity, and may yield products that are extremely difficult to purify. Frequently the isolation of one component from the mixture will cause destruction or racemization of other fractions. However, chromatographic techniques have simplified purification procedures used in both biochemical and hot-atom labeling.

8-2 CHEMICAL METHODS

There exist many good procedures for the chemical synthesis of the more common carbon-14-labeled organic compounds. One of the best sources of such procedures is the compilation by Murray and Williams,[1] which describes about 400 syntheses; however, for many of the syntheses optimum conditions have not been established. Short bibliographies of syntheses are also available.[2,3] Catch[4] discusses the synthesis of carbon-14 compounds, as well as other problems concerning the use of carbon-14. Almost all the numerous publications of Catch (The Radiochemical Centre, Amersham, England) and Pichat (Labeled Molecules Section, Saclay, France) relate to the preparation of relatively complex labeled compounds. Another source of procedures for preparing labeled compounds is the *Journal of Labelled Compounds*. This journal also contains abstracts of methods reported in the current literature for preparing labeled compounds.

In general, any organic compound that can be synthesized in the laboratory can be labeled. However, the specific labeling of complicated molecules may be difficult and expensive if high molar radioactivity is

required. Certain complex geochemicals, such as petroleum crudes and coal tar, that cannot be duplicated in the laboratory cannot be labeled in a representative way. The impossibility of representative labeling definitely limits the application of such analytical techniques as isotope-dilution analysis.

8-2a PLANNING A SYNTHESIS

Before the chemical synthesis of a carbon-14-labeled compound is undertaken, a reaction scheme must be chosen that will satisfy most of the following requirements:

1 give a high yield.
2 introduce the carbon-14 as near the last step of the synthesis as possible.
3 introduce the carbon-14 in a known position in the molecule.
4 provide a product of high radiochemical purity.
5 ensure adequate specific activity, which for biological work may be 1 to 50 mc/mmole, and for organic chemistry, 1 to 10 mc/mole.

A labeled compound for which preparative methods are not well established should be synthesized as follows: First, the synthesis is performed with nonradioactive materials on the desired scale until optimum conditions are established. Product purity is checked by the usual chemical and physical methods. Then, the experiment is carried out at the tracer level to establish the nature of impurities and to determine the yield of desired product by isotope-dilution analysis. At this point it may also be desirable to verify the specificity of labeling. Finally, the procedures developed in the nonlabeled and tracer-level runs are carefully duplicated, usually with amounts of carbon-14 in the range 1 to 100 mc or more. There are both advantages and disadvantages in working at high specific activities. An advantage is that the yield, and often the purity, can be increased by dilution at a stage for which isolation might normally be a problem. The techniques of paper, thin-layer, gas-liquid, and column chromatography are most convenient for small amounts of material. A disadvantage is the difficulty of completely removing all high-specific-activity impurities. This problem is very serious for critical isotope-effect and reaction-mechanism studies for which it is almost always preferable to prepare the desired compound at the level of specific activity best suited to the study rather than to resort to dilution of high-specific-activity compounds. A carbon-14 concentration of 1 to 10 mc/mole is usually suitable.

If it is desirable to use a vacuum line or other closed system, quantities must be limited to a few millimoles. Such a system is mandatory for gaseous and volatile liquid products. Barium carbonate-^{14}C of isotopic abundance from 30 to 80% is readily available; at this level the cost of carbon-14 risked per preparation may be prohibitive beyond the one- or two-millimole quantity. In exceptional cases, the isotopic abundance

of carbon-14 in barium carbonate-^{14}C is as high as 90% (nearly 56 c/mole).

The weight of barium carbonate-^{14}C required for a synthesis is inversely proportional to the atom percent (isotopic abundance) of carbon-14 in it; this relationship is shown graphically by the isograms in Fig. 8-1 for the small quantities used in most syntheses. Larger or smaller amounts can be calculated readily by extrapolation. The atom percent of carbon-14 is a value furnished with each lot of barium carbonate-^{14}C.

MULTIPLE LABELING   Multiple isotope substitution provides for the formation of many structurally distinguishable compounds; for example, Murray and Williams[5] have calculated that five such tetramethylammonium iodides can be produced by the exhaustive methylation of ammonia with methyl-[6] iodide. Catch[6] describes the many species that result from the single and multiple labeling of succinic acid. He also reminds his readers that uniformly labeled glucose is

FIG. 8-1   Radioactivity isograms for barium carbonate-^{14}C.

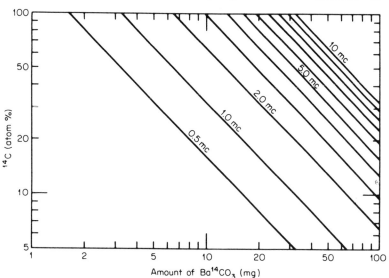

Amount of Ba^{14}CO$_3$ (mg)

a composite of 63 labeled molecular forms. The multiplicity of structures complicates nomenclature. This nomenclature problem is discussed by Murray and Williams.[5] Since isotopically pure carbon-14 is not available, it is impossible to substitute carbon-14 for all carbon atoms in a molecule. The preparation of a simple two-carbon compound, acetic acid-^{14}C, from barium carbonate-^{14}C whose carbon is in one case 50% carbon-14 and in another 0.01% (adequate for most tracer work) demonstrates the arithmetic of multiple labeling.

$$^{14}CO_2 \quad (0.50)$$
$$\downarrow \text{ LiAlH}_4$$
$$^{14}CH_3OH \quad (0.50)$$
$$\downarrow \text{ I}_2, \text{ P}$$
$$\downarrow \text{ Mg}$$
$$\downarrow \ ^{14}CO_2 \quad (0.50)$$
$$^{14}CH_3{}^{14}CO_2H, \ ^{14}CH_3CO_2H$$
$$(0.25) \qquad\qquad (0.25)$$
$$CH_3{}^{14}CO_2H, \ CH_3CO_2H$$
$$(0.25) \qquad\quad (0.25)$$

$$^{14}CO_2 \quad (0.0001)$$
$$\downarrow \text{ LiAlH}_4$$
$$^{14}CH_3OH \quad (0.0001)$$
$$\downarrow \text{ I}_2, \text{ P}$$
$$\downarrow \text{ Mg}$$
$$\downarrow \ ^{14}CO_2 \quad (0.0001)$$
$$^{14}CH_3{}^{14}CO_2H, \ ^{14}CH_3CO_2H$$
$$(0.00000001) \quad (0.00009999)$$
$$CH_3{}^{14}CO_2H, \ CH_3CO_2H$$
$$(0.00009999) \quad (0.99980001)$$

This subject is discussed briefly in Sec. 3-4c. In most reactions the chemical yield will be less than 100%. Normal isotope effects will tend to keep the percent of labeled compounds actually produced less than the value calculated. On the basis of the results of one study,[7,8] which showed that the rate of rupture of a ^{14}C—^{14}C bond is faster than that of a ^{12}C—^{14}C bond, it appears possible that the formation of a doubly labeled molecule might be favored kinetically over that of a singly labeled molecule.

PRECAUTIONS   The position of labeling is particularly important in studies of reaction mechanisms and isotope effects. In general, it is desirable to introduce the label during the latest possible step of a series of steps that constitute a synthesis. If the preparation is not well understood, it is best to confirm the position of labeling by use of a suitable degradation (see Chap. 10). In the synthesis of labeled compounds, it is necessary at times to distinguish between chemical yield and radiochemical yield. In the normal preparative chemistry of nonlabeled compounds, the recovery of pure reaction product may be attended by a large mechanical loss incurred during the isolation and purification of the product. In the same way, loss of the product will occur during radiochemical preparations if the maximum radioactivity possible in the product is desired. However, in most preparations the product can be diluted with carrier and (for practical purposes) essentially all the radioactive product of a reaction can be recovered. In a long series of reactions involving carbon-14-labeled compounds, this addition of carrier would result in a slight dilution in each isolation (including crystallizations). This method of achieving maximum radiochemical yield has the major disadvantage that any highly radioactive contaminant formed in any of the steps of a synthesis may be carried along undiluted into the final product. If no carrier were added, then the contribution made by the radioactive contaminant to the total radioactivity of the final product probably would be very small after purification of the product. For example, if the desired compound were isolated 99% pure, it would contain 1% of contaminant. Both the chemical and the radiochemical purity of the product would be 99%. However, if a reaction yields equimolar amounts of desired product A and contaminant B, both labeled, it may be advantageous to dilute 100-fold with the nonlabeled form (carrier) of A in order to recover all that compound. Even though in subsequent steps the diluted form of A might then be purified to 99% chemical purity, its *radiochemical purity* would not be 99%. Instead, the 1% of undiluted contaminant

B (if carried in its entirety) would contribute as much radioactivity to the final purified product as would be contributed by the desired product, A. The radiochemical purity of the final purified product would therefore be 50%. This disadvantage is overcome by adding a small amount of the contaminant in its nonradioactive form. Such an isotopic diluent for a substance whose carrying is undesirable is called a "holdback" carrier. The addition of a holdback carrier naturally must be followed by repurification of the product; possibly a second or third addition of holdback carrier will be needed. It must be remembered that the objective in using a holdback-carrier procedure is to remove the *labeled* contaminant; the addition may cause an increase in the chemical contamination. The problem of purification is discussed in Sec. 4-1 also. In ensuring maximum purity, gas-liquid chromatography, paper chromatography, infrared spectroscopy, and zone-melting procedures may be invaluable. Conscientious commercial suppliers of radiochemical products usually offer information regarding radiochemical purity based on the results of carrier-dilution analysis, paper chromatography, and autoradiography. Also, information may be given regarding optimum storage conditions, as well as the rate of self-irradiation damage if it is known.

Preparations of submillimolar quantities of labeled compounds are often fraught with possibilities for their destruction through air-oxidation, volatilization, peroxide oxidation, hydrolysis, reduction, bacterial action, etc.; these difficulties would be of little significance for macro quantities. For example, Ostwald, Adams, and Tolbert[8a] observed that small quantities of alanine in nonsterile solution are decarboxylated by bacterial action if left standing at room temperature. Dauben and Payot[8b] found that when cholesterol is stored in the presence of air, it is oxidized, and that this oxidation requires both radiation and oxygen, since

cholesterol-[14]C *in vacuo* and unlabeled choesterol in air are stable.

8-2b LABORATORY EQUIPMENT AND PRACTICE

Preparative work at the tracer level with 0.01 to 1 mole of a labeled organic compound can usually be done with the standard equipment found in any organic chemistry laboratory. Even such volatile compounds as methyl-^{14}C iodide can be prepared in good yield without the use of a vacuum line. Because carbon-14 compounds of high specific activity are expensive and somewhat hazardous, work with them requires greater emphasis on safety and yield than is given in work with unlabeled organic compounds. However, the requirements for safety are not nearly so great for carbon-14 as they are for many other isotopes. Such problems as radiation protection, instrumentation, decontamination, and waste disposal are already discussed in Chap. 7. The purpose of this section is to describe techniques and equipment that facilitate work with both low-level and high-level carbon-14-labeled compounds.

FUME HOODS It is desirable to have available two types of fume hoods, one for general chemical work and the other for vacuum-line work that involves both syntheses and the combustion of samples for analytical purposes. A most practical general-purpose radiochemical fume hood is described by Ward.[9] Service facilities needed will vary depending on the nature of the work to be done. Both sides of the hood should have outlets for electricity, cold water, steam, gas, vacuum, and air. A standard drain should be provided for water, even though local regulations may call for an additional "hot" drain for the disposal of small volumes of radioactive wastes. For occasional use, a hood 6 ft wide is adequate; for extended work, an 8-ft hood is desirable. The floor of the hood should be seamless and depressed in order to contain spilled radioactive materials. Baffles located above and below the door ensure that the flow of air is smooth, even when the hood door is closed. Automatic louvres may be used in the exhaust stack to permit outside air to enter the stack if the hood door is more than two-thirds closed. A "by-pass" hood serves the same purpose, and no tampering with the stack is necessary. The hood walls may be sprayed ("cocooned") with a strippable plastic to facilitate their decontamination. However, in the usual organic laboratory, such a film becomes badly splattered before it becomes contaminated. Its use is not recommended for work with carbon-14.

The so-called "California" hood is very suitable for housing a lattice frame, which is ideal for mounting vacuum lines, small furnaces, carbon-14 combustion apparatus, and any other permanently mounted equipment that requires rigid support. An efficient lattice-frame hood is available commercially.[9a] An ordinary walk-in hood is likewise useful and provides adequate draft.

VACUUM SYSTEMS Elaborate vacuum systems of manifolds are not as popular as they once were for use in handling carbon-14-labeled compounds. The great reduction in the cost of barium carbonate-^{14}C has resulted in a decrease in the emphasis on yield. At the same time, there has been a switch to low-level bench-scale syntheses, partly as an outcome of the development of efficient liquid-scintillation counters.

Much practical information about the construction and use of vacuum lines is given by Sanderson[10] and by Calvin and co-authors.[11] Several practical vacuum lines are also described by Murray and Williams.[1]

PUMPS Possibly the simplest vacuum pump is a water aspirator. It provides sufficient reduction in pressure (to about 20 mm) for most distillations and even for simple transfers when used in conjunction with a Dry-Ice cold trap. Mechanical pumps of several sizes

are commercially available; they vary in speed, noise, and ultimate vacuum produced. A good pump will transfer several liters of gas per minute at a few microns pressure. It will be usable for many years if it is properly protected from volatile compounds and corrosive gases, such as those produced in the distillation of liquids that contain the halides of phosphorus and of sulfur. A simple vacuum system that includes adequate protection for the pump is shown in Fig. 8-2. In addition to the pump, the equipment consists of a Cartesian manometer, G, of range from 0.1 to 10 mm; a trap, K, of 500- to 1000-ml capacity and filled with potassium hydroxide pellets; and a Dry-Ice or liquid-nitrogen trap, T, fabricated from a large Dewar blank. If the lower outlet is properly positioned, as much as 150 ml or more of a volatile liquid can be trapped out before it is necessary to drain the trap through the Teflon stopcock. The bores of stopcocks and tubing should be moderately large to minimize pressure drop in the pumping system.

Diffusion Pumps The flexibility and ultimate utility of most vacuum lines are increased through the use of a diffusion pump. Pumps are available commercially in which either mercury or a high-boiling oil is used. The oil-diffusion pump is the more popular, because it is compact and of durable metal construction and it does not present the hazard of mercury vapor. The pump is available in a large number of sizes; the small units (capacities of 5 to 10 liters/sec at 10^{-4} mm) are adequate for any usual laboratory application. The oil-diffusion pump must be protected by a liquid-nitrogen-cooled, high-vacuum type trap and provided with a bypass to avoid pumping large volumes of oxidizing gases such as oxygen through the hot oil, usually dioctyl phthalate (Octoil). If these precautions are observed, the oil-diffusion pump will give long maintenance-free service. Oil-diffusion pumps require a backing pressure of 100 μ or less; since requirements may vary from one diffusion pump to another, the

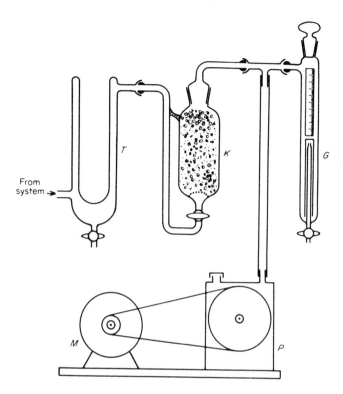

FIG. 8-2 Simple vacuum system. (*M*, motor; *P*, pump; *G*, Cartesian manometer; *K*, trap of KOH pellets; and *T*, Dry-Ice or liquid-nitrogen trap.)

From system →

manufacturer's recommendations should be followed. Unless the history of a used mechanical pump is known, it is best to buy a new pump for use as a backing pump. The minimum diffusion-pump system, ready for insertion between the mechanical fore pump and the vacuum manifold, is shown in Fig. 8-3. Provision is made for connection to a vacuum gage.

Toepler Pumps If noncondensable organic compounds are to be transferred, it is necessary to use a Toepler pump unless·the gas can be generated within the closed system. Toepler pumps may be either manual or automatic in operation. Their use permits the nearly quantitative transfer of a gas from a part of a system in which it is present at a low pressure to another part of the system where the pressure may be substantially higher. This vacuum technique is especially useful for the transfer of carbon-14 dioxide,

deuterium, and tritium, as well as for handling volatile liquids when liquid nitrogen is not available. A compact, automatic Toepler pump of superior design has been described by Urry and Urry[12] (Fig. 8-4). Its operation is similar to that of other mercury-piston type pumps. The lower chamber is filled to *A* with mercury, the pump is connected to the vacuum line, and both the upper and lower chambers are evacuated. The gas is then permitted to enter the upper chamber through the input valve *C*. The sealed tungsten-wire contacts at points *1*, *2*, and *3* are connected to a simple control system, which requires only a DPST ac relay modified to control the pump and the air input (details of construction are given in the original article[12]). The designers found that a pump which has an upper-chamber (piston) volume of 800 cc and a cycling time of 35 sec can remove 99.85% of the gas in a 2-liter system in about

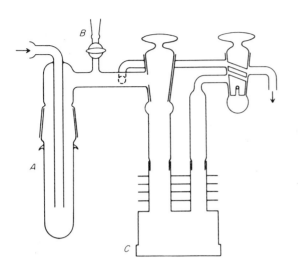

FIG. 8-3 Oil-diffusion-pump assembly. (*A*, liquid-nitrogen-cooled trap; *B*, vacuum-gage connection; *C*, diffusion pump.)

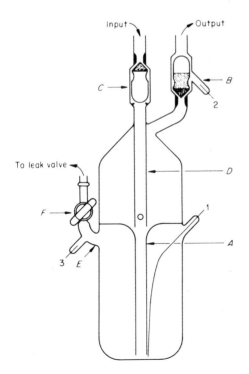

FIG. 8-4 Automatic Toepler pump. (*From G. Urry and W. H. Urry, Rev. Sci. Instr.*, **27**, 819 (1956), *with permission.*)

10 minutes. If only an occasional gas transfer is made, it is possible to dispense with the automatic feature of the pump by substituting capillary stopcocks at *B* and *C* and a two-way stopcock at *F*. Only 5 to 10 cycles are usually necessary, and this operation is not unduly tedious. The greatest grief may come from not turning the stopcocks at the proper moments or in the proper order.

INSTRUMENTS FOR MEASURING PRESSURE The barometer-type manometer is accurate down to only about 10 mm and readable to 1 mm of mercury. The Cartesian (or Dubrovin) manometer can be read accurately to 1 mm of mercury and, in its commercial forms, is very useful for determining pressure in routine vacuum distillations. The Cartesian manometer presents the pressure range, 0 to 10 mm mercury, on a 100-mm scale that is graduated in 1-mm divisions. The simple rotating form of the McLeod pressure gage becomes useful at pressures still lower than 1 mm and duplicates much of the range of thermal gages such as the Pirani gage, which is useful in the pressure range produced by oil- or mercury-diffusion pumps. The McLeod gage has three principal disadvantages: (1) it does not give continuous readings, (2) it is insensible to condensable vapors such as water or ammonia, because it depends on compression, and (3) it loses mercury to the vacuum system where the mercury often reacts with gases in the system to deposit solid products on the inner walls of the measuring device.

The most common instruments used for measuring very low pressures are thermal gages, which depend on the fact that the heat conductance of a gas varies with its pressure. Such gages are sensitive only at low pressures, have a linear output only for a small part of the usable range, and depend on the heat conductivity of the particular gas being measured (the sensitivity for different gases can vary as much as 10:1). A thermal gage consists of a heated surface and a temperature-sensing device. The latter can be a resistance

wire (as in the Pirani gage), thermocouple, or a thermistor. Most thermal gages are useful from 10^{-3} to 1 mm, but the thermistor-type thermal gage (commercially available from Kinney Vacuum Division of The New York Air Brake Co., Boston, Mass.) has been built in such a way as to extend the useful range to relatively high values of pressure. This is done by enclosing the thermistor element in a metallic cylinder having very small dimensions. The thermistor-type thermal gage has the advantage that it is linear over a wider pressure range and is less subject to the effect of corrosive materials in the vacuum line. Heated-filament gages, such as the Pirani, can be damaged or caused to change in calibration if exposed to hydrocarbons or to corrosive gases such as chlorine. It is advisable to use a glass joint and a stopcock between the vacuum line and the gage if the line is to be used for preparative purposes.

Several different ionization gages are available; they cover the range from atmospheric pressure to 10^{-12} mm. They have the disadvantage that certain gases poison filament emission and that the accessory amplifiers and power supplies are unnecessarily complicated for a simple vacuum line. Most often one is merely interested in knowing that a vacuum line has been pumped down to 10^{-3} mm of mercury and that it will maintain that vacuum when isolated from the pump.

VACUUM LINES A simple vacuum manifold with accessory equipment for the carbonation of a Grignard reagent with carbon-14 dioxide is shown in Fig. 8-5. The manifold together with the oil-diffusion-pump assembly shown in Fig. 8-3, a mechanical backing pump, and a Pirani gage, constitute a complete vacuum line. Numerous references to descriptions of vacuum lines are given by Murray and Williams[1] and by Calvin and coauthors.[11] In the apparatus shown in Fig. 8-5, manifold outlets *A*, *B*, *C*, and *D* lead respectively to the Grignard reaction vessel, carbon-14 dioxide generator, mercury manometer, and a cylinder of helium or

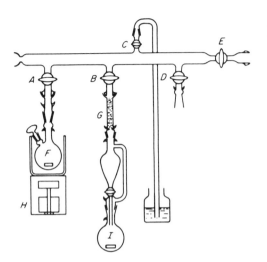

FIG. 8-5 Manifold for the carbonation of a Grignard reagent.

nitrogen. Stopcock E isolates the manifold from the pumping system during carbonation of a Grignard reagent or during other reactions or gas transfers.

In the use of this high-vacuum line for a Grignard carbonation, the procedure is as follows. Drying tube G is charged with Drierite, and H is filled with concentrated sulfuric acid. The required amount of barium carbonate-^{14}C is added to flask I. The entire system is then evacuated and filled with helium. A slight excess of Grignard reagent is then added to flask F and is frozen immediately with liquid nitrogen. The system is evacuated again and is isolated from the pump. Flask F is warmed to about $-20°$ to $-10°$, and its contents is stirred with a magnetic stirring bar. In Flask I, carbon-14 dioxide is generated by the reaction of sulfuric acid with barium carbonate-^{14}C. After absorption of the carbon-14 dioxide is complete, the Grignard addition product is cooled with liquid nitrogen to trap all the carbon-14 dioxide. The flask is warmed to room temperature to complete the reaction. The line is then filled with helium or liquid nitrogen prior to removal of flask F and subsequent decomposition of the Grignard complex. It is advisable to provide an Ascarite

trap to recover any possible excess of carbon-14 dioxide evolved during the decomposition.

Nystrom[13] finds that the yield of benzoic-^{14}C acid prepared by the procedure given by Murray and Williams[1] is only 50% and that high yields (80 to 90%) of benzoic acid can be obtained by reacting 40 to 50 mmoles of phenylmagnesium bromide in ether with 10 mmoles of carbon-14 dioxide at $0°$ for 1 hr.

Outlet D on the manifold may be used to accommodate all-glass ampoules. One type of ampoule that is simple and very useful is commonly known as a break-seal tube (Fig. 8-6). It is available commercially in the form shown (Fig. 8-6A). A number of these may be equipped with $\frac{12}{30}$ standard-taper inner joints and drawn out to facilitate sealing (Fig. 8-6B). A break–seal tube so modified can then be attached to the vacuum line to receive an aliquot of labeled compound and, while still cold, be sealed off and removed for cold storage or for immediate use in another reaction. When the break-seal tube is to be used on a vacuum line, it can be joined at its open end to the outer section of another $\frac{12}{30}$ joint (Fig. 8-6C). A short length of fresh heavy-walled rubber tubing may be substituted if the glass-to-glass distance is

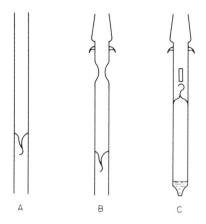

FIG. 8-6   A break-seal tube.

kept very short to minimize absorption by the rubber. Once the vacuum line is evacuated and is ready to receive the sample, it is a simple matter to break the tip with the enclosed magnet.

The most satisfactory lubricants for vacuum-line apparatus are those of the hydrocarbon type. Silicone and fluorocarbon greases are useful for work with corrosive gases such as chlorine but are more likely to striate when the stopcock is turned.

PRACTICAL LABORATORY APPARA-TUS   Descriptions follow of a number of pieces of equipment that facilitate work with both labeled and unlabeled organic compounds.

PIPETTERS   Pipetting by mouth is not a safe procedure in any laboratory and especially not in a radiochemical laboratory. Very elaborate and costly micro syringe fillers are commercially available, but the 1-cc tuberculin type syringe provided with an adapter is usually adequate for filling micro pipets. For larger pipets, the simple pipetter described by Hood[14] is most useful.

STIRRERS FOR USE IN CLOSED SYSTEMS   A number of devices are in use for agitating solutions in closed systems. Among these are sonic stirrers, enclosed-armature induc-

tion stirrers,[15] mercury-seal stirrers, high-speed wire stirrers, shakers, magnetic stirrers, and the Tru-bore stirrer. The two stirrers mentioned last are adequate for most purposes. The magnetic stirrer may be used for stirring most nonviscous liquids. As an antibumping device, the glass bar is superior to the plastic (Teflon, Kel-F, etc.) but at times produces an objectionable amount of powdered glass. The lozenge-shaped bar that is coated with Teflon or Kel-F produces less debris and should be used for preparing analytical samples. The Tru-bore stirrer consists of a uniformly ground shaft and hollow-ground $\frac{19}{38}$ standard-taper adapter. The shaft can be lubricated with a light-bodied silicone grease; if this is done, the assembly is gastight. The commercial model comes with a glass paddle, which may be advantageously discarded in favor of a Teflon blade cut in crescent shape to fit both the diameter of the neck and the contour of the flask.

CHROMATOGRAPHIC COLUMNS   Many pieces of laboratory apparatus, such as burets, filter funnels, and separatory funnels, can be made to serve as chromatographic columns. A column designed for chromatography should incorporate a sintered-glass support, a Teflon-plug stopcock, and Teflon sleeves. Several columns are described by Hagdahl.[16] For adsorption chromatography a useful column which has the advantage that it cannot run dry is shown in Fig. 8-7. The use of Teflon sleeves between the inner joint of the addition funnel (not shown) and the outer joint of the column, as well as the use of Teflon-plug stopcocks in both pieces, makes lubrication unnecessary. In the construction of any chromatographic column, it is desirable to minimize the dead space below the sintered-glass support by careful glass-blowing and by the use of capillary tubing.

DISTILLATION APPARATUS   The theoretical aspects and practice of distillation have been discussed quite extensively in other works.[17,18,19,20,21]   Purification of organic

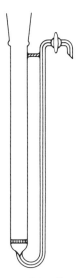

FIG. 8-7 Chromatographic column that will not run dry.

compounds by fractional distillation can be very effective for 5-ml volumes or more. For smaller volumes, losses increase, and the efficiency does not compare with that of microcrystallizations, which can be very effective for as little as 50 mg of solid. This limitation in quantity does not apply to the simple distillation or transfer of a volatile substance from one vessel to another in a vacuum line. Unfortunately, volatile contaminants distil too. For routine distillations of 5- to 1000-ml volumes of liquids boiling at temperatures up to 200°, the simple distillation assembly shown in Fig. 8-8 is convenient. It is robust and requires very little bench space. The distance between flasks need be only sufficient to accommodate a heating mantle or oil bath. The Dry-Ice-cooled condenser is fabricated from a Dewar blank. A water-cooled condenser or simple air condenser is also satisfactory. The apparatus is adequate for many vacuum distillations, especially in the stripping of a low-boiling solvent.

A fraction cutter is a valuable accessory for distillations made under reduced pressure. A number of these devices are described by Carney;[18] some are commercially available. A simple fraction cutter and take-off head is shown in Fig. 8-9. A Teflon-plug stopcock is recommended for the control of reflux ratio, since a lubricated glass stopcock can be very troublesome. A certain amount of reflux control is also made possible by offsetting the tip of the cold-finger condenser.

SUBLIMATORS For the purification of many compounds, sublimation is more satisfactory than crystallization, because the recovery of product is much more efficient and because less manipulation is involved. Even at normal pressures, sublimation can yield purified fractions of iodoform, benzoic acid, many fatty acids, many α-amino acids, salicylic acid, acetylsalicylic acid, phthalic anhydride, acetanilide, β-naphthol, cholesterol, quinones, camphor, coumarin, anthracene, naphthalene, and many other

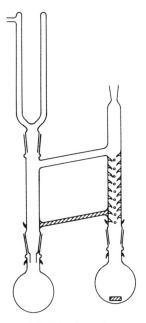

FIG. 8-8 Simple and versatile distillation apparatus.

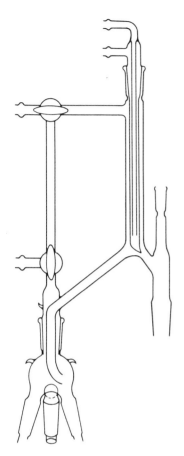

FIG. 8-9 Combined take-off head and fraction cutter.

inverted over a container in the manner of a funnel, whereupon the solid can be dislodged with a spatula and collected. The residues may be washed out with a solvent. The straight-tube version should be very useful for solids of intermediate-to-high vapor pressure. For compounds that have very low vapor pressures, such as malonic acid and some of the amino acids, it is desirable to keep the distance between the sublimand and the condensing surface as short as possible and to use a vacuum of 50 μ or better. A vacuum that is too high may cause some loss of sublimate. The crystalline form of the sublimate and the degree of adherence of the sublimate to the condenser will depend on the rate of sublimation and the temperature of the condenser. A stream of air may be substituted for water if a higher temperature is required. Lower temperatures can be achieved by use of an open vacuum-jacketed condenser, which can be filled with Dry Ice or liquid nitrogen.

The sublimation apparatus described by Ronzio[23] is suitable for subliming preparative samples. The problem of breaking the seal in this and in larger sublimators is solved by using a ball joint. This difficulty

compounds. At reduced pressures such relatively heat-sensitive compounds as malonic acid are readily sublimed. The practice of sublimation is discussed by Cheronis[22] and by Ronzio.[23] A simple water-cooled sublimator is shown in Fig. 8-10. This design permits the use of a sintered-glass filter cup or filter disk and eliminates the need to mechanically transfer small quantities following filtration. A sophisticated version[24] of the straight-tube sublimator described by Catch[25] is shown in Fig. 8-10B. Mallory built this model around $\frac{50}{30}$ spherical joints to sublime 1 to 20 g of solid. It has the advantage that it can be

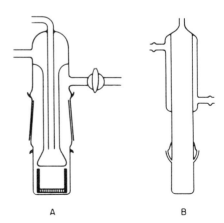

A   B

FIG. 8-10 Two types of vacuum-sublimation apparatus. (*B, by permission of J. Chem. Educ.*)

can also be overcome by using an O-ring joint. The commercially available[23a] McCarter vacuum sublimation apparatus uses such a connection and can accommodate a 100-g charge.

GAS-LIQUID CHROMATOGRAPHS Purification of less than 5 ml of an organic liquid by distillation is difficult and inefficient. Chromatography is very useful for both analyzing and purifying small quantities (see Chap. 12). High-specific-activity carbon-14 compounds are usually made in quantities of the order of 1 to 10 mmole. In such preparations, Pichat[23a] and co-workers have found gas chromatography ideally suited to the purification of carbon-14-labeled compounds and their separation from complex reaction mixtures. In chromatography the substances to be separated are distributed between two phases; one mobile, the other stationary. The mobile phase is either a liquid or a gas; the stationary phase is a solid or a liquid. If the mobile phase is a gas, the system is a gas (or vapor-phase) chromatograph; if the stationary phase is a liquid, the apparatus is a gas-liquid chromatograph. The latter uses capillary columns coated with a liquid or columns filled with an inert supporting material, such as firebrick, that has been impregnated with 5 to 40 wt % or more of the liquid phase. The use of coated capillary columns makes it possible to analyze samples in quantities of 10 to 100 pg. Large, filled preparative columns of 12.5- to 25-mm diameter are used to separate samples of liquids and of low-melting solids that weigh as much as 10 g or more. Capillary columns can be constructed that have 200,000 or more theoretical plates; short preparative columns may have only a few hundred plates. The selectivity of the liquid phase can be far more decisive in the separation of two substances than the theoretical efficiency of the column. For example, in the separation of an aliphatic compound from an aromatic compound, advantage may be taken of the fact that an aliphatic compound is held more firmly than an aromatic

compound on a paraffin liquid phase. However, if the liquid phase is an aromatic compound, the aliphatic compound will be eluted first. The selectivity of the liquid phase may be altered by additives; thus, a 10 wt % solution of stearic acid in silicone oil DC 550 is a more satisfactory liquid phase for the separation of the low-molecular-weight fatty acids than is the oil alone.

The use of a column for separations in preparative chemistry depends on the choice of a selective phase on which the substances to be separated have widely differing retention volumes. If this condition is met, samples as large as 1 g can be separated on a 12.5 mm × 2.5 m column without serious broadening of the peaks. Manual operation becomes somewhat tedious for large quantities. About 20 g of a mixture can be chromatographed in 8 hr if 20 min is required for each separation. Fraction collectors can be very simple for manual operation and may consist of a two-way Teflon-plug capillary stopcock and two 6-in. test tubes immersed in crushed ice or Dry Ice–acetone. Simple cold traps are described by Anderson.[26] An apparatus for preparative vapor-phase chromatography is discussed by Kirkland;[27] he describes the construction and operation of sample-injection systems, columns, fraction collectors, etc. If solenoid valves are used, it is certainly possible to control the automatic change of traps by determining the time lapse between the appearance of individual fractions and then setting a program timer to control each solenoid at the proper time. An automatic fraction collector for gas chromatography is described by Kronmueller.[28] It is frequently advantageous to distil the collected material to separate it from the small amount of the column liquid phase that is carried into the trap. Much practical information on gas chromatography is contained in the monograph by Bayer,[29] as well as in the many books on the subject listed in Sec. 12-2b. Reviews on gas chromatography appear every two years in *Analytical Chemistry*.

For solids, gas-liquid chromatography has its nearest counterpart in the zone-melting technique. However, the latter is only a purification process and can accommodate only a relatively pure compound; commercial equipment is limited to moderately large quantities (i.e., several grams or more). However, zone melting *can* be done on milligram quantities.

DECONTAMINATION   Various phases of health physics are considered in Chap. 7. Common sense dictates that contamination of bench tops, glassware, and counting equipment be controlled to avoid interference in measurements of radioactivity. The greatest difficulty arises when compounds of high molar radioactivity are being prepared at the same time tracer experimentation is being done with materials having 10^{-5} times less activity. To minimize cross-contamination, it is advisable to set aside one area or room for syntheses with high-level materials and for storage of glassware used for that work. Glassware is readily decontaminated in a vat that contains hot sulfuric acid and just enough nitric acid to oxidize any residual organic matter that is on the glassware. The nitric acid is replenished from time to time. Such a cleaning bath requires a special hood having a lined stack and is therefore expensive. A hood, duct, and blower-impeller of polyvinyl chloride (PVC) is impervious to fumes from a bath of sulfuric and nitric acids. For most purposes the usual chromic acid cleaning solution, contained in a 5- or 10-gal earthenware vessel, is adequate if activity levels are very low.

For detecting spills of radioactive solids or liquids, as well as leaks of radioactive gas, the most useful accessory is the portable, thin-window Geiger counter (see Sec. 11-3). For monitoring purposes, the clicking sound from the speaker is more valuable than the indication on the meter. Moreover, the meter is usually off calibration, makes the equipment bulky, and adds to its cost. Transistorized battery-operated monitors will un-

doubtedly replace the more bulky ac-operated units.

The wearing of rubber gloves and dust respirators is certainly not warranted for most work with carbon-14 compounds at the tracer level. High-level compounds should be treated with about the same degree of caution as certain of the more toxic aromatic amines or beryllium compounds. Thin, rough-surfaced, rubber household gloves should be worn for cleaning up spills, handling chromatograms, and making hazardous transfers. The less comfortable throw-away plastic gloves are also useful.

8-2c ROUTES TO CLASSES OF CARBON-14-LABELED COMPOUNDS

A number of good methods are available for preparing compounds specifically labeled in a single position. Some of the more general methods are listed in the following paragraphs according to the class of compound. A few specific methods will be described for compounds that are particularly important as intermediates in synthesis procedures.

Carboxyl-labeled acids can be conveniently prepared by carbonation of organomagnesium halides with carbon-14 dioxide or by hydrolysis of nitriles that are formed by the reactions of organic halides with an alkali-metal cyanide or cuprous cyanide. If both methods are suitable for the preparation, the carbonation procedure should be used, because carbon-14 dioxide is much less expensive than is a metal cyanide-^{14}C. A large complicated carboxylic-^{14}C acid can be prepared either by starting with the next lower homolog or by degradation and resynthesis. Thus, stearic-^{14}C acid might be prepared labeled in the carboxyl group either by starting with its next lower homolog, margaric acid, and proceeding as follows

$$C_{16}H_{33}CO_2H \rightarrow C_{16}H_{33}COCl \rightarrow C_{16}H_{33}CH_2OH \rightarrow$$
$$C_{16}H_{33}CH_2Cl \rightarrow C_{16}H_{33}CH_2MgCl \rightarrow$$
$$C_{17}H_{35}{}^{14}CO_2H$$

or by degrading unlabeled stearic acid to margaric acid by the Barbier-Wieland degradation or Hoffman rearrangement and then proceeding as above.

The malonic ester synthesis and acetoacetic ester synthesis can be used to label either the carboxyl carbon or the α-carbon atom. Mono- and disubstituted labeled malonic esters can be hydrolyzed to corresponding acids, which on being heated lose one carboxyl group to give mono- and disubstituted acetic acids. The procedure is wasteful of carbon-14 if the malonic ester is labeled in the carboxyl group, because nearly half the labeled carbon will be removed as carbon-14 dioxide. An example of "going up" the series by means of the malonic ester synthesis is the preparation of the labeled, even, normal C_{20}- to C_{30}-acids and their derivatives, the starting material being stearic acid. The sequence for each addition of two carbons is

$$C_{17}H_{35}CO_2H \rightarrow C_{17}H_{35}CH_2OH \rightarrow$$
$$C_{17}H_{35}CH_2X \rightarrow C_{18}H_{37}{}^{14}CH(CO_2C_2H_5)_2 \rightarrow$$
$$C_{18}H_{37}{}^{14}CH_2CO_2H$$

Other reactions that may prove useful for synthesizing labeled carboxylic acids are the Perkin, Reformatsky, Knoevenagel, and Michael reactions. A reaction similar to the Michael reaction is the 1,4-addition of radioactive hydrogen cyanide to α,β-unsaturated esters.

α-*Amino acids* can be prepared by use of potassium cyanide-^{14}C in the Strecker synthesis or by means of the Gabriel phthalimide synthesis, an α-bromo ester being the starting material. The azlactone synthesis can be used to synthesize α-amino acids from aldehydes by condensation of the latter with benzoyl glycine. Pichat, Herbert, and Mizon[29a,29b] have described the synthesis of carbon-14-labeled δ-aminolevulinic acid, glutamic acid, ornithine, arginine, and proline.

Labeled *acid chlorides* are most conveniently prepared by reacting the carboxylic acid with thionyl chloride. Phosphorus trichloride is less useful than thionyl chloride, because the former does not react quantitatively. Phosphorus pentachloride is often used to prepare acid chlorides for the Friedel-Crafts acylations, since the reactions can be run consecutively without isolation or purification of the acid chloride.

Labeled *acid anhydrides* can be prepared by heating the corresponding acid chloride with the sodium salt of the corresponding acid. If the highly radioactive salt is available and if tracer-level acid anhydride-^{14}C is desired, it is convenient to add the salt and a catalytic amount of phosphoric or sulfuric acid to a large excess of the anhydride and then to distil the mixture (see Sec. 4-1). An anhydride of higher molecular weight can be obtained by treating the labeled acid with acetic anhydride in the presence of a catalytic amount of sulfuric or phosphoric acid and then separating the reaction products by fractional distillation. This procedure has been used successfully to prepare benzoic anhydride-^{14}C.

Labeled *esters* are prepared most readily from acids by conversion of the acid to the acid chloride followed by the addition of an excess of the alcohol. A labeled methyl ester is conveniently prepared by the addition of diazomethane to a solution of the labeled carboxylic acid in ether; an ethyl ester is prepared by reacting the sodium salt of the acid with ethyl phosphate at temperatures near 185°.

Labeled *alcohols* are prepared easily by the reduction of carboxyl-labeled acids or their derivatives with lithium aluminum hydride. Methanol-^{14}C can be prepared in yields from 85 to 95% by the reduction of carbon-14 dioxide with lithium aluminum hydride according to the procedure of Nystrom and Brown[30] or to a modification[31] thereof. Each procedure tends to minimize impurities derived from the solvents used in the reaction. Both low-molecular-weight and intermediate-molecular-weight alcohols have been prepared by catalytic hydrogenation.[32,33] Many labeled secondary alcohols can be obtained from the reaction of Grignard reagents with aldehydes and from the reduction of the appropriate ketone with lithium aluminum hydride. Labeled tertiary alcohols are readily prepared by the reaction of a ketone with a suitable Grignard reagent.

Aldehydes of low molecular weight are prepared by rather specific syntheses. Thus, formaldehyde-^{14}C can be prepared by the catalytic oxidation of methanol-^{14}C, and acetaldehyde-1,2-^{14}C can be prepared by the acid hydrolysis of labeled acetylene. The labeled aromatic aldehydes can be prepared by the catalytic reduction of the carboxyl-labeled acid chlorides (Rosenmund reaction). Newer reagents, particularly lithium-*t*-butoxy-aluminohydride,[34] undoubtedly will be very useful in the preparation of aldehydes from acid chlorides

The broad scope of this reaction, as well as its tolerance of nitro, cyano, and carbethoxy substituents, should make it a valuable route from the carboxylic acids to the corresponding aldehydes.

Aldehydes can also be prepared from nitriles and from *N,N*-dimethylamides by the use of lithium triethoxyaluminohydride in ether solution.[35,36] In the case of *t*-amides, both aliphatic and aromatic aldehydes can be obtained in yields of 80 to 90%. For the nitrile reduction, the yields vary from 70% for aliphatic nitriles to 90% for aromatic nitriles.

Many aldehydes can be prepared by reduction of acid chlorides or esters with lithium aluminum hydride followed by oxi-

dation with specially prepared manganese dioxide.[37,38,39] If lithium aluminum deuteride or lithium aluminum tritide is used, it is possible to prepare an aldehyde that is doubly labeled. The reaction is most useful when applied to compounds of the allyl alcohol and benzyl alcohol types.

The simple aliphatic *ketones* can be prepared in labeled form by pyrolysis of the heavy-metal salts of labeled acids. Mixed aliphatic-aromatic ketones and diaryl ketones can be synthesized in a variety of ways including the Friedel-Crafts reaction, the dialkyl or diaryl cadmium reaction with acid chlorides, the Grignard reaction on nitriles and, in some instances, the pinacol rearrangement.

Aromatic hydrocarbons are available via syntheses that require only three- or four-step reactions. Thus, phenanthrene-9-^{14}C is readily prepared from the phosphorus pentoxide catalyzed Wagner rearrangement of 9-fluorene-methanol-10-^{14}C.[40] Catch and Evans[40a] describe the high-yield synthesis of several labeled polycyclic aromatic hydrocarbons, including anthracene-9-^{14}C, methyl-substituted benzanthracenes-^{14}C, and 1,2,5,6-dibenzanthracene-9-^{14}C. Carbon-14 has been introduced into benzene by the cyclizing polymerization of acetylene in the presence of a nickel carbonyl catalyst.[41] The carbon-14 atom is introduced into position 1 of the benzene ring by condensation of the Grignard reagent prepared from pentamethylene dibromide with ethyl acetate-1-^{14}C. The 1-methyl-cyclohexanol-1-^{14}C so obtained is then catalytically dehydrated and dehydrogenated. This method makes possible the preparation, in successive reactions, of toluene, benzoic acid, and benzene.

8-2d ROUTES FROM SIMPLE LABELED COMPOUNDS

It is not unusual to proceed through eight to ten stages from carbon-14 dioxide to the labeled reaction intermediate. Yields become

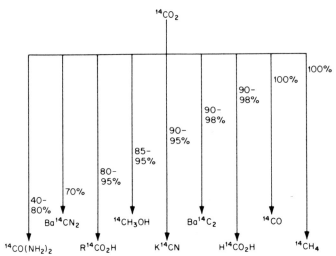

FIG. 8-11 Synthesis scheme based on carbon-14 dioxide. (*Courtesy of R. F. Nystrom.*)

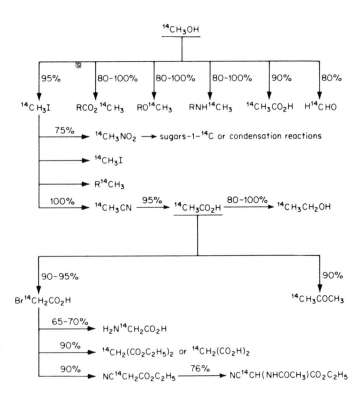

FIG. 8-12 Synthesis scheme based on methanol-^{14}C. (*Courtesy of R. F. Nystrom.*)

important in multistep syntheses, and one sequence of reactions may be better than another. Certain key intermediates may be used for the preparation of a great number of labeled compounds. Three very useful starting compounds are sodium (or potassium) cyanide-^{14}C, barium carbide-^{14}C, and methanol-[14]C. Murray and Williams[1] provide procedures for the preparation of each of these compounds from carbon-14 dioxide. Andreeva and Kostikova[41a] found that the carbon of potassium cyanide exchanges readily with the carbon-14 of barium carbonate-^{14}C at 800°. They recommend the use of this reaction for the preparation of labeled potassium cyanide. By their procedure, the potassium cyanide is extracted with liquid ammonia. The extent of dilution with carbon-12 depends on the amount of potassium cyanide used (relative

to the amount of barium carbonate-^{14}C); dilution is usually not a problem. Pichat, Mizon, and Herbert[41b] describe a procedure that is a modification of the one used by Andreeva and Kostikova for the preparation of potassium cyanide; it is probably the best procedure now available.

Several schemes based on sodium (or potassium) cyanide-^{14}C, barium carbide-^{14}C, and methanol-^{14}C are shown in Figs. 8-11 through -15.[42]

8-3 BIOCHEMICAL METHODS

Many organic chemists are not familiar with biochemical methods and are therefore reluctant to use them in preparing tracer compounds.

Yield is as important in a biochemical as in a purely chemical synthesis, but few

FIG. 8-13   Synthesis scheme based on sodium cyanide-[14]C. (*Courtesy of R. F. Nystrom.*)

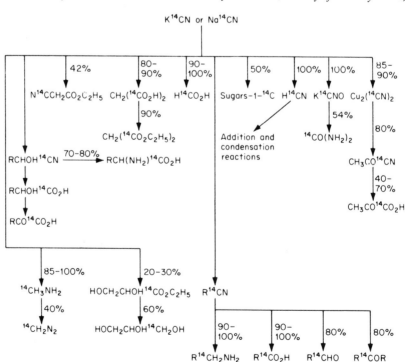

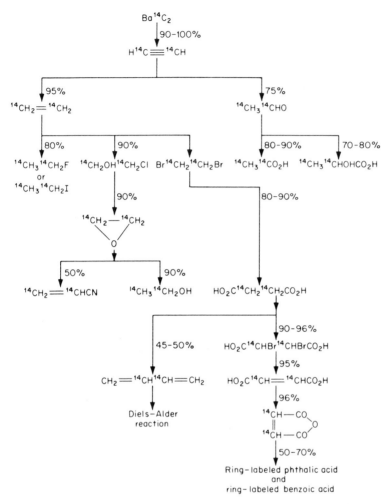

FIG. 8-14   Synthesis scheme based on barium carbide-^{14}C.   (*Courtesy of R. F. Nystrom.*)

biochemical processes provide a single product in high yield. Carbon-14 dioxide must be the starting material for the biochemical method of labeling, as it is for the chemical method. Photosynthesis is certainly the most important biochemical method for preparing labeled compounds from carbon-14 dioxide. The scale of operation may vary greatly. In one case it may involve the assimilation of carbon-14 dioxide by algae such as *Chlorella vulgaris* or by detached leaves, and in another by full-sized plants in a hermetically sealed greenhouse.[43] In some instances, trees have been grown in plastic bags that contain carbon-14 dioxide. The assimilation of carbon-14 dioxide by means other than photosynthesis, for example, by exchange with carboxyl groups, is not practical, because the usual metabolic path leads *toward* carbon dioxide rather than from it. Perhaps the most interesting applications of photosynthesis to labeling have been made with *Chlorella*,

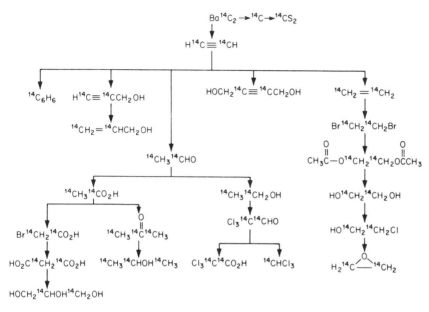

FIG. 8-15   Alternative synthesis scheme based on barium carbide-^{14}C.

which is both resistant to radiation[44] and efficient in its utilization of carbon-14 dioxide. Godward's observation that the radiation resistance of algae is inversely proportional to the size of their chromosomes (*Chlorella* chromosomes are unresolvable with the ordinary microscope) provides further guidance in the selection of suitable biochemical systems. Carbon-14 dioxide that is used to grow this alga can have a molar radioactivity as high as 4 c. After exposure of the algae, most of the carbon-14 is in the uniformly labeled lipid fraction from which many saturated and unsaturated fatty acids can be obtained. Uniformly labeled oleic, linoleic, linolenic, stearic, and palmitic acids, produced from *Chlorella*, are now commercially available. The level of radioactivity is high: 50 mc/mmole. Also commercially available are a large number of uniformly labeled L-amino acids that have molar radioactivities in the range from 70 to over 200 mc/mmole. Unfortunately for the supplier, *Chlorella* does not yield each amino acid in quantities

proportional to demand! A system based on the growth of algae has the advantage that the carbon-14 dioxide can be recovered, virtually undiluted, by burning the waste fractions.

8-4 "HOT ATOM" METHODS

The tediousness of isotopic labeling by chemical or biochemical synthesis has resulted in a search for more direct methods of labeling. Recoil labeling and radiation-induced labeling have partially satisfied the demand for a simple method of labeling a few organic compounds of medium-to-high molecular weight. For several reasons, not the least of which is cost, tritium has been used with greater success than has carbon-14.

If momentum is to be conserved, an atom produced in a nuclear transformation must have recoil energy. The chemical consequences of nuclear recoil energy were recognized and studied many years ago by Lind and Bardwell.[45] General information about nuclear recoil chemistry (including radiation-induced reactions and ion-acceleration methods) is to be found in a number of reviews.[46-51]

8-4a NUCLEAR-RECOIL LABELING

The transformation of atoms by nuclear reactions yields species that are produced in unusual energy states. Often, the increased energy is manifest in the form of electronic excitation, ionization, and high kinetic energy. The effectiveness of nuclear-recoil labeling depends on the neutron cross section of the irradiated atom, the half-life of the product nuclide, the radiation resistance of the compounds being irradiated, and other factors.

It is interesting to compare carbon-14 recoil labeling with tritium recoil labeling. In the nuclear reaction

$$^{14}N + n \rightarrow [^{15}N] \rightarrow ^{14}C + p$$

the cross section for thermal neutrons is small—only 1.75 barns.[52] The ejection of a proton from the unstable ^{15}N produces a recoiling carbon-14 atom of 40- to 45-kev energy. In the reaction $^6Li(n,\alpha)^3H$ for producing tritium, the cross section for thermal neutrons is 945 barns. The nascent tritium has a high recoil energy (i.e., 2.74 Mev) and can travel a distance of 40 μ in an organic solid.[53] Because it has such a high kinetic energy, recoiling tritium can be effective in heterogeneous systems, for example, in a mixture of lithium carbonate and an organic compound. The relatively smaller kinetic energy, greater mass, and higher charge of recoiling carbon-14 limit its range in condensed phases and make necessary the use of a homogeneous system. The half-life of carbon-14 is nearly 500 times longer than that of tritium; therefore, if no factors other than half-life are considered, the specific activity of the carbon-14 produced in the labeled molecule will be proportionately smaller. In the labeling of a complex compound such as reserpine,[54] the level of

specific activity need not always be high, and recoil labeling may be the only practical route to the labeled compound.

The great difference between the kinetic energies of recoiling tritium and recoiling carbon-14 has little direct bearing on the labeling process, since chemical reaction with either nuclide cannot occur until the nuclide is slowed to less than 100 ev. At the time of its formation, the recoiling carbon-14 is a quadruply charged negative ion having a recoil energy of about 45 kev.[48] All bonds of the parent nitrogen are broken; the negative charge is soon lost through collisions.[55] The degradation of energy is thought[46] to take place in discrete processes. The initial loss to 15,000 ev produces electronic excitation. Further loss of energy below that value occurs through scattering. The last few hundred electron volts of energy is dissipated in a relatively small volume. The volume in which the last 25 to 50 ev is lost is sometimes referred to as a "hot spot"; it is here that the recoiling carbon-14 can displace another atom in the lattice. If a carbon atom is displaced, the original lattice structure is retained; if a hydrogen atom is displaced, then a homolog or closely related molecule results. Possibly 0.1 to 10% of the recoiling carbon-14 atoms may react in either of these two ways. The displacement is neither specific nor uniformly random. It is further complicated by the fact that both reactants and products are subject to radiation fields so intense as to cause a great variety of cleavage and recombination reactions. Consequently, the application of this method to labeling with carbon-14 yields a small amount of a nonuniformly labeled product having low specific radioactivity and gross amounts of radioactive impurities.

EXPERIMENTAL PROCEDURES   Some techniques used for recoil labeling are described by Wolf.[46,47]   One of the problems in using neutron fluxes of the order of 10^{13} neutrons/cm^2/sec is the gamma heating of the organic sample. Most organic compounds are unstable at high temperatures, therefore some provision must be made for cooling the irradiation vessels. It is possible to irradiate several hundred grams of a solid or liquid in a quartz or aluminum container. The nitrogen essential to the nuclear reactions may be a constituent atom in the compound itself. If the compound contains no nitrogen, it may be converted to an amide, hydrazide, or other nitrogen-containing derivative. If this conversion is neither convenient nor possible, then a compound that contains a relatively large amount of nitrogen may be added; 2-methylpyrazine is such a compound. The duration of irradiation depends on the radiation stability of the organic compound. Aromatic compounds can be irradiated safely for a much longer time than can compounds such as amino acids.

It is instructive to examine in detail one experiment in recoil labeling, for example, the study made by Visser and co-workers[56] of the recoil labeling of toluene-^{14}C. They examined the toluene-^{14}C produced by the thermal-neutron irradiation of a solution that contained 30 mole% of 2-methylpyrazine in benzene. After the solution had been irradiated for 80 hr at 1.34×10^{13} neutrons/cm^2/sec, carrier was added. The solution was washed repeatedly with 40% sulfuric acid and then with water and was dried. The toluene in the benzene-toluene solution was freed of most of the benzene by fractional distillation and was further purified by being passed several times through a gas-liquid chromatograph. The difficulty normally encountered in purifying recoil-labeled compounds is demonstrated by the 6% difference in specific radioactivity between the first and last cuts of the toluene-^{14}C peak. The distribution of radioactivity was determined by oxidizing part of the toluene-^{14}C to benzoic-^{14}C acid. Degradation of the benzoic-^{14}C acid by means of the Schmidt reaction showed that 85.7% of the activity was in the methyl group. The distribution (relative to the methyl

group) of the remaining 14.3% of the activity in the ring was established by a degradation scheme published by Steinberg and Sixma.[57] The degradation showed the following distribution of radioactivity in the ring: carbon-1, 7.65%; carbon-2,6, 3.68%; carbon-3,5, 2.00%; carbon-4, 0.99%.

If all the activity had been found in the methyl group (synthesis product), the carbon-14 label would have been introduced by simple hydrogen replacement in the benzene molecule. Partial labeling of the ring shows that some "re-entry" of carbon-14 has taken place and that the nonrandom nature of the labeling rules out (according to Visser and co-workers[56]) a mechanism in which a symmetrical intermediate plays the only role.

One fact remains obvious in all nuclear-recoil studies, namely, that thorough purification of the products is mandatory. Muxart and Pinte[58] found that in the reaction of 5,6-benzacridine with slow neutrons

$+ n$

$+$

20 purification steps were necessary, including chromatography, recrystallization, and derivatization, to attain a reasonably constant level of radioactivity for 5,6-benzacridine-^{14}C. The same difficulty was experienced by Wolf and Anderson[59] in the purification of anthracene-^{14}C and acridine-^{14}C produced from the neutron irradiation of acridine. Wolfgang[60] irradiated mixtures of nitrogen with ethane or methane in the gas phase. Here too, the principal products formed were hydrocarbons having one carbon atom more than the number of carbon atoms in the substances that were irradiated. The interesting observation was made that the neutron irradiation of air yields carbon-14 monoxide as the chief product. Neutron-capture reactions of nitrogen in gaseous anhydrous ammonia have been studied by Yang and Wolf.[61] Methane-^{14}C is the only significant product of this reaction, whereas the neutron irradiation of methylamine in the absence of ammonia gives a complex mixture of products. Cacace and Wolf[62] showed that most of the methane is produced by radiation-induced reduction of methylamine and methyleneimine, the latter two compounds being the "primary" products. Although tritium labeling by the Wilzbach process is claimed to be improved by the addition of argon, Yang and Wolf found that neon and xenon have no moderating effect in the reaction of recoiling carbon-14 with gaseous ammonia.

Extensive tabulations of carbon-14 recoil-labeled compounds have been made by Wolf.[46,47] Wolf's tables omit the nuclear reaction that yields a labeled organic compound in curie amounts, namely, the neutron irradiation of beryllium nitride. The major product obtained from this reaction (see Sec. 1-2) is methane, but, because it is not a very useful compound of carbon-14, it is usually oxidized to carbon-14 dioxide. Even with an ideal compound, such as beryllium nitride or aluminum nitride, it is necessary to use a large amount of target material, a long irradiation time, and a high neutron flux in order to produce one curie of carbon-14. These nitrides meet the necessary requirements, namely, high nitrogen content, stability to irradiation, and low neutron absorption by the metal (beryllium in particular). Neutron irradiation of less ideal substances, such as ammonium sulfate and ammonium bromide,[63,64] produced about 1 μc of the principal product per gram of irradiated compound. This is in striking contrast to the existing industrial capabilities for producing 20 c of barium carbonate-^{14}C from a single processing of irradiated beryllium nitride. The possibilities for producing great quantities of carbon-14 from *stable* nitrogen compounds have been enhanced by the construction of new reactors having a flux as high as 10^{15} neutrons/cm^2/sec.

8-4b RADIATION-INDUCED LABELING

Labeled organic compounds can be prepared by exposing a mixture of an organic compound and a labeled substrate to a source of ionizing radiation. This method of labeling has been relatively successful with tritium, the tritium serving as its own radiation source. The technique, devised by Wilzbach,[65] of mixing multicurie amounts of tritium gas with an organic compound produces labeled compounds having specific activities of 1 mc/mg or higher. The method is simple and inexpensive and does not require protective shielding or the facilities of a nuclear reactor. Here too, there is great destruction of the organic compound; less than 0.1% of it may survive after several days of irradiation.

Carbon-14 is much more costly than tritium and at best has less than one-thousandth the specific activity of tritium. The fact that carbon-14 can be its own radiation source is apparent from the observation by Skraba, Burr, and Hess[66] that 100-mc lots of methanol-^{14}C yielded more than 5 mc of labeled ethylene glycol-^{14}C and smaller amounts of glycerol-^{14}C and erythritol-^{14}C. The yield is excellent compared with that of recoil labeling, but a synthesis that requires several years is not useful from a practical standpoint.

Carbon-14 has also been found[67] in carbon dioxide and in organic substances that have been held in contact with a carbon-14 source.

A number of studies have been made in which an internal source of radiation has been used. Aliprandi and Cacace[68] recovered ten labeled carboxylic acids resulting from the beta irradiation in a gaseous mixture of pentane, carbon-14 dioxide, and pure krypton that contained 3% krypton-85. Yields of the individual acids produced after a 48-day irradiation were determined. Altogether, the recovered acids accounted for about 0.4% of the starting activity. Cacace and co-workers[69] found that beta rays from thallium-204 in a gaseous mixture of carbon-14 dioxide and benzene gives labeled benzoic acid. The substitution of an electrical discharge for thallium-204 gives benzoic acid in amounts sufficient for it to be identified by paper chromatography.

Turton[70] has also studied a number of radiation-induced reactions by use of krypton-85 as the radiation source. The benzene–carbon-14 dioxide system yielded benzoic acid that contained 98% of its activity in the carboxyl group. Benzaldehyde produced in the same reaction was found to have only 41.3% of its total radioactivity in the carbonyl group. The total amount of radioactivity incorporated in both these compounds was less than 0.1%. The second system studied was a mixture of pyridine and carbon-14 dioxide. This system yielded labeled picolinic, nicotinic, and isonicotinic acids, all labeled exclusively in the carboxyl group. Substitution of labeled acetylene for carbon-14 dioxide produced pyridine derivatives in which side chains contained essentially all the radioactivity.

Several radiation-induced reactions have been studied in which an external radiation source was used. The radiation of a mixture of *n*-pentane and carbon-14 dioxide[71] with 35-kv x rays produced results similar to those from the irradiation with beta particles from krypton-85.[68] G-values were calculated for the ten carboxylic acids that were isolated. Cacace and Guarino[72] describe the gamma-ray-induced labeling of aliphatic hydrocarbons in a mixture of methane-^{14}C, propane, and xenon. Eight hydrocarbons were identified, and their relative radioactivities were evaluated by the use of a flow ionization chamber located directly following the thermal conductivity cell of a gas chromatograph (see Sec. 12-1b).

Radioactive biacetyl-1-^{14}C was prepared[73] by irradiating a mixture of acetone and methyl-^{14}C iodide with ultraviolet light of 2537-A wavelength. After the irradiation, carbon-14 was present in every product that contained methyl radicals; this fact indicated that the process by which acetone yields methyl and acetyl radicals is reversible.

Radiation by 40-Mev helium ions was used by Garrison and co-workers[74] to oxidize oxygenated solutions of acetic acid to glycolic and oxalic acids.

Radiation can be used to remove groups, as well as to add them. Downes,[75] using gamma radiation from a cobalt-60 source, found that $G(CO_2)$ for the decarboxylation of sodium benzoate was 0.73 ± 0.03 and suggested that sodium benzoate be used as a radiation dosimeter. He found also that both the gamma and the x-ray irradiation of aerated aqueous solutions of labeled benzoic acid yields o-, m-, and p-hydroxybenzoic acids in the ratio 9:5:4. A similar study was made of the radiation-induced oxidation of carboxyl-labeled salicylic acid.

8-4c ACCELERATED-ION LABELING

Labeling with carbon-14 may also be accomplished by impinging $(^{14}C)^+$, $(^{14}CO)^+$, and $(^{14}CO_2)^+$ ions on a thin layer of an organic compound. Such bombardment of organic targets provides a method of synthesizing labeled molecules that are almost carrier free. However, yields are so small that the addition of carrier is essential to the isolation of the product. The advantage of carrier-free synthesis is thus lost.

Guillaume[76] labeled acetamide, citric acid, succinic acid, benzoic acid, and benzoates by depositing them in a very thin layer on the cathode of a cell that contained carbon-14 dioxide at a pressure less than 1 mm of mercury. In this attenuated atmosphere, a potential of 500 volts produces a discharge current of 100 to 150 μa across the electrodes. The average discharge time was not given.

Cacace, Giacomello, and Zifferero[77] placed the organic material to be irradiated in a thin layer on the collector plate of an isotope separator. Bombardment of the organic layer with the carbon-14 ions caused replacement of carbon-12 atoms by carbon-14 atoms in 0.1 to 2% of the impacts. Fragmentation and polymerization of the organic target also occurred.

Aliprandi and Cacace[78] have bombarded cholesterol with 30-kv carbon-14 ions in a mass spectrograph. They identified the labeled products cholesterol, trans-dehydroandrosterone, and a number of less complex molecules. Lemmon and co-workers[79] continuously distilled benzene onto the chilled target of a mass spectrometer during irradiation with a 2-kv $(^{14}C)^+$ beam (10^{-10} to 10^{-9} amp). A small amount of toluene-^{14}C was isolated along with the benzene-^{14}C. Such syntheses are extremely inefficient in terms of radiochemical yield—a 10^{-6}-amp beam will produce only 1 μc of benzene-^{14}C in 10 hr.

Other studies similar to those cited above have been made by Aliprandi and co-workers,[80,81] by Croatto and Giacomello,[82] by Terrence,[83] and by Palm and Calvin.[84] Palm and Calvin used 5-Mev electrons from a linear accelerator to irradiate mixtures of presumed primordial gases. One such mixture contained methane-^{14}C, ammonia, hydrogen, and water. The object of the experiment was the study of primordial organic chemistry; the use of labeled methane made possible a more sensitive determination of the fate of carbon. Urea was isolated as the major component, and gaseous products were examined in a cursory manner with a mass spectrometer. Many other components remain to be identified.

It appears that investigations of "hot atom" chemistry have raised more questions than they have answered. Future investigations in this area will probably be devoted more to the understanding of the mechanisms of high-energy reactions and less to their use in synthesis as such.

CITED REFERENCES

[1] A. Murray, III, and D. L. Williams, "Organic Syntheses with Isotopes," part I, Interscience Publishers, New York, 1958. (Unfortunately, the index follows Part II of the two-volume set.)

[2] J. C. Nevenzel, R. F. Riley, D. R. Howton, and G. Steinberg, "Bibliography of Syntheses with Carbon Isotopes," United States Atomic Energy Commission Report UCLA-316 (1954).

[3] J. C. Nevenzel, R. F. Riley, D. R. Howton, and G. Steinberg, "Bibliography of Syntheses with Carbon Isotopes," United States Atomic Energy Commission Report UCLA-395 (1957).

[4] J. R. Catch, "Carbon-14 Compounds," Butterworth Inc., Washington, D.C., 1961.

[5] A. Murray, III, and D. L. Williams, "Organic Syntheses with Isotopes," part I, Interscience Publishers, New York, 1958, p. 3.

[6] J. R. Catch, "Carbon-14 Compounds," Butterworth Inc., Washington, D.C., 1961, pp. 60–63.

[7] A. M. Brodskii, R. A. Kalinenko, and K. P. Lavrovskii, Proc. Acad. Sci., USSR, Phys. Chem. Sect. (Eng. Transl.), **124**, 43 (1959).

[8] A. M. Brodskii, R. A. Kalinenko, and K. P. Lavrovskii, Proc. Acad. Sci., USSR, Phys. Chem. Sect. (Eng. Transl.), **126**, 517 (1959).

[8a] R. Ostwald, P. T. Adams, and B. M. Tolbert, *J. Am. Chem. Soc.*, **74**, 2425 (1952).

[8b] W. G. Dauben and P. H. Payot, *J. Am. Chem. Soc.*, **78**, 5657 (1956).

[9] D. R. Ward, "Design of Laboratories for Safe Use of Radioisotopes," United States Atomic Energy Commission Report AECU-2226 (Nov., 1952), pp. 18–19.

[9a] Walrus Manufacturing Company, Decatur, Illinois.

[10] R. T. Sanderson, "Vacuum Manipulation of Volatile Compounds," John Wiley & Sons, Inc., New York, 1949.

[11] M. Calvin, C. Heidelberger, J. C. Reid, B. M. Tolbert, and P. F. Yankwich, "Isotopic Carbon," pp. 127–231, John Wiley & Sons, Inc., New York, 1949.

[12] G. Urry and W. H. Urry, *Rev. Sci. Instr.*, **27**, 819 (1956).

[13] A. Murray, III, and D. L. Williams, "Organic Syntheses with Isotopes," part I, pp. 86 ff, Interscience Publishers, New York, 1958.

[13a] R. F. Nystrom, personal communication to the authors, November, 1966.

[14] S. L. Hood, *Anal. Chem.*, **24**, 2020 (1952).

[15] M. Calvin, C. Heidelberger, J. C. Reid, B. M. Tolbert, and P. F. Yankwich, "Isotopic Carbon," pp. 336–338, John Wiley & Sons, Inc., New York, 1949.

[16] L. Hagdahl in E. Heftmann, "Chromatography," pp. 56–85, Reinhold Publishing Corp., New York, 1961.

[17] A. Weissberger, Ed., "Technique of Organic Chemistry," vol. IV, Interscience Publishers, New York, 1950.

[18] T. P. Carney, "Laboratory Fractional Distillation," The Macmillan Company, New York, 1949.

[19] N. D. Cheronis in A. Weissberger, "Technique of Organic Chemistry," vol. VI, pp. 57–107, Interscience Publishers, New York, 1954.

[20] C. S. Robinson and E. R. Gilliland, "Elements of Fractional Distillation," 4th ed., McGraw-Hill Book Company, Inc., New York, 1950.

[20a] L. Pichat, C. Baret, J.-P. Guermont, and M. Audinot, in "Radioisotopes in the Physical Sciences and Industry," p. 145, vol. III, International Atomic Energy Agency, Vienna, 1962.

[21] R. T. Sanderson, "Vacuum Manipulation of Volatile Compounds," John Wiley & Sons, Inc., New York, 1948.

[22] N. D. Cheronis in A. Weissberger, "Technique of Organic Chemistry," vol. VI, pp. 84–96, Interscience Publishers, New York, 1954.

[23] A. R. Ronzio in A. Weissberger, "Technique of Organic Chemistry," vol. VI, pp. 380–384, Interscience Publishers, New York, 1954.

[23a] Nester/Faust Manufacturing Corporation, Box 565, Newark, Delaware.

[24] F. B. Mallory, *J. Chem. Educ.*, **39**, 261 (1962).

[25] J. R. Catch, "Carbon-14 Compounds," p. 39, Butterworth, Inc., Washington, D.C., 1961.

[26] B. C. Anderson in H. J. Noebels, R. F. Wall, and N. Brenner, Eds., "Gas Chromatography," p. 331, Academic Press Inc., New York, 1961.

[27] J. J. Kirkland in V. J. Coates, H. J. Noebels, and I. S. Fagerson, Eds., "Gas Chromatography," pp. 203–222, Academic Press Inc., New York, 1958.

[28] G. Kronmueller in H. J. Noebels, R. F. Wall, and N. Brenner, Eds., "Gas Chromatography," pp. 199–206, Academic Press Inc., New York, 1961.

[29] E. Bayer, "Gas Chromatography," English ed., Elsevier Publishing Co., New York, 1961.

[29a] L. Pichat and M. Herbert, *Bull. Soc. Chim. France*, 673 (1957).

[29b] L. Pichat, J. Mizon, and M. Herbert, *Bull. Soc. Chim. France*, 1787, 1792 (1963).

[30] R. F. Nystrom and W. G. Brown, *J. Am. Chem. Soc.*, **69**, 2548 (1947).

[31] J. D. Cox and R. J. Warne, *J. Chem. Soc.*, 3167 (1950).

[32] P. T. Adams, R. E. Selff, and B. M. Tolbert, *J. Am. Chem. Soc.*, **74**, 2416 (1952).

[33] H. Hauptmann, P. T. Adams, and B. M. Tolbert, *J. Am. Chem. Soc.*, **74**, 2423 (1952).

[34] H. C. Brown and B. C. Subba Rao, *J. Am. Chem. Soc.*, **80**, 5377 (1958).

[35] H. C. Brown, *J. Chem. Educ.*, **38**, 173 (1961).

[36] H. C. Brown, C. J. Shoaf, and C. P. Garg, *Tetrahedron Letters*, no. 3, 9 (1959).

[37] J. Attenburrow, A. F. B. Cameron, J. H. Chapman, R. M. Evans, B. A. Hems, A. B. A. Jansen, and T. Walker, *J. Chem. Soc.*, 1094 (1952).

[38] R. M. Evans, *Quart. Rev. (London)*, **13**, 61 (1959).

[39] C. D. Robeson, *Org. Chem. Bull.*, **32**, no. 1 (1960).

[40] C. J. Collins, *J. Am. Chem. Soc.*, **70**, 2418 (1948).

[40a] J. R. Catch and E. A. Evans, *J. Chem. Soc.*, 2787, 2790, 2796 (1957).

[41] H. Pichat, *Proc. Intern. Conf. Peaceful Uses At. Energy, 2nd*, Geneva, 1958, **20**, 82 (1958).

[41a] O. I. Andreeva and G. I. Kostikova in "Radioisotopes in the Physical Sciences and Industry," p. 111, vol. III, International Atomic Energy Agency, Vienna, 1962.

[1b] L. Pichat, J. Mizon, and M. Herbert, *Bull. Soc. Chim. France*, 1787 (1963).

[42] Figs. 8-13 through -16 are taken wholly or in part from the lecture notes of Prof. Robert F. Nystrom, Radiocarbon Laboratory, University of Illinois. They are used here with his kind permission.

[43] S. Aronoff, "Techniques of Radiobiochemistry," pp. 66–67, The Iowa State College Press, Ames, Iowa, 1956; anonymous, *Nucleonics*, **14**, 103 (1956).

[44] M. B. E. Godward, *Nature*, **185**, 706 (1960).

[45] S. C. Lind and D. C. Bardwell, *J. Am. Chem. Soc.*, **46**, 2003 (1924).

[46] A. P. Wolf in E. Segré, G. Friedlander, and W. E. Meyerhoff, Eds., "Annual Review of Nuclear Science," vol. 10, pp. 259–290, Annual Reviews, Inc., Palo Alto, Calif., 1960.

[47] A. P. Wolf, *Angew. Chem.*, **71**, 237 (1959).

[48] P. E. Yankwich, *Can. J. Chem.*, **34**, 301 (1956).

[49] J. E. Willard in J. G. Beckerley, M. D. Kamen, D. F. Mastick, and L. I. Schiff, Eds., "Annual Review of Nuclear Science," vol. 3, pp. 193–220, Annual Reviews, Inc., Palo Alto, Calif., 1953.

[50] J. E. Willard in D. W. Scott, "Annual Review of Physical Chemistry," vol. 6, pp. 141–170, Annual Reviews, Inc., Palo Alto, Calif., 1955.

[51] K. Svoboda, J. Cifka, and K. Panek, *Jaderna Energie*, **6**, 326 (1960).

[52] D. J. Hughes and R. B. Schwartz, "Neutron Cross Sections," United States Atomic Energy Commission Report BNL-325, 2d ed. (1958).

[53] F. S. Rowland, *Proc. Intern. Conf. Peaceful Uses At. Energy, 2nd*, Geneva, 1958, **20**, 87 (1958).

[54] V. Santoro and G. Minozyi, *Ric. Sci. Suppl.*, **29**, 2243 (1959).

[55] C. F. MacKay and W. F. Libby, *J. Am. Chem. Soc.*, **79**, 6366 (1957).

[56] R. Visser, C. R. Redvanly, F. L. J. Sixma, and A. P. Wolf, *Rec. Trav. Chim.*, **80**, 533 (1961).

[57] H. Steinberg and F. L. J. Sixma, *Rec. Trav. Chim.*, **79**, 679 (1960).

[58] R. Muxart and G. Pinte, *Bull. Soc. Chim. France*, 1675 (1956).

[59] A. P. Wolf and R. C. Anderson, *J. Am. Chem. Soc.*, **77**, 1608 (1955).

[60] R. Wolfgang, *Proc. Intern. Conf. Peaceful Uses At. Energy, 2nd*, Geneva, 1958, **29**, 326 (1958).

[61] Y. V. Yang and A. P. Wolf, *J. Am. Chem. Soc.*, **82**, 3315 (1960).

[62] F. Cacace and A. P. Wolf, *J. Am. Chem. Soc.*, **87**, 5301 (1965).

[63] P. E. Yankwich and J. D. Vaughan, *J. Am. Chem. Soc.*, **76**, 5851 (1954).

[64] P. E. Yankwich and W. R. Cornman, *J. Am. Chem. Soc.*, **77**, 2096 (1955).

[65] K. E. Wilzbach, *J. Am. Chem. Soc.*, **79**, 1013 (1957).

[66] W. J. Skraba, J. G. Burr, and D. N. Hess, *J. Chem. Phys.*, **21**, 1296 (1953).

[67] *Chem. Abstr.*, **53**, 21209i (1959); G. Mayr, *Ric. Sci. Suppl.*, **29**, 542 (1959).

[68] B. Aliprandi and F. Cacace, *Gazz. Chim. Ital.*, **89**, 2268 (1959).

[69] *Chem. Abstr.*, **54**, 17316g (1960); F. Cacace, G. Ciranni, G. Giacomello, and M. Zifferero, *Ric. Sci. Suppl.*, **28**, 2131 (1958).

[70] C. N. Turton, *Proc. Intern. Conf. Peaceful Uses At. Energy, 2nd*, Geneva, 1958, **20**, 91 (1958).

[71] F. Cacace, A. Guarino, and E. Possagno, *Gazz. Chim. Ital.*, **89**, 1837 (1959).

[72] F. Cacace and A. Guarino, *Nature*, **186**, 632 (1960).

[73] S. N. Naldrett, *Can. J. Chem.*, **33**, 750 (1956).

[74] W. M. Garrison, H. R. Haymond, W. Bennett, and S. Cole, *J. Chem. Phys.*, **25**, 1282 (1956).

[75] A. M. Downes, *Australian J. Chem.*, **11**, 154 (1958).

[76] M. Guillaume, *Nature*, **182**, 1592 (1958).

[77] F. Cacace, G. Giacomello, and M. Zifferero, *Energia Nucl.* (Milan), **5**, 287 (1958).

[78] B. Aliprandi and F. Cacace, *Ann. Chim.* (Rome), **46**, 1204 (1956).

[79] R. M. Lemmon, F. Mazzetti, F. L. Reynolds, and M. Calvin, *J. Am. Chem. Soc.*, **78**, 6414 (1956).

[80] B. Aliprandi, F. Cacace, L. Cieri, G. Giranni, R. Masironi, and M. Zifferero in R. C. Extermann, Ed., "Radioisotopes in Scientific Research," p. 146, vol. II, Pergamon Press, New York, 1958.

[81] B. Aliprandi, F. Cacace, and G. Giacomello, *Ric. Sci. Suppl.*, **26**, 3029 (1956).

[82] *Chem. Abstr.*, **55**, 14113d (1961); U. Croatto and G. Giacomello, *Atti. Soc. Ital. Progr. Sci.*, **1**(45), 208 (1956).

[83] R. T. Terrence, "The Chemical Interaction of Accelerated Carbon-14 Ions with Benzene," United States Atomic Energy Commission Report UCRL-9603 (1961); Ph.D. Thesis, University of California.

[84] C. Palm and M. Calvin, *J. Am. Chem. Soc.*, **84**, 2115 (1962).

GENERAL REFERENCES

(*a*)   A. Murray, III, and D. L. Williams, "Organic Syntheses with Isotopes," part I, Interscience Publishers, New York, 1958.

(*b*)   M. Calvin, C. Heidelberger, J. C. Reid, B. M. Tolbert, and P. F. Yankwich, "Isotopic Carbon," John Wiley & Sons, Inc., New York, 1949.

(*c*)   J. R. Catch, "Carbon-14 Compounds," Butterworth Inc., Washington, D.C., 1961.

(*d*)   M. D. Kamen, "Isotopic Tracers in Biology," 3d ed., Academic Press, Inc., New York, 1957.

(*e*)   L. Pichat, "Synthèses Chimiques de Molécules Marquées par les Isotopes," *Chim. Mod.*, **7**, no. 50, 1962.

(*f*)   H. R. Schutte, "Radioaktive Isotope in der Organischen Chemie und Biochemie," Weinheim, Verlag Chemie 1966; esp. Tabelle 2, pp. 270-594, 'Synthesen[14] C-markierter organischer Verbindungen' from literature to March, 1966.

CHAPTER
9
DERIVATIZATION OF CARBON-14-LABELED COMPOUNDS

9-1 INTRODUCTION

Derivatization, that is, the preparation of derivatives for the purpose of identifying organic compounds, is basic to organic chemistry and therefore requires no special introduction. A derivatization is nothing more than a small-scale synthesis. Derivatives are used to good advantage in carbon-14 isotope tracer chemistry for the particular purpose of facilitating the purification and radioassay of isotopically labeled compounds. Many isotopically labeled compounds, especially those that are liquids or gases at room temperature and pressure, are difficult to obtain in pure form convenient for radioassay. Usually, such compounds are converted to suitable solid derivatives that can be purified to constant molar radioactivity and that can serve as good weighing forms.

Numerous derivatization procedures that have been worked out in detail on micro, semimicro, and macro scales are described in the texts listed at the end of this chapter and in the extensive literature on the synthesis of organic compounds. If the available literature is used together with a general knowledge of procedures for organic syntheses, derivatives that meet a particular requirement can almost always be prepared.

9-2 AGREEMENT AMONG THE MOLAR RADIOACTIVITIES OF DERIVATIVES AND THEIR PRECURSOR

Perhaps the fact is obvious that the molar radioactivity of a pure isotopically labeled compound is equal to the molar radioactivity of any pure derivative prepared from that compound provided (a) the derivative and the precursor have the same number of isotopically labeled positions, (b) no isotope dilution occurs as, for example, through addition of carrier or through an isotope-exchange reaction (see Chap. 4), and (c) no isotope fractionation (see Chap. 5) occurs during derivatization. The agreement of the molar radioactivities among derivatives and their precursor is a necessary consequence of the fact that each mole of each of the derivatives and of the precursor contains the same total number of radioactive atoms. If the derivative and its precursor have different numbers of labeled positions, their molar radioactivities will be in the ratio of small whole numbers. If, for example, methanol-^{14}C is used to prepare dimethyl-^{14}C phthalate, the molar radioactivity of the ester will necessarily be twice that of the methanol-^{14}C from which it was prepared.

If carrier is intentionally or inadvertently allowed to enter the reaction vessel during the derivatization, the relationship of the molar radioactivity of the compound to that of the derivative will be altered. Exchange reactions may have the same deleterious effect as the addition of carrier.

9-3 DESIDERATA FOR DERIVATIVES

The physical and chemical properties of a derivative suitable for use in radiochemical work are much the same as those of a derivative prepared for any other purpose. A good derivative, most often a crystalline solid, should be easily, and preferably quantitatively, formed from the precursor. The isolation of the derivative from chemical and radiochemical contaminants should not be too difficult. The chemical composition and molecular weight of the derivative must be known. The preparation of a solid derivative that has a molecular weight much greater than that of the precursor often facilitates the handling of a small quantity of a radioactive material. A good derivative is usually a good weighing form that can be exposed to the atmosphere without change in composition. Since the usual purpose of derivatization during a radiochemical study is to aid in the radiochemical assay of the precursor, a derivative that can be conveniently radioassayed is required. For example, it would be shortsighted to prepare a derivative that contained nitro groups if nitro groups were known to interfere with the method of chemical or radiochemical assay to be used. For certain reasons, a derivative may be unsuitable; it may not be soluble in the scintillator counting medium, it may have polar groups that cause quenching, or it may be colored (e.g., 2,4-dinitrophenylhydrazones) and therefore be unsuited for scintillation counting.

9-4 DERIVATIVES AS AIDS TO PURIFICATION AND AS CRITERIA OF PURITY

A useful derivative has some physical and chemical properties that are different from those of its precursor. Consequently, a derivative can often be obtained free of chemical and radiochemical impurities even though purification of the precursor may be difficult or even impossible.

A common test of the chemical and radiochemical purity of a carbon-14-labeled compound consists in the radioassay of that compound after each of several successive purifications. When the specific radioactivity remains constant, the labeled compound is assumed to be free of both labeled and unlabeled contaminants. This test is, for obvious reasons, most reliable when the successive purifications are performed by different methods or by modifications of the same method. For example, the purification of a crystalline labeled compound by successive recrystallizations from two or more different solvents is likely to be much more effective than repeated recrystallizations from the same solvent.

The formation of a derivative is a logical extension of the test for purity by purification to constant specific radioactivity. If a compound and one or more of its derivatives, the properties of all of which differ from each other, are found to have the same molar radioactivity, it is reasonably certain that the compound and its derivatives are pure and that the measured molar radioactivity is correct. This fact has been applied in establishing the accuracy of a method of radio-assaying carbon-14 compounds.[1]

9-5 ISOTOPE FRACTIONATION DURING DERIVATIZATION

Isotope fractionation of carbon-14 may accompany many low-yield derivative-forming reactions. The consequent difference between the molar radioactivity of the derivative and that of its precursor can result in some error in a tracer experiment. This error is usually so small that it can be neglected in ordinary tracer studies (see Chap. 5).

Theoretically, most carbon-14 isotope effects that occur during derivatization could be eliminated completely by making the derivative-forming reaction quantitative (see Chap. 5). However, this ideal is rarely attained in laboratory practice. A much more practical method of avoiding isotope fractionation during derivatization is to choose a derivative that can be prepared by use of a reaction which does not involve the isotopically labeled center (see Chap. 5). For example, if acetophenone-α-^{14}C is derivatized by formation of the semicarbazone, some carbon-14 fractionation may occur because of the difficulty of effecting quantitative conversion to the derivative. The consequent carbon-14 isotope effect caused by derivatization at the carbon-14-labeled position could result in a derivative having a molar radioactivity of, perhaps, 1 or 2% less than that of the acetophenone-α-^{14}C, which the derivative is intended to represent. However, choice of a derivative prepared by attack on the aromatic ring at a position remote from the carbon-14 rather than on the carbon-14-labeled carbonyl group itself would eliminate even the 1 to 2% error caused by the carbon-14 isotope effect. Thus, m-nitroacetophenone, formed by nitration of the aromatic nucleus,

$$C_6H_5{}^{14}COCH_3 \xrightarrow{HNO_3} m\text{-}O_2NC_6H_4{}^{14}COCH_3$$

would be a more suitable derivative of acetophenone-α-^{14}C for use in a tracer study that required the highest order of accuracy.

9-6 DERIVATIZATION OF CARBON-14 DIOXIDE

Carbon-14 dioxide is the one carbon-14-labeled compound that is handled and radioassayed more frequently than any other. Combined in the form of barium carbonate-^{14}C, it is a primary source of the carbon-14 radioactivity used in the preparation of carbon-14-labeled organic compounds. Carbon-14 dioxide is also the product of many chemical and biochemical processes and is, of course, an ultimate oxidation product of all carbon-14-labeled organic substances. The methods of separation, purification, and derivatization of carbon-14 dioxide and of radioassay of its derivatives are therefore of first importance to those interested in carbon-14 techniques. Carbon-14 dioxide can be purified by absorption in aqueous alkaline solutions and can thereby be completely separated from relatively inert gases, such as nitrogen, oxygen, and carbon monoxide. The alkali-metal carbonate and bicarbonate that form on dissolution of the carbon-14 dioxide can be considered to be derivatives. The total radioactivity per unit volume of solution can be measured by radioassaying a test portion of the solution. For example, the portion can be decomposed with acid in an apparatus arranged so that the released carbon-14 dioxide can be swept with commercial-grade carbon dioxide into an ionization chamber and then counted.

Barium carbonate-^{14}C is frequently used as a solid derivative of carbon-14 dioxide. The carbon-14 dioxide is bubbled through two or three successive traps that contain saturated solutions of barium hydroxide from which the carbon-14 is quantitatively precipitated as barium carbonate-^{14}C. An inert sweep gas, such as nitrogen, can be used conveniently to exclude atmospheric carbon dioxide. The precipitated barium carbonate-^{14}C is collected on a sintered-glass disk under an inert, carbon dioxide free atmosphere. The precipitate is washed thoroughly with freshly boiled distilled water to remove excess barium hydroxide, is then washed quickly with acetone, and is dried for several hours at 125°. Test portions of the barium carbonate-^{14}C can be counted as the infinitely thick solid, or weighed aliquots of the barium carbonate-^{14}C can be decomposed with acid to carbon-14 dioxide, which is counted as a gas. For some purposes, it is convenient to handle barium carbonate-^{14}C in solution. This is possible by the use of the sequestering agent, Versene.[2] Calcium carbonate-^{14}C has also been used in place of barium carbonate-^{14}C as a solid derivative[3] of carbon-14 dioxide.

For many types of tracer studies, the alkaline-earth salts of carbon-14 dioxide are suitable as derivatives. However, they must be handled judiciously if they are used in isotope-fractionation studies or in any other type of tracer study that requires very accurate radioassays. In the case of barium carbonate-^{14}C, exchange with atmospheric carbon dioxide must be prevented.[4] Likewise, excess barium hydroxide must be removed completely from barium carbonate-^{14}C that is subsequently exposed to air; in this way, the possibility of isotopic dilution by barium carbonate formed from atmospheric carbon dioxide is eliminated. Even when all the usual precautions are taken in handling the barium carbonate-^{14}C, very precise and accurate radioassays of the material may be difficult to attain. Barium carbonate-^{14}C therefore appears to be something less than a perfect derivative of carbon-14 dioxide. A stable and easily prepared solid derivative that could be recrystallized to constant specific radioactivity would be preferred. Even though carboxylic acids can be prepared as derivatives

by treatment of carbon-14 dioxide with Grignard reagents, this technique has rarely been used, because it requires anhydrous conditions.

Another derivative, the Hyamine salt of carbon-14 dioxide, has been assayed by liquid scintillation counting; it is soluble in toluene.[5]

9-7 TABULATION OF TYPICAL DERIVATIVES OF CARBON-14-LABELED COMPOUNDS

Examples of some of the derivatives that have been prepared successfully from about sixty carbon-14-labeled compounds are listed in Table 9-1. The labeled compounds derivatized are arranged according to their functional groups; the subheadings of Table 9-1 designate the functional groups. In most instances the method of radioassaying the carbon-14-labeled derivative is indicated in the third column of the table, since the selection of a suitable derivative may depend on the method of radioassay to be used. References to the literature are given in all cases. If the articles cited do not describe the derivatization procedure in detail, a well-known procedure was used. Such well-known procedures are published in one or more of the texts listed among the general references at the end of this chapter.

For brevity, symbols are used in the third column of Table 9-1 to indicate the methods of assaying the derivatives. Thus, SC indicates solid counting (normally as $Ba^{14}CO_3$); LSC indicates liquid-scintillation counting, WC refers to wet combustion, DC means dry combustion, and ICC indicates ionization-chamber counting of a gas, which is normally carbon-14 dioxide.

Some derivatives are also degradation products. Therefore, in some instances, the information given in Chap. 10 may be useful in the location of suitable derivatives.

Table 9-1   Typical derivatives of carbon-14-labeled compounds

Labeled compound derivatized	Derivative	Method of assaying derivative	References
Carbon dioxide molecule			
Carbon dioxide	Barium carbonate	SC	4, 5, 6, 7
	Barium carbonate	ICC	8
	Calcium carbonate	SC	2
	Toluene-soluble salt of Hyamine	LSC	3
	Barium carbonate dissolved in Versene	—	1
Carboxyl			
Formic acid	S-Benzylthiuronium formate	WC, ICC	11
Acetic acid	p-Nitrobenzyl acetate	WC, ICC	9
	S-1-Naphthylmethyl-thiuronium acetate	WC, ICC	13
Propionic acid	Sodium propionate	SC	14
Amino acids (also proteins)	Hyamine complex	LSC	12
Bromoacetic acid	Benzylamine salt	WC, ICC	10
Trichloroacetic acid	S-Benzylthiuronium trichloroacetate	WC, ICC	15
Malonic acid	3-(2-Furanyl)-propenoic acid	WC, ICC	10
Carboalkoxy			
n-Butyl acetate	N-Benzylbutyramide	WC, ICC	16
Hydroxyl			
Methanol	N-Methyl-(α-naphthyl)-carbamate	DC, ICC	17
	Methyl-3,5-dinitro-benzoate	WC, ICC	9
Ethyl alcohol	Ethyl-3,5-dinitrobenzoate	DC, SC	19
2-Butanol	sec-Butyl-p-toluene-sulfonate	DC, SC	18
Benzyl alcohol	Phenylacetic acid	DC, SC	21
β-Phenylethyl alcohol	β-Phenylpropionic acid	DC, SC	21
Glycerol	Glycerol tribenzoate	SC	20
Cyclohexanol	Cyclohexanone	WC, ICC	22
Halide			
Methyl iodide	Phenyltrimethyl-ammonium iodide; tetramethylammonium iodide	—	24
Chloroform	Trichloroacrylic acid	WC, ICC	15

Table 9-1 (*Continued*)

Labeled compound derivatized	Derivative	Method of assaying derivative	References
Halide (**continued**)			
Benzyl chloride	Phenylacetic acid	DC, SC	21
β-Phenylethyl chloride	β-Phenylpropionic acid	DC, SC	21
Bromobenzene	1,2-Diphenylethylene	WC, ICC	23
Carbonyl (**aldehyde**)			
Formaldehyde	Dimedone	DC, ICC	25
Acetaldehyde	p-Nitrophenylhydrazone	DC, SC	29
Glucose	Osazone	—	28
Benzaldehyde	2,4-Dinitrophenyl-hydrazone	WC, ICC	26
p-Hydroxybenzaldehyde	m-Nitrobenzohydrazone	(Derivative used for purification)	27
Glyceric acid	Ethyl glycerate	SC	20
Glyoxal	Bis-phenylhydrazone	SC	52
Carbonyl (**ketone**)			
Acetone	2,4-Dinitrophenyl-hydrazone	WC, ICC	30
		SC	31
	Semicarbazone	WC, ICC	13
Acetophenone	2,4-Dinitrophenyl-hydrazone	DC, ICC	32
	Semicarbazone	DC, ICC	35
m-Chloro-, p-chloro-, p-methoxy-, p-methyl-, and m-nitroacetophenones	2,4-Dinitrophenyl-hydrazones	WC, ICC	36
Benzophenone	2,4-Dinitrophenyl-hydrazone	WC, ICC	23
Pyruvic acid	1,5-Diphenyl-2,3-pyrrolidinedione	SC	34
Acetoacetic ester	Copper enolate	SC	33
Cyclohexanone	Semicarbazone	WC	22
	2,4-Dinitrophenyl-hydrazone	ICC	22
Quinone			
2-Methyl-1,4-naphthoquinone	Diacetate	WC, ICC	37
Activated methylene group			
Nitromethane	Glucose and mannose	SC	38, 39

Table 9-1 (*Continued*)

Labeled compound derivatized	Derivative	Method of assaying derivative	References
Amino			
Methylamine	Methylphenylthiourea	WC, ICC	13
Ethylenediamine	Dibenzenesulfonamide	WC	40
	Dibenzamide	ICC	40
Glycine	Benzoyl derivative	Not counted directly	42
Aniline	p-Dimethylamino-azobenzene	—	43
2,2-Diphenyl-2-p-tolylethylamine	2,2-Diphenyl-2-p-tolylethylamine hydrochloride	WC, ICC	41
Cyclopropylethylamine	Benzamide	DC, proportional counting of $^{14}CO_2$	53
Cyano			
Hydrogen cyanide	Alanine	—	44
Acetonitrile	p-Chloroacetophenone	WC, ICC	9
Olefinic or acetylenic bonds			
Styrene	Styrene dibromide	WC, ICC	35
Methyl cinnamate	Methyl dibromo-cinnamate	WC, ICC	35
β-Nitrostyrene	1,2-Dimethyl-4-nitro-5-phenylcyclohexene	WC, ICC	35
Phenylpropiolic acid	Phenyldibromo-propionic acid	—	46
Butadiene	Meerwein reaction with diazotized p-nitroaniline	WC, ICC	45
Aromatic ring			
Benzene	Nickel cyanide clathrate	DC, ICC	47
	o-Benzoylbenzoic acid	DC, ICC, SC	47
	m-Dinitrobenzene	—	54
Anthracene	Anthraquinone	DC, ICC, SC	48
Mesitylene	Hexahydromesitylene	?	49
Side chains on aromatic rings			
Toluene	Benzoic acid	?	50
Ethylbenzene	p-Nitrobenzoic acid	WC, ICC	51
Diethylbenzene (m and p)	Phthalic acids	WC, ICC	51

References for Table 9-1

[1] E. I. Wyatt, "Carbon-14, Beta Ionization Chamber Method," Method No. 9 0733172 (3-19-53), *Oak Ridge National Laboratory Master Analytical Manual*, TID-7015, sec. 9.

[2] F. W. Morthland and W. G. Brown, *J. Am. Chem. Soc.*, 78, 469 (1956).

[3] J. M. Passman, N. S. Radin, and J. A. D. Cooper, *Anal. Chem.*, 28, 484 (1956).

[4] W. G. Dauben, J. C. Reid, and P. E. Yankwich, *Anal. Chem.*, 19, 828 (1947).

[5] A. Fry, *J. Am. Chem. Soc.*, 75, 2686 (1953).

[6] R. B. Duff and A. H. Knight, *Chem. Ind. (London)*, 1469 (1955).

[7] A. K. Das Gupta and C. K. N. Nair, *J. Sci. Ind. Res. (India)*, 15B, 1 (1956); *Chem. Abstr.*, 50, 14385i (1956).

[8] O. K. Neville, *J. Am. Chem. Soc.*, 70, 3499 (1948).

[9] D. N. Hess, *J. Am. Chem. Soc.*, 73, 4038 (1951).

[10] G. A. Ropp, *J. Am. Chem. Soc.*, 72, 4459 (1950).

[11] J. G. Burr, W. G. Brown, and H. E. Heller, *J. Am. Chem. Soc.*, 72, 2560 (1950).

[12] M. Vaughan, D. Steinberg, and J. Logan, *Science*, 126, 446 (1957).

[13] G. A. Ropp, W. A. Bonner, M. T. Clark, and V. F. Raaen, *J. Am. Chem. Soc.*, 76, 1710 (1954).

[14] G. R. Burns, *J. Am. Chem. Soc.*, 77, 6615 (1955).

[15] C. H. Shuford, Jr., D. L. West, and H. W. Davis, *J. Am. Chem. Soc.*, 76, 5803 (1956).

[16] G. A. Ropp, *J. Am. Chem. Soc.*, 72, 2299 (1950).

[17] R. F. Nystrom, W. H. Yanko, and W. G. Brown, *J. Am. Chem. Soc.*, 70, 441 (1948).

[18] J. D. Roberts, W. Bennett, R. E. McMahon, and E. W. Holroyd, Jr., *J. Am. Chem. Soc.*, 74, 4283 (1952).

[19] J. D. Roberts and J. A. Yancey, *J. Am. Chem. Soc.*, 74, 5943 (1952).

[20] A. P. Doerschuk, *J. Am. Chem. Soc.*, 73, 821 (1951).

[21] W. G. Dauben and P. Coad, *J. Am. Chem. Soc.*, 71, 2928 (1949).

[22] J. D. Roberts, D. A. Semenow, H. E. Simmons, Jr., and L. A. Carlsmith, *J. Am. Chem. Soc.*, 78, 601 (1956).

[23] C. J. Collins and W. A. Bonner, *J. Am. Chem. Soc.*, 77, 92 (1955).

[24] L. M. Nazarova, M. G. Shirmazan, and Y. K. Syrkin, *Dokl. Akad. Nauk SSSR*, 90, 1045 (1953); *Chem. Abstr.*, 48, 7539f (1954).

[25] A. R. Jones and W. J. Skraba, *J. Am. Chem. Soc.*, 74, 2437 (1952).

[26] W. A. Bonner and C. J. Collins, *J. Am. Chem. Soc.*, 75, 4516 (1953).

[27] K. Kratzl and G. Billek, *Monatsh. Chem.*, 85, 845 (1954).

[28] C. E. Becker and H. G. Day, *J. Biol. Chem.*, 201, 795 (1953).

[29] K. Schmid, P. Fahrni, and H. Schmid, *Helv. Chim. Acta*, 39, 708 (1956).

[30] A. Roe and E. L. Albenesius, *J. Am. Chem. Soc.*, 74, 2402 (1952).

[31] D. E. Koshland and F. H. Westheimer, *J. Am. Chem. Soc.*, 72, 3383 (1950).

[32] V. F. Raaen, A. K. Tsiomis, and C. J. Collins, *J. Am. Chem. Soc.*, 82, 5502 (1960).

[33] G. L. Curran, *J. Biol. Chem.*, 191, 775 (1951).

[34] W. R. Vaughan and D. I. McCane, *J. Org. Chem.*, 20, 143 (1955).

[35] G. A. Ropp, V. F. Raaen, and A. J. Weinberger, *J. Am. Chem. Soc.*, 75, 3694 (1953).

[36] G. A. Ropp and V. F. Raaen, *J. Chem. Phys.*, 22, 1223 (1954).

[37] C. J. Collins, *J. Am. Chem. Soc.*, 73, 1038 (1951).

[38] J. C. Sowden, *Science*, 109, 229 (1949).

[39] J. C. Sowden, *J. Biol. Chem.*, 180, 55 (1949).

[40] E. F. Phares and M. V. Long, *J. Am. Chem. Soc.*, 77, 2556 (1955).

[41] B. M. Benjamin and C. J. Collins, *J. Am. Chem. Soc.*, 78, 4952 (1956).

[42] A. I. Krasna, P. Peyser, and D. B. Sprinson, *J. Biol. Chem.*, 198, 421 (1952).

[43] O. Hromatka and L. H. Schlager, *Monatsh. Chem.*, 85, 29 (1954).

[44] J. A. Bos, *Experientia*, 7, 258 (1951).

[45] G. A. Ropp and V. F. Raaen, *J. Am. Chem. Soc.*, 76, 4484 (1954).

[46] D. Y. Curtin, E. W. Flynn, and R. F. Nystrom, *J. Am. Chem. Soc.*, **80**, 4599 (1958).
[47] A. P. Wolf, C. S. Redvanly, and R. C. Anderson, *Nature*, **176**, 831 (1955).
[48] A. P. Wolf and R. C. Anderson, *J. Am. Chem. Soc.*, **77**, 1608 (1955).
[49] A. V. Grosse and S. Weinhouse, *Science*, **104**, 402 (1946).
[50] V. I. Savushkina, S. V. Syavtsillo, and A. P. Terent'ev, *Dokl. Akad. Nauk SSSR*, **102**, 1139 (1955); *Chem. Abstr.*, **50**, 4804i (1956).
[51] R. M. Roberts, G. A. Ropp, and O. K. Neville, *J. Am. Chem. Soc.*, **77**, 1764 (1955).
[52] F. Shafizadeh, M. L. Wolfram, and P. McWain, *J. Am. Chem. Soc.*, **81**, 1229 (1959).
[53] G. E. Cartier and S. C. Bume, *J. Am. Chem. Soc.*, **85**, 932 (1963).
[54] C. D. Hurd, R. V. Levetan, and A. R. Macon, *J. Am. Chem. Soc.*, **84**, 4515 (1962).

CITED REFERENCES

[1] C. J. Collins and G. A. Ropp, *J. Am. Chem. Soc.*, **77**, 4160 (1955).
[2] E. I. Wyatt, "Carbon-14, Beta Ionization Chamber Method," Method No. 9 0733172 (3-19-53), *Oak Ridge National Laboratory Master Analytical Manual*, TID-7015, sec. 9.
[3] F. W. Morthland and W. G. Brown, *J. Am. Chem. Soc.*, **78**, 469 (1956).
[4] P. E. Yankwich, *Science*, **107**, 2791 (1948).
[5] J. M. Passman, N. S. Radin, and J. A. D. Cooper, *Anal. Chem.*, **28**, 484 (1956).

GENERAL REFERENCES

(*a*) R. L. Shriner, R. C. Fuson, and D. Y. Curtin, "The Systematic Identification of Organic Compounds," 4th ed., John Wiley & Sons, Inc., New York, 1956.
(*b*) "Tables for Identification of Organic Compounds," Chemical Rubber Publishing Co., Cleveland, Ohio, 1960.
(*c*) N. D. Cheronis and J. B. Entrikin, "Semimicro Qualitative Organic Analysis," 2d ed., Interscience Publishers, Inc., New York, 1957.
(*d*) Houben-Weyl, "Methoden der Organischen Chemie," vol. II, Analytische Methoden, 4th ed., George Thieme, Stuttgart, 1953.
(*e*) S. Veibel, "The Identification of Organic Compounds," 4th ed., G. E. C. Gad, Copenhagen, 1954.
(*f*) F. Wild, "Characterization of Organic Compounds," 2d ed., Cambridge University Press, Cambridge, England, 1958.
(*g*) F. Schneider, "Qualitative Organic Microanalysis," John Wiley & Sons, Inc., New York, 1946.
(*h*) M. Calvin, C. Heidelberger, J. C. Reid, B. M. Tolbert, and P. F. Yankwich, "Isotopic Carbon," John Wiley & Sons, Inc., New York, 1949.
(*i*) A. Murray and D. L. Williams, "Organic Syntheses with Isotopes," Part I, Interscience Publishers, Inc., New York, 1958.
(*j*) J. R. Catch, "Carbon-14 Compounds," Butterworth Inc., Washington, D.C., 1961.
(*k*) N. D. Cheronis, 'Micro and Semimicro Methods,' in A. Weissberger, "Technique of Organic Chemistry," vol. VI, pp. 479–571, Interscience Publishers, Inc., New York, 1954.
(*l*) N. D. Cheronis and J. B. Entrikin, "Identification of Organic Compounds," Interscience Publishers, Inc., New York, 1963.
(*m*) N. D. Cheronis and T. S. Ma, "Organic Functional Group Analysis," Interscience Publishers, a Division of John Wiley & Sons, Inc., 1964.
(*n*) H. Koch and W. Haaf, *Ann. Chem.*, **618**, 251 (1958); describes a method potentially useful for derivatizing labeled branched olefins and alcohols by conversion to carboxylic acids.

PROBLEMS

9-1. A sample of pure glucose that had a specific radioactivity of 0.10 μc/mg was converted to the phenylosazone. Part of the purified derivative was burned in oxygen; the carbon-14 dioxide produced was precipitated as $Ba^{14}CO_3$, which was washed thoroughly and dried. Calculate the radioactivity of the $Ba^{14}CO_3$ in counts/min/mg.

9-2. A mixture of equal weights of acetone-2-^{14}C that had a molar radioactivity of 2.70 mc and of methylethyl-2-^{14}C ketone that contained an unknown amount of carbon-14 activity was precipitated quantitatively as a mixture of 2,4-dinitrophenylhydrazones-^{14}C. After the derivative mixture was washed and dried, 20 mg of it was assayed by wet combustion and was found to contain 0.210 μc of radioactivity. Calculate the molar radioactivity of the methylethyl-2-^{14}C ketone.

9-3. In an attempt to make a close estimate of the molar radioactivity of a sample of chloroacetic-2-^{14}C acid, the following data were obtained: (a) molar radioactivity determined by dry combustion of a weighed sample of the acid, 1.21 mc; (b) molar radioactivity of carbon-14 dioxide produced by van Slyke oxidation, 0.52 mc; (c) molar radioactivity of the p-phenylphenacyl ester, 1.24 mc; and (d) molar radioactivity of malonic-2-^{14}C acid produced via reaction with potassium cyanide and hydrolysis, 1.25 mc. How should the best value of the molar radioactivity be calculated and why?

9-4. A 0.2-g precipitate of $Ba^{14}CO_3$ was found to have a molar radioactivity 10% lower than expected. Assuming the error was caused by dilution due to absorption of atmospheric carbon dioxide in unremoved barium hydroxide, calculate the minimum volume of air that would have had to contact the precipitate to cause the error. Assume that air contains 0.05% carbon dioxide by volume.

9-5. In Problem 9-4, how much air could have caused the 10% error if the major cause was exchange of $Ba^{14}CO_3$ with atmospheric carbon dioxide? Assume that a simple single-pass exchange occurred.

CHAPTER
10
DEGRADATION

Degradation, as applied in connection with uses of carbon-14 and carbon-13 in organic chemistry, is the process by which a labeled molecule is broken down to permit determination of the relative carbon isotope concentration in different positions within the molecule. Since the number of proven degradation procedures is limited, the search for new and improved procedures is a continual one. The feasibility of proposed tracer experiments with carbon isotopes often is decided by the availability of suitable degradation methods. Although problems related to synthesis of labeled compounds, assay methods, etc., can usually be overcome or bypassed, the problem of developing a satisfactory degradation scheme can be exceedingly difficult. This chapter is a brief introduction to the literature of methods of degrading organic compounds labeled with isotopic carbon. A complete critical review of such methods would fill many chapters, particularly if all the chemical reactions potentially useful for degrading labeled molecules were discussed.

Like an ideal derivatization, an ideal degradation gives a quantitative yield of products. Unfortunately, few ideal degradations are known. In practice, 50% yield of a degradation product is usually acceptable; many times, a yield much smaller than 50% is the maximum attained.

In semimicro or macro tracer studies of chemical systems employing pure chemicals, it is highly desirable to isolate a pure degradation product. In such cases, the degradation preferably should give a product having the properties previously indicated (Chap. 9) as being essential to a good derivative. If such a product cannot be obtained, the degradation product should at least be convertible to a good derivative. Benzoic acid, for example, is a good degradation product, because it can be freed from neutral impurities by extraction with base. Being only slightly soluble in water, it can be recovered easily from the aqueous extract by acidification. Benzoic acid can also be purified by recrystallization and by sublimation. In contrast with benzoic acid, acetic acid as a degradation product ordinarily would require derivatization; its solubility in water increases the difficulty of isolating it.

In some microscale biochemical tracer studies, the small scale and the complexity of the chemistry involved make impossible the isolation of pure degradation products or their derivatives. The results obtained from such studies should never be reported without a clear statement of the possible errors that may have resulted from radioassaying relatively crude degradation products. Unfortunately, such a statement of possible errors has sometimes been omitted. Indeed, some authors are apparently unaware of this source of error.

The recently developed technique of combined gas chromatography and simultaneous ionization-chamber radioassay of the effluent (Sec. 12-1b) is a boon to the separation and radioassay of small amounts of degradation products. The handling of volatile liquids as degradation products is greatly facilitated by this technique.

10-2 SOURCES OF ERROR IN DEGRADATIONS

An acceptable degradation *must* yield a product whose molar radioactivity (or isotope concentration if carbon-13 is the tracer nuclide) represents accurately that of the atom or group whose molar radioactivity is sought. This requirement may not be satisfied if the degradation is accompanied by an *isotope dilution, isotope exchange,* or *isotope fractionation.*

10-2a ERRORS DUE TO ISOTOPE DILUTION

There are cases in which benzoic-7-^{14}C acid fails as a degradation product, because it is diluted by unlabeled benzoic acid from a second source, formed, for example, from a side reaction that accompanies the degradation. Similarly, carbon-14 dioxide as a degradation product may sometimes be diluted by carbon dioxide produced unknowingly either by oxidation of an unlabeled part of the molecule degraded or by oxidation of unremoved solvent or of other unlabeled contaminant. Dauben and Coad[1] found that the decarboxylation of phenylacetic-1-^{14}C acid over copper chromite yields carbon dioxide produced by oxidation of toluene, the unlabeled product of the decarboxylation. Using phenylacetic acid labeled in the methylene group, they demonstrated that decarboxylation over copper chromite at 230° produces carbon dioxide that contains 0.6% of the carbon-14 originally present in the methylene-carbon position. Even earlier,[2] it was shown that the pyrolysis of the barium salt of methyl-labeled acetic acid produces barium carbonate which contains some of the carbon-14 from the methyl group. From this work, it follows that pyrolysis of barium acetate-1-^{14}C can yield barium carbonate-^{14}C that has been diluted by carbon atoms from the methyl group.

Other cases of this kind include the Hofmann degradation of acetamide-2-^{14}C,[3] which leads to some oxidation of the methyl group to carbon dioxide. Intentional isotope dilution of labeled compounds just prior to their degradation deserves special mention. Occasionally, this technique has been used to provide a large quantity of material for degradation when only a few milligrams of the impure material to be degraded was obtainable. At first, it may appear to be an ideal way to provide the necessary bulk of material, and indeed it may be in some instances. However, this advantage cannot be gained entirely without risk. The risk is that very small amounts of undiluted impurities may contaminate one or more of the degradation products; a resulting error in a measured specific radioactivity might be far out of proportion to the weight percent of impurity retained in the degradation product radioassayed. This type of error is discussed in Sec. 8-2a. The probability that dilution might introduce an error in any particular case depends on the difficulty of removing contaminants from the degradation product and on the care taken to ensure the radiochemical purity of all samples radioassayed.[6] Before an isotope dilution is made intentionally just prior to a degradation, all possible indirect consequences of the dilution should be considered.

A problem similar to that associated with intentional isotope dilution arises in the degradation of molecules into two very similar chemical species that have vastly different molar radioactivities. The oxidation of a substituted benzoin is an example

If the carbon-14 is distributed about equally between the benzoic-α-^{14}C acid and the toluic-α-^{14}C acid and if the oxidation is complete, then the separation and the subsequent application of the usual criteria for purity will suffice. On the other hand, if the molar radioactivities of the benzoic-α-^{14}C acid and p-toluic-α-^{14}C acid produced are in the ratio $1:50$, the presence of only 2% of p-toluic-α-^{14}C acid in the benzoic-α-^{14}C acid fraction could cause an error of almost 100% in the determination of the latter. If all attempts to achieve radiochemical purity of the benzoic-α-^{14}C acid fail, the only solution to this problem may be to add holdback carrier (see Sec. 8-2a). The addition of nonradioactive p-toluic acid (about 10% of the sample weight) followed by recrystallization and/or sublimation will then remove most of the contaminant radioactivity. This procedure should be repeated until the radioassay

remains constant. In practice, one or two such cycles are usually adequate.

Crystallization—or other purification—of degradation products to constant specific radioactivity is usually an effective way to avoid errors due to the presence of high-specific-activity impurities. However, such purification must not be considered to be infallible (see Sec. 9-4).

10-2b ERRORS DUE TO ISOTOPE EXCHANGE

There may be many possible causes of "misplacement" of carbon-14 atoms during degradations. An unpredicted exchange reaction or molecular rearrangement induced by the conditions used for the degradation might occur during the degradation and thus alter the distribution of carbon-14 within the labeled molecule. Studies[4] of mixtures of certain salts of organic acids labeled in the carboxyl group have indicated that exchange reactions involving the carbon atoms of the carboxyl group can occur at elevated temperatures.

$$CH_3CH_2{}^{14}CO_2Na + CH_3CO_2Na \underset{}{\overset{300-400°}{\rightleftharpoons}}$$
$$CH_3CH_2CO_2Na + CH_3{}^{14}CO_2Na$$

It is apparent that degradations by pyrolytic processes should be examined carefully before they are applied as degradative methods.

Another interesting example of an unexpected "exchange" reaction at an elevated temperature is the interaction between sodium formate and sodium carbonate-^{14}C observed by Grant and Turner[5]

$$NaO_2CH + Na_2{}^{14}CO_3 \xrightarrow[250°]{H_2O}$$
$$NaO_2{}^{14}CH + Na_2{}^{14}CO_3$$

Since the reverse process was not observed, this interaction apparently is not a true isotope-exchange reaction.

It is possible that in isotopic studies involving very high specific activities of carbon-14, radiation from or recoil effects of the carbon-14 nucleus might induce chemical changes that could cause the appearance of carbon-14 in unexpected degradation products and thus lead to erroneous conclusions (see Sec. 6-2).

10-2c ERRORS DUE TO ISOTOPE EFFECTS

A carbon-14 isotope effect may occur during a degradation if a bond or bonds to the labeled position in the molecule degraded are critically involved in the degradation reaction (see Chap. 5). Although such a carbon-14 isotope effect may influence the measured molar radioactivity of a degradation product, the influence is ignored regularly in carbon-14 tracer studies, because it is usually small and other considerations are more pressing. However, this error due to isotope fractionation is not necessarily negligible in experiments that demand high accuracy. For a one-step reaction involving the labeled center, a 7% isotope effect at 50% yield could lower the specific radioactivity of the degradation product to 93.5% of that of the compound degraded. A sequence of three 50%-yield reactions, each critically involving the labeled center, could have a net effect of lowering the specific radioactivity of the ultimate degradation product by about 18%. Such estimates apply if the 50% yields are the result of incomplete conversion during the degradation reactions and are not due simply to mechanical loss of product during handling. If side reactions that accompany a degradation cause the low yield, the situation becomes complex, and the consequences of isotope fractionation cannot be estimated unless a thorough study of the system is made (see Chap. 5).

10-3 DEGRADATION METHODS

Some organic reactions are used repeatedly to degrade compounds labeled with isotopic carbon. In this section the application of a number of these reactions is discussed, sometimes in detail. A systematic arrangement according to reaction type is used as far as possible.

The reliability of the degradation methods outlined here varies widely. Much depends on the skill of the experimentalist and his attention to details. The information given here should be used primarily as an aid to locating in the original literature those procedures suited to a particular need. It is strongly recommended that even previously validated degradative procedures be tested anew with specifically labeled compounds by each investigator. This testing will help the novice to gain confidence in his own technique and may reveal unsuspected deviations from normality in degradative methods that previously have been taken for granted. Above all, any untested degradative procedure should be validated by application to specifically labeled compounds before it is used.

In organic chemical tracer studies made with isotopic carbon, the difficult degradations are those in which carbon-to-carbon bonds must be cleaved to isolate particular carbon atoms or groups in the form of compounds that can be radioassayed. It is difficult to cleave carbon-to-carbon bonds selectively and efficiently. With few exceptions, the degradations discussed in the following paragraphs involve carbon-to-carbon bond cleavage. To simplify the discussion, the position of carbon-14 in the molecules degraded usually is not indicated.

I SEPARATION OF THE CARBON OF CARBOXYL GROUPS

A. DECARBOXYLATION Many carboxylic acids lose carbon dioxide when heated, others only when heated in the presence of an amine such as quinoline. The decarboxylation reaction is frequently useful for isolating, as carbon dioxide, the carbon of the carboxyl group of an acid of the aromatic series

$$ArCO_2H \xrightarrow[\Delta]{\text{quinoline}} ArH + CO_2\uparrow$$

In this equation Ar represents an aromatic group. In such a simple decarboxylation, the carbon atom attached to the carboxyl group acquires a hydrogen atom.

Certain nonaromatic acids, namely, β-keto acids and acids with highly electronegative *alpha* substituents, undergo rapid decarboxylation at low temperatures. Labeled acetoacetic acid[7] and labeled trichloroacetic acid[8] have been degraded by decarboxylation to acetone and chloroform, respectively. The decarboxylation of labeled malonic acids is discussed in Sec. 5-6a. Numerous modifications of the simple decarboxylation reaction have been used to degrade compounds labeled with isotopic carbon. Frequently, oxidizing agents such as potassium permanganate, chromic acid, and hydrogen peroxide achieve both release of the carboxyl-group carbon as carbon dioxide and partial oxidation of the group originally attached to the carboxyl group. Some examples of such degradation reactions are described elsewhere.[9] Among the decarboxylations with broadest applicability is the use of ninhydrin[9] to decarboxylate α-amino acids. The amino group is reduced to ammonia, and the other group originally attached to the *alpha* carbon atom is separated as an aldehyde. A number of studies of other types of decarboxylation of labeled acids are described more recently. For example, Grovenstein and Ropp[10] studied bromodecarboxylation, Smith and Fahey[11] studied base-catalyzed acylative decarboxylation, and Seltzer, Hamilton, and Westheimer[12] studied an enzymatic decarboxylation. These reactions are potentially useful as means of degrading labeled organic acids.

As mentioned earlier in this chapter, pyrolytic decarboxylation of carboxylic acid salts has been used to degrade the labeled organic acids, but the results are not always reliable.[9] The Hunsdiecker reaction of silver salts, as well as modifications of this reaction, are sometimes useful. Barton and Porter[13] used it as the second step in the degradation of a labeled ketone

$$\underset{\underset{CH_3}{|}}{\overset{\overset{CH_3}{|}}{CH_3-C}}---\underset{\underset{CH_3}{|}}{\overset{\overset{CH_3}{|}}{C}}-CO-CH_3$$

$$\downarrow HNO_3$$

$$\underset{\underset{CH_3}{|}}{\overset{\overset{CH_3}{|}}{CH_3-C}}---\underset{\underset{CH_3}{|}}{\overset{\overset{CH_3}{|}}{C}}-CO_2H$$

$$\downarrow \begin{array}{l} Br_2 \text{ or } I_2 \\ \text{with silver salt} \end{array}$$

$$\underset{\underset{CH_2}{|}}{\overset{\overset{CH_3}{|}}{CH_3-C}}---\underset{\underset{CH_3}{|}}{\overset{\overset{CH_3}{|}}{C}}-X + CO_2$$

Mitchell[14] used the Hunsdiecker reaction to decarboxylate carbon-14-labeled potassium benzoate.

B. DECARBONYLATION The decarbonylation of certain acids in concentrated sulfuric acid results in the separation of the carboxyl-group carbon as carbon monoxide. Decarbonylation was used as the initial step in the degradation of labeled citric acid.[15] A study of the decarbonylation of several other labeled acids in concentrated sulfuric acid was reported more recently.[16]

Decarbonylation of esters and triketones is included at this point for convenience, even though they contain no carboxyl group. *Alpha*-keto esters such as ethylpyruvate[17] undergo thermal decarbonylation. The carboethoxy-group carbon atom is released as carbon monoxide. The original α-carbon atom becomes the "carbo" atom of the carboalkoxy group in the new ester formed. Thus, ethyl pyruvate yields carbon monoxide and ethyl acetate.

Triketones undergo decarbonylation catalyzed by aluminum chloride, cupric acetate, or sodium hydroxide. Tracer studies[18] have shown that for diphenyl triketone and its p-methoxy derivative, only the center carbonyl group is lost as carbon monoxide.

C. STEPWISE DEGRADATION OF CARBOXYLIC ACIDS BY THE SCHMIDT REACTION

The Schmidt reaction[19] was used by Phares[20] and others to degrade aliphatic carboxylic acids.

$$RCH_2CO_2H + HN_3 \xrightarrow{H_2SO_4} RCH_2NH_2 + CO_2\uparrow$$

The carbon dioxide evolved comes from the carboxyl group. The amine is then oxidized to the next lower acid in the series.

$$RCH_2NH_2 \xrightarrow[NaOH]{KMnO_4} RCO_2H$$

These reactions can be repeated to achieve stepwise degradation of a straight-chain, saturated carboxylic acid. The method was applied to the degradation of specifically labeled acetic,[20] propionic,[20] and butyric[21] acids; a procedure that gives the degradation products in yields of 65% or more is described in detail.[20] Since little cross-contamination by carbon-14 between individual carbon positions was observed, the method is reliable—at least for the acids studied. Degradation of succinic acid to carbon dioxide and ethylenediamine by the Schmidt reaction is performed best by converting the acid to succinic anhydride.[22] Maleic and fumaric acids can be degraded by way of reduction to succinic acid and conversion of the succinic acid to the anhydride. Wolf, Redvanly, and Anderson[23] used thallous acetate in degrading acetic acid by the Schmidt reaction. Rabinowitz and Pritzker[23a] discuss the limitations of the Schmidt degradation method. They find that noncarboxylic, oxidizable, carbon-14-labeled groups in compounds to be degraded by the Schmidt method may contribute, in many cases, to the carbon-14 dioxide that is recovered. They recommend that a blank be run to obtain a correction factor if accurate results are desired.

D. USE OF THE CURTIUS REARRANGEMENT

The Curtius rearrangement[9] has been used like the Schmidt reaction for degrading organic acids.

E. DARZENS-MENTZER STEPWISE DEGRADATION OF CARBOXYLIC ACIDS

The elegant method of Darzens and Mentzer[24] provides for the stepwise degradation of linear, aliphatic carboxylic acids; it includes a second-order Beckmann rearrangement of an α-diketone monoxime. The method was reinvestigated by Dauben, Hoerger, and Petersen,[25] who applied it to carbon-14-labeled fatty acids. It has the advantage that the individually degraded carbon atoms are recovered in the form of carboxyl-labeled benzoic acid, which is easily purified and assayed. The overall yield from the acid to its next-lower homolog is about 50 to 75%, and no extraneous carbon dioxide can be introduced inadvertently. The steps of the reaction are exemplified by the scheme

$$RCH_2CO_2H \xrightarrow{SOCl_2} RCH_2COCl \xrightarrow[AlCl_3]{C_6H_6}$$

$$\underset{RCCOC_6H_5}{\overset{NOH}{\|}} \xleftarrow[RONO]{H^+} RCH_2COC_6H_5$$

$$\xrightarrow[OH^-]{p\text{-}CH_3C_6H_4SO_2Cl} RCN + C_6H_5CO_2H$$

The nitrile may be hydrolyzed by heating under reflux for 24 hr in an alcoholic solution of potassium hydroxide; the process is then repeated to isolate the α-carbon of the original acid. The procedure requires neither special apparatus nor strong oxidizing agents. Dauben, Hoerger, and Petersen[25] provide a detailed procedure specifically for the degradation of palmitic acid and list the results of the degradations of carbon-14-labeled pentadecanoic, myristic, tridecanoic, stearic, and margaric acids.

A semimicro procedure based on the Darzens-Mentzer degradation is used to degrade unsaturated fats.[26] The fats are converted to the free unsaturated acids; the acids are then separated by crystallization and are hydrogenated to prevent their oxidation and isomerization. In this way the carboxyl carbon of the oleic, linoleic, or linolenic acid is removed and is isolated as the carboxyl carbon of benzoic acid.

F. ROSEMAN DEGRADATION OF CARBOXYLIC ACIDS

Roseman[27] developed an efficient method of degrading carboxylic acids and proved that it is reliable when applied to specifically labeled acetic and lactic acid in the manner shown below. Thus, of the carbon atoms of the acid degraded, the 2-substituted benzimidazole (I or V) contains all the carbon atoms; the 2-benzimidazolecarboxylic acid (III) contains the carbon atom of the carboxyl group and the *alpha* carbon atom; the benzimidazole (IV) contains the carbon atom of the carboxyl group; and the carbon dioxide contains the *alpha* carbon atom. The 2-substituted benzimidazole (V) from lactic acid can also be degraded by the iodoform reaction to iodoform, which contains the *beta* carbon atom of the lactic acid. The Roseman method has the advantage that it can be used to degrade micro quantities of carboxylic acids.

For acetic acid the equations are

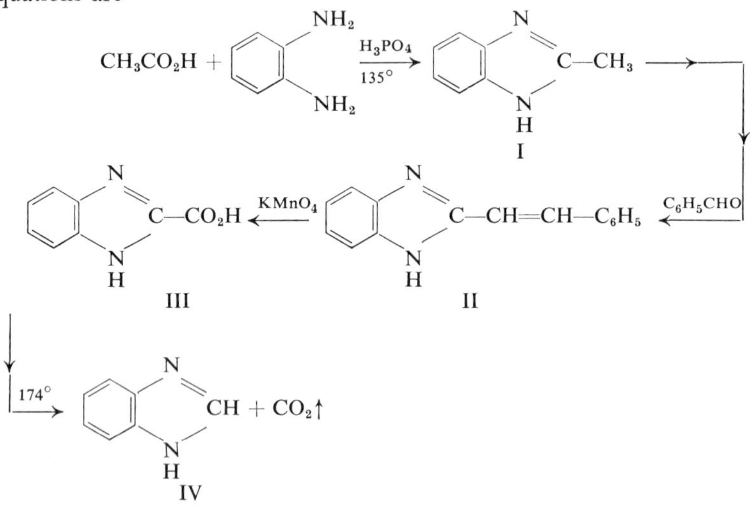

With lactic acid the reactions are similar:

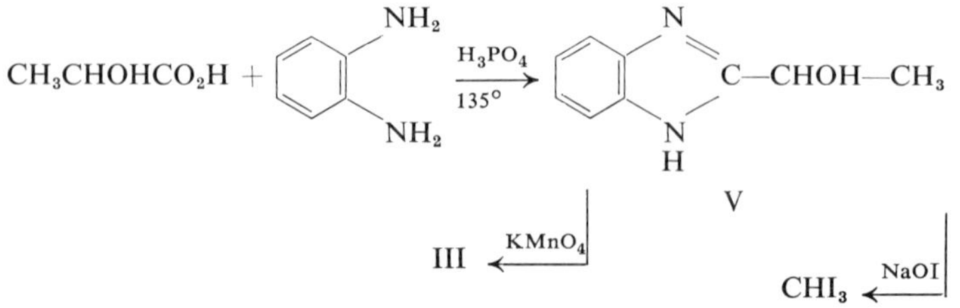

Another reaction that can be used for degradative purposes is the ketonic decarboxylation of aliphatic acids. The thermal decarboxylation of the iron(II) salts of an aliphatic acid and of benzoic acid affords a good yield of an alkyl phenyl ketone. Raaen and Beach[27a] found that all the carbon dioxide eliminated in the decarboxylation reaction comes from the carboxyl group of the aliphatic acid. Thus, iron(II) laurate and iron(II) benzoate decarboxylate smoothly at 300°. The molar radioactivity of the carbon

$$(C_6H_5{}^{14}CO_2)_2Fe + (C_{11}H_{23}CO_2)_2Fe \rightarrow$$
$$2\,C_{11}H_{23}{}^{14}COC_6H_5 + 2\,FeO + 2\,CO_2\uparrow$$

dioxide was negligible; cross contamination was less than 0.5%. Granito and Schultz[27b] studied the applicability of this reaction to a large number of unlabeled aliphatic and aromatic acids.

II CLEAVAGE OF MULTIPLE CARBON-TO-CARBON BONDS

A double or triple bond in a carbon chain frequently is a convenient site for a degradative attack. Such a bond is usually highly susceptible to attack by oxidizing agents; oxidation can lead to immediate or ultimate cleavage of the chain. Some typical cleavages of labeled compounds at multiple bonds are described in the following sections.

A. OXIDATION BY CHROMIC ACID

Cleavage of olefinic bonds by oxidation with chromic acid is illustrated by the procedure of Raaen and Collins,[28] who used it to degrade labeled 1,2-diphenyl-1-o-tolylethylene and 1,1-diphenyl-2-o-tolylethylene (see below). Small samples of the olefins were stirred 45 min as a solution in 75 ml of glacial acetic acid that contained 2.80 g of chromium trioxide. The solutions were then heated 15 min on a steam bath, poured onto ice, and extracted with chloroform. Acid fractions were recovered from the chloroform layers by extraction into 10% sodium hydroxide solution. These acid fractions were purified by recrystallization from water and by sublimation. The ketones were isolated by evaporating the chloroform from the neutral chloroform fractions and then adding alcohol and 2,4-dinitrophenylhydrazine reagent. The 2,4-dinitrophenylhydrazones were recrystallized from tetrahydrofuran—ethyl alcohol.

B. OXIDATION BY THE PROCEDURE OF LEMIEUX AND VON RUDLOFF

Bonner, Stehr, and do Amaral[29] adapted the

procedure of Lemieux and von Rudloff[30] to degrade labeled 3-phenyl-1-butene. The methylene group was converted to formaldehyde; its dimedone derivative was assayed for carbon-14

$$CH_3\overset{|}{CH}—CH=CH_2 \xrightarrow[KMnO_4]{HIO_4}$$

$$CH_2O + \text{other products}$$

A solution of 4 g of paraperiodic acid in 400 ml of water was neutralized with sodium carbonate. The 3-phenyl-1-butene was added; the mixture was stirred rapidly while a solution of 0.33 g of potassium permanganate in 25 ml of water was added in four equal portions over 1 hr. After two additional hours of stirring, excess permanganate was destroyed by the addition of sufficient sodium bisulfite. The oxidation mixture was extracted with four portions of ether. The aqueous layer was filtered through Celite, and the filtrate was treated with a slight excess of an aqueous solution of dimedone reagent. The formaldehyde derivative precipitated immediately (0.47 g, 40.3% yield; m.p., 187 to 187.5°). It was recrystallized from 60% ethyl alcohol prior to radioassay.

C. OXIDATIVE CLEAVAGE AT A CARBON-TO-CARBON TRIPLE BOND

Bothner-By[31] used potassium dichromate and sulfuric acid to cleave 4-bromotolan at the triple bond

$$\text{(diagram)} \xrightarrow[H_2SO_4]{K_2Cr_2O_7}$$

The labeled 4-bromotolan (0.45 g), 1.00 g of powdered potassium dichromate, and 3.0 ml of 3.4 M sulfuric acid were refluxed for $\frac{1}{2}$ hr. The mixture was cooled, diluted with water, and extracted with two 5-ml portions of ether. The mixture of acid products was

extracted from the ether into saturated sodium bicarbonate solution which, when acidified, yielded a greenish mixture of solids as a precipitate. An additional ether extraction, bicarbonate treatment, and acidification yielded a colorless solid. Fractional sublimation yielded 11 mg of pure benzoic acid (m.p., 120 to 121°). The residues in the sublimer were purified by recrystallization from aqueous alcohol and vacuum sublimation yielding p-bromobenzoic acid (120 mg; m.p., 251 to 252°).

D. OZONOLYSIS

Reaction with ozone is described[32] as the most general and reliable procedure for the cleavage and location of double bonds. The action of ozone yields ozonides (often dangerously explosive), whose decomposition gives carbonyl compounds related to the two doubly bonded parts of the molecule. The danger resulting from the accumulation of large amounts of ozonides in the macro procedure is essentially eliminated in the small-scale degradative application. Detailed instructions for the construction and operation of a portable semimicro ozonizer are available.[33] The apparatus is simple and inexpensive; it consists of four Pyrex units, namely, a bubbler to indicate oxygen throughput, a single Berthelot tube for the generation of ozone, a reaction vessel, and a tube filled with soda lime for the decomposition of excess ozone. Although the use of only one short Berthelot tube results in inefficient oxygen-to-ozone conversion, it is still possible to ozonize a millimole of an olefin in only 5 min. As a safety precaution, the transformer, mounting stand, and external foil should be adequately grounded, and the high-tension lead should be insulated properly. The design of the apparatus tends to minimize shock hazard. The value of the method for degradations is enhanced if the ozonization is conducted in excess ethanolic 2,4-dinitrophenylhydrazine sulfate solution[34] (the reagent can be prepared conveniently as a 0.1 M solution). The acid reaction medium decomposes the ozonide as it is formed, and the 2,4-dinitrophenylhydrazones of the degradation fractions are obtained in high yield. Also, the amount of precipitate formed indicates the progress of the reaction. The application of the method to carbon-14 compounds is illustrated by the ozonolysis of stilbene-α-^{14}C and its conversion to benzaldehyde-α-^{14}C 2,4-dinitrophenylhydrazone. This process is described in detail by Bonner and Collins.[35]

E. HYDROXYLATION PRELIMINARY TO GLYCOL CLEAVAGE   In some cases it is convenient to cleave a carbon-to-carbon chain at a double bond by hydroxylation to the glycol and cleavage of the glycol with a reagent such as lead tetraacetate. The details of a hydroxylation of labeled allylbenzene are reported by Fort and Roberts[36]

$$C_6H_5CH_2—CH{=}CH_2 + H_2O_2 \xrightarrow{HCO_2H}$$
$$C_6H_5CH_2—CHOH—CH_2OH$$

Allylbenzene (0.30 g) was stirred with 5 ml of 98 to 100% formic acid and 0.9 ml of 30% hydrogen peroxide. After 15 min the mixture was homogeneous. It was then allowed to stand at room temperature for several hours. Formic acid was distilled off under reduced pressure. The residue was boiled with a 20% solution of sodium hydroxide in the presence of some ethyl alcohol. The saponification mixture was diluted with water, and the 3-phenylpropane-1,2-diol was collected by continuous ether extraction. Peroxides were removed, the ether distilled off, and the concentrate was used for reaction with lead tetraacetate (Part III below).

Prelog and co-workers[37] used osmium tetroxide to hydroxylate a labeled cyclic olefin in preparing it for subsequent cleavage by lead tetraacetate and oxidation to a dicarboxylic acid.

III CLEAVAGE OF CHAINS AT CARBON ATOMS BEARING HYDROXYL GROUPS

A. MONOHYDROXY COMPOUNDS   The primary carbon atom of a primary alcohol

can be isolated as carbon dioxide by oxidation of the alcohol to an acid and removal of the carboxyl group by the Schmidt reaction or the Curtius rearrangement. Roberts and Mazur[38] oxidized the labeled cyclopropylcarbinol in an alcoholic mixture to cyclopropane-carboxylic acid with sodium permanganate. Treatment of this acid with hydrazoic acid converted it to the amine and carbon dioxide. The cyclopropylamine was then converted to the benzoate for radioassay. The other component of the alcoholic mixture, cyclobutanol, was oxidized by the permanganate to succinic acid. The succinic acid was then degraded to carbon dioxide and ethylenediamine by Curtius rearrangement of the diazide as described by Benson and Bassham.[39]

Benson and Bassham[39] also demonstrated that the secondary hydroxyl group in malic acid can be oxidized by chromic acid

$$HO_2C—CH_2—CHOH—CO_2H \xrightarrow{CrO_3}$$
$$2\,CO_2 + CH_3CO_2H$$

The two carbon dioxide molecules originate in the carboxyl groups. The position-2 carbon atom in malic acid appears as the carboxyl group in the acetic acid.

When a hydroxyl group is on the position-2 carbon atom of a carbon chain and is also next to a methyl group, the haloform reaction can be used to effect cleavage between the position-1 and position-2 carbon atoms.

When a hydroxyl group and an amino group are on adjacent carbon atoms of a chain, a glycol-type cleavage with periodic acid is possible, as in the degradation of a labeled amino acid reported by Delluva[40]

$$CH_3CHOHCH(NH_2)CO_2H \xrightarrow{HIO_4}$$
$$CH_3CHO + HCO_2H + CO_2$$

B. DIHYDROXY AND POLYHYDROXY COMPOUNDS   Periodic acid[41,42] and lead tetraacetate[42] are well known as reagents that cleave chains having hydroxyl groups on adjacent carbon atoms. These reagents have been used widely to degrade labeled carbohydrates. A typical procedure was applied by Fort and Roberts[36] to the cleavage of 3-phenylpropane-1,2-diol that was prepared by hydroxylation of allylbenzene

$$C_6H_5CH_2-CHOH-CH_2OH \xrightarrow{Pb(OAc)_4}$$
$$C_6H_5CH_2-CHO + CH_2O$$

The 3-phenylpropane-1,2-diol concentrate was stirred at room temperature with lead tetraacetate and anhydrous potassium carbonate in 5 ml of benzene. The formaldehyde produced was extracted from the reaction mixture into water and was converted to the dimedone derivative (m.p., 191 to 191.6° after recrystallization from methanol). The benzene layer was filtered. Benzene was distilled off. The residue of phenylacetaldehyde was converted to the dimedone derivative (m.p., 168.5 to 169.8° after recrystallization from methanol).

A general procedure for the quantitative determination of the hydroxymethylene group is that which uses periodate in the way Frush and Isbell[43] applied it to a carbon-14-labeled aldopentose.

Table 10-1 at the end of this chapter supplies references to degradations of a number of labeled dihydroxy and polyhydroxy compounds. References to degradations of labeled glucose, fructose, and other related polyhydroxy compounds are also given in Table 10-1; the degradation of such materials will not be discussed here.

IV CLEAVAGE OF CARBON CHAINS AT KETO GROUPS

A. THE IODOFORM REACTION The iodoform reaction is commonly used to cleave acetyl groups. The methyl group is converted to iodoform, which precipitates from solution

$$R-COCH_3 + 4 NaOH + 3 I_2 \rightarrow$$
$$R-CO_2Na + CHI_3\downarrow + 3 NaI + 3H_2O$$

Any other group that can be oxidized to an

acetyl group under the conditions of the iodoform reaction is also cleaved

$$R-CHOHCH_3 + 2 NaOH + I_2 \rightarrow$$
$$R-COCH_3 + 2 NaI + 2 H_2O$$

The yield of iodoform is never quantitative but is sufficient to permit the reaction to be used effectively to degrade small samples of labeled compounds. Every milligram of methyl group can produce 33 mg of iodoform; the ease with which small samples can be degraded is thereby improved. Iodoform can be purified readily by vacuum sublimation.

Meinwald[44] used the iodoform reaction to degrade carbon-14-labeled geronic acid. A 623-mg quantity of the organic acid was dissolved in an aqueous solution of sodium carbonate, 3 g of potassium iodide was added, and Chlorox was added dropwise until no more iodoform precipitated. The iodoform was collected on a filter, washed with water, and vacuum-dried; 1.07 g (75%) yield) of crude iodoform was obtained. The iodoform was purified by two sublimations made at 50° and 0.1 mm pressure. The difference between the specific radioactivities of the doubly sublimed sample and the crude sample was only about 0.4%.

B. MODIFICATIONS OF THE IODOFORM REACTION Different research workers have altered the conditions of the iodoform reaction to suit their various needs in degrading labeled compounds. Although most workers appear not to have had difficulties in using the iodoform reaction in degrading labeled substances, some deviation from normality has been mentioned.[45]

In their degradation of labeled pinacolone, Roberts and Yancey[46] preferred to use sodium hypobromite and to convert the methyl group to carbon tetrabromide. A mixture of 1.0 g of pinacolone, 1.8 ml of bromine, 12 g of sodium hydroxide, and 40 ml of water was stirred for 3 hr at 0 to 10°. The carbon tetrabromide that precipitated was steam distilled, collected on a filter, dried between filter papers, and sublimed twice. The yield was 1.5 g (46%); m.p., 95°.

The residue from the steam distillation was acidified with concentrated sulfuric acid. After 13 g of silver sulfate was added, the mixture was again steam distilled. Water was distilled out at reduced pressure from the neutralized distillate. The residue of sodium trimethylacetate was converted to the *p*-bromophenacyl ester for carbon-14 assay.

C. OTHER METHODS

Various other methods of cleavage of chains at keto groups are available. If the keto group is not adjacent to a methyl group, the haloform reaction usually fails. Another possibility consists in reduction of the carbonyl group and degradation by one of the methods described in Part IIIA. Sometimes the resulting hydroxyl group can be dehydrated to an olefin, which can then be cleaved by one of the methods already discussed.

Alkaline ketone cleavage as applied by Raaen and Collins[28] has been used in several cases to cleave labeled ketones

A small sample[28] of the benzhydryl-*o*-tolyl ketone was heated at reflux temperature for 24 hr with 75 ml of 25% potassium hydroxide in methanol. The solution was poured onto ice and was extracted three times with 50-ml portions of ether. The alkaline residue was acidified, and the precipitated *o*-toluic acid was collected and purified by three recrystallizations from methanol (20%)-water followed by vacuum sublimation. In lieu of purification, the diphenylmethane in the crude neutral fraction was oxidized to benzophenone. The oxidation was effected in an

acetic acid–chromic acid solution heated on the steam bath for 1 hr. The benzophenone was recovered by precipitation as the 2,4-dinitrophenylhydrazone derivative, which was recrystallized from tetrahydrofuran—ethyl alcohol to a melting point of 239 to 240°.

V DEGRADATION OF GROUPS ATTACHED TO AROMATIC NUCLEI

The resistance of aromatic nuclei to attack by many reagents that attack nonaromatic groups is the basis of procedures for degrading a variety of labeled organic compounds. More often than not, aromatic rings, when present, are the chief focal points in planning a degradation scheme.

The attack of strong oxidizing agents, such as aqueous alkaline permanganate or potassium dichromate–aqueous sulfuric acid, on a carbon chain attached to an aromatic ring generally results in the production of some benzoic acid. The carbon atom that is originally *alpha* to the ring normally becomes the carbon of the carboxyl group in the benzoic acid. For a variety of reasons, such oxidations frequently lead to low yields of benzoic acid. If the organic compound is extremely insoluble in water, poor contact with the aqueous oxidizing solution may result in very slow reaction. If, on the other hand, a high concentration of oxidizing agent, a high temperature, or a prolonged reaction time is necessary to oxidize a highly unreactive benzene derivative, the benzoic acid produced may also be oxidized partially or even completely. Some oxidation of the benzene ring often accompanies the degradation of any except the most easily oxidized side chains. Accordingly, the carbon-14 dioxide produced on strong oxidation of most carbon-14-labeled side chains can be expected to be diluted with some unknown amount of unlabeled carbon dioxide that results from partial ring destruction. If, therefore, such carbon-14 dioxide is collected and radioassayed during the course of a carbon-14 tracer experiment, the measured specific radioactivity may well be meaningless and totally unrelated to other specific radioactivities measured during the experiment. As was pointed out earlier in this chapter, basing the results of a tracer experiment on a measured specific radioactivity of carbon-14 dioxide can be hazardous if there is any possibility of dilution by carbon dioxide from a second source.

In general, electron-withdrawing substituents such as the nitro group stabilize aromatic rings toward destruction by oxidizing agents; electron-releasing substituents, particularly the hydroxyl substituent, render these rings more susceptible to oxidation. These facts can be useful in planning degradation schemes.

Besides benzene rings and substituted benzene rings, other rings with aromatic character may serve as centers of stability on which a degradation scheme can be based. The pyridine ring, which is highly resistant to oxidation—particularly in an acid aqueous medium—is a typical example.

Some biaryl type structures can be partly degraded in such a way that one aromatic nucleus is degraded and the other nucleus is left intact. Similarly, one ring of some fused-ring systems may be destroyed leaving the other ring or rings intact. Although these simple principles are well known, they have not yet been applied to many carbon-14-labeled, cyclic organic compounds.

A. DEGRADATION OF A CHAIN OR GROUP ATTACHED TO ONLY ONE AROMATIC NUCLEUS

Degradation of a side chain occurs most readily if there is a multiple bond *alpha* to the ring or if the *alpha* carbon atom is already partially oxidized, as for example, to a substituted benzyl alcohol. Thus, Ropp and Raaen[47] oxidized labeled 1-(*p*-nitrophenyl)-butadiene-1,3 to *p*-nitrobenzoic acid, Eberhardt[48] oxidized labeled *p*-methoxycinnamic acid to *p*-anisic acid, and Curtin, Flynn, and Nystrom[49]

oxidized labeled phenylpropiolic acid to benzoic acid. Labeled 1-phenylcyclohexene was oxidized by Schaeffer and Collins[50] first to δ-benzoylvaleric acid, then to benzoic acid

A mixture of 500 mg of 1-phenylcyclohexene, 40 ml of acetone, 2.5 g of potassium permanganate, and 80 ml of water was stirred 15 min. Manganese dioxide was removed by filtration, and the acetone was distilled off by use of a steam bath. The filtrate was extracted with chloroform, then made acid with dilute sulfuric acid, and extracted with ether. The ether extract was washed with water and was then evaporated to give δ-benzoylvaleric acid; the yield was 205 mg (31%). The acid was purified by alternate recrystallization from hexane and water until its melting point was 77 to 78°. For further oxidation to benzoic acid, 400 mg of the δ-benzoylvaleric acid was refluxed for 3 hr with 2 g of potassium permanganate, 2 ml of a 10% aqueous solution of sodium hydroxide, and 30 ml of water. After the mixture was cooled, excess permanganate was removed with sodium bisulfite, and the manganese dioxide was collected on a filter and washed with water. The filtrate was extracted with chloroform and was then acidified with dilute sulfuric acid. By ether extraction, 210 mg (88% yield) of crude benzoic acid was recovered. Schaeffer and Collins[50] also achieved oxidation of the 1-phenylcyclohexene by chromic acid oxidation of the nitrosochloride derivative. Scardiglia and Roberts[51] used permanganate oxidation of the dinitrophenylmercapto derivative. In some instances, benzene nuclei have been introduced deliberately into the structure of labeled molecules or formed by dehydrogenation to facilitate subsequent degradation. Currell and Fry[52] degraded labeled isobutyraldehyde by the reactions

$$CH_3—CH—CHO \quad + \quad \text{(C}_6\text{H}_5)—MgBr$$
$$\overset{|}{CH_3}$$

$$\text{(C}_6\text{H}_5)—CO_2H \xleftarrow{HNO_3} \text{(C}_6\text{H}_5)—CHOH—CH(CH_3)_2$$

The carbonyl carbon of the aldehyde was thus isolated as the *alpha* carbon of benzoic acid. Pines and Shaw[53] used platinized alumina at 280° to aromatize chain-labeled ethylcyclohexane. The ethylbenzene was then oxidized to benzoic acid. Dimethylcyclohexane was present in the ethylcyclohexane used originally; therefore, phthalic acid was present in the benzoic acid recovered.

The alkylbenzenes generally are difficult to oxidize to benzoic acid in high yields. Roberts, Ropp, and Neville[54] found it expedient to use other means than direct oxidation to benzoic acid for degrading labeled ethylbenzene

$$\text{(C}_6\text{H}_5)C_2H_5 \xrightarrow[O_2N]{HNO_3} \text{(C}_6\text{H}_4)CO_2H$$

and

$$\text{(C}_6\text{H}_5)C_2H_5 \xrightarrow[\text{ultraviolet light}]{Br_2}$$

$$\left[\text{(C}_6\text{H}_5)CHBrCH_3\right] \xrightarrow[KOH]{KMnO_4} \text{(C}_6\text{H}_5)CO_2H$$

Both schemes gave better yields of degradation product than did direct oxidation with alkaline permanganate. For degradation of labeled *n*-propylbenzene, Roberts and Brandenburger[55] used another variation

$$\text{(C}_6\text{H}_5)C_3H_7 \xrightarrow[\text{succinimide}]{N\text{-bromo-}} \text{(C}_6\text{H}_5)CHBrCH_2CH_3$$

$$\downarrow \text{pyridine}$$

$$\text{(C}_6\text{H}_5)CH=CHCH_3$$

$$\text{(C}_6\text{H}_5)CHOHCHOHCH_3 \xleftarrow[\text{(2) KOH}]{\text{(1) } H_2O_2, HCO_2H}$$

$$\downarrow HIO_4$$

$$\text{(C}_6\text{H}_5)—CHO + CH_3CHO$$

By this scheme all three carbon atoms of the chain can be separated, because the acetaldehyde produced can be further degraded by the iodoform reaction. In the case of labeled *n*-butylbenzene, oxidation to benzoic acid with permanganate was used.[56]

The oxidations of 2-(3-pyridyl)-piperidine[57] and of nicotine[58] exemplify degradations that are based on the stability of a nucleus other than the benzene nucleus

$$\xrightarrow{HNO_3}$$

$$\xrightarrow{HNO_3}$$

B. DEGRADATION OF A CHAIN OR GROUP HAVING A CARBON ATOM ATTACHED TO TWO AROMATIC NUCLEI

When two aromatic rings are attached to a carbon atom to be isolated by degradation, oxidation by permanganate or chromic acid to benzophenone or a benzophenone derivative is often possible. One example involving a labeled triarylethylene was cited above.[28] Benjamin, Schaeffer, and Collins[59] supply another useful example

C. SELECTIVE RING DESTRUCTION IN BIARYLS AND FUSED RING SYSTEMS

Labeled biphenyl was degraded to benzoic acid by Wynberg and Wolf,[60] who used a procedure developed by Colbert and Hensley.[61] About 0.5 g of biphenyl was stirred for 5 hr at 40 to 50° with 3.0 g of chromium trioxide and 35 ml of glacial acetic acid. The yield of benzoic acid was 35 to 47%.

Some degradations involving ring opening in labeled fused-ring systems are reported. For example, Collins, Burr, and Hess[62] degraded benz[a]anthracene that was labeled with carbon-14 in positions 5 and 6

This series of reactions was necessary to isolate as carbon dioxide the position-6 carbon of the hydrocarbon degraded.

VI DEGRADATION OF RINGS

Apart from the selective opening of aromatic rings mentioned in Part V above, the degradation of labeled rings in such a way that each of the ring carbon atoms is isolated can be a formidable task.

A. AROMATIC RINGS

Aromatic rings are often first hydrogenated to saturated rings, which are then degraded as indicated below under Part VI-B. In addition, direct degradation without preliminary dearomatization is possible in some cases. Several examples are cited here in which phenol derivatives are used. The methods were developed by Ehrensvärd.[63] Tyrosine can be degraded via p-hydroxybenzoic acid and phenol.[63,64] The fate of the ring carbon atoms is shown with the aid of numbers that refer to the positions in the ring of tyrosine

(average of 1 and 4)

The p-hydroxybenzoic acid can be converted by strong nitration to picric acid. Three carbon atoms are isolated as bromopicrin

The phenol can be converted by alkylation to p-(t-butyl)phenol, which is oxidized to trimethylpyruvic acid

The p-hydroxybenzoic acid can then be nitrated to the dinitro derivative for a second degradation to bromopicrin

Thus, the radioactivity of each of the six carbon atoms of the tyrosine ring can be calculated, because atoms 2 and 6 are equivalent, and atoms 3 and 5 are equivalent. Similar methods were used to degrade the ring in phenylalanine.[63] Gilvarg and Bloch[65] also used such methods to degrade the phenylalanine ring after a preliminary oxidation and Schmidt reaction to convert the ring to aniline.

Eberhardt and Schubert[66] used similar processes to degrade labeled vanillin; these authors refer to a number of papers that supply useful experimental details.

The ring of labeled p-methoxycinnamic acid was degraded similarly.[67] The method they used to degrade p-hydroxybenzoic acid is described by Reio and Ehrensvärd.[68]

B. SIX-MEMBERED NONAROMATIC RINGS
Labeled cyclohexanol,[69] and thereby its immediate precursors, aniline and phenol, were degraded by Roberts and coworkers[69] by the scheme shown in the equations below (numbers in parentheses

designate the carbons from the six original ring positions).

For the purpose at hand, it was not necessary to carry the degradation further. The 1,3-diaminopropane was essentially free of carbon-14. Total degradation of the ring could have been accomplished by one additional oxidation to malonic acid, which can be decarboxylated to separate carbon 3 or carbon 5 from carbon 4. Correction for errors due to the carbon-14 isotope effect must be made.

C. OTHER RINGS
A number of other carbon-14-labeled rings of various sizes, with and without heteroatoms, have been degraded partially or completely. In general, the reactions used are much the same as those used to degrade compounds without rings. The degradation of labeled cyclobutanone by Semenow, Cox, and Roberts[70] is an interesting example. Numbers and a letter are used as aids in following the paths of the atoms

The glycol was also cleaved with periodate to acetaldehyde and acetone; the acetone was degraded further

$$\overset{(3)}{C}H_3\overset{(4)}{C}HO + \overset{(a,2)}{C}H_3-\overset{(1)}{C}O-\overset{(a,2)}{C}H_3$$

$$\downarrow NaOI$$

$$\overset{(a,2)}{C}HI_3$$

Since carbon atoms 2 and 4 are equivalent in cyclobutanone, determination of the molar radioactivities of the several degradation products provided a measure of, and a cross-check on, the molar radioactivities of the four carbon atoms in cyclobutanone.

VII MISCELLANEOUS DEGRADATION METHODS

A number of degradation methods used for labeled compounds have not so far been referred to in this chapter. Several of these have been described by Calvin and co-workers.[9] Others are referred to among the references that accompany Table 10-1.

The Hofmann degradation has been used in several instances although, as mentioned earlier,[3] it may lead to minor difficulties when applied to labeled acetamide. Dauben and co-workers[71] used barium hypobromite to degrade labeled phenylacetamide to benzylamine hydrochloride. The same process was used by Brown, Cerwonka, and Anderson.[72]

Sixma and Hendricks[73] used an electrochemical oxidation to isolate the position-2 carbon of ethyl bromide.

To degrade labeled benzophenone so as to determine what fraction of the total activity is in the rings, the method used by Bonner and Collins[74] is convenient. They used a Beckmann type rearrangement of the ketone hydrazone.[75] Half the carbon-14 originally present in the rings of the benzophenone is isolated as acetanilide.

Bonner, Stehr, and do Amaral[29] used

Raney nickel to cleave labeled 2-phenyl-1-propanol

$$CH_3—CH—CH_2OH \xrightarrow[\substack{\text{absolute ethyl} \\ \text{alcohol, reflux}}]{\text{Raney nickel,}} CH_3—CH_2$$

Cleavage occurred between carbon atoms 1 and 2. Carbon atoms 2 and 3 were isolated as the 2,4-diacetylamino derivative of ethyl benzene.

10-4 PUBLISHED DEGRADATION PROCEDURES

Table 10-1 is an extensive list of organic compounds that have been labeled with isotopic carbon and degraded. References to the original literature are given in all cases. The arrangement in the table is according to the class of compound degraded; within a class, the compounds are listed in the order of increasing molecular complexity. There are some exceptions to this arrangement. Functional groups that play no vital part in the degradation are ignored in some cases. For example, some methoxy and nitro derivatives are tabulated with hydrocarbons, and some nitrogen compounds are listed under "VIII. Aromatic Rings" rather than under "IX. Nitrogen Compounds."

Table 10-1   Published procedures used for degradation of organic compounds labeled with isotopic carbon

Compound degraded	Carbon positions determined	Ref.
I. Hydrocarbons		
$\overset{3}{C}H_3\overset{2}{C}H{=}\overset{1}{C}H_2$	1, 2, 3	62
$\overset{1}{C}H_2{=}\overset{2}{C}{=}\overset{3}{C}H_2$	1, 2, 3	96
$C_6H_5CH_3$	Methyl	91
	Methyl group, ring atoms (total)	41
$\overset{2}{C}H_2\overset{1}{C}H_3$ on cyclohexane (S)	1, 2	103
$C_6H_5\overset{1}{C}H_2CH_3$	1	121
$C_6H_5\overset{1}{C}H_2\overset{2}{C}H_3$	1, 2	143
m-Xylene	Methyl groups, ring atoms (total)	41
$C_6H_5\overset{1}{C}H_2\overset{2}{C}H_2\overset{3}{C}H_3$	1, 2, 3	119
$C_6H_5\overset{1}{C}H{=}\overset{2}{C}H_2$	1	144
$C_6H_5\overset{3}{C}H_2\overset{2}{C}H{=}\overset{1}{C}H_2$	1	59

Table 10-1   (*Continued*)

Compound degraded	carbon positions determined	Ref.

I. Hydrocarbons (continued)

Compound degraded	carbon positions determined	Ref.
$\overset{3}{C_6H_5}\overset{2}{C}H\overset{1}{CH}=CH_2$ with CH_3 branch	3	58
$\overset{1}{C_6H_5}CH_2CH_2CH_2CH_3$	1	120
$\overset{4}{C}H_3\overset{3}{C}H_2\overset{2}{C}H\overset{1}{C}H_3$ with C_6H_5 branch	1, 2	21
$\overset{1}{C}H_2=\overset{2}{C}H\overset{3}{C}H\overset{4}{C}H_3$ with C_6H_5 branch	1, 2, 3, 4	21
C_6H_5- (cyclohexene, *)	*	132, 133
C_6H_5- (cyclopentene)	All carbons of cyclo-pentene ring	92
Dimethylcyclohexane (3 isomers)	Methyl	103
$(C_6H_5)_2\overset{1}{C}H\overset{2}{C}H_2C_6H_5$	1, 2	15, 17
$C_6H_5\overset{2}{C}H=\overset{1}{C}(C_6H_5)_2$	1, 2	37
$(C_6H_5)_2\overset{1}{C}=\overset{2}{C}$ with *o*-tolyl and H	1, 2	105
C_6H_5, C_6H_5 on $\overset{1}{C}=\overset{2}{C}$ with *o*-tolyl and H	1, 2	105
p-$BrC_6H_4\overset{1}{C}\equiv\overset{2}{C}C_6H_5$	1	23
p-$CH_3OC_6H_4\overset{3}{C}H_2\overset{2}{C}H=\overset{1}{C}H_2$	1	59
p-$CH_3OC_6H_4\overset{3}{C}H\overset{2}{C}H=\overset{1}{C}H_2$ with CH_3 branch	3	58

Table 10-1   (Continued)

Compound degraded	Carbon positions determined	Ref.

I. Hydrocarbons (continued)

$p\text{-}O_2NC_6H_4\overset{1}{C}H\!=\!\overset{2}{C}H\overset{3}{C}H\!=\!\overset{4}{C}H_2$ 1   127

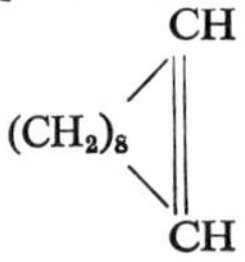

$(CH_2)_8$ with CH=CH bridge   1, 2   104

$C_6H_5\overset{}{C}\!=\!\overset{*}{C}H$ (acenaphthylene)   *   16

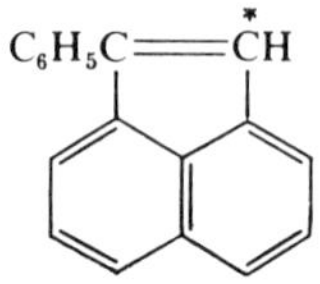

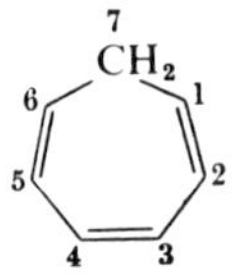

(cycloheptatriene, CH₂ = 7)   (1 + 2 + 5 + 6 + 7)   74

Bitropyl:

(bitropyl structure)   (1 + 2 + 3 + 6 + 7 +1′ + 2′ + 3′ + 6′ + 7′), (1 + 1′)   74

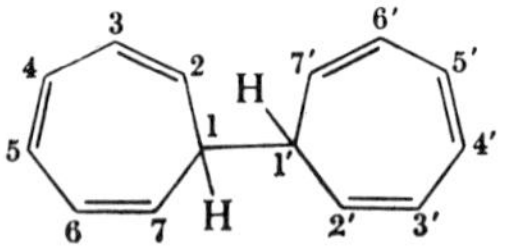

Squalene:

$CH_3C\!=\!\left[CHCH_2CH_2C\right]\!=\!CHCH_2\text{-}$ with CH_3 and H_3C All   49

Copolymers of styrene and methylstyrene   (Degraded to original monomers only)   93

II. Carboxylic acids

CH_3CO_2H	1, 2	3, 14, 128, 147
$(CH_3CO_2)_2Ba$	1, 2	62
CH_3CO_2H	1	4
$CH_3CH_2CO_2H$	1	97, 112, 164
$CH_3CH_2CONH_2$	1, 2, 3	159
$CH_3CH_2CO_2H, CH_3CO_2H$	All	101, 160
$CH_3CH_2CH_2CO_2H$	All	161
$CH_3CH_2CH_2CO_2C_2H_5$	(2 + 3 + 4)	94, 95
$(CH_3)_3\overset{3}{C}\!-\!\overset{2}{C}\overset{1}{O}_2H$	1, 2, 3	129

Table 10-1 (*Continued*)

Compound degraded	Carbon positions determined	Ref.
II. Carboxylic acids (*continued*)		
$-CO_2H$	Carboxyl, ring (total)	114
CO_2H (*)	*	85
$C_6H_5CO_2H$	Carboxyl	50
$p\text{-}CH_3OC_6H_4CO_2H$	Carboxyl	117
$C_6H_5CH_2CO_2H$	Carboxyl	27, 40, 44
$\overset{3}{C_6H_5}\overset{2}{CH_2}\overset{1}{CH_2CO_2H}$	1, 3	59, 144
CH_3O—⟨⟩—$\overset{3}{CH}=\overset{2}{CH}\overset{1}{CO_2H}$	(3 + ring)	53
$(C_6H_5)_3\overset{2}{C}\!-\!\overset{1}{CO_2H}$	2	123
$(C_6H_5)_2\overset{3}{CH}\overset{2}{CH}\overset{1}{CO_2H}$ $\|$ C_6H_5	2, 3	15
$CH_3(CH_2)_nCO_2H$ ($n = 11, 12, 13, 14, 15$)	Carboxyl	46
Linolenic acid: $CH_3(CH_2CH{=}CH)_3(CH_2)_7CO_2H$ (also for linoleic and oleic acids)	Carboxyl	65
$C_6H_5\overset{3}{C}{\equiv}\overset{2}{C}\!-\!\overset{1}{CO_2H}$	3	43
Tropic acid: $C_6H_5\overset{2}{C}H\overset{1}{CO_2H}$ $\|$ CH_2OH	2, ring	82
	Carboxyl	45
$HO_2CCH_2CH_2CO_2H$	1, 2	11, 49, 78
Fumaric acid	2	2
	1, 2	102
CO_2H CO_2H	Carboxyl	113

Table 10-1 (*Continued*)

Compound degraded	Carbon positions determined	Ref.
II. Carboxylic acids (*continued*)		
Phthalic acid	Ring (total)	34
	Carboxyl	103
$HO_2C(CH_2)_8CO_2H$	All	153
$\overset{1}{C}O_2H$ / CH_3CHCH \ CO_2H ; $H_2CCH_2CO_2H$	1	140
$\overset{*}{C}O_2H$ / CH_3CHCH \ CO_2H ; CH_3CHCO_2H	*	141
$CH_3CHCH(CH_3)CO_2H$	*	141
$\overset{*}{C}O_2H$ / CH_3C \ CO_2H		
III. Aldehydes; ketones		
CH_3CHO	1, 2	162
$(CH_3)_2CH\overset{1}{C}HO$	1	42
D-Glucose	All	68
$C_6H_5\overset{3}{C}H_2\overset{2}{C}H_2\overset{1}{C}HO$	1	143
$\overset{*}{C}HO$ | $C_6H_5COCHC_6H_5$	*	72
CH_3COCH_3	1, 2	122, 126, 160
$CH_3\overset{2}{C}H\overset{1}{C}OCH_3$ | CH_3	1	145
$\overset{1}{C}H_3\overset{2}{C}OC(CH_3)_3$	1	118
$\overset{4}{C}H_3\overset{3}{C}{-}\overset{2}{C}O\overset{1}{C}H_3$ with CH_3 branches	1, 2, 3, 4	129

Table 10-1   (*Continued*)

Compound degraded	Carbon positions determined	Ref.

III. Aldehydes; ketones (continued)

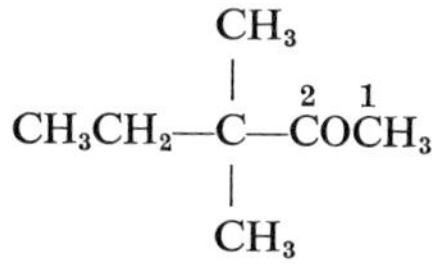

$$CH_3CH_2-\overset{\overset{\displaystyle CH_3}{|}}{\underset{\underset{\displaystyle CH_3}{|}}{C}}-\overset{2}{C}\overset{1}{O}CH_3$$

2 — 149

$$CH_3\overset{\overset{\displaystyle CH_3}{|}}{\underset{\underset{\displaystyle CH_3}{|}}{C}}-\overset{\overset{\displaystyle CH_3}{|}}{\underset{\underset{\displaystyle CH_3}{|}}{C}}-\overset{2}{C}\overset{1}{O}CH_3$$

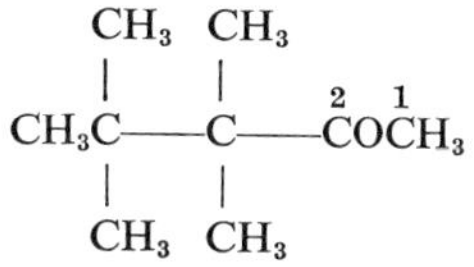

2 — 7, 149

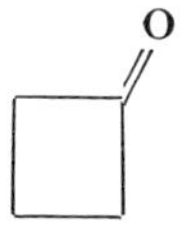

All — 134

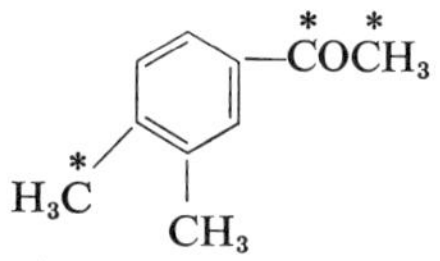

* — 86

$C_6H_5COC_6H_5$ — Carbonyl, ring — 18

$C_6H_5\overset{2}{C}O\overset{1}{C}H(C_6H_5)_2$ — 1, 2 — 10

$\overset{1}{C_6H_5}CO\overset{2}{C}H(C_6H_5)_2$ — 1, 2 (total ring activity in two possible positions) — 10

$$C_6H_5\overset{1}{C}\overset{\overset{\displaystyle O}{\|}}{-}\overset{2}{C}(C_6H_5)_3$$

1, 2 — 64

$$\overset{\displaystyle C_6H_5}{\underset{p-CH_3C_6H_4}{\diagdown}}\overset{1}{C}H\overset{\overset{\displaystyle O}{\|2}}{C}-C_6H_5$$

1, 2 — 8

$$(C_6H_5)_2\overset{1}{C}H\overset{\overset{\displaystyle O}{\|2}}{C}-C_6H_4CH_3\text{-}p$$

1, 2 — 8

$$\overset{\displaystyle C_6H_5}{\underset{o-CH_3C_6H_4}{\diagdown}}\overset{2}{C}H\overset{1}{C}OC_6H_5$$

1, 2 — 105

$$(C_6H_5)_2\overset{2}{C}H\overset{1}{C}OC_6H_4CH_3\text{-}o$$

1, 2 — 105

Table 10-1 (*Continued*)

Compound degraded	Carbon positions determined	Ref.
III. Aldehydes; ketones (*continued*)		
$C_6H_5\overset{2}{C}H\overset{1}{C}OC_6H_4CH_3$-$p$ $\quad\vert$ $\quad C_6H_4CH_3$-p	1, 2	76
$(p\text{-}CH_3C_6H_4)_2\overset{2}{C}H\overset{1}{C}OC_6H_5$	1, 2	76
$(p\text{-}CH_3OC_6H_4)_2\overset{OH}{\underset{\vert}{C^1}}$ $\quad\vert$ $\quad p\text{-}CH_3OC_6H_4C^2{=}O$	1, 2	52
$(C_6H_5)_2\overset{OH}{\overset{\vert}{C^1}}{-}\overset{O}{\overset{\Vert}{C^2}}{-\!-\!-}C_6H_4CH_3$-$o$	1, 2	52
$o\text{-}CH_3C_6H_4\overset{OH}{\overset{\vert}{C^1}}{-}\overset{O}{\overset{\Vert}{C^2}}{-\!-}C_6H_5$ $\qquad\vert$ $\qquad C_6H_5$	1, 2	52
$(C_6H_5)_2\overset{OH}{\overset{\vert}{C^1}}{-}\overset{O}{\overset{\Vert}{C^2}}{-\!-}C_6H_5$	1, 2	52
$p\text{-}CH_3OC_6H_4COCOC_6H_5$	1, 2	117
$C_6H_5CO\overset{*}{C}OCOC_6H_5$	*	117
IV. Quinones		

	2	34
V. Hydroxyl compounds		
$CH_2{=}CHCH_2OH,\ CH_2{=}CHCH_2Br$	1, 3	99
$CH_3CHOHCH_2CH_3$	1	111, 138
$\overset{4}{C}H_2{=}\overset{3}{C}H\overset{2}{C}H_2\overset{1}{C}H_2OH$	1, 2, 3, 4	139
$(CH_3)_3C\overset{1}{C}H_2CH_2OH$	1	113, 115, 131
$(CH_3)_2\overset{1}{C}OH\overset{2}{C}H(CH_3)_2$	1, 2	113, 115, 131
$(CH_3)_3C\overset{1}{C}OH(CH_3)_2$	1	118

Table 10-1 *(Continued)*

Compound degraded	Carbon positions determined	Ref.
V. Hydroxyl compounds *(continued)*		
△—CH₂OH (with * above)	*, ring (total)	88, 109, 114
(cyclobutanol) OH	All	88, 109, 114, 134
(CH₂)₈ bridged CH₂ / CHOH	1, 2	104
△—²CH₂¹CH₂OH	1, 2, ring (total)	32
△—¹CHOH²CH₃	1, 2, ring (total)	32
(cyclopentanol, 3 2 1 / 4 5)—OH	1, (2 + 3 + 4 + 5)	32
(bicyclic) O=C OCCH₃	*	113
C₆H₅²CH₂¹CH₂OH	2	80
C₆H₅³CH₂²CH₂¹CH₂OH	1, 2, 3	59, 71
C₆H₅³CH²CH₂¹CH₂OH | CH₃	3	58
C₆H₅³CH₂²CHOH¹CH₃	1, 2, 3	59, 128
erythro-C₆H₅³CH²CHOH¹CH₃ | CH₃	3	58
CH₃CH(C₆H₅)¹CHOHCH₃	1	22
C₆H₅²CH₂¹COH(C₆H₅)₂	1, 2	29
C₆H₅²CHOH¹CH(C₆H₅)₂	Phenyl (total) at two possible locations	38

Table 10-1   (*Continued*)

Compound degraded	Carbon positions determined	Ref.
V. Hydroxyl compounds (*continued*)		
$(C_6H_5)_2\overset{2}{C}H\overset{1}{C}H(OH)C_6H_5$	1, 2, phenyl (total) on 2-C	19
$C_6H_5\overset{1}{C}HOH\overset{2}{C}H_2C_6H_4CH_3\text{-}p$	1, 2	9, 33
$p\text{-}CH_3C_6H_4\overset{1}{C}HOH\overset{2}{C}H_2C_6H_5$	1, 2	9, 33
$p\text{-}CH_3OC_6H_4\overset{3}{C}H_2\overset{2}{C}H_2\overset{1}{C}H_2OH$	1, 2, 3	59
$p\text{-}CH_3OC_6H_4\overset{3}{C}H\text{—}\overset{2}{C}H_2\overset{1}{C}H_2OH$ 　　　　　　$\vert$ 　　　　　　CH_3	3	58
$p\text{-}CH_3OC_6H_4\overset{3}{C}H_2\overset{2}{C}HOH\overset{1}{C}H_3$	1, 2, 3	59
$erythro\text{-}p\text{-}CH_3OC_6H_4\overset{3}{C}H\overset{2}{C}HOH\overset{1}{C}H_3$ 　　　　　　　　　$\vert$ 　　　　　　　　　CH_3	3	58
Ergosterol	Side-chain	1
$(\overset{1}{C}H_3)_2\overset{2}{C}OH\overset{3}{C}HOH\overset{4}{C}H_3$	All	115
$(CH_3)_2COHCOH(CH_3)_2$	Chain, methyl	51, 106
$\overset{1}{C}H_2OH$ 　$\overset{2}{\vert}$ $C_6H_5\overset{}{C}HOH$ 　$\overset{3}{\vert}$ 　CH_3	1, (2 + 3)	20
$(C_6H_5)_2\overset{2}{C}OH\overset{1}{C}HOHC_6H_4CH_3\text{-}p$	1	8
$\phantom{p\text{-}CH_3C_6H_4}OH\ \ \ OH$ $\phantom{p\text{-}CH_3C_6H_4}\vert_2\ \ \ \vert_1$ $p\text{-}CH_3C_6H_4C\text{——}CH$ $\phantom{p\text{-}CH_3C_6H_4}\vert\ \ \ \ \ \vert$ $\phantom{p\text{-}CH_3C_6H_4}C_6H_5\ \ C_6H_5$	1, 2, phenyl (total) on 2-C	8
$\phantom{o\text{-}tolyl}OH\ \ \ OH$ $\phantom{o\text{-}tolyl}\vert_1\ \ \ \ \vert_2$ $o\text{-tolyl-}C\text{——}C\text{-}C_6H_5$ $\phantom{o\text{-}tolyl-}\vert\ \ \ \ \ \vert$ $\phantom{o\text{-}tolyl-}C_6H_5\ \ H$	1, 2	105
$CH_2OHCHOHCH_2OH$	1	135

Table 10-1   (*Continued*)

Compound degraded	Carbon positions determined	Ref.
V. Hydroxyl compounds (*continued*)		
$$\begin{array}{c} CHO \\ | \\ HO-CH \\ | \\ HC-OH \\ | \\ HC-OH \\ | \\ CH_2OH \end{array}$$	5	63, 107
Glucose	1	73
Fructose	All	26
Sorbose	All	12, 148
VI. Hydroxy acids		
$CH_3CHOHCO_2H$	All	128, 162
	2	50
	1, (2 + 3)	75
$\overset{2}{C_6H_5}\overset{1}{CHOHCO_2H}$	1, 2	98
$p\text{-}CH_3OC_6H_4-CH_2-\overset{\overset{\displaystyle OH}{|}}{\underset{\underset{\displaystyle C_6H_5}{|}}{\overset{1}{C}}}-CO_2H$	1	40, 70
$p\text{-}CH_3OC_6H_4-\overset{\overset{\displaystyle OH}{|}}{\underset{\underset{\displaystyle C_6H_5}{|}}{\overset{2}{C}}}-\overset{1}{C}O_2H$	1, 2	117
naphthalene—OH, —CO₂H	Carboxyl	28
α-D-Galactometasaccharinic acid: $$\begin{array}{c} CO_2H \\ | \\ HCOH \\ | \\ CH_2 \\ | \\ HOCH \\ | \\ HCOH \\ | \\ CH_2OH \end{array}$$	All	146

Table 10-1 (*Continued*)

Compound degraded	Carbon positions determined	Ref.
VI. Hydroxy acids (*continued*)		
α-D-Glucosaccharinic acid: 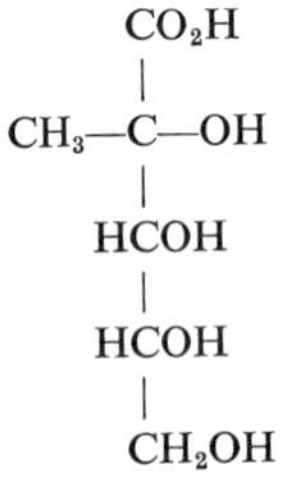	All	146
α-D-Isosaccharinic acid: 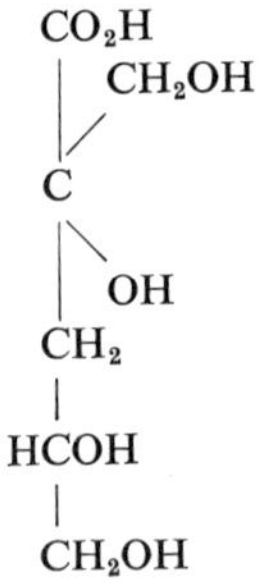	All	146
$\overset{2}{C}H_3COH(CO_2H)_2$	2	162
$HO_2CCH_2CHOHCO_2H$	Methylene	11
Tartaric acid	2	157
Citric acid	All	156
VII. Keto acids		
CH_3COCO_2H	Carboxyl	77, 154
$CH_3COCO_2C_2H_5$	1	30
$\overset{4}{C}H_3\overset{3}{C}O\overset{2}{C}H_2\overset{1}{C}O_2H$	All	155
$CH_3COCH_2CO_2C_2H_5$	1, 2, (3 + 4)	13, 87
Levulinic acid:	All	49
$\overset{*}{C}H_3CO(CH_2)_3C(CH_3)_2CO_2H$	*	89
$\overset{10}{C}H_3(CH_2)_6\overset{3}{C}OCH_2CO_2C_2H_5$	Sum of 3–10	110
$C_6H_5\overset{2}{C}O\overset{1}{C}O_2H$	1, 2	6
$C_6H_5\overset{2}{C}OCO_2H$	2	123, 125

α-D-Glucosaccharinic acid:

CO_2H

$CH_3—C—OH$

$HCOH$

$HCOH$

CH_2OH

α-D-Isosaccharinic acid:

CO_2H
$\quad CH_2OH$

C

$\quad OH$
CH_2

$HCOH$

CH_2OH

Levulinic acid:

$\overset{1}{H}O_2\overset{}{C}—\overset{2}{C}H_2\overset{3}{C}H_2\overset{4}{C}O\overset{5}{C}H_3$

Table 10-1 (*Continued*)

Compound degraded	Carbon positions determined	Ref.
VII. Keto acids (continued)		

| 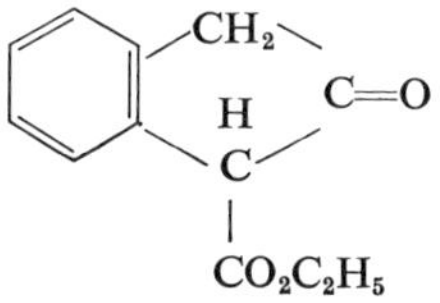 | Carboxyl, remainder of molecule (total) | 31 |

| 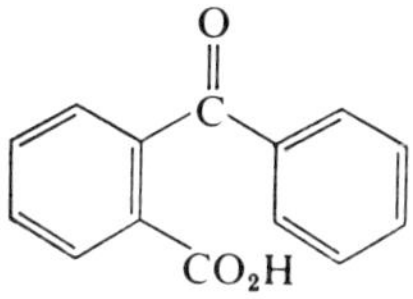 | Carboxyl, remainder of molecule (total) | 124 |

| 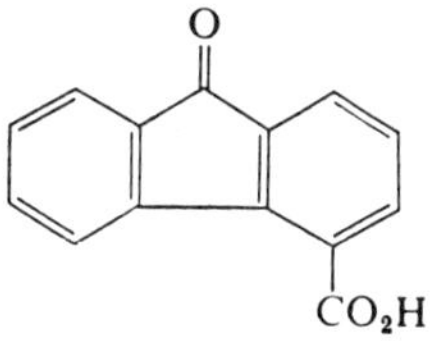 | Carboxyl, remainder of molecule (total) | 36 |

| 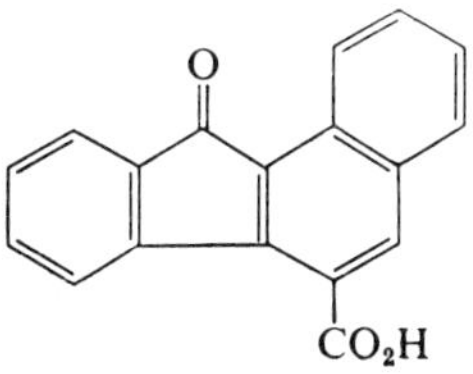 | Carboxyl, remainder of molecule (total) | 39 |

| $\overset{1}{HO_2CCH_2CH_2COCO_2H}$ | 1 | 57, 163 |

VIII. Aromatic rings

C_6H_5OH	All	25
$C_6H_5NH_2$	All	116
$C_6H_5CH_2CHNH_2CO_2H$	Ring	47, 66, 67
Tyrosine:		
$p\text{-}HOC_6H_4CH_2CH(NH_2)CO_2H$	Ring	5, 55
Vanillin: 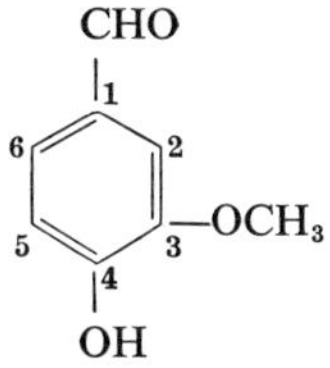	2, 5, 6	54

| $CH_3OC_6H_4CH{=}CHCO_2CH_3$ | All | 108, 137 |

Table 10-1   (*Continued*)

Compound degraded	Carbon positions determined	Ref.
IX. Nitrogen compounds		
α-Amino acids in general	Carboxyl	60
$CH_2NH_2CO_2H$	1, 2	56
Leucine:	All	150
$(CH_3)_2CHCH_2CHCO_2H$ 丨 NH_2		
Isoleucine:	All	151
$CH_3CH_2CH-CHCO_2H$ 丨 丨 CH_3 NH_2		
$\overset{1}{H}O_2CCHNH_2(CH_2)_2\overset{5}{C}O_2H$	1, 5 (2 + 3 + 4 + 5)	90 69
$\overset{1}{C}H_2OHCH(CO_2H)NHCOCH_3$	1	84
$CH_3CH\overset{2}{O}HCH(NH_2)\overset{1}{C}O_2H$	1, 2	48
Folic acid:	Carboxyl	158

	7	130
Anabasine:	*	81
	2, 3	61
Nicotine:	1, 2 (of 5-membered ring)	83
	2, 3 (of 6-membered ring)	61
Nicotinic Acid:	2, 3	61

Table 10-1   (*Continued*)

Compound degraded	Carbon positions determined	Ref.

IX. Nitrogen compounds (*continued*)

$C_6H_5CH_2OC_6H_4$ —CH(H)—*CH(H)—NO_2 with C_6H_5, C_6H_5 attached via $N{=}N$ *   100

$C_6H_5CH_2OC_6H_4$—CH(H)—*CH(H)—NO_2 ... C_6H_5, C_6H_5, $N{=}N$ *   100

Compound degraded	Carbon positions determined	Ref.
$(C_6H_5)_2\overset{1}{C}OH\overset{2}{C}H(NH_2)C_6H_5$	1, 2	10
$p\text{-}CH_3OC_6H_4\overset{3}{C}H\overset{2}{C}H_2\overset{1}{C}H_2NH_2$ with CH_3	3	58
$(C_6H_5)_2\overset{1}{C}OH\overset{2}{C}H(NH_2)C_6H_5$	1, 2	35
Alloxanic acid:	Carboxyl	79

Alloxanic acid structure:

$O{=}C$ — $N{-}R^1$ ring, $C{=}O$, $HO{-}C$ — $N{-}R^2$, CO_2H

Compound degraded	Carbon positions determined	Ref.
Hyoscyamine:	*	24

Hyoscyamine structure: $N{-}CH_3$ bridged ring, H, CH_2OH, $OCOCHC_6H_5$, * marked position.

X. Halogen, sulfur compounds

Compound degraded	Carbon positions determined	Ref.
$(CH_3)_3CC\overset{1}{C}l(CH_3)_2$	1	118
$CH_3\overset{1}{C}H_2Cl$	1	121
CH_3CH_2Br	1, 2	142
$\overset{3}{C}H_2{=}CHCH_2Cl$	3	136
$\overset{3,3'}{(CH_2}{=}CHCH_2O)_2SO$	3,3'	136

Table 10-1   (*Continued*)

Compound degraded	Carbon positions determined	Ref.

X. Halogen, sulfur compounds (continued)

$$\overset{3}{CH_2}=CHCH_2-O$$
$$SO$$
$$n-C_5H_{11}-O$$

3   136

Gliotoxin: *   152

References for Table 10-1

[1] G. Alexander, A. M. Gold, and E. Schwenk, *J. Am. Chem. Soc.*, **79**, 2967 (1957).

[2] M. B. Allen and S. Ruben, *J. Am. Chem. Soc.*, **64**, 948 (1942).

[3] H. S. Anker, *J. Biol. Chem.*, **166**, 219 (1946).

[4] S. Aronoff, V. Haas, and B. A. Fries, *Science*, **110**, 476 (1949).

[5] J. Baddiley, G. Ehrensvärd, E. Klein, L. Reio, E. Saluste, and R. Stjernholm, *J. Biol. Chem.*, **183**, 777 (1950).

[6] K. Banholzer and H. Schmid, *Helv. Chim. Acta*, **39**, 548 (1956).

[7] S. Barton and C. R. Porter, *J. Chem. Soc.*, 2483 (1956).

[8] B. M. Benjamin and C. J. Collins, *J. Am. Chem. Soc.*, **78**, 4329 (1956).

[9] B. M. Benjamin and C. J. Collins, *J. Am. Chem. Soc.*, **78**, 4952 (1956).

[10] B. M. Benjamin, H. J. Schaeffer, and C. J. Collins, *J. Am. Chem. Soc.*, **79**, 6162 (1957).

[11] A. A. Benson and J. A. Bassham, *J. Am. Chem. Soc.*, **70**, 3939 (1948).

[12] C. T. Bishop, *Science*, **117**, 715 (1953).

[13] M. Blecher and S. Gurin, *J. Biol. Chem.*, **209**, 953 (1954).

[14] P. Blicharski and J. Swiderski, *Roczniki Chem.*, **31**, 1317 (1957).

[15] W. A. Bonner, *J. Am. Chem. Soc.*, **81**, 1181 (1959).

[16] W. A. Bonner and C. J. Collins, *J. Am. Chem. Soc.*, **75**, 2303, 3831 (1953).

[17] W. A. Bonner and C. J. Collins, *J. Am. Chem. Soc.*, **75**, 5372 (1953).

[18] W. A. Bonner and C. J. Collins, *J. Am. Chem. Soc.*, **77**, 99 (1955).

[19] W. A. Bonner and C. J. Collins, *J. Am. Chem. Soc.*, **78**, 5587 (1956).

[20] W. A. Bonner and T. W. Greenlee, *J. Am. Chem. Soc.*, **81**, 2122 (1959).

[21] W. A. Bonner, C. E. Stehr, and J. R. do Amaral, *J. Am. Chem. Soc.*, **80**, 4732 (1958).

[22] W. A. Bonner and D. D. Tanner, *J. Am. Chem. Soc.*, **80**, 1447 (1958).

[23] A. A. Bothner-By, *J. Am. Chem. Soc.*, **77**, 3293 (1955).

[24] A. A. Bothner-By, R. S. Schutz, R. F. Dawson, and M. L. Solt, *J. Am. Chem. Soc.*, **84**, 52 (1962).

[25] A. T. Bottini and J. D. Roberts, *J. Am. Chem. Soc.*, **79**, 1458 (1957).

[26] C. Brice and A. S. Perlin, *Can. J. Biochem. Physiol.*, **35**, 7 (1957).

[27] E. V. Brown, E. Cerwonka, and R. C. Anderson, *J. Am. Chem. Soc.*, **73**, 3735 (1951).

[28] K. Burgdorf, H. Grisebach, H. Kracker, and F. Weygand, *Chem. Ber.*, **87**, 87 (1954).

[29] J. G. Burr, *J. Am. Chem. Soc.*, **75**, 1990 (1953).

[30] M. Calvin and R. M. Lemmon, *J. Am. Chem. Soc.*, **69**, 1232 (1947).
[31] W. L. Carrick and A. Fry, *J. Am. Chem. Soc.*, **77**, 4381 (1955).
[32] G. E. Cartier and S. C. Bunce, *J. Am. Chem. Soc.*, **85**, 932 (1963).
[33] L. S. Ciereszko and J. G. Burr, Jr., *J. Am. Chem. Soc.*, **74**, 5431 (1952).
[34] C. J. Collins, *Nucleonics*, **7**, 44 (1950).
[35] C. J. Collins, *J. Am. Chem. Soc.*, **77**, 5517 (1955).
[36] C. J. Collins and B. M. Benjamin, *J. Am. Chem. Soc.*, **75**, 1644 (1953).
[37] C. J. Collins and W. A. Bonner, *J. Am. Chem. Soc.*, **75**, 5379 (1953).
[38] C. J. Collins and W. A. Bonner, *J. Am. Chem. Soc.*, **77**, 92 (1955).
[39] C. J. Collins, J. G. Burr, and D. N. Hess, *J. Am. Chem. Soc.*, **73**, 5176 (1951).
[40] C. J. Collins and O. K. Neville, *J. Am. Chem. Soc.*, **73**, 2471 (1951).
[41] S. M. Csicsery and H. Pines, *J. Am. Chem. Soc.*, **84**, 3939 (1962).
[42] D. Currell and A. Fry, *J. Am. Chem. Soc.*, **78**, 4377 (1956).
[43] D. Y. Curtin, E. W. Flynn, and R. F. Nystrom, *J. Am. Chem. Soc.*, **80**, 4599 (1958).
[44] W. G. Dauben and P. Coad, *J. Am. Chem. Soc.*, **71**, 2928 (1949).
[45] W. G. Dauben, C. F. Hiskey, and M. A. Muhs, *J. Am. Chem. Soc.*, **74**, 2082 (1952).
[46] W. G. Dauben, E. Hoerger, and J. W. Petersen, *J. Am. Chem. Soc.*, **75**, 2347 (1953).
[47] W. G. Dauben, J. C. Reid, P. E. Yankwich, and M. Calvin, *J. Am. Chem. Soc.*, **68**, 2117 (1946).
[48] A. M. Delluva, *Arch. Biochem.*, **45**, 443 (1953).
[49] F. Dituri, S. Gurin, and J. L. Rabinowitz, *J. Am. Chem. Soc.*, **79**, 2650 (1957).
[50] W. v. E. Doering, T. I. Taylor, and E. F. Schoenwaldt, *J. Am. Chem. Soc.*, **70**, 455 (1948).
[51] J. F. Duncan and K. R. Lynn, *Australian J. Chem.*, **10**, 7 (1957).
[52] J. F. Eastham, J. E. Huffaker, V. F. Raaen, and C. J. Collins, *J. Am. Chem. Soc.*, **78**, 4323 (1956).
[53] G. Eberhardt, *J. Am. Chem. Soc.*, **78**, 2832 (1956).
[54] G. Eberhardt and W. T. Schubert, *J. Am. Chem. Soc.*, **78**, 2835 (1956).
[55] G. Ehrensvärd, "Records of the Second International Congress of Biochemistry (1952)," Société d'Edition d'Enseignement Supérieur, Paris, 1952, p. 73.
[56] G. Ehrensvärd and R. Stjernholm, *Acta Chem. Scand.*, **3**, 971 (1949).
[57] E. A. Evans and L. Slotin, *J. Biol. Chem.*, **141**, 439 (1941).
[58] A. W. Fort and R. E. Leary, *J. Am. Chem. Soc.*, **82**, 2494 (1960).
[59] A. W. Fort and J. D. Roberts, *J. Am. Chem. Soc.*, **78**, 584 (1956).
[60] I. D. Frantz, R. B. Loftfield, and W. W. Miller, *Science*, **106**, 544 (1947).
[61] A. R. Friedman and E. Leete, *J. Am. Chem. Soc.*, **85**, 2141 (1963).
[62] B. A. Fries and M. Calvin, *J. Am. Chem. Soc.*, **70**, 2235 (1948).
[63] H. L. Frush and H. S. Isbell, *J. Res. Nat. Bur. Std.*, **51**, 167 (1953).
[64] A. Fry, W. L. Carrick, and C. T. Adams, *J. Am. Chem. Soc.*, **80**, 4743 (1958).
[65] W. P. Gibble, E. B. Kurtz, Jr., and A. E. Kelley, *J. Am. Oil Chemists' Soc.*, **33**, 66 (1956).
[66] C. Gilvarg and K. Bloch, *J. Am. Chem. Soc.*, **72**, 5791 (1950).
[67] C. Gilvarg and K. Bloch, *Federation Proc.*, **10**, 189 (1951).
[68] G. A. Greathouse, *J. Am. Chem. Soc.*, **79**, 4505 (1957).
[69] R. W. Hendler and C. B. Alfinson, *J. Biol. Chem.*, **209**, 55 (1954).
[70] E. C. Hendley and O. K. Neville, *J. Am. Chem. Soc.*, **75**, 1995 (1953).
[71] E. C. Horning and M. G. Horning, *J. Org. Chem.*, **11**, 95 (1946).
[72] H. O. House, *J. Am. Chem. Soc.*, **78**, 2298 (1956).
[73] H. S. Isbell, J. V. Karabinos, H. L. Frush, N. B. Holt, A. Schwebel, and T. T. Galkowski, *J. Res. Nat. Bur. Std.*, **48**, 163 (1952).
[74] G. Juppe and A. P. Wolf, *J. Am. Chem. Soc.*, **83**, 337 (1961).
[75] J. Katz, S. Abraham, and I. L. Chaikoff, *Anal. Chem.*, **27**, 155 (1955).
[76] L. W. Kendrick, B. M. Benjamin, and C. J. Collins, *J. Am. Chem. Soc.*, **80**, 4057 (1958).
[77] H. A. Krebs and W. A. Johnson, *Biochem. J.*, **31**, 645 (1937).
[78] M. Kushner and S. Weinhouse, *J. Am. Chem. Soc.*, **71**, 3558 (1949).

[79] H. Kwart, R. W. Spayd, and C. J. Collins, *J. Am. Chem. Soc.*, **83**, 2579 (1961).

[80] C. C. Lee and J. W. T. Spinks, *Can. J. Chem.*, **31**, 761 (1953).

[81] E. Leete, *J. Am. Chem. Soc.*, **78**, 3520 (1956).

[82] E. Leete, *J. Am. Chem. Soc.*, **82**, 612 (1960).

[83] E. Leete and K. J. Siegfried, *J. Am. Chem. Soc.*, **79**, 4529 (1957).

[84] M. Levine and H. Tarver, *J. Biol. Chem.*, **184**, 427 (1950).

[85] R. B. Loftfield, *J. Am. Chem. Soc.*, **73**, 4707 (1951).

[86] R. P. Lutz and J. D. Roberts, *J. Am. Chem. Soc.*, **84**, 3715 (1962).

[87] H. Lux, *Chem. Ber.*, **62**, 1824 (1929).

[88] R. H. Mazur, W. N. White, D. A. Semenow, C. C. Lee, M. S. Silver, and J. D. Roberts, *J. Am. Chem. Soc.*, **81**, 4300 (1959).

[89] J. Meinwald, *J. Am. Chem. Soc.*, **77**, 1617 (1955).

[90] L. L. Miller and W. F. Bale, *Arch. Biochem.*, **48**, 361 (1954).

[91] J. J. Mitchell, *J. Am. Chem. Soc.*, **80**, 5848 (1958).

[92] L. K. Montgomery and J. D. Roberts, *J. Am. Chem. Soc.*, **82**, 4750 (1960).

[93] F. W. Morthland and W. G. Brown, *J. Am. Chem. Soc.*, **78**, 469 (1956).

[94] E. H. Mosbach, E. F. Phares, and S. F. Carson, *J. Am. Chem. Soc.*, **73**, 5477 (1951).

[95] E. H. Mosbach, E. F. Phares, and S. F. Carson, *Arch. Biochem. Biophys.*, **33**, 179 (1951).

[96] R. T. Mullen and A. P. Wolf, *J. Am. Chem. Soc.*, **84**, 3214 (1962).

[97] P. Nahinsky and S. Ruben, *J. Am. Chem. Soc.*, **63**, 2275 (1941).

[98] O. K. Neville, *J. Am. Chem. Soc.*, **70**, 3499 (1948).

[99] R. F. Nystrom and J. C. Leak, *J. Am. Chem. Soc.*, **75**, 3039 (1953).

[100] W. E. Parham, C. Serres, Jr., and P. R. O'Connor, *J. Am. Chem. Soc.*, **80**, 588 (1958).

[101] E. F. Phares, *Arch. Biochem. Biophys.*, **33**, 173 (1951).

[102] E. F. Phares and M. V. Long, *J. Am. Chem. Soc.*, **77**, 2256 (1955).

[103] H. Pines and A. W. Shaw, *J. Am. Chem. Soc.*, **79**, 1474 (1957).

[104] V. Prelog, H. J. Urech, A. A. Bothner-By, and J. Wüersch, *Helv. Chim. Acta*, **38**, 1095 (1955).

[105] V. F. Raaen and C. J. Collins, *J. Am. Chem. Soc.*, **80**, 1409 (1958).

[106] V. F. Raaen and C. J. Collins, *J. Am. Chem. Soc.*, **80**, 4432 (1958).

[107] R. E. Reeves, *J. Am. Chem. Soc.*, **63**, 1476 (1941).

[108] L. Reio and G. Ehrensvärd, *Arkiv Kimi*, **5**, 301 (1953).

[109] E. Renk and J. D. Roberts, *J. Am. Chem. Soc.*, **83**, 878 (1961).

[110] J. D. Roberts, R. Armstrong, R. F. Trimble, Jr., and A. M. Burg, *J. Am. Chem. Soc.*, **71**, 843 (1949).

[111] J. D. Roberts, W. Bennett, R. E. McMahon, and E. W. Holroyd, Jr., *J. Am. Chem. Soc.*, **74**, 4283 (1952).

[112] J. D. Roberts and M. Halmann, *J. Am. Chem. Soc.*, **75**, 5759 (1953).

[113] J. D. Roberts, C. C. Lee, and W. H. Saunders, *J. Am. Chem. Soc.*, **76**, 4501 (1954).

[114] J. D. Roberts and R. H. Mazur, *J. Am. Chem. Soc.*, **73**, 3543 (1951).

[115] J. D. Roberts, R. E. McMahon, and J. S. Hine, *J. Am. Chem. Soc.*, **72**, 4327 (1950).

[116] J. D. Roberts, D. A. Semenow, H. E. Simmons, Jr., and L. A. Carlsmith, *J. Am. Chem. Soc.*, **78**, 601 (1956).

[117] J. D. Roberts, D. R. Smith, and C. C. Lee, *J. Am. Chem. Soc.*, **73**, 618 (1951).

[118] J. D. Roberts and J. A. Yancey, *J. Am. Chem. Soc.*, **77**, 5558 (1955).

[119] R. M. Roberts and S. G. Brandenberger, *J. Am. Chem. Soc.*, **79**, 5484 (1957).

[120] R. M. Roberts, S. G. Brandenberger, and S. G. Panayides, *J. Am. Chem. Soc.*, **80**, 2507 (1958).

[121] R. M. Roberts, G. A. Ropp, and O. K. Neville, *J. Am. Chem. Soc.*, **77**, 1764 (1955).

[122] A. Roe and E. L. Albenesius, *J. Am. Chem. Soc.*, **74**, 2402 (1952).

[123] G. A. Ropp, *J. Am. Chem. Soc.*, **80**, 6691 (1958).

[124] G. A. Ropp, *J. Org. Chem.*, **25**, 1255 (1960).

[125] G. A. Ropp, *J. Am. Chem. Soc.*, **82**, 4252 (1960).

[126] G. A. Ropp, W. A. Bonner, M. T. Clark, and V. F. Raaen, *J. Am. Chem. Soc.*, **76**, 1710 (1954).

[127] G. A. Ropp and V. F. Raaen, *J. Am. Chem. Soc.*, **76**, 4484 (1954).

[128] S. Roseman, *J. Am. Chem. Soc.*, **75**, 3854 (1953).

[129] T. S. Rothrock and A. Fry, *J. Am. Chem. Soc.*, **80**, 4349 (1958).

[130] J. C. Sauer and J. L. Cairns, *J. Am. Chem. Soc.*, **79**, 2660 (1957).

[131] W. H. Saunders, *J. Am. Chem. Soc.*, **78**, 6127 (1956).

[132] F. Scardiglia and J. D. Roberts, *Tetrahedron*, **1**, 343 (1957).

[133] H. J. Schaeffer and C. J. Collins, *J. Am. Chem. Soc.*, **78**, 124 (1956).

[134] D. A. Semenow, E. F. Cox, and J. D. Roberts, *J. Am. Chem. Soc.*, **78**, 322 (1956).

[135] F. Shafizadeh and M. L. Wolfram, *J. Am. Chem. Soc.*, **78**, 2498 (1956).

[136] S. H. Sharman, F. F. Caserio, R. F. Nystrom, J. C. Leak, and W. G. Young, *J. Am. Chem. Soc.*, **80**, 5970 (1958).

[137] H. Shimanzona, W. T. Schubert, and F. F. Nord, *J. Am. Chem. Soc.*, **80**, 1992 (1958).

[138] A. F. Shulgin, *J. Am. Chem. Soc.*, **77**, 2338 (1955).

[139] M. S. Silver, P. R. Shafer, J. E. Nordlander, C. Rüchardt, and J. D. Roberts, *J. Am. Chem. Soc.*, **82**, 2646 (1960).

[140] O. Simamura and N. Inamoto, *Bull. Chem. Soc. Japan*, **28**, 529 (1955).

[141] O. Simamura, T. Suehiro, N. Inamoto, and T. Tsuyuki, "Elucidation of the Mechanism of the Michael Reaction with Carbon-14 as a Tracer," Radioisotopes in Scientific Research, vol. II, p. 21, Pergamon Press, 1958.

[142] F. L. J. Sixma and H. Hendricks, *Koninkl. Ned. Akad. Wetenschap., Proc.*, **59B**, 61 (1956).

[143] L. H. Slaugh, *J. Am. Chem. Soc.*, **81**, 2262 (1959).

[144] W. B. Smith and J. D. Anderson, *J. Am. Chem. Soc.*, **82**, 656 (1960).

[145] W. B. Smith, R. E. Bowman, and T. J. Kmet, *J. Am. Chem. Soc.*, **81**, 997 (1959).

[146] J. C. Sowden, M. G. Blair, and D. J. Kuenne, *J. Am. Chem. Soc.*, **79**, 6450 (1957).

[147] J. C. Sowden and E. K. Pohlen, *J. Am. Chem. Soc.*, **80**, 242 (1958).

[148] J. C. Sowden and R. R. Thompson, *J. Am. Chem. Soc.*, **80**, 2236 (1958).

[149] M. Stiles and R. P. Mayer, *J. Am. Chem. Soc.*, **81**, 1497 (1959).

[150] M. Strassman, L. A. Locke, A. J. Thomas, and S. Weinhouse, *J. Am. Chem. Soc.*, **78**, 1600 (1956).

[151] M. Strassman, A. J. Thomas, L. A. Locke, and S. Weinhouse, *J. Am. Chem. Soc.*, **78**, 228 (1956).

[152] R. J. Suhadolnik and R. G. Chenoweth, *J. Am. Chem. Soc.*, **80**, 4391 (1958).

[153] H. J. Urech and V. Prelog, *Helv. Chim. Acta*, **40**, 477 (1957).

[154] M. F. Utter, F. Lipmann, and C. H. Werkman, *J. Biol. Chem.*, **158**, 521 (1945).

[155] S. Weinhouse, G. Medes, and N. F. Floyd, *J. Biol. Chem.*, **155**, 143 (1944).

[156] S. Weinhouse, G. Medes, and N. F. Floyd, *J. Biol. Chem.*, **166**, 691 (1946).

[157] A. Weissbach and D. B. Sprinson, *J. Biol. Chem.*, **202**, 1023 (1953).

[158] F. Weygand, A. Wacker, and V. Schmied-Korwarzik, *Experientia*, **6**, 184 (1950).

[159] A. P. Wolf, B. Gordon, and R. C. Anderson, *J. Am. Chem. Soc.*, **78**, 2657 (1956).

[160] A. P. Wolf, C. S. Redvanly, and R. C. Anderson, *J. Am. Chem. Soc.*, **79**, 3717 (1957).

[161] H. G. Wood, R. W. Brown, C. H. Werkman, and C. G. Stuckwisch, *J. Am. Chem. Soc.*, **66**, 1812 (1944).

[162] H. G. Wood, N. Lifson, and V. Lorber, *J. Biol. Chem.*, **159**, 475 (1945).

[163] H. G. Wood, C. H. Werkman, A. Hemingway, and A. O. Nier, *J. Biol. Chem.*, **139**, 483 (1941).

[164] H. G. Wood, C. H. Werkman, A. Hemingway, A. O. Nier, and C. G. Stuckwisch, *J. Am. Chem. Soc.*, **63**, 2140 (1941).

CITED REFERENCES

[1] W. G. Dauben and P. Coad, *J. Am. Chem. Soc.*, **71**, 2928 (1949).

[2] B. A. Fries and M. Calvin, *J. Am. Chem. Soc.*, **70**, 2235 (1948).

[3] J. R. Catch, *Anal. Chem.*, **29**, 1726 (1957).

[4] R. Nakai, M. Sugii, and H. Nakao, *J. Am. Chem. Soc.*, **81**, 1003 (1959).

[5] D. G. Grant and H. S. Turner, *Nature*, **165**, 153 (1950).

⁶ G. A. Ropp, *J. Chem. Educ.*, **34**, 60 (1957).

⁷ S. Weinhouse, G. Medes, and N. F. Floyd, *J. Biol. Chem.*, **155**, 143 (1944).

⁸ J. Bigeleisen and T. L. Allen, *J. Chem. Phys.*, **19**, 760 (1951).

⁹ M. Calvin, C. Heidelberger, J. C. Reid, B. M. Tolbert, and P. F. Yankwich, "Isotopic Carbon," chap. 11, John Wiley & Sons, Inc., New York, 1949.

¹⁰ E. Grovenstein, Jr., and G. A. Ropp, *J. Am. Chem. Soc.*, **78**, 2560 (1956).

¹¹ G. G. Smith and D. M. Fahey, *J. Am. Chem. Soc.*, **81**, 3391 (1959).

¹² S. Seltzer, G. A. Hamilton, and F. H. West-heimer, *J. Am. Chem. Soc.*, **81**, 4018 (1959).

¹³ S. Barton and C. R. Porter, *J. Chem. Soc.*, 2483 (1956).

¹⁴ J. J. Mitchell, *J. Am. Chem. Soc.*, **80**, 5849 (1958).

¹⁵ S. Weinhouse, G. Medes, and N. F. Floyd, *J. Biol. Chem.*, **166**, 691 (1946).

¹⁶ G. A. Ropp, *J. Am. Chem. Soc.*, **82**, 4252 (1960).

¹⁷ M. Calvin and R. M. Lemmon, *J. Am. Chem. Soc.*, **69**, 1232 (1947).

¹⁸ J. D. Roberts, D. R. Smith, and C. C. Lee, *J. Am. Chem. Soc.*, **73**, 618 (1951).

¹⁹ H. Wolff, 'The Schmidt Reaction,' in "Organic Reactions," R. Adams, Ed.-in-Chief, vol. III, chap. 8, John Wiley & Sons, Inc., New York, 1946.

²⁰ E. F. Phares, *Arch. Biochem. Biophys.*, **33**, 173 (1951).

²¹ E. H. Mosbach, E. F. Phares, and S. F. Carson, *Arch. Biochem. Biophys.*, **33**, 179 (1951).

²² E. F. Phares and M. V. Long, *J. Am. Chem. Soc.*, **77**, 2556 (1956).

²³ A. P. Wolf, C. S. Redvanly, and R. C. Anderson, *J. Am. Chem. Soc.*, **79**, 3723 (1957).

²³ᵃ J. L. Rabinowitz and B. Pritzker, *Anal. Chem.*, **36**, 403 (1964).

²⁴ G. Darzens and C. Mentzer, *Compt. Rend.*, **213**, 268 (1941).

²⁵ W. G. Dauben, E. Hoerger, and J. W. Petersen, *J. Am. Chem. Soc.*, **75**, 2347 (1953).

²⁶ W. P. Gibble, E. B. Kurtz, Jr., and A. E. Kelley, *J. Am. Oil Chemists' Soc.*, **33**, 66 (1956).

²⁷ S. Roseman, *J. Am. Chem. Soc.*, **75**, 3854 (1953).

²⁷ᵃ Unpublished work of V. F. Raaen and R. Beach.

²⁷ᵇ C. Granito and H. P. Schultz, *J. Org. Chem.*, **28**, 879 (1963).

²⁸ V. F. Raaen and C. J. Collins, *J. Am. Chem. Soc.*, **80**, 1413 (1958).

²⁹ W. A. Bonner, C. E. Stehr, and J. R. do Amaral, *J. Am. Chem. Soc.*, **80**, 4732 (1958).

³⁰ R. U. Lemieux and E. von Rudloff, *Can. J. Chem.*, **33**, 1701 (1955).

³¹ A. A. Bothner-By, *J. Am. Chem. Soc.*, **77**, 3295 (1955).

³² H. Gilman, "Organic Chemistry," 2d ed., vol. 1, p. 636, John Wiley & Sons, Inc., New York, 1943.

³³ W. A. Bonner, *J. Chem. Educ.*, **30**, 452 (1953).

³⁴ R. L. Shriner, R. C. Fuson, and D. Y. Curtin, "The Systematic Identification of Organic Compounds," 4th ed., p. 219, John Wiley & Sons, Inc., New York, 1956.

³⁵ W. A. Bonner and C. J. Collins, *J. Am. Chem. Soc.*, **75**, 4517 (1953).

³⁶ A. W. Fort and J. D. Roberts, *J. Am. Chem. Soc.*, **78**, 588 (1956).

³⁷ V. Prelog, H. J. Urech, A. A. Bothner-By, and J. Wuersch, *Helv. Chim. Acta*, **38**, 1095 (1955).

³⁸ J. D. Roberts and R. H. Mazur, *J. Am. Chem. Soc.*, **73**, 3542 (1951).

³⁹ A. A. Benson and J. A. Bassham, *J. Am. Chem. Soc.*, **70**, 3939 (1948).

⁴⁰ A. M. Delluva, *Arch. Biochem. Biophys.*, **45**, 443 (1953).

⁴¹ E. L. Jackson, 'Periodic Acid Oxidation,' in R. Adams, W. E. Bachmann, L. F. Fieser, J. R. Johnson, and H. R. Snyder, Eds., "Organic Reactions," chap. 8, vol. II, John Wiley & Sons, Inc., New York, 1944.

⁴² R. Criegee, 'Oxidations with Lead Tetraacetate and Periodic Acid,' in W. Foerst, Ed., "Newer Methods of Preparative Organic Chemistry," p. 1, Interscience Publishers, New York, 1948; also R. Criegee, 'Newer Investigations on Oxidation with Lead Tetraacetate,' in W. Foerst, Ed., "Newer Methods of Preparative Organic Chemistry," pp. 367–388, Academic Press, New York, 1963.

⁴³ H. L. Frush and H. S. Isbell, *J. Res. Nat. Bur. Std.*, **51**, 167 (1953).

⁴⁴ J. Meinwald, *J. Am. Chem. Soc.*, **77**, 1620 (1955).

⁴⁵ W. A. Bonner and D. D. Tanner, *J. Am. Chem. Soc.*, **80**, 1448 (1958).

⁴⁶ J. D. Roberts and J. A. Yancey, *J. Am. Chem. Soc.*, **77**, 5561 (1955).

[47] G. A. Ropp and V. F. Raaen, *J. Am. Chem. Soc.*, **76**, 4484 (1954).

[48] G. Eberhardt, *J. Am. Chem. Soc.*, **78**, 2832 (1956).

[49] D. Y. Curtin, E. W. Flynn, and R. F. Nystrom, *J. Am. Chem. Soc.*, **80**, 4599 (1958).

[50] H. J. Schaeffer and C. J. Collins, *J. Am. Chem. Soc.*, **78**, 131 (1956).

[51] F. Scardiglia and J. D. Roberts, *Tetrahedron*, **1**, 343 (1957).

[52] D. Currell and A. Fry, *J. Am. Chem. Soc.*, **78**, 4377 (1956).

[53] H. Pines and A. W. Shaw, *J. Am. Chem. Soc.*, **79**, 1474 (1957).

[54] R. M. Roberts, G. A. Ropp, and O. K. Neville, *J. Am. Chem. Soc.*, **77**, 1764 (1955).

[55] R. M. Roberts and S. G. Brandenberger, *J. Am. Chem. Soc.*, **79**, 5484 (1957).

[56] R. M. Roberts, S. G. Brandenberger, and S. G. Panayides, *J. Am. Chem. Soc.*, **80**, 2507 (1958).

[57] E. Leete, *J. Am. Chem. Soc.*, **78**, 3520 (1956).

[58] E. Leete and K. J. Siegfried, *J. Am. Chem. Soc.*, **79**, 4529 (1957).

[59] B. M. Benjamin, H. J. Schaeffer, and C. J. Collins, *J. Am. Chem. Soc.*, **79**, 6162 (1957).

[60] H. Wynberg and A. P. Wolf, *J. Am. Chem. Soc.*, **85**, 3308 (1963).

[61] J. C. Colbert and C. L. Hensley, *J. Am. Chem. Soc.*, **62**, 3257 (1940).

[62] C. J. Collins, J. G. Burr, and D. N. Hess, *J. Am. Chem. Soc.*, **73**, 5176 (1951).

[63] G. Ehrensvärd, "Records of the 2nd Intern. Congress of Biochemistry in Paris, 1952," p. 72, Société d'Edition d'Enseignement Supérieur, Paris, 1952; *Chem. Abstr.*, **47**, 4397c (1953).

[64] J. Baddiley, G. Ehrensvärd, E. Klein, L. Reio, and E. Saluste, *J. Biol. Chem.*, **183**, 777 (1950).

[65] C. Gilvarg and K. Bloch, *J. Am. Chem. Soc.*, **72**, 5791 (1950).

[66] G. Eberhardt and W. J. Schubert, *J. Am. Chem. Soc.*, **78**, 2835 (1956).

[67] H. Shimanzonà, W. J. Schubert, and F. F. Nord, *J. Am. Chem. Soc.*, **80**, 1992 (1958).

[68] L. Reio and G. Ehrensvärd, *Arkiv Kemi*, **5**, 301 (1953).

[69] J. D. Roberts, D. A. Semenow, H. E. Simmons, Jr., and L. A. Carlsmith, *J. Am. Chem. Soc.*, **78**, 601 (1956).

[70] D. A. Semenow, E. F. Cox, and J. D. Roberts, *J. Am. Chem. Soc.*, **78**, 3221 (1956).

[71] W. G. Dauben, J. C. Reid, P. E. Yankwich, and M. Calvin, *J. Am. Chem. Soc.*, **72**, 121 (1950).

[72] E. V. Brown, E. Cerwonka, and R. C. Anderson, *J. Am. Chem. Soc.*, **73**, 8735 (1951).

[73] F. L. J. Sixma and H. Hendricks, *Proc. Koninkl. Ned. Akad. Wetenschap.*, **59B**, 61 (1956).

[74] W. A. Bonner and C. J. Collins, *J. Am. Chem. Soc.*, **78**, 5587 (1956).

[75] D. E. Pearson and C. M. Greer, *J. Am. Chem. Soc.*, **71**, 1895 (1949).

GENERAL REFERENCES

(*a*) M. Calvin, C. Heidelberger, J. C. Reid, B. M. Tolbert, and P. F. Yankwich, "Isotopic Carbon," chap. 11, John Wiley & Sons, Inc., New York, 1949.

(*b*) M. D. Kamen, "Isotopic Tracers in Biology," 3d ed., Academic Press Inc., New York, 1957.

(*c*) S. Aronoff, "Techniques of Radiobiochemistry," chap. 1, State College Press, Ames, Iowa, 1956.

(*d*) A. Murray, III, and D. L. Williams, "Organic Syntheses with Isotopes," part I, 'Compounds of Isotopic Carbon,' Interscience Publishers, New York, 1958.

(*e*) J. R. Catch, "Carbon-14 Compounds," Butterworth Inc., Washington, D.C., 1961.

PROBLEMS

10-1. Acetone-1-^{14}C having a radioactivity of 1.50 mc/g was degraded by the iodoform reaction. The acetic acid produced was isolated as the pure *p*-nitrobenzyl ester. Calculate (*a*) the molar radioactivity and (*b*) the radioactivity in μc/g of that derivative; assume that no isotope effect occurs during the degradation.

10-2. Malonic-1-^{14}C acid having a radioactivity of 10.6 μc/g was condensed with benzaldehyde-α-^{14}C having a total radioactivity of 16.5 μc/g. The benzaldehyde-α-^{14}C was later shown to be contaminated with 3.0 wt % benzoic-α-^{14}C acid produced in the aldehyde by air oxidation. Calculate (*a*) the specific radioactivity of the pure cinnamic acid produced in the condensation; assume that there was no isotope effect. (*b*) By what procedure could the cinnamic acid be degraded to determine the percent of its radioactivity in the carbon atom *alpha* to the ring?

10-3. If the presumed intermediate, benzalmalonic acid, in the condensation described in Problem 10-2 underwent decarboxylation with an *intramolecular* isotope effect of 5.0% ($k_{12}/k_{14} = 1.050$), what would be the molar radioactivity of the cinnamic acid?

10-4. Glucose-1-^{13}C that contained 20.0% excess carbon-13 at the labeled position was converted to an aldoheptose by a cyanohydrin synthesis in which cyanide that contained the normal 1.1% abundance of carbon-13 was used. Calculate (*a*) the percent excess carbon-13 in the carbon dioxide formed by total combustion of the heptose and (*b*) the percent excess carbon-13 in the carbon dioxide formed by total combustion of the phenyl osazone prepared from the heptose. For practice, search the appropriate references in Chap. 10 to locate a method suitable for degrading the aldoheptose in such a way that the position-2 carbon could be isolated as carbon dioxide for mass spectrometric analysis to prove that the position-2 carbon contained all the excess carbon-13 present in the molecule.

10-5. For a carbon-14-labeled substituted benzil

$$R-\!\!\!\left\langle\,\,\right\rangle\!\!\!-^{14}CO-CO-\!\!\!\left\langle\,\,\right\rangle\!\!\!-R'$$

the mass of substituent R was 29 and that of R′ was 57. The specific radioactivity of the substituted benzil was 23.8 $\mu c/g$. After a benzilic acid rearrangement, the substituted benzilic acid was degraded by decarboxylation. The radioactivity of the carbon-14 dioxide collected was 0.125 $\mu c/ml$ at 25° and 740 mm.

(*a*) Calculate the percent migration for the R-substituted aromatic nucleus and also for the R′-substituted nucleus.

(*b*) If the results calculated in (*a*) were suspected of being slightly in error due to the occurrence of a normal carbon-14 isotope effect during the decarboxylation, how would the results be influenced by correcting for the isotope effect?

10-6. From information given in Chap. 10 or from a general knowledge of organic chemistry, suggest practical ways to: (*a*) determine the percent of the carbon-14 radioactivity in the carbonyl group of a sample of *o*-benzoylbenzoic acid that also contains radioactivity in the carboxyl group, (*b*) determine the distribution of carbon-14 radioactivity between the position-1 carbon atom and the position-8 carbon atom of 1-nitroanthracene labeled only in positions 1 and 8, (*c*) determine the distribution of carbon-14 radioactivity between the two aromatic rings in the carbon-14-labeled 4-(*p*-nitrophenyl)benzoic acid.

10-7. Dituri, Gurin, and Rabinowitz degraded a sample of biosynthetic squalene and showed that the principal distribution of carbon-14 in this polymeric material is as indicated by the stars in the formula

$$\left[\overset{*}{C}H_3C\!=\!CHCH_2\overset{*}{C}H_2C\!=\!CHCH_2\overset{*}{C}H_2C\!=\!CHCH_2\right.\!\!\!-$$
$$\left.\underset{CH_3}{|}\qquad\underset{CH_3}{|}\qquad\underset{CH_3}{|}\right]$$

Suggest degradative routes to prove that this is the distribution of the label. Compare the suggested methods with those used by Dituri, Gurin, and Rabinowitz.

10-8. Collins and Bonner degraded 1,2,2-triphenylethanol labeled in the rings with carbon-14. The fraction of the radioactivity in the ring at position 1 was determined. Suggest independently (*a*) a suitable degradation and compare it with that used by Bonner and Collins (note the possibility of an error due to prolonged oxidation), (*b*) how the results would be affected by this prolonged oxidation.

CHAPTER
11
ASSAY OF CARBON-14 COMPOUNDS

11-1 INTRODUCTION

Work with radioactive materials may require measurement of the strength of a radioactive source and measurement of the dose received by an irradiated volume or mass of a substance. The unit of measurement of source radioactivity is the curie (c), at one time defined as the disintegration rate associated with 1 g of radium. Today the curie is the unit used to describe *any* radioactive source having a decay rate of 3.700×10^{10} dps. Often counting equipment, especially scintillation counters, provide data in counts per minute. It is therefore worth remembering that a curie refers to that quantity of a nuclide that has a decay rate of 2.22×10^{12} dpm. Because the curie is a very large unit, it is often convenient to use instead millicurie (mc) and microcurie (μc), which are one-thousandth and one-millionth of a curie, respectively. The preferred expression for level of radioactivity is specific radioactivity, that is, the disintegration rate of a radioisotope per unit amount of the sample (e.g., millicuries per milligram, microcuries per milliliter, millicuries per mole, etc.). Generally, it is desirable to describe the radioactivity of carbon-14 compounds at the tracer level in millicuries per mole (mc/mole). Compounds with very high molar radioactivity are conveniently measured in the unit millicuries per millimole (mc/mmole). Use of the molar radioactivity terminology is especially desirable when mechanism studies are made that describe large numbers of labeled related compounds. If a single compound is used throughout a study or if the specific radioactivity of a mixture of compounds is measured, then it may be convenient—or even necessary—to express the measurement in terms of radioactivity units per gram or per milliliter. The use of such arbitrary and loose units as "counts," "counts/min," "counts/min/g," and "disintegrations/min" should be discouraged.

The half-life of carbon-14 is 5745 ± 50 y.[1,2] Carbon-14 decays to nitrogen with the emission of a beta particle whose maximum energy is about 0.156 Mev.[3] Beta particles are high-speed electrons ejected from nuclei as a result of nuclear disintegration. Unlike alpha particles, they do not have discrete values of energy and are thought not to be one of the nuclear subparticles. Primary beta particles show a continuous energy distribution whose mean energy bears no exact relationship to the maximum energy. Empirical formulas for calculating radiation dosage contain a factor, $\frac{1}{3}$, which is the approximate ratio of the average energy to the maximum energy. The remaining two-thirds of the total energy is lost through the emission of an antineutrino, a neutral particle possibly of zero mass. The interaction of the antineutrino with matter is extremely weak; there is therefore no possibility of its interference with the measurement of beta radiation.

When a beta particle passes through a gas, there is a Coulombic repulsion between the moving electron and the negatively charged electrons of the atom. This interaction may lead simply to excitation of the atom, or, if the effect is great, to removal of an electron from an atom or molecule. The average amount of energy lost in the production of one ion pair (electron + positively charged atom or molecule) amounts to 30 to 35 ev for the common gases. The average carbon-14 beta particle of 45-kev energy can therefore produce about 1500 ion pairs. The ion pairs are quickly neutralized by recombination. In the presence of suitable electrodes, the ionization produced by nuclear radiation provides the means by which nuclear disintegrations can be detected.

Carbon-14 beta particles have a maximum range of about 22 cm in air and 0.1 mm in aluminum foil. The effectiveness of a shield against alpha or beta particles is related to the density and to the thickness of the shield. This relationship may be expressed as

$$F = dx = (mg/cm^3)cm = mg/cm^2$$

where F, d, and x are the absorption factor, density, and thickness of the absorber, respectively. The density-thickness, mg/cm^2, is often used to describe the window of a Geiger-Müller counter (e.g., 1.4 mg/cm^2). The relatively weak radiation from carbon-14 simplifies the confinement of radiation but makes its detection difficult. No single system of detecting and counting weak beta particles offers a perfect solution.

There are six fundamentally different methods for detecting the soft betas from carbon-14: detection in the Geiger and proportional regions, ion-current measurement, autoradiography, liquid scintillation, and use of semiconductors. Choice of the best method must be based on a consideration of several factors including sensitivity, precision, speed, intensity limits, and cost. Unfortunately, performance is approximately proportionate with cost, and cost may vary from a few cents for autoradiographic apparatus to $15,000 or more for a sophisticated liquid-scintillation counter.

Beta radiation from carbon-14 is readily detected with an end-window Geiger-Müller counter. The window is very thin (1 to 2 mg/cm^2) and is therefore fragile. The popularity of thin-window counters results largely from their low cost and relative simplicity. A thin-window Geiger-Müller tube is almost always used in the portable, laboratory monitor found in every carbon-14 laboratory. With the exception of autoradiographic methods, the thin-window Geiger-Müller counting system is the least sensitive and the least precise. Samples are difficult to prepare for measurement with it, and it is necessary to correct for self-absorption and back-scattering. The counting efficiency is about 5%. Windowless detectors are useful for solid compounds but are subject to contamination by volatile samples. They are more efficient than thin-window counters and are also more costly.

Labeled gases such as carbon-14 dioxide may be used to fill or partly fill the detecting tubes, both in proportional and Geiger-Müller systems. The efficiency of such gas counting systems approaches 100%, but their use is restricted to a limited number of gases. They are especially useful for detecting small amounts of radioactivity in gases having low specific radioactivity.

Ionization chambers can be used to detect the radioactivity of gaseous samples over a range from a few counts per minute to 10^6 counts/min. The problems of sample geometry and self-absorption are eliminated. The combustion of organic compounds to carbon dioxide is a well-developed technique by which most organic compounds are oxidized quantitatively. The ionization chamber, like the Geiger-Müller tube, is a simple device; it is little more than a tin can fitted with a well-insulated probe on one end and a stopcock on the other for filling. When used with a good vibrating-reed electrometer, the ionization chamber provides a moderately fast means for making very accurate measurements of carbon-14 radioactivity. Its use at very low levels of radioactivity is tedious. A further disadvantage is the high cost of the electrometer.

The determination of carbon-14 radioactivity by liquid-scintillation counting is a relatively recent development. The method possesses many of the features desired in a counting system except that it is costly. It is less precise than the gas-proportional or ionization-chamber counting methods but is very sensitive. It accommodates a range of sample sizes from the smallest measurable amount to 20 ml or larger, depending on the volume of the cell. It is often necessary to correct for somewhat unpredictable chemical quenching; highly colored samples are not counted at all by liquid-scintillation counting techniques.

Autoradiographic methods are useful for the qualitative information they give, especially when used in conjunction with paper chromatography. The autoradiographic method is the least accurate and least sensitive of all the possible methods; it is discussed in Chap. 13.

The use of semiconductors for particle detection is a recent innovation; there is no literature on their application to the detection of weak beta particles from carbon-14. Semiconductors behave very erratically in the presence of organic vapors. The detector would have to be encapsulated in a very thin, inert, nonconducting envelope, or the carbon-14-labeled compound would have to be present in some standard form such as carbon-14 dioxide.

11-2 EXTERNAL COUNTING OF SOLIDS, LIQUIDS, AND GASES

Thin-window and windowless counters can be used to determine the carbon-14 content of solids, liquids, and gases. Formerly solid counting of carbon-14 was the most commonly used method. Although this method lacks accuracy and sensitivity, it is considered to have the advantages of low cost, adaptability to automation, and simplicity. The simplicity of the approach is deceptive, however, for solid counting is subject to many experimental errors.

Labeled liquids and solids are usually deposited on shallow plastic, metal, or glass cups called planchets. They are often 1 in. in diameter. The difficulties arising in the determination of radioactivity on planchets result from variations in self-absorption, scattering, and geometry. These factors are illustrated in Fig. 11-1.

As thicker and thicker samples of a labeled material are prepared for counting, the counting rate increases rapidly at first, then begins to level off, and eventually approaches a constant value. The sample thickness for which all carbon-14 beta particles emitted from the lowest layers are absorbed by the sample itself is about 25 mg/cm². Samples of this thickness or thicker are said to be "infinitely thick." This saturation value for the counting rate is proportional to the specific

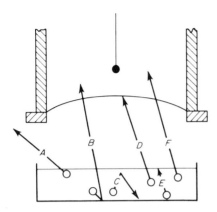

FIG. 11-1   Fate of beta particles: *A*, lost due to unfavorable geometry; *B*, backscattered from planchet and counted; *C*, self-scattered; *D*, absorbed by window; *E*, absorbed by sample; *F*, counted. (*Adapted from* NUCLEAR-CHICAGO TECHNICAL BULLETIN NO. **7**.)

radioactivity of the sample, not to its total radioactivity.

Deposits that are 1 mg/cm² or less in thickness have negligible self-absorption but are difficult to spread or "plate" uniformly. If an end-window Geiger-Müller tube is used as the detector, further absorption takes place in the air between the sample and the window and in the window itself. To withstand atmospheric pressure, the window must be at least 1-mg/cm² thick. A window that is 2-mg/cm² thick will absorb about half the radiation from carbon-14.

The location of the detecting tube with respect to the sample determines the probability that the beta particle will enter the tube. It is important that the geometry of this arrangement be as constant as possible throughout a series of measurements.

Backscattering can be a serious cause of error and varies greatly (as much as 25%) with the nature of the compound and the material on the planchet. Such scattering results from the reflection, back to the sample surface, of beta particles originally directed *away* from the detecting tube. Backscattering is most noticeable in samples that contain heavy elements

(e.g., in Ba¹⁴CO₃) and for planchets made of copper or other elements of high atomic number. Even for aluminum planchets, the count rate was found[4] to be 110 ± 1% of the value observed when extremely thin organic membranes were used as supports. The grain size and smoothness of the layer of sample have an added effect on backscattering. Taken together, these effects are sufficient reason for converting all carbon-14 samples to a common chemical form, usually barium carbonate-¹⁴C.

If small samples must be counted, the maximum efficiency can be increased from 5% to as much as 50% by going from an end-window counter to a windowless counter, using thin samples, and choosing planchets that cause maximum backscatter.

11-2a   PREPARATION OF ORGANIC SAMPLES

Techniques for preparing organic samples as well as their inorganic derivatives are reviewed by a number of authors.[5,6,7,8,9] The detection of carbon-14 in flowing gases is discussed in detail in Sec. 12-1b.

Organic solids are most readily counted at infinite thickness; however, a large amount of sample (25 to 100 mg) is needed. If thin films of known thickness are counted with an end-window or windowless counter, then it is necessary to extrapolate to zero thickness. This extrapolation is done by plotting count rates against thickness for samples of known radioactivity. Such self-absorption curves have been plotted for carbon-14-labeled barium carbonate, glucose, and fatty acids.[10] Berson and Yalow[11] describe a method for sample-absorption correction that requires only the counting of a duplicate sample to which has been added a known quantity of a standard carbon-14-labeled compound of negligible mass. The following is quoted from the procedure of Berson and Yalow:[12]

If *U* and *S* represent the number of microcuries of C¹⁴ present in the unknown sample and the added standard, respectively, A is the counting rate of the unknown sample and B is the counting rate of the duplicate unknown sample containing the added known quantity of S, then

$$cU = A$$
$$cU + cS = B$$

where c is the counting rate per microcurie of C^{14} under the particular conditions of assay and is the same for both samples. These equations permit determination of the C^{14} content of the unknown sample in absolute units (microcuries) if that of the standard is known. However, it is frequently necessary to know only the relative C^{14} contents of different unknown samples or the C^{14} content in terms of a standard. Then

$$U = [A/(B - A)]S$$

and unknown samples of varying and undetermined weights may readily be assayed relative to the standard and to each other without further correction for absorption in the samples.

The further suggestion was made that the added radioactivity should be at least as great as, preferably much greater than, that expected to be present in the unknown sample.

Organic solids can be dissolved in a suitable volatile solvent and then plated out by evaporation of the solvent. Kordecki and Gandy[13] use this technique to precisely plate stearic acid-1-^{14}C from its solution in benzene. Calvin and co-authors[14] provide detailed plating data for a large number of pure organic compounds. Sample spinners and sample dryers are aids to uniform plating; these are available commercially. Spinners for rotating the planchet during application of the solution or during the drying can be improvised from inexpensive 2- or 4-watt timing motors. The source of heat may be an electric hair dryer or a red-Pyrex infrared lamp. The possibility that the sample will react with the planchet, especially at elevated temperatures, must be considered. Seaman and Stewart[15] found that there is loss of activity when (hexadecyl-1-^{14}C)-trimethylammonium bromide is counted in glass planchets. Samples that do not adhere well and are easily wafted away may be anchored by using in the solvent a very small amount of a binding agent, such as Collodion. Compounds normally considered nonvolatile can show significant losses when plated out in a thin layer on an open planchet. As a result of such volatilization, it may be difficult to reproduce count rates; in the case of flow counters, serious contamination can result. Hamilton and Moreland[16] greatly reduced the volatility of samples by coating the plated samples with a clear acrylic plastic. The coatings so applied were 0.4-to-0.8 mg/cm^2 thick, a thickness sufficient to cause significant absorption and therefore some decrease in the counting rate.

Other efforts to secure uniform sample deposits have been made. Solutions of solids have been pipetted onto paper disks made of lens tissue or filter paper.[17] Various devices have been used to ensure that the paper is uniformly impregnated. The accuracy of radioactivity measurements made on deposits so obtained is poor.

Liquids may also be measured in planchets. One procedure[18] specifies the use of 1% aerosol in the sample to cause it to spread evenly on cupped stainless-steel planchets. Samples are then covered with a thin Mylar film. McCready[19] used agar as a binder to produce uniform deposits of aqueous solutions that contained carbon-14 compounds. The layer so produced had reproducible self-absorption of less than 20%.

Nonvolatile liquid samples are easily counted if they spread smoothly on the planchet. A wetting agent can be added to liquids having objectionably high surface tension; those which creep require that a repellent be spread around the periphery of the planchet.[7] Solids can be dissolved in nonvolatile liquids such as formamide and ethylene glycol. The solutions are then counted with a thin-window or windowless counter. Carbon-14 has been determined in animal tissues by dissolving them in hot formamide. Aliquots of the solution are then deposited on disks of lens tissue centered in the planchets.[20] Moyer and Isbell[21] measured carbon-14 present in an alkali-metal cyanide by adding a known weight of glucose to the cyanide to convert it to a glucose derivative and then dissolving the derivative in a known volume of formamide. Carbon-14 dioxide from barium carbonate-^{14}C was converted to potassium carbonate-^{14}C, and the latter was counted in ethylene glycol solution. The procedure for carbon-14 dioxide seems unduly complicated. The use of a nonvolatile solvent requires moderately large samples or high molar radioactivity because of the greatly reduced efficiency.

Isbell, Frush, and Holt[22] describe a procedure for the radioassay of both carbon-14 and tritium by means of a windowless gas-flow proportional counter. Water-soluble nonvolatile compounds that contain both isotopes in a uniform film of sodium-O-(carboxymethyl)cellulose were determined with the proportional counter and were then re-counted in the presence of a screen capable of just stopping all tritium radiation. Suitable calibration curves were used to determine the amount of tritium and carbon-14 present. Satisfactory analyses are claimed for samples that contained less than 0.005 μc of tritium and 0.001 μc of carbon-14 (compare the autoradiographic resolution of doubly labeled compounds described in Secs. 13-1 and -7).

Energetic beta particles can give up energy through the production of *bremsstrahlung*. Bremsstrahlung are identical with continuous x rays and have energies ranging from zero to near the maximum energy of the beta particle. The radiation is caused by a change in the velocity or direction of the beta particle as it enters the electrical field of an atom. The amount of bremsstrahlung produced increases with increase in the kinetic energy of the beta particle and with increase in the atomic number of the absorber. The effect is particularly noticeable for electrons of energy of 1 Mev or greater. For carbon-14, the amount of energy lost in this way is small, but these x rays are readily detected on the outside of a vial that contains 10 mc

or more of barium carbonate-^{14}C for which $^{14}C/^{12}C \cong 1$ or greater. The measurement of carbon-14 radioactivity via its bremsstrahlung can be done but is neither very practical nor very accurate. A procedure in which an ionization chamber is used for making such measurements on beta-emitting nuclides is described by Tompkins, Wish, and Burnett.[23]

11-2b COMBUSTION OF SAMPLES AND CONVERSION OF CARBON-14 DIOXIDE TO BARIUM CARBONATE-^{14}C

The counting of solids and liquids in their original chemical form presents many complications. Some of these difficulties, such as nonuniform absorption and backscattering, are mentioned above. Other problems arise from differences in electrical conductivity, reaction with the planchet, and sample volatility. Windowless detectors are especially subject to contamination by volatile samples. To standardize these factors as much as possible, it is desirable to use a common chemical form. Among gases, the best choice is carbon dioxide, an ultimate oxidation product of all carbon compounds. If a solid is needed, it is only reasonable to choose an insoluble carbonate. The preferred compound is barium carbonate; its advantages and disadvantages are discussed later.

Combustion of labeled organic samples can be accomplished by wet or dry methods. Detailed combustion procedures are described in Sec. 11-5d. The Pregl type combustion procedure, in which medical oxygen is the sweep gas, is obviously unsuitable if barium carbonate-^{14}C is to be counted. Carbon-14 dioxide evolved from a combustion can be either absorbed directly in barium hydroxide solution or absorbed in sodium hydroxide solution and then converted to barium carbonate-^{14}C. Many detailed procedures are available; typical sample preparations are described by Tolbert and Siri[5] and by Walker and Lougheed.[24] Barium hydroxide is only slightly soluble (0.1 mole/ liter) at room temperature and has less speed and capacity for absorbing carbon dioxide than does a 1 M solution of sodium hydroxide. No isotope fractionation has been observed during the absorption of carbon-14 dioxide in alkaline media.[25] In the procedure that requires the use of excess sodium hydroxide, Walker and Lougheed[24] dilute the sodium hydroxide–sodium carbonate solution to volume in a volumetric flask. An aliquot of the resulting solution is neutralized to the phenolphthalein end point with hydrochloric acid solution. Excess barium chloride is then added, followed by sufficient carbonate-free sodium hydroxide solution to make the solution alkaline. The solution is then just neutralized with 0.1 M hydrochloric acid. This technique is claimed to yield a fine and uniform precipitate of barium carbonate-14C.

The procedure described by Tolbert and Siri[5] calls for the addition of an amount of ammonium chloride or ammonium nitrate equal in moles to the amount of sodium hydroxide used for the absorption. A slight excess of barium chloride solution is then added. The precipitate is protected from the atmosphere and is permitted to stand in a warm place to increase the size of the crystals. Blank determinations must be made to confirm the absence of carbonate in the sodium hydroxide.

Barium hydroxide has the advantage that it can be separated readily from barium carbonate. However, the use of a strongly basic anion-exchange resin should simplify the removal of small amounts of carbonate from sodium hydroxide.

More than 16 mg of barium carbonate is produced from the combustion of 1 mg of carbon. The result of this dilution is an increase in self-absorption and a consequent loss of sensitivity. Self-absorption may be reduced somewhat by preparing the calcium salt. Little[26] outlines a procedure in which the sodium hydroxide solution that contains carbonate-14C is treated with a mixture of calcium and magnesium chlorides. (Magnesium chloride eliminates the formation of gelatinous precipitates and the consequent need for heating.) After the reagent is added, the solution is titrated to a thymol blue end point with hydrochloric acid. The precipitated calcium carbonate-14C is then collected as an infinitely thick sample on filter paper. The counting rate compared with that of barium carbonate-14C is 1.85 ± 0.08 times greater. Infinitely thick plates of either calcium carbonate-14C or properly digested barium carbonate-14C can be made by pouring the solution and precipitate onto a 1-in.-diameter disk of filter paper mounted in a buchner type funnel. The sample is washed with water and then with ethyl alcohol and is dried. Samples may be deposited on copper or aluminum plates by slurrying the barium carbonate-14C in ethyl alcohol and then pouring the slurry into a solid-sample plate maker. Evaporation of the solvent leaves an adherent carbonate deposit. The above procedures are described and illustrated by Tolbert and Siri.[27] Barium carbonate-14C plates of reportedly excellent reproducibility have been prepared by centrifugation of previously precipitated barium carbonate-14C from its slurry in ethyl alcohol diethyl ether.[28] The apparatus used was a special demountable metal holder made to fit into a 250-ml trunnion cup.

Barium carbonate-14C samples can be contaminated by short-lived disintegration products of radon and thorium. These are contained in atmospheric dust collected during filtration. It has been suggested that filtered samples of low radioactivity be permitted to stand for at least 4 hr before they are counted.[29] Static charges that develop when glass planchets are used can produce variations in counting. Perkins and MacDonald[30] were able to improve count reproducibility by spraying the lower glass surface with an antistatic aerosol spray, such as a quaternary ammonium compound. Others[31] have found errors in carbon-14 and tritium measurements of nonconducting samples when a gas-flow counter was used.

11-2c INSTRUMENTATION

The Geiger-Müller counting tube is a rather simple device. It consists of a pair of co-axially oriented electrodes. The center conductor is a fine wire that serves as the positive electrode; the outer cylindrical conductor is the cathode. The space between the electrodes is filled to about 0.1 atm or more with a mixture of a rare gas and a polyatomic organic compound or of a rare gas and a halogen. A typical filling is a mixture of argon and ethyl alcohol or 0.1% chlorine in neon. The nature and amount of gas used are determined by the region (proportional or Geiger-Müller) in which the counter is used.

Proportional counters frequently are operated at atmospheric pressure, Geiger-Müller tubes at pressures of the order of 0.1 to 0.2 atm, although some tubes are filled to near atmospheric pressure. The use of an anode of very small diameter results in a higher voltage gradient. The ionizing particles cause current to flow in short pulses. The nature of the pulses varies with the potential applied to the electrodes. It is this variation that determines whether the detector behaves as an ionization chamber, proportional counter, or Geiger-Müller tube. The effect of increasing voltage is shown in Fig. 11-2. Voltage ranges will vary depending on the nature of the gas. In the first voltage range from 0 to about 10 volts, the applied voltage is so low that most ions recombine. Collection is much more efficient from 10 to 45 volts, but the voltage chosen (voltage range 2) for ion chambers is usually between 45 and 500 volts. In voltage range 3 (500 to 800 volts), electrons and ions may acquire sufficient kinetic energy to enable them to ionize other molecules on impact. The resulting gas amplification may vary from unity to 10^4 or more. The increase in pulse

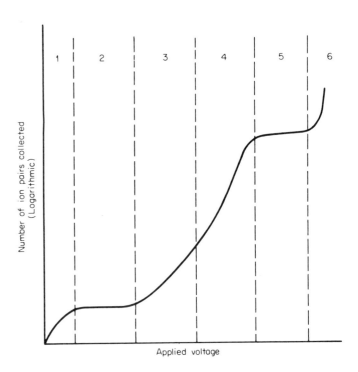

FIG. 11-2 Schematic designation of variation of signal output with voltage for common counting chambers.

size from gas amplification is proportional to the initial ionization—hence the term *proportional* counter. The number of ion pairs collected also increases with the potential, which may be in the range from 500 to 800 volts. In voltage range 4, strict proportionality is lost. Geiger-Müller detection occurs in voltage range 5, in which the operating voltage is usually between 800 and 1500 volts. In the Geiger-Müller region, the discharge (or avalanche) is propagated throughout the length of the chamber; in the proportional region the discharge is limited to the region in which ions were produced by the original radioactive particle. The gas multiplication factor for a Geiger-Müller counter may be as large as 10^8 or larger. All the pulses produced in this region will be about the same height. In voltage range 6, the voltage is high enough to permit the triggering of a continuous discharge. Such a discharge can shorten the life of or destroy a Geiger-Müller tube.

In the Geiger-Müller tube, the collection of electrons is very fast; the movement of the positive-ion sheath to the cathode is much slower and accounts for the long resolving time of this counting tube. If one of the rare-gas ions strikes the cathode, it may dislodge an electron. This electron may in turn initiate another discharge accompanied by a pulse that is indistinguishable from the one produced by the orginal ionizing event. Either electronic or chemical means can be used to stop (or quench) the counter action as soon as possible after an avalanche. Electronic circuits are sometimes used to drop the voltage on the tube below the threshold voltage for about 0.1 msec. For external sample counting, it is simpler to use a chemical quenching agent, usually a polyatomic organic molecule such as ethyl alcohol. The quenching action consists in the transfer of charge from the argon or helium ions to the quenching molecule. The organic molecule ions are dissociated at the cathode and do not dislodge secondary

electrons. The organic quenching vapor is gradually depleted by this process and, as a result, the lifetime of the tube is about 10^9 counts. Quenching may also be accomplished with halogens. A typical filling might consist of 0.1% chlorine in neon and argon at a few centimeters pressure. Bromine can also be used. The dissociated halogen atoms recombine, and the quenching agent is not the limiting factor in tube life. The starting voltage may be lower than 275 volts; an operating voltage of about 300 to 400 volts is common for halogen-quenched end-window detectors.

Thin-window Geiger-Müller tubes with window thickness of 1.5 mg/cm² or less are costly, but the increased sensitivity makes their purchase justifiable. The tubes usually are accompanied by an instruction and specification sheet, with which is included the recommended operating voltage or a strip-recorder plot of counts/min versus voltage. To conserve the life of the tube, the operating voltage should be in the lower 20 to 30% of the plateau. The operating characteristics can be determined by plotting the counting rate against voltage for a carbon-14-labeled sample placed at a fixed distance from the tube. The resulting plot will resemble Fig. 11-3, which illustrates the starting voltage (*A*), threshold voltage (*B*), working voltage (*C*), plateau (*D*), and continuous-discharge region (*E*). Good organically quenched

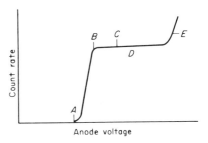

FIG. 11-3 Characteristic curve for a Geiger-Müller tube.

Geiger-Müller tubes have plateau slopes of less than 3% per 100 volts; halogen-quenched tubes have a slightly steeper slope.

The end of useful tube life is indicated by erratic counting, continuous discharge, cessation of counting, or greatly increased slope of the counting plateau. A new Geiger-Müller tube shielded with 2 in. of lead usually will have a background count of 14 to 25 counts/min. In the absence of shielding, this rate will possibly double. The upper limit to the counting rate is the resolving time of the tube, usually 400 μsec.

Thin-window and windowless counters are easily adapted to automatic sample changing and counting. Manufacturers of counting instruments offer equipment that automatically feeds sample planchets to a shielded counter. After a preset number of counts have accumulated, the sample number and counting time are printed out. The cycle is then repeated. It is stated[32] that in one automatic, windowless flow counter, 1-in.-diameter samples of infinitely thick barium carbonate-^{14}C and absolute specific activity of 1.0 dpm/mg can be counted to a 5% probability error in about 100 min.

Carbon-14 standards are available from manufactures of radiochemicals and from the U.S. Bureau of Standards. The standard sodium bicarbonate-^{14}C may be used to prepare standard plates of barium carbonate-^{14}C. Disks that contain a carbon-14-labeled plastic are useful for checking survey meters. In most instances, radioactivity measurements involve a series of comparisons; whether the radioactivity of a compound is 1.0 or 1.1 mc/mole is unimportant. The determination of absolute radioactivity is needed for radiocarbon dating and for compounds that are to be sold but is seldom needed for other purposes.

In a review of end-window counting, L'vova and Bochkarev[33] estimate the error of this method to be $\pm 10\%$. With careful sample preparation and attention to geometry, it should be possible to radioassay

barium carbonate-^{14}C samples with an error of $\pm 5\%$ or less. In some experimentation, errors of this magnitude are tolerable. One advantage of end-window or windowless counting is its adaptability to classroom procedures. A justification for its use is the need to have equipment that will also count other isotopes, for example, phosphorus-32 or sulfur-35. Compounds that contain these tracer elements are not readily converted to gases for counting in ion chambers or proportional counters. Serious experimentation with carbon-14 should not depend on the counting of external samples with either thin-window or windowless counters.

A thin-window Geiger-Müller tube used in the laboratory as part of a simple radioactivity monitor is indispensable in surveying for radiation contamination on the person, bench top, and glassware. It also serves to monitor laboratory background radioactivity (including the next-door neighbor's cobalt-60 source that is carefully shielded on all sides but the back!). Ideally, such a monitor should be light in weight and should have transistorized circuitry and dual a-c and battery-operated power supplies. The use of a halogen-quenched Geiger-Müller detector simplifies the high-voltage requirement. A *carefully* calibrated meter is certainly not needed. A loudspeaker within the unit is the best indicator of counting rate; a flashing light is almost useless.

11-3 INTERNAL GAS COUNTING IN THE GEIGER AND PROPORTIONAL REGIONS

Internal gas-phase counting of carbon-14 has been reviewed by Kalab and Broda[34] and by Christman and Wolf.[35]

The counting of carbon-14 samples in Geiger-Müller tubes is not common. The necessity for a filling at relatively low pressure and for mixtures of other gases with the labeled carbon dioxide makes the method somewhat cumbersome for routine measurements. Brown and Miller[36] used a counter tube filled with a mixture of carbon dioxide (200 mm mercury) and a small amount of carbon disulfide. An external quenching circuit (Neher-Pickering) was used. Melhuish[37] used essentially the same filling: carbon disulfide to 20 ± 2 mm mercury and carbon dioxide to between 150 and 200 mm mercury. He found that 80% of the disintegrations were recorded, an efficiency of 50 to 100 times that of an end-window counter used with solid samples. Carbon-14 dioxide from a sample that contained 4×10^{-3} $\mu c/g$ of carbon-14 gave counting rates that were about equal to the background count of 25 counts/min. The error was said to be $\pm 1\%$. Benzene has been used as the quenching agent; labeled benzene or gasoline vapor is useable as a single-component filling; and a wide variety of hydrocarbons such as ethylene, hexane, heptane, and others may constitute part of a filling with labeled carbon dioxide. A modified Geiger-Müller tube of large capacity was used to count up to 0.5 atm pressure of carbon-14 dioxide from samples that contained as much as 50 mg of carbon without the addition of other gases;[38] the gas-handling apparatus and associated electronic circuits are described. Mann and co-workers[39] used internal gas counters in both the proportional and Geiger regions to recalibrate the National Bureau of Standards (U.S.A.) carbon-14 solution standards. Kalab and Broda[34] show that, with suitable electronics, it is possible to obtain good plateaus with counters filled with unpurified carbon-14

dioxide as the only filling. Plateaus of length up to 1200 volts and slopes of 0.25% per 100 volts were obtained by use of strong amplification and by isolation of the counting circuit from the effect of after-discharges. The electronic equipment is described by Kalab in a separate publication;[40] it consists of an amplifier of 0.3-mv sensitivity, together with an interrupting circuit that breaks the connection between the counting tube and the recording system for predetermined times of the order of 4×10^{-4} to 4×10^{-3} sec. Measurements with unmixed carbon dioxide show that the plateau extends from the proportional region to the region of limited proportionality. Addition of benzene shifts the plateau part way into the Geiger region. Addition of carbon disulfide radically changes the counter behavior, the result of which change is an extended plateau in the Geiger region. The efficiency of the counter for carbon-14 dioxide is stated to be $92.5 \pm 4.5\%$, which value reflects the uncertainty in the value for the carbon-14 standard whose true value was known to only $\pm 5\%$.

The counter tube used by Kalab and Broda is illustrated in Fig. 11-4, and the vacuum system for filling it is shown in Fig. 11-5; both should be generally useful for internal gas-counting systems. The counting tube as described is small, having a volume of less than 30 ml. The body is a brass tube 9.6 cm long and 1.8 cm in diameter. The glass caps are cemented to the metal with a thermosetting resin. The anode is a 0.1-mm-diameter

FIG. 11-4   Diagram of the counter tube. (*From B. Kalab and E. Broda*, INTERN. J. APPL. RADIATION ISOTOPES, **13**, *191 (1962), with permission.*)

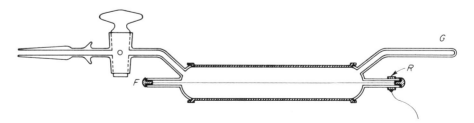

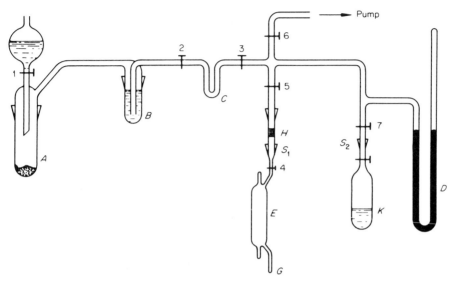

FIG. 11-5 Counter-filling manifold. *A*, barium carbonate-^{14}C sample; *B*, magnesium perchlorate; *C*, U-trap cooled with liquid nitrogen; *D*, manometer; *E*, counter tube; *G*, cold finger cooled with liquid nitrogen; *H*, sintered-glass filter to remove dust; *K*, storage vessel for nonlabeled carbon dioxide or other filling gases. (*From B. Kalab and E. Broda*, INTERN. J. APPL. RADIATION ISOTOPES, **13**, *191* (*1962*), *with permission.*)

tungsten wire welded to a metal cap at *F* and led out to a brass sleeve, *R*, to which the connecting wire is soldered. The spaces between the ends of the wire and the glass are filled with a wax that is stable to high vacuum. The tube is similar in pattern, but not in construction, to the gas counter recommended by Glascock.[41] The condensing tube permits submersion of that part of the counting tube in liquid nitrogen. The gas-counting tube of Bernstein and Ballentine[41,42] has no condensing tube, but one end is kept free of glass-to-metal seals; that end may be immersed in liquid nitrogen. The filling system shown in Fig. 11-5 is relatively simple. The barium carbonate-^{14}C is decomposed with dilute perchloric acid. The frozen carbon dioxide is freed of air by continued pumping and is then warmed after being isolated from the generating and pumping systems. All or part of the carbon dioxide

may be used. The filling pressure is determined from the pressure read on the manometer, the volume of the manifold, and the volume of the counter tube. The vessel *K* may be omitted if the filling system is to be used in the manner described by Kalab and Broda.[34] With this method, it is possible to detect as little as 4×10^{-9} mc of carbon-14. In a review, Broda and Kalab[43] compared it with the other principal methods for determining carbon-14. The barium carbonate-^{14}C was prepared by wet combustion of the sample, absorption of the carbon dioxide in sodium hydroxide solution, addition of a solution that contained barium ions, and collection of the barium carbonate on a filter followed by washes with ethyl alcohol and ether. Since combustion requires 20 min, the use of two wet-combustion apparatuses was suggested to save time during this operation.

For determining very low levels of carbon-14 radioactivity, proportional counting systems are superior to the use of the ionization chamber and possibly are more accurate than the scintillation counter. For samples of moderate radioactivity (1 to 5 mc/mole) the proportional-counter procedure is not as fast and is no more accurate than the combination of an ionization chamber with a good vibrating-reed electrometer. Systems for counting internal gas samples are not adaptable to automatic changers. Flow proportional counters are very useful for the detection of radioactivity in flowing gases. Their applications in this area are discussed in Sec. 12-1b.

11-4 SCINTILLATION COUNTING

A number of early fundamental experiments in nuclear physics depended on the examination, under a microscope, of the scintillations of the zinc sulfide phosphor. One example was the investigation, by Rutherford in 1911, of the angular distribution of α-scattering in metal foils. These observations helped to establish the nuclear model. The development of the vacuum tube was eventually responsible for the replacement of the scintillator by ionization chambers and Geiger-Müller counters. Later, the advent of multiplier phototubes, good organic scintillators, linear amplifiers, and recorders led to the restoration and rapid development of scintillation counting techniques. In one or another of its many forms the scintillation counter can be used to detect and measure the energy of weak or energetic and of light or heavy charged particles at low or high counting rates.

A scintillation counter consists of a scintillation detector (solid, liquid, or gas) that produces light pulses when excited by ionizing radiation, a multiplier phototube that converts the light pulses to photoelectrons within the tube and amplifies them, and a counting system that can furnish information (pulse-height analysis) on the energy spectrum of the radiation and can discriminate against noise.

Scintillation counting has proved so versatile and convenient for the measurement of both carbon-14 and tritium that a great volume of publications, including a number of reviews,[44-52] has resulted.

11-4a INSTRUMENTATION

No attempt will be made here to describe the electronic components of a scintillation counting system. That information is available in books on electronic instrumentation and in the literature provided for the operation of commercial liquid-scintillation counters.

Photoelectric emission in a multiplier phototube depends on the presence of a metallic coating that has a low work function. The work function, ϕ, of a substance is defined as the least amount of energy that must be supplied to remove an electron from that substance. The most effective photoelectron emitters are the alkali metals and their alloys. The cesium-antimony emitter is frequently used, because it has a high quantum yield and because it has a response cutoff in the infrared region of the spectrum that helps to reduce the amount of thermionic emission. A given type of multiplier phototube may vary widely in its degree of thermionic emission; tubes that are free of such spurious emission seem to be more a matter of accident than of design. Since, on the average, less than one photoelectron results from each scintillation produced by a weak beta emitter, it is impossible to distinguish signal from thermionic "noise." Cooling the phototube greatly reduces the amount of thermionic emission. The remaining noise is nearly eliminated by the use of a pair of multiplier phototubes in coincidence. The phototube noise in the two channels is independently random, whereas the scintillation pulses from the sample occur simultaneously in both channels. With the use of appropriate circuitry, it is possible to pass only the coincidental pulses and to reject in each channel pulses that differ by a few tenths of a microsecond. Instruments equipped for pulse-height selection also reject both the very weak, but abundant, noise pulses and those pulses whose size is greater than would be expected from carbon-14 beta particles.

In addition to their use for separating signal from noise, discriminators are used to further sort the spectra of pulses from two beta-emitting isotopes in a single sample.[53–57] According to Rapkin,[51] the measurement of two beta emitters in the same sample is possible if they differ in energy by a factor of about 4. The most common simultaneous measurement is that of carbon-14 and tritium. Kabara and co-workers[55] find that a modern dual-channel spectrometer can be used to differentiate these isotopes with a single count at one high-voltage setting as readily as with separate counts at different high-voltage settings. The simultaneous measurement of other pairs of radioisotopes was reviewed by Rapkin.[51]

The thermionic noise generated in a multiplier phototube is markedly greater at room temperature than at 0°. The amplitude of the noise pulse is of the same order of magnitude as that of the pulse generated by tritium beta particles in a liquid-scintillator medium. Therefore, it is common practice to cool the assembly that consists of changer, multiplier phototube, shielding, sample, and preamplifier by enclosing it in a small food freezer. Temperatures are regulated to be in the range from −10° to 0°. With new multiplier phototubes that have been improved with respect to noise reduction, it is possible to build room-temperature coincidence type liquid scintillation counters that are adequate for measuring carbon-14. The new bialkali photocathode RCA-8575 is typical of the improved multiplier phototubes. It is adaptable to systems that now use the 56AVP, 6810A, or 7264 tube type. Horrocks[57a]

describes a room-temperature liquid-scintillation spectrometer (for alpha-emitting nuclides) that uses the new bialkali multiplier phototube. He finds that this counting system has comparable detection efficiency, with lower background, compared with one that uses a freezer-cooled conventional multiplier phototube. There is a trend toward the use of multiplier phototubes having more dynodes; a 13-dynode phototube can be used without a preamplifier.

Scintillation counters are readily adaptable to automatic sample changing. High-speed 200-sample changers are a boon to the investigator, because great numbers of samples can be counted with automatic replication over a 24-hr period. Some models print out sample number, time, and scaler counts, together with values for channel ratios. An instrument exists into which predetermined backgrounds may be dialed before the count of a series of samples is started; thus, the display and printout of data show net counts. One commercial instrument can be set to automatically reject samples having less than a preselected radioactivity level. Such bypassing saves time when it is necessary to scan large numbers of samples, for example, in the determination of the radioactivity of chromatographic eluants. Loading all samples into the changer at one time permits phosphorescence in glass vials to decay, minimizes the fogging of vials, and ensures a more constant sample temperature.

11-4b SCINTILLATORS AND SOLVENTS

The basic liquid scintillator system is a three-component solution that consists of an organic solvent, a primary solute that converts the beta-particle energy to light quanta, and a secondary solute that shifts the wavelength of the light to a value that matches the response of the photocathode.

A solvent must meet several requirements if it is to be used in liquid-scintillation counting. It must permit an efficient transfer of energy from the beta particle to the scintillator, that is, it must not "quench." The solvent must also dissolve both the sample and the scintillating solutes. It should not freeze at normal counting temperatures. A large number of organic solvents were tested in original studies by Kallmann and Furst,[58,59] and by Hayes, Rogers, and Sanders.[60] Since then no especially important single solvents have been announced, although many combination solvents have been recommended for special counting problems. The best solvents in general use are aromatic hydrocarbons. The effectiveness of a liquid-scintillator solvent can be evaluated by adding a fixed percentage of scintillator to each solvent and then determining the relative pulse height for each solution. Typical solvents are xylene, phenylcyclohexane, toluene, ethylbenzene, benzene, anisole, cumene, and p-cymene in order of decreasing pulse height. The individual xylenes differ in efficiency, and p-cymene derived from wood products contains contemporary carbon (about 13 dis/min per gram of solvent). Toluene is the most commonly used solvent, because it is inexpensive, readily purified, and very efficient.

The alkylbenzenes are good solvents for most *nonpolar* substances; no really good solvent has been found for the scintillation counting of *polar* substances. Combination solvents are therefore used to improve the performance of a good chemical solvent. Methanol, ethyl alcohol, or the bis-(2-alkoxyethyl)ethers can be added to toluene; naphthalene can be added to p-dioxane. Use of combination solvents will be discussed in more detail in Sec. 11-4b.

Solvent purity should not be overlooked. Scintillator solutions made with dioxane-naphthalene may appear to perform well when first prepared but deteriorate rapidly if the dioxane is impure. Spectrographic grade dioxane is usable as received. Other grades of dioxane should be purified, possibly by distillation and chromatography over alumina or Florisil. Kas'yanova and Nesynov[61] recommend a three-step purification procedure for toluene. One liter of toluene is shaken with 20 ml of concentrated sulfuric acid for 15 to 20 min. After 24 hr the toluene layer is passed through a column that contains an upper layer of silica gel and a lower layer of alumina. The toluene is then distilled (56% recovery).

Several secondary solvents are used to form soluble salts or complexes of carbon dioxide, amino acids, proteins, etc. Typical secondary solvents are Hyamine 10-X [trade name for p-(diisobutylcresoxyethoxyethyl)dimethylbenzylammonium chloride monohydrate], Primene 81-R[62] (trade name for a mixture of tertiary alkyl primary C_{12}–C_{14} amines), and ethanolamine.

The most commonly used primary and secondary scintillator solutes, their formulas, and fluorescence maxima are shown in Table 11-1. Aside from cost, the main differences between scintillators are solubility, self-quenching properties, and tendency to maintain a given counting efficiency over a range of scintillator concentration. For some scintillators such a plateau is never reached because of solubility limitations. With others, the counting efficiency may rise, level off, and then decrease as a result of self-quenching at high concentration.

Of all the primary scintillators (also called phosphors or fluors) available, 2,5-diphenyloxazole (PPO) is the most widely used. Its selection is based on its good performance and relatively low cost. The usefulness of p-terphenyl is limited because of its low solubility at low temperatures, but it is a good and relatively inexpensive scintillator for room-temperature applications. One scintillator that can be used as a single solute is 2,5-bis-[2-(5-*tert*-butylbenzoxazoyl)]-thiophene (BBOT). It is claimed to be more soluble, stable, and resistant to quenching than are the other scintillator solutes. However, it is used very little.

Table 11-1 *Commonly used primary and secondary scintillating solutes*

Solute	Formula	Wavelength of fluorescence maximum, $m\mu$
Primary		
2,5-Diphenyloxazole (PPO)	*(structural formula)*	380
2-Phenyl-5-(4-biphenylyl)-1,3,4-oxadiazole (PBD)	*(structural formula)*	370
Anthracene	*(structural formula)*	445
p-Terphenyl (*p*-TP)	*(structural formula)*	346
2,5-Bis-[2-(5-*tert*-butyl-benzoxazoyl)]-thiophene (BBOT)	*(structural formula)*	435
Secondary		
1,4-Bis-2-(5-phenyl-oxazolyl)-benzene (POPOP)	*(structural formula)*	420
1,4-Bis-2-(4-methyl-5-phenyloxazolyl)benzene (dimethyl POPOP)	*(structural formula)*	430
2-(1-Naphthyl)-5-phenyl-oxazole (α-NPO)	*(structural formula)*	405
1,4-Bis-2-(5-α-naphthyl-oxazolyl)-benzene (α-NOPON)	*(structural formula)*	442

The secondary scintillator shifts the wavelength of the light emitted by the primary scintillator to a region in which the multiplier phototube shows greater sensitivity. Small concentrations (0.5 g/liter or less) of secondary scintillator give an advantageous increase in efficiency when the energies involved are low, as they are in the counting of tritium; improvement is noticeable for carbon-14 as well. The most widely used secondary scintillator is 1,4-bis-2-(5-phenyloxazolyl)benzene (POPOP), which dissolves with difficulty in the usual solvents. It is therefore advantageous to use the comparable and no more costly 1,4-bis-2-(4-methyl-5-phenyloxazolyl)benzene (i.e., dimethyl POPOP).

II-4c PREPARATION OF SAMPLES

Samples are said to be either integral or external. A sample is integral if it, together with an organic phosphor, is dissolved or suspended in a solvent; it is external if the phosphor is not dissolved with the sample. External samples are considered in Chap. 12. Liquid-scintillation counting usually requires an integral sample. Since the sample in solution is contained in a vial, it may be counted over and over again or set aside for comparison with other samples at some later time. Internal-sample counting has the merits of high sensitivity, good geometry, energy discrimination, and low background count. The fact that dilute solutions of fluorescent organic compounds in aromatic solvents are good scintillation detectors was first announced independently by Reynolds, Harrison, and Salvini[63] and by Kallmann.[64] The usefulness of terphenyl, diphenyl, anthracene, and stilbene as crystalline scintillators had already been observed. Reynolds and co-workers used benzene solutions of naphthalene, as well as of other phosphors such as anthracene and terphenyl. Background was kept low by coincidence circuitry. Photons were generated by Compton electrons produced within the vial by gamma radiation from a cobalt-60 source. Kallmann recognized the short decay time in the scintillation process and emphasized the need for pure phosphors and solvents. He used solutions of toluene or xylene that contained fluorene, carbazole, phenanthrene, or anthracene.

COUNTING VIALS To choose the most suitable vessels for counting radiocarbon at natural-abundance levels, Leger and Tamers[65] calibrated counting vials that had various sizes and shapes. They concluded that for the systems they studied the highest sensitivity was obtained with the 60-ml container. For most scintillation counting ultimate sensitivity is not the objective; therefore, the 20-ml vial has been adopted as the most practical size. Vials may be of glass, quartz, or polyethylene. Most glasses contain potassium-40 in various amounts but sufficient to constitute a significant part of the background count. At least one manufacturer[66] produces vials from a glass to which no potassium was added. Another source of background activity results from the activation of glass by exposure to sunlight or fluorescent light. This phosphorescence decays over a period of several hours; it can be troublesome with quartz vials as well. Fortunately, phosphorescence of glass is a single-photon event, not counted by multiplier phototubes in coincidence if reasonable care has been taken to minimize exposure of the vial to intense ultraviolet light. Screw-cap closures are usually of polyethylene or cork-tinfoil, and although the vials are reusable, the caps are not. The solvent toluene slowly diffuses through the polyethylene lining causing dissolution of the cement in the cap. Samples such as labeled hydrocarbons that might diffuse through should not be stored in vials that have polyethylene or polyethylene-lined caps if the samples are to be counted again at a later time. Such samples will show a count rate that diminishes with time. Polyethylene containers have been used to advantage for counting tritium-labeled samples.[67]

As compared with glass, medium-density polyethylene is better from the standpoint of increased efficiency and lower background. Many organic liquids will penetrate polyethylene containers. These include ketones, aldehydes, esters, benzene, toluene, higher alcohols, oils, silicone fluids, and chlorinated hydrocarbons. The U.S. Public Health Service has warned that temporary storage of such compounds in polyethylene bottles can result in the development of an explosive concentration of organic vapors in a confined space. The flash point (40°F) of toluene is just a little higher than the temperature of the freezer and is dangerously low for room-temperature operation.

SOLUBLE SAMPLES   Simplicity of sample preparation is often cited as the principal advantage of liquid-scintillation counting. Unlike other counting systems that depend on a common counting form, the scintillation-counting system will accept almost any sample that will dissolve, be converted to a soluble salt, form a gel, or be capable of suspension in the scintillator solution. Such adaptability is not without its price, and a large number of investigations have been made to determine the best method for working with a particular compound.

Most organic compounds are soluble in toluene; if they do not quench excessively, they can be counted in a solution composed of 5 g of PPO, 0.3 g of POPOP, and sufficient toluene to make 1 liter. The Packard Instrument Company also recommends a scintillator solution prepared by dissolving 4 g of BBOT in 1 liter of toluene. The volume of scintillator solution used is not extremely critical. A dispenser that delivers 15 ml of solution is a convenience. Such dispensers are easily made or can be purchased.[68] Liquid samples are conveniently weighed in unsealed melting-point tubes and are then flushed into the counting vial with part of the scintillator solution.

CARBON DIOXIDE   Compounds that quench excessively, are insoluble, or are highly colored may have to be converted to carbon dioxide before they can be counted. A number of amines are satisfactory for the formation of soluble salts from labeled carbon dioxide. Two such amines, Hyamine 10-X and Primene 81-R, were referred to in Sec. 11-4b.

The use of the hydroxide of Hyamine 10-X is discussed in detail by Rapkin.[69] Hyamine carbonate is readily soluble in toluene, although Passmann, Radin, and Cooper[70] describe its use in toluene-methanol solution. These authors found that samples as large as 5 mmoles can be counted with an efficiency of 33 to 67%. Hyamine is widely used for trapping carbon-14 dioxide but is expensive and causes quenching. Therefore, it should be used in only slight excess over the amount of carbon-14 dioxide to be absorbed. A quenching correction should be made for each sample if accuracy is required.

Primene 81-R is a mixture of branched-chain amines that has been used by Oppermann and co-workers[71] to absorb carbon dioxide. They distil Primene in vacuo to obtain a colorless distillate which on dilution with methanol to 0.2 to 0.25 M Primene solution provides a very efficient absorbent for carbon dioxide. The Primene–carbon dioxide complex is claimed to be stable at room temperature and compatible with a scintillation fluid consisting of 3 g of PPO per liter of toluene. Moderate amounts of Primene do not quench.

Jeffay and Alvarez[72] have used a solution of ethanolamine, ethylene glycol monomethyl ether (Cellosolve), and toluene; a volume ratio of 1:8:10 was found best. The scintillator used was 5 to 6 g of PPO per liter of solvent; it produced a carbon-14 counting efficiency of 50%. Absorption of carbon dioxide is quantitative. Carbon dioxide can also be absorbed in ethanolamine-methanol (3:20 v/v). When absorption is complete, 1 to 10 ml of this solution is made up to 20 ml with a scintillator solution prepared from 4 g of BBOT in toluene. Higher counting efficiency can be achieved by using as much as 6 to 12 g of BBOT per liter of toluene. Woeller[73] has compared phenylethylamine with Hyamine for the absorption of carbon-14 dioxide; he concluded that phenylethylamine was the better reagent from the standpoint of viscosity, quenching, cost, and capacity for carbon dioxide. To increase the solubility of the carbonate, Woeller adds methanol to the usual toluene-PPO-POPOP scintillator system. The scintillator mixture that contains the amine can be used directly to absorb carbon-14 dioxide. The solution is then poured into the counting vial; toluene is the washing liquid. Davidson and Oliverio[73a] likewise find that 2-phenylethylamine is a good inexpensive absorbent for carbon dioxide. They recommend that the amine be purified by distillation at reduced pressure. Once purified, it is stable for one year if refrigerated in brown bottles.

Derivatives other than organic and inorganic salts have been used to determine carbon-14 dioxide. Dowben[74] used the gas to carbonate a phenyl Grignard reagent. The carboxyl-labeled benzoic acid that resulted was then counted in a liquid-scintillation counter. The methods for scintillation counting of insoluble derivatives will be discussed later.

AQUEOUS SAMPLES The scintillation counting of carbon-14 seldom requires the measurement of aqueous samples, because most organic materials are soluble in the more efficient nonpolar solvents and because the combustion product, carbon dioxide, can be complexed as a toluene-soluble salt. On the other hand, tritium samples are often burned to provide the common counting form, water. Occasionally, it is necessary to determine the radioactivity of carbohydrates, amino acids, and other water-soluble substances. Only a limited number of mixed-solvent systems have been found useful.

It is difficult to overcome problems of immiscibility, freezing at low temperatures, and quenching. Water and ethyl alcohol are severe quenchers. Dioxane is reasonably efficient but has a relatively high freezing point. One scintillator solution that is useful for aqueous systems is similar to that of Kaufman and co-workers;[75] it consists of 7 g of PPO, 0.3 g of POPOP, 100 g of naphthalene, and sufficient spectrographic grade dioxane to make 1 liter of solution; it is satisfactory for tritium as well as carbon-14. A 15-ml quantity of this mixture will accept 1 ml of aqueous sample. Even if less than 1 ml of aqueous sample is available or is required, it is advisable to dilute the sample to 1 ml with water. If the dilution is not made, the mixture may freeze. Because water is a strong quencher, the efficiency will remain constant only if the same amount is used each time. Loewus[76] modified the naphthalene-dioxane mixture to permit its use at temperatures below 0°. The modification consisted in replacing a portion of the dioxane with bis-(2-methoxyethyl)ether (diglyme) or bis-(2-ethoxyethyl)ether (diethyl carbitol). Loewus claims that the addition of 2 ml of either of these ethers will allow 15-ml samples that contain 1 ml of water to be counted at −4° with better than 90% of the efficiency (for tritium) of the pure naphthalene-dioxane system. For carbon-14 the use of a very low temperature is not so critical, and it might be as satisfactory to raise the temperature a little for all counting. Bruno and Christian[77] describe a system that consists of "1 part xylene, 3 parts dioxane, and 3 parts Cellosolve, with 1.0% PPO, 0.05% POPOP, and 8.0% naphthalene." They report that this system is twice as efficient as a similar one that contains ethyl alcohol instead of Cellosolve.

Bray[78] developed a solvent system capable of handling aqueous solutions of salts and of other soluble materials; the system consists of 60 g of naphthalene, 4 g of PPO, 0.200 g of POPOP, 100 ml of methanol, 20 ml of ethylene glycol, and sufficient dioxane to make 1 liter.

Whenever possible, the amount of water used should be adjusted to provide the optimum "figure of merit"[79] for the scintillating solution used. The figure of merit is the product of water volume, W, and counting efficiency, E. If values for EW are plotted against W, the peak in the resulting curve will show the optimum W that should be used. If both tritium and carbon-14 are of interest, then the advantage of a low temperature must also be considered. For example, Baxter, Fanning, and Swartz[80] found, in a study of ten different scintillation solvents, that the highest counting efficiencies and figure-of-merit values were observed at $-15°$. They attributed this fact to the wider discriminator settings possible at the lower temperature, for which background and tube noise were at a minimum. The solvent system found to be best contained 0.4% PPO, 8.0% naphthalene, 300 ml of Cellosolve, 300 ml of dioxane, and enough toluene to make 1 liter. The volume of water that can be added to 10 ml of such a solution is 0.5 ml, which is less than can be used in many systems but is certainly adequate for most purposes. For the particular system studied, the amount of residual water present in the component solvents amounted to 40% of the water added.

INSOLUBLE SOLIDS It is not always practical to convert labeled materials to a soluble form. However, it is possible to count these materials in the form of *suspensions*. At first, attempts were made to disperse solids in the counting medium without the help of gels. The results obtained were unsatisfactory, because the count rate declined as settling occurred. Although some of the difficulty caused by quenching was removed, other problems such as self-absorption in the suspended particles gave trouble, a difficulty that continues to be serious in the counting of such weak beta emitters as tritium. The disadvantage of

settling was eliminated by the use of scintillating gels. Suspensions of solids in aluminum stearate gel scintillators were described by Funt and Hetherington.[81] They found that by adding aluminum stearate (2 to 7 wt %) to the liquid scintillation solution, it is possible to radioassay a wide variety of colorless salts and insoluble inorganic materials. The agent selected by White and Helf[82] to perform the same function was Thixcin, a derivative of castor oil. The gel is prepared by adding 25 g of Thixcin powder to one liter of scintillator in a blender. After the mixture is homogenized for 3 min, it is clear and fluid; a 22-ml volume of it can support as much as 1 g of suspended solid. Ott and co-workers[83] and Gordon and Wolfe[84] describe the use of Cab-O-Sil for thickening scintillating solutions. Cab-O-Sil, which is finely divided silica, disperses rapidly in ordinary scintillation solutions to produce an optically clear counting medium. Gordon and Wolfe found that as much as 12% Cab-O-Sil can be incorporated into the scintillator solution to suspend still larger amounts of radioactive material, but that the gel becomes too thick to permit adequate dispersion of the sample. Such counting systems are stable for 1 to 2 weeks; however, it is recommended that they be prepared daily to maintain reproducible conditions. The sample (up to 1.3 g of aqueous radioactive solution or 3.0 g of finely powdered sample) is weighed into a 20-ml vial. The vial is then filled with scintillating gel, shaken a few times, cooled, and counted. Gordon and Wolfe claim counting efficiencies as high as 65% for carbon-14 and 14% for tritium. A suspended plastic scintillator was used by Jenkinson[85] to determine the carbon-14 in large numbers of aqueous samples obtained from the decomposition, in soil, of labeled plant material.

Filter paper impregnated with the labeled sample can also be counted in heterogeneous systems. The procedures by which a labeled compound is collected on a filter paper or separated on a paper chromatogram and counted are discussed in Chap. 12.

Steinberg[86] reports the use of solid scintillators suspended in aqueous solutions of radioactive substances. Scintillators such as PPO and anthracene, as well as filaments and plastic beads,[87] can be used to count such compounds as sodium bicarbonate-^{14}C in aqueous solution. Wetting agents are used to disperse the solid scintillator in the aqueous solution. Solid scintillators are relatively inefficient for counting tritium, but efficiency up to 50 % is reported for carbon-14.

Cluley[88] studied the suspension scintillation counting of barium carbonate-^{14}C in a scintillating mixture that contained Degussa Aerosil,[89] a silica similar to Cab-O-Sil. At constant Aerosil concentration (usually 4 w/v %), the ratio of count rate to weight of suspended barium carbonate decreased somewhat with increase in the weight of barium carbonate. At constant concentration of barium carbonate, the counting efficiency decreased with increase in the concentration of Aerosil. Therefore, for any experiment in which careful comparisons are to be made, it is desirable to keep the concentration of silica constant and the weight of all the barium carbonate-^{14}C samples nearly the same.

In the experiments described by Cluley, the barium carbonate was ground in a glass mortar for about 30 sec. The required amount of it was then weighed out and added to a counting vial that contained 0.400 ± 0.003 g of Aerosil; 10 ml of the scintillator solution (3 g of PPO in 1 liter of toluene) was added. The mixture was then shaken vigorously for 2 min on a mechanical shaker, stored in the scintillation counter for 10 min, and then counted. A similar sample that contained inactive barium carbonate was used to determine the background count rate.

The suspension-counting method is relatively insensitive to variation in particle size. White and Helf[82] report only small differences in counting efficiency among suspensions of 60-, 120-, 325-, and 400-mesh particles. It is thought that the reduction of self-absorption achieved with the finer precipitates is canceled by the greater loss of light from scattering. The suspension-counting method for barium carbonate-^{14}C has been investigated further by Gilly and Bisci.[90]

Occasionally, small amounts of high-specific-activity substances are adsorbed on the wall of a counting vial. This adsorption results in a decrease in the counting rate. Blanchard and Takahashi[91] eliminate the adsorption of several polymeric compounds on the wall of the counting vial by use of a scintillator solution that contains 3 w/v % Cab-O-Sil.

The base, Hyamine, solubilizes many complex substances such as amino acids,[92] animal tissues,[93] purines and pyrimidines,[94] and proteins.[95] If Hyamine solutions are heated to increase the rate of dissolution, the solutions of some substances will turn yellow. Some insoluble materials are effectively solubilized by ultrasonic agitation. Herberg[95] observed that for certain Hyamine-protein-toluene solutions very high count rates are obtained even in the absence of a radioactive isotope and of a scintillation phosphor. The phosphorescence observed in these systems required several days to decay. The effect is most noticeable for large quantities of proteins and can be eliminated by using Hyamine base prepared from carefully purified quaternary ammonium chloride. Acidification of the Hyamine-protein-toluene solution is also effective in eliminating the phosphorescence. Francis and Hawkins[95a] describe a scintillator solution for counting as much as 3 ml of aqueous solution that contains a maximum of 100 mg of protein and electrolytes. The solution is prepared by dissolving the conventional phosphors PPO and POPOP in a mixture of 2-phenylethylamine, ethanol, and toluene.

Samples of colored materials such as carotenoids and chlorophylls can be bleached[86] with microliter volumes of chlorine water.

The optimum efficiency for carbon-14 and tritium is almost completely restored in bleached carotenoid samples; the treatment of chlorophyll samples is less successful.

GASES The need to count labeled gases with scintillation-counting equipment seldom arises. The scintillation counting of non-integral samples of gases and liquids is discussed in Chap. 12. Feates[97] describes a simple apparatus in which carbon-14 dioxide and carbon-14 monoxide can be separated for rapid measurement of the molar radioactivity of each. The apparatus is a combination of McLeod gage, gas buret, Toepler pump, and scintillation counter. The scintillation cell is prepared by carefully depositing (by sublimation) anthracene on one surface. The efficiency for carbon-14-labeled gases is high; the method can be applied to very small quantities of gas (1 μmole) of low activity with 99% reproducibility. A notable feature of the apparatus is the use of an external standard to provide corrections for day-to-day variations in the efficiency of the multiplier-phototube assembly.

11-4d   QUENCHING

The phenomenon of quenching has been mentioned from time to time. The quenching or attenuation of scintillation pulse heights may be caused by chemical action or by simple absorption of light. Chemical quenching results from the interaction of a substance with the solvent or solute components in such a way that the efficiency of energy transfer is decreased. The energy may be dissipated as heat instead of in light pulses. In the second type of quenching, colored substances absorb light whose wavelength is in the region of maximum fluorescence. Light is also blocked by suspended substances such as mixtures of barium carbonate and Cab-O-Sil; the effect imposes a limit on the sample size of suspended materials, even if large amounts can be supported.

Hayes, Rogers, and Sanders[98] found that amines, ketones, chloro- and bromobenzene, and thiophene all show pronounced quenching. Aldehydes, mercaptans, oxygen, and water are also strong quenchers. Some heterocyclic compounds quench; benzoic acid, which is used frequently as an easily purified and chemically stable carbon-14 standard, quenches to the extent of 3.5% per 10 mg in 15 ml of scintillator solution.[99] To reduce the quenching effect of water, naphthalene is often added to systems designed for aqueous samples. Dobbs[100] found, however, that although naphthalene increases the efficiency of counting labeled methyl benzoate, its addition to solutions that contain large amounts of labeled benzoic acid causes a significant decrease in counting efficiency. Dobbs concludes that the quenching mechanism in the two systems is basically different. Oxygen can be removed by displacement with argon or nitrogen. The exchange rate is so rapid, however, that it would be difficult to handle samples without incurring exchange with air. Attempts to remove oxygen are probably not worthwhile or applicable to routine counting. It is important to remember that standards are usually prepared and sealed in an atmosphere of nitrogen and therefore count with higher efficiency than those prepared in air.

The simple absorption of light by some colored substances is so great that they cannot be counted at any practical concentration. Typical of such substances are the 2,4-dinitrophenylhydrazones of aldehydes and ketones. Color quenching by other compounds, for example, carbon-14-labeled nitro compounds, can be greatly reduced by the use of suitable wavelength shifters.[101] Sometimes a small amount of color can be removed by treating the sample with peroxide[102] or by destroying the chromophore with a reducing agent such as sodium borohydride.[103] Sometimes the only practical way to handle materials that quench badly is to burn them to carbon dioxide. The carbon-14 dioxide is then absorbed, preferably in a nonquenching base. Because quenching is so unpredictable and because instrument variations occur from day to day, it is advisable to make regular determinations of counting efficiency. Davidson[94] discusses three methods of determining the degree of quenching. One method consists in diluting the sample. If a sample is counted in 5 ml of scintillation solvent and then is counted again after the addition of 10 ml more of the solvent, the count rate will increase for samples that quench. A second method for determining quenching is more quantitative; it involves the addition of an internal standard. The third method requires the simultaneous determination of counts occurring in two different portions of the energy spectrum followed by a comparison of the ratio for the two channels with the ratio observed for compounds known not to quench.

Peng[104] describes an extrapolation method that is the reverse of the dilution method;[94] it consists in adding larger and larger amounts of sample. The solution is counted after each addition to obtain data for a plot of count rate *vs* sample weight. The specific counting rate for an unquenched sample is then determined by extrapolating to zero weight. Absolute efficiency must be determined by counting a nonquenching standard.

The *internal-standard method* for measuring quenching can be applied to the counting of heterogeneous as well as homogeneous scintillating systems. After the sample has been counted, a small quantity of an absolute standard is added to the counting vial. When the sample plus internal standard are re-counted, the increase in counts is attributed to the added standard. If the count-rate increase is the same as it would be in the absence of the sample, then no quenching has occurred. If the actual increase in count rate is only 95 % of the expected increase, then the sample has caused 5 % quenching. The amount of internal standard that is added

should be small so as not to disturb the solute-to-solvent ratio; also, the internal standard should not quench, a reason for not using benzoic acid. Radioactivity standards labeled with carbon-14 are available from the U.S. National Bureau of Standards, and secondary standards are sold by manufacturers of scintillation-counting equipment. The accuracy of pipetting liquid standards, such as labeled toluene, in the 10-to-25 μl range is poor. The problem of internal-standard addition can be simplified by the use of a standard quenching curve for samples of known weight and composition. Toporek[105] used such a curve to determine quenching in the scintillation counting of carbon-14-labeled plasma proteins. When the internal-standard method is used, the efficiency determination depends on the difference between two counts. Accuracy decreases if the sample is more radioactive than the standard. It is best to add an amount of standard that contains about ten times the amount of carbon-14 in the sample.

In the *channels-ratio technique*, the problem of determining counting efficiency for each of many samples by the accurate addition of an internal standard to each and then re-counting can become very laborious. The alternative method by which the efficiency can be related quantitatively to the ratio of the counting rates in two channels of the pulse-height spectrum is described in several publications.[106–110]. Quenching decreases the amount of light produced in the scintillating solution and thereby causes a decrease in the height of the output pulse from the multiplier phototube. The result is a downward shift in the pulse-height spectrum. For tritium much of the pulse-height spectrum may be degraded to the noise level; the spectrum of carbon-14 will be shifted toward that of tritium, thus making their simultaneous determination difficult. The downward shift of the pulse-height spectrum caused by quenching is shown in Fig. 11-6. Bush[110] studied the channels-ratio method, first used

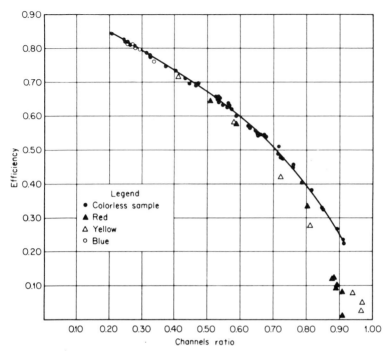

FIG. 11-6   Spectrometer channels in relation to beta spectra. (*From E. T. Bush,* ANAL. CHEM., **35,** *1024 (1963), with permission.*)

by Baillie,[106] to determine the overall effect of instrument variables. The positions of the counting channels indicated in Fig. 11-6 were chosen in such a way as to minimize statistical errors and at the same time to provide a calibration curve of maximum linearity. It was possible to minimize statistical errors by using the total portion of the spectrum included within the counting channels to calculate the efficiency. A calibration curve, established for a wide range of quenching agents, is shown in Fig. 11-7. The shape of the curve is determined by the position of the windows L_1-L_2 and L_2-L_3 and is therefore affected by the gain and discriminator settings. Optimum settings are not possible for samples having a wide range of quenching, but better performance is possible with samples having

a narrower quenching range. Wang[111] has observed that the quenching effect of Hyamine can be minimized by use of a wide window and higher voltages. At higher multiplier-phototube voltages, the background increases, but at the same time the pulse sizes gradually assume a more random distribution.

Bush found that a single quenching-correction curve was adequate for all solvents, quenching agents, and scintillators studied but that colored samples diverged from the chemical-quenching curve as the color became more intense. A special calibration curve is recommended for highly colored samples that contain carbon-14.

The channels-ratio method has the advantage that, with a dual-channel instrument, only one measurement is needed.

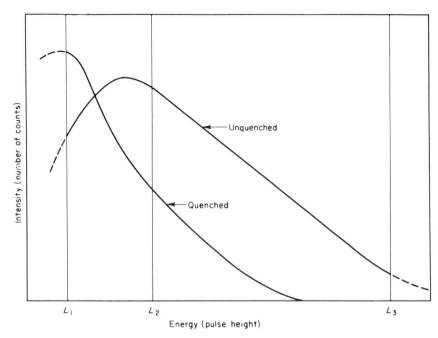

FIG. 11-7 Quenching curve for ^{14}C samples containing 100 μl of labeled toluene. Wide-channel (L_1-L_3) efficiency *vs.* ratio of counts in channels $(L_1-L_2)/(L_1-L_3)$. (*From E. T. Bush,* ANAL. CHEM., **35,** *1024 (1963), with permission.*)

Errors in weighing the internal standard are eliminated, as are possible interactions with the standard that might change the efficiency of the measurement. The amount of time required to reach a given statistical precision may be great if the level of radioactivity is low; this delay can be a disadvantage if many samples are to be counted. In the study made by Bruno and Christian,[108] an average error of $\pm 1.9\%$ was reported for a number of determinations in which aniline was the quenching agent. A calibration curve determined from a mixture of quenchers and colored substances would provide corrections that are less accurate.

Users of instruments that do not have dual channels can take advantage of the "balanced quenching" technique described by Ross.[112] If errors of $\pm 5\%$ can be tolerated,

the technique permits the counting of solutions that contain substantial amounts of quenching agents.

QUENCH DETERMINATION BY EXTERNAL STANDARDIZATION A gamma radiation source such as cesium-137 or cobalt-60 can be placed external to a liquid scintillation sample to generate Compton electrons within the vial. Quenching agents in the sample will affect the induced spectrum in much the same way that they affect the photon spectrum from the sample itself. Funt and Hetherington[113] used excitation from an externally mounted cesium-137 source to study the kinetics of quenching in liquid scintillators. Horrocks[114] used the same radionuclide to study the counting efficiency of carbon-14. Higashimura and co-workers[115] determined the effect of chemical quenchers, color quenchers, and diluents on the counting efficiency of carbon-14 samples. Cesium-137, cerium-144, and pitchblende were used as external standards. Perhaps the earliest use of an external standard for efficiency determination is that by Fleishman and Glazunov[116] to determine the efficiency for counting potassium-40, cesium-137, and strontium-90.

Schrodt, Gibbs, and Cavanaugh[117] used automatic external standardization in a Tri-Carb[118] liquid-scintillation spectrometer. They chose radium-226 for this application, because it (together with its steady-state mixture of daughter radionuclides) provides a relatively smooth Compton spectrum that extends to about 2 Mev (Fig. 11-8).

To determine the degree of quenching, it is necessary to prepare a correlation curve. Data for its preparation are obtained by counting a series of samples, each containing a known amount of carbon-14 and a different amount of quenching agent to cover the range from quench-free to nearly totally quenched solutions. The samples are counted with and without the external standard. The correlation curve (Fig. 11-9) is then prepared by plotting the calculated efficiencies as ordinate and the external-standard count rate as abscissa. Unfortunately, such a calibration is most accurate only for experimentation in which the same scintillator solution, the same volume of solution, and the same quenching agents are present. The data (Fig. 11-10) of Schrodt, Gibbs, and Cavanaugh[117] show that minor variations in volume will not be critical for samples having volumes of about 15 ml.

FIG. 11-8 Induced spectrum generated by Compton electrons from ^{226}Ra (gain and voltage settings for Tri-Carb). [*From A. G. Schrodt, J. A. Gibbs, and R. E. Cavanaugh (a paper presented at the American Nuclear Society, San Francisco, December 3, 1964), with permission from the authors.*]

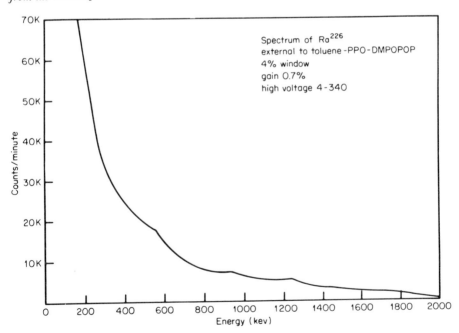

Spectrum of Ra^{226}
external to toluene -PPO-DMPOPOP
4% window
gain 0.7%
high voltage 4-340

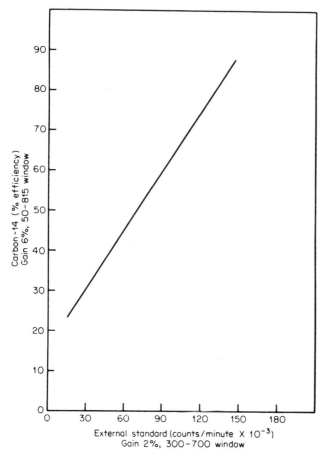

FIG. 11-9 Correlation curve for carbon-14 counting efficiency related to the count rate of a ^{226}Ra external standard (gain and window settings for Tri-Carb). (*From A. G. Schrodt, J. A. Gibbs, and R. E. Cavanaugh in S. Rothchild, "Advances in Tracer Methodology," vol. 2, p. 157, New England Nuclear Corporation, Boston, 1965, with permission.*)

According to the procedure recommended[117] for most radioisotopes, one counting channel is reserved for the external standard only. Three channels are therefore necessary for the simultaneous determination of carbon-14 and tritium. For a given quenched sample counted for a preset time, the procedure is as follows. On the first count the sample is counted in both channels 1 and 2; channel 3 provides the background count for the external standard. On the second count the sample plus external standard are counted in channels 1 and 2; channel 3 provides the external standard count. To calculate the degree of quenching and to correct for it,

the only information required is the data from channels 1 and 2 of the first count and from channel 3 of the second count (the level of radioactivity of the external standard is so great that the background in channel 3 can be neglected). The count rate from channel 3 is then used together with the correlation curve to determine the necessary correction (or corrections) for the radioisotope (or radioisotopes) counted in channels 1 and 2.

A number of important advantages are claimed for the automatic external-standard technique. It is unnecessary, as compared with the internal-standard technique, to alter the sample or to make time-consuming

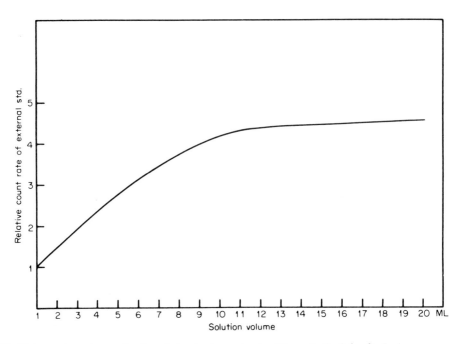

FIG. 11-10 Volume dependence of external standard count rate. (*From A. G. Schrodt, J. A. Gibbs, and R. E. Cavanaugh in S. Rothchild, "Advances in Tracer Methodology," vol. 2, p. 116, New England Nuclear Corporation, Boston, 1965, with permission.*)

weighings. It is possible to measure samples that contain quencher in a wide range of concentration. The statistical accuracy of the efficiency determination is independent of the sample count rate.

ADVANTAGES AND LIMITATIONS OF SCINTILLATION COUNTING The scintillation-counting method is highly efficient and sensitive, is capable of accepting samples that have a wide range of radioactivity, and often requires a minimum amount of time for sample preparation. Modern commercial counters will automatically count as many as 200 samples and are therefore useful for 24 hr a day, even though they are unattended.

Among the disadvantages of the liquid-scintillation method are its high cost and greater electronic complexity. Modern in-struments have been made much more reliable through the incorporation of semi-conductor devices but continue to be much less robust than, for example, the ionization chamber–vibrating-reed electrometer combin-ation.

A disadvantage of scintillation counting is that corrections for quenching are often insufficiently accurate for a careful inves-tigation. Also, there is a tendency to prepare and count more samples than would be prepared and counted if a less automatic instrument were available. Often there is a good reason for frequent counts of replicate samples. Counting vials are sometimes im-perfect, and the sample count rate will vary from vial to vial. In an automatic scintillation counter the vial will be replaced in a different position each time. Such repositioning also averages the nonuniform response to an external standard that results from variations in the thickness of glass. For the routine counting of large numbers of samples for which quenching is not a problem, the scintillation counter is the instrument of choice. Each manufacturer has attempted to outdo his competitors in the sophistication of the instrument. The result is a baffling array of controls; the occasional user finds it necessary to expend a great amount of time in consulting the operating manual and in adjusting the instrument for optimum performance. The problem is greater if, because of the instrument's versatility, it is shared with others who use it to count tritium, phosphorus-32, sulfur-35, etc. Even for limited numbers of samples the newer less-automatic (and less-expensive) liquid-scintillation counters will be most useful for counting a wide range of carbon-14 activity with modest accuracy. For accurate, occasional counting of a great variety of substances at moderate activity levels, oxidation to carbon dioxide followed by ionization-chamber counting is preferred. For most work, the only additional nuclear instrumentation needed is an inexpensive radiation monitor equipped with a thin-window Geiger-Müller tube.

11-5 IONIZATION-CHAMBER COUNTING

Proportional counting tubes, Geiger-Müller tubes, and ionization chambers are all ionization counters. However, in this section "ionization chamber" will be used to mean a detector that operates in the region of simple ionization without gas amplification. Excellent reviews that describe the use of ionization chambers for measuring weak-beta emitters are given by Tolbert[119] and by Tolbert and Siri.[120]

11-5a IONIZATION CHAMBERS AND THEIR CONSTRUCTION

A simple circuit for ionization-chamber counting is shown in Fig. 11-11. Radiation

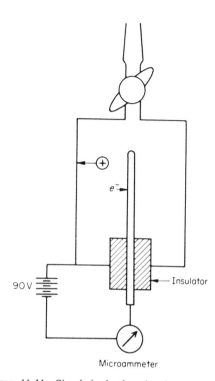

FIG. 11-11 Simple ionization chamber.

causes ionization of the gas in the chamber. In the presence of an electric field, the electrons and ions each migrate to the electrodes of opposite charge. For each carbon-14 disintegration that occurs, about 1500 ion pairs are formed; their collection results in the flow of a very small current. Circuits of the type shown in Fig. 11-11, though too insensitive for most measurements, have been used to determine carbon-14 dioxide during the production of barium carbonate-^{14}C.

A modification of the simple ionization chamber is used to measure a very small ionization current. It incorporates a guard ring (Fig. 11-12) that completely isolates the outer cylindrical section of the insulator from the inner section, thus permitting any electrical leakage across the surface of the insulator to be bypassed directly to ground.

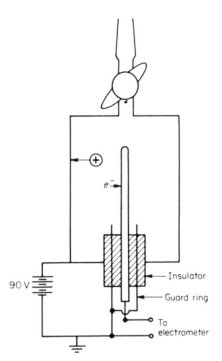

FIG. 11-12 Simple ionization chamber with a guard ring.

The shape and size of an ionization chamber significantly affect its efficiency; depending on the need, sizes from a few cubic centimeters to 22 liters have been used. Small flow-type ionization chambers have been used to assay radioactivity in flowing-gas systems. Such chambers are readily adapted to the monitoring of radioactivity in effluents from a gas chromatograph (see Sec. 12-1b). Methods by which radioactive compounds can be converted to a form suitable for introduction into an ionization chamber are discussed later.

The choice of an insulator to isolate the probe from the chamber proper requires consideration of more than just the volume resistivity or surface resistivity of insulator materials. Mica, many glasses, sapphire, quartz, steatite, polymethylmethacrylates, polyethyl-

ene, polystyrene, polytetrafluoroethylene, and polytrifluorochloroethylene all show high volume resistance. Glass, however, is very susceptible to moisture adsorption. The most satisfactory materials for the center probe insulator are polyethylene, polytetrafluoroethylene, polytrifluorochloroethylene, and sapphire; polyethylene and sapphire insulators are found in two commonly used commercial ionization chambers. All these insulators show relatively good piezoelectric characteristics and minimum charge soak-in. Polytrifluorochloroethylene insulators have proved serviceable in Borkowski type ionization chambers used at the Oak Ridge National Laboratory. They have a more reproducible background current and require less time to come to equilibrium than do chambers equipped with a sapphire insulator. The center probe should not be subjected to unnecessary mechanical stress; aside from that precaution, the ionizaton chamber is a robust detector that will last for many years if given reasonable care. Care of the instrument consists in protecting the probe end of the assembly with a dust cap and periodically cleaning the disassembled chamber. Often grease from the stopcock enters the chamber. Such contamination is readily removed with chloroform or a similar solvent. The insulators and the probe assembly can be washed with ethyl alcohol and distilled water. The presence of a small trace of a salt on an insulator can greatly increase its surface conductivity. For this reason the insulators and probe assembly of the ionization chamber should not be handled with bare hands. Usually a cleaned and reassembled chamber requires several hours to reach chemical and electrical equilibrium.

Materials for the construction of radiation detectors and shields must be selected with care. Almost all commonly used metals contain radium. Elements related to the lanthanide or actinide series usually show varying but appreciable contamination. For example, carefully refined lead contains radioactivity due to ^{210}Pb (RaD). The half-life of this isotope is about 20 y; therefore, this source of residual radioactivity can be reduced by using "aged" lead recovered from the plumbing in old buildings. Other metals such as platinum, tin, cadmium, and antimony are stated[121] to have high and variable levels of radioactivity. Potassium-40 is a radioactive contaminant of most glass. Borosilicate glass produced since 1958 is often contaminated with other radionuclides,[122] presumably from fallout of radioactive alkali that is eventually incorporated with the alkali normally used in making borosilicate glass. Pure copper, brass (lead-free), and mild and stainless steels are all satisfactory for ionization-chamber construction. Commercial ionization chambers are made of stainless steel, a material particularly useful because of its resistance to chemical corrosion. Possible contamination from glass, Kovar seals, solder, and other construction materials has been investigated; the results are summarized in NBS Handbook 86.[123]

11-5b FILLING GAS

The efficiency of ion formation varies from gas to gas. A detailed discussion of the process of ionization as it is affected by the type and energy of the ionizing particle as well as by the filling gas is given by Franzen and Cochran.[124] The constant W (the energy in electron volts lost per ion pair produced) for energetic electrons in gases varies from a value of 22 for xenon to 42 for helium. Values of W for other gases fall between those for xenon and helium; for the more common gases they are: carbon dioxide, 32.9; oxygen, 30.9; air, 34.0; nitrogen, 35.0; and methane, 27.3.[125] It will be seen that the W-value for air is about that expected on the basis of the values known for the major components of air. Such agreement is not general; sometimes the addition of a contaminant gas may greatly alter the W-value for the major component. A minimum value of W occurs for a particular concen-

tration of each impurity gas. In ionization-chamber and proportional counting, it is therefore important that the ratios of the gases in the mixtures used be kept as constant as is practicable throughout a series of measurements. In the ionization-chamber assay of carbon-14, the gas counted is usually carbon-14 dioxide, although compounds have been cracked and counted as methane. Labeled volatile hydrocarbons have been counted in ionization chambers, but their W-values are by no means constant.

11-5c MEASUREMENT OF IONIZATION-CHAMBER CURRENT

For an ionization chamber of average size (250 ml), about half the energy from carbon-14 dioxide is absorbed by the gas (if the filling is air); the remaining energy is absorbed by the metal walls of the container. It is instructive to calculate the ionization current produced by 0.1 μc of carbon-14 dioxide in a carbon dioxide filling. If it is assumed that the average beta particle has an energy of 45,000 ev, that 33 ev produce an ion pair, and that the efficiency is 50%, then

$$\text{rate of energy emission} = (3.7 \times 10^3)(45,000)$$
$$= 1.67 \times 10^8 \text{ ev/sec}$$
$$\text{number of ions} = (1.67 \times 10^8)/(2 \times 33)$$
$$= 2.5 \times 10^6 \text{ ion pairs/sec}$$
$$\text{charge carried} = (2.5 \times 10^6)(1.6 \times 10^{-19})$$
$$= 4.0 \times 10^{-13} \text{ coulomb/sec}$$
$$= 4.0 \times 10^{-13} \text{ amp}$$

Such small currents cannot be measured with an ordinary microammeter, nor even with a sensitive laboratory galvanometer. Instruments that are capable of measuring the small electric charges collected in an ionization chamber are known as electroscopes or electrometers. The gold-leaf electroscope and the Lauritsen electroscope are examples of the first of these; they are simple and reliable radiation detectors. Electroscopes differ from electrometers in that they do not require a continuous external voltage for operation. They are seldom used in the laboratory as a measuring instrument, but the principle of the quartz fiber instrument is applied in the *pocket dosimeter* used to measure cumulative radiation exposure.

Electrometers as well as electroscopes can be voltage- or current-measuring devices. The electrometer is usually thought of as a vacuum-tube device. The vacuum tube chosen for such service must have a very small grid current, usually 10^{-15} amp or less. Direct-current electrometers are used in the "cutie pie" a portable beta-gamma ionization chamber type of survey meter. As a rule the dc electrometer is not nearly as sensitive and stable as the vibrating-reed electrometer, but some commercially available[126] instruments perform very well. Despite its sensitivity, the dc electrometer cannot distinguish between signal and input-tube variations; both are amplified alike. The instrument is therefore subject to much drift over the period of time normally needed to measure ion current. The most sensitive and stable device for measuring small direct currents is the vibrating-reed electrometer (also called the vibrating-capacitor electrometer). It can detect less than 10^{-17} amp and is the instrument used for the accurate routine determination of low radioactivity in an ionization chamber and for the continuous indication of radioactivity in a flow system. Fairstein[127] gives much useful information on the application of electrometers to the measurement of ionization currents.

METHOD OF MEASUREMENT   The current that flows in an ionization chamber can be measured in two different ways. One of these is the "high-resistance-leak" method; the other, the "rate-of-charge" method. Ionization-chamber counting systems such as those available commercially[128] can be used either way.

The high-resistance-leak method is useful for the continuous determination of ionization in an ionization chamber. Such a determination *must* be made if changes in the radioactivity of a gas flowing through the ionization chamber are to be observed. In the high-resistance-leak method, a high resistance is connected between the feedback line and the input lead of the electrometer. Resistors having values of 10^8, 10^{10}, and 10^{12} ohms are often incorporated in a turret switch that is part of the preamplifier assembly. The speed of response of the electrometer is greater for the lower-valued resistor. Some control over the response speed can be exercised by the manufacturer; the fastest possible response speed is desirable if the instrument is to be used to monitor the effluent of a gas chromatograph. The high-resistance-leak method can be used to measure[129] the current in a closed ionization chamber as well as in one in which the gas flows. Such a measurement is seldom used and is not as accurate as the alternate rate-of-charge method.

The inherent capacity of the head of the vibrating-reed electrometer is about 10 pf or less; consequently, very little current is required to give the system an appreciable charge. For this reason, currents of the order of 10^{-12} amp or less are usually measured by the rate-of-charge method. The sensitivity of the electrometer is great enough to permit the measurement of carbon-14 activity as low as 5×10^{-15} curie per milligram of barium carbonate.[130]

Once the ionization chamber is filled (usually to atmospheric pressure), it is placed on the electrometer head and is connected to a polarizing voltage that may be 90 to 180 volts or more. If the chamber contains less than 0.01 μc of carbon-14 radioactivity, it is advisable to allow the chamber to remain on the electrometer head, with the input shorted, for about 10 min. Several rates of charge are then measured. In its simplest form, such a measurement can consist in observation of the meter on the electrometer, starting a stopwatch when the needle is at $\frac{1}{10}$ of full scale, and stopping the watch when the meter reading is $\frac{9}{10}$ of full scale.

For relatively long charging periods such a procedure is surprisingly accurate but is too laborious. Often a modified high-speed strip-chart recorder is used in an arrangement that provides for automatic switching of a timer. The input to the recorder is adjusted so that full scale on the electrometer meter corresponds to full scale on the strip-chart recorder (usually a 1-ma recording milliammeter or a 25-mv recording potentiometer). Installation of microswitches or mercury switches in the recorder is relatively simple. Microswitches are more satisfactory than mercury switches, because the mercury pool in the latter shifts position unpredictably if noise from the switching operation is fed back to the recorder. The use of a recorder is helpful if very-low-level measurements are made. Alpha pulses from both the chamber and the filling gas can be spotted on the recorded trace, and the necessary corrections can be made.

For samples of moderate to high levels of radioactivity, the strip-chart recorder is an unnecessary, complicated, and expensive adjunct to the counting system. A relatively simple and robust electrical timer can be used in its place. One such instrument that employs a pair of meter relays has been in use for several years at the Oak Ridge National Laboratory. The circuit for it is shown in Fig. 11-13.

The resistances that are in series with the input signal were needed to bring the total resistance of the external circuit up to the value specified for the electrometer used (in this case a Cary Model 31 vibrating-reed electrometer). Relays MR-1 and MR-2 are 1-ma meter relays;[131] relays RY-1 and RY-2 are fast-acting 12,000-ohm relays. Meter relay MR-2 is set to make contact at about 10% of full scale, and MR-1 to make contact at about 90 to 100% of full scale, thus relays RY-2 and RY-1, respectively, are

FIG. 11-13 Timer-control circuit for use with a vibrating-reed electrometer. (*Reproduced with permission from API Instruments Company, Chesterland, Ohio.*)

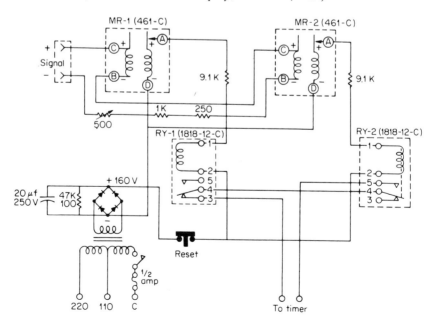

actuated to start and stop the clock. A micro switch that operates automatically with the grounding of the electrometer head can serve to reset the control. Substitution of the newer taut-band meter movements for the models shown (Assembly Products 461-C) should give even better reproducibility of timing.

For a 250-ml chamber that contains 0.1 μc of radioactivity, about 50 sec is needed to charge a 10-pf-capacity electrometer to 3 volts. To calibrate the ionization chamber–electrometer counting system, carbon-14 dioxide from a sample of standard barium carbonate-^{14}C or sodium carbonate-^{14}C can be swept into the ionization chamber with the filling gas normally used. A reference standard is almost a necessity for determining absolute radioactivities (the precision of such determinations is more important than the accuracy) and for judging the performance of the counting system. A useful secondary standard consists of a piece of uranium metal wrapped in aluminum foil (to stop alpha particles) and secured to the end of the chamber opposite the probe. Tolbert and Siri[129] suggest filling a cylinder with the counting gas (e.g., CO_2) and a calculated amount of carbon-14 dioxide. The resulting gas can then be aliquoted into ionization chambers to calibrate them. An alternate suggestion was to paint part of the inside wall of the reference chamber with Aqua-Dag that contains a small amount of a nonvolatile stable organic compound. One difficulty encountered with the latter procedure, as well as with the uranium reference chamber, is that neither will respond to a change in pressure in the same way in which a chamber that contains a gaseous carbon-14 compound responds. Fortunately, such differences in sample geometry seldom amount to more than a few tenths of 1%. Whatever the reference standard chosen, it should contain a carbon-14 equivalence that is of the same order of magnitude as that of the samples used—it should not contain much less than 0.1 μc-equivalent of carbon-14.

11-5d COMBUSTION OF LABELED ORGANIC COMPOUNDS

Changes in combustion procedures continue to receive much interest. More than 150 years ago Gay-Lussac and Thenard achieved oxidation in a closed system by mixing the sample with potassium chlorate. Combustion methods were perfected during the next 100 years by Berzelius, Liebig, and finally Pregl. Much of the effort in elemental microanalysis is devoted to simplifying methods, shortening analysis time, and extending techniques to progressively smaller quantities of materials. The advent of rapid combustion procedures is more important than automation in converting carbon-14 compounds to carbon-14 dioxide.

Oxidation procedures may be classified into two major categories, dry and wet. Dry combustion procedures include modifications of the Pregl microcombustion, the Schöniger-Hempel oxygen-flask technique, and the sodium peroxide fusion. The wet combustion procedures are limited to oxidation by persulfate and by Van Slyke–Folch solutions. Regardless of which technique is chosen, the demands on the analyst are not as great as they are for elemental microanalyses. Unless tritium or deuterium is to be measured, there is no need to isolate the water formed in the reaction; unless barium carbonate is being prepared for solid counting, there is less need to be concerned about the introduction of extraneous carbon dioxide. It *is* important that all carbon-14 atoms be converted to carbon-14 dioxide and that the carbon-14 dioxide be swept quantitatively—or at least reproducibly—into the collecting apparatus.

MODIFIED   PREGL   COMBUSTION METHOD The Pregl micro combustion method is the most reliable and generally applicable means for burning carbon compounds. Tube fillings and absorbents are available to permit the combustion of compounds that contain almost any imaginable substituent. A simple combustion train has been described;[132,133] it is intended primarily for use in burning carbon-14 compounds for the filling of ionization chambers. The apparatus consists of a tank of 5% carbon dioxide in oxygen (medical oxygen), a pressure regulator, a combustion tube and furnace, and a rotameter flowmeter. A similar apparatus (Fig. 11-14), which is a modification of that described by Tolbert, has been used very successfully at the Oak Ridge National Laboratory. It retains the salient feature of Tolbert's apparatus, that is, the use of an oxygen–carbon dioxide mixture that contains 5 to 7% carbon dioxide. Two kinds of "medical oxygen" are sold. Medical oxygen for therapeutic use is U.S.P., 99+% oxygen, whereas oxygen for use in anesthesis contains about 5% carbon dioxide and is the grade that should be used. The chief alterations are the provision for automatic oxygen cutoff when the ionization chamber is full and the use of cobaltocobaltic oxide (Co_3O_4) instead of quartz as the combustion-tube filling. The new filling[134] makes possible the burning of samples of organic compounds at lower temperatures and at flow rates as high as 50 ml/min. In addition to the above changes, the pressure-relief bubbler and rotameter flowmeter were eliminated to advantage. The fritted-disk pressure regulator (normally used with the Van Slyke–Folch procedure) and a trap for oxides of nitrogen are part of the modified apparatus. The changes described permit the accurate determination of carbon-14 in a 2- to 30-mg sample in 20 min, which includes the time required for all weighing operations and calculations.

Compounds having an angular methyl group,[135] for example, steroids and other oxidation-resistant compounds, tend to give methane on combustion. When tritium is present, cross-contamination can become serious if the oxidation is incomplete. Use of the efficient cobaltocobaltic oxide catalyst reduces cross-contamination from tritium to 0.2% or less at sweep rates that permit total absorption of water.

The use of cobaltocobaltic oxide is described by Večeřa, Šnobl, and Synek[136] in a series of papers on organic quantitative analysis. Večeřa and Šnobl[137] also investigated the use of manganese dioxide for the absorption of nitrogen oxides and give detailed instructions for preparing a hydrated amorphous $MnO(OH)_2$ gel that has

FIG. 11-14 Apparatus for dry combustion.

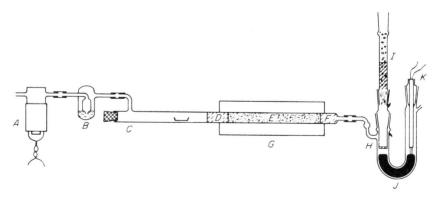

suitable absorption properties; the *Chemical Abstracts* reference includes these directions. Kainz and Mayer[138] learned that several factors influence the absorption of nitrogen oxide. Of most importance is the grain size and water content of the manganese dioxide. Nitrogen oxide absorption improves greatly with decreasing grain size and is hastened by absorptively bound water. The equation for the reaction is presumed to be

$$MnO_2 + H_2O + 2\,NO_2 \rightleftharpoons Mn(NO_3)_2\text{—}H_2O$$

The effectiveness of the absorbent is excellent at room temperature, but the efficiency falls as the temperature is raised, since the absorption product decomposes thermally above 50°. This information indicates that the best location for the active manganese dioxide is between the combustion tube and the Drierite (or other water absorbent).

Precipitated manganese dioxide prepared as described by Attenburrow and co-workers[139] is perfectly satisfactory for the absorption of nitrogen oxides if it is not thoroughly dry. The procedure for the preparation of this catalyst is as follows. A 390-ml volume of 40% sodium hydroxide and a solution of 280 g of manganous sulfate tetrahydrate in 500 ml of water are added simultaneously over a 1-hr period to a hot stirred solution of 320 g of potassium permanganate in 2 liters of water. The resulting very finely divided solid may be washed by decantation and filtration or separated by centrifugation. The solid should be washed with 5% sulfuric acid solution and then with water to ensure that all alkaline residues are removed. If the solid is not washed, then alkaline residues will slowly absorb and exchange carbon-14 dioxide from one sample to another. The manganese dioxide is dried at 100° to remove most of the water; then it is crushed and sieved. To provide an excellent oxidant for benzylic and allylic hydroxides, the fines can be dried further. Active manganese dioxide is also available from commercial sources.[140]

Instructions for the preparation of the cobaltocobaltic oxide catalyst are given by Gawargious and MacDonald.[141] The preparation is essentially as follows. A solution of 88 g of oxalic acid dihydrate in 300 ml of water is added to a solution of 145 g of cobalt nitrate hexahydrate in 200 ml of water. The precipitate is collected on a filter and is washed with water and then with ethyl alcohol. The washed precipitate is mixed to a paste with water and with an amount of starch that is about the same as the dry weight of the precipitate. The paste is dried at 110° and is then ignited at 550 to 600° for 2 to 3 hr. The ignition is accompanied by the evolution of a great volume of smoke and must be done in the draft of a hood! The low-density catalyst that results is carefully broken up with a spatula and sieved to obtain a 14-to-40 mesh portion. The catalyst is used at a furnace temperature of about 650°.

The apparatus described above is adequate for oxidizing carbon-14 compounds that contain carbon, hydrogen, oxygen, the halogens (except fluorine), sulfur, and nitrogen. If other compounds are to be burned satisfactorily, one of many modified combustion fillings must be used. A universal combustion-tube filling that can be used successfully with organometallic compounds as well as with compounds that contain fluorine, phosphorus, silicon, boron, and other elements is described by Yeh.[142] Reviews on organic microchemistry that cover elemental analysis are published frequently in the Annual Reviews section of the April issues of *Analytical Chemistry*. One such review is that by Ma and Gutterson.[143]

Sample weight is relatively unimportant if the combustion products are swept into the ionization chamber with inactive carbon dioxide. When other sweep gases are used, the rates of drift observed may not vary linearly with sample weight. Such variations are especially noticeable in the dry-combustion procedure that uses medical oxygen. Here it has been found[144] that in the filling of a 250-ml ionization chamber, a sixfold increase (from 5 to 30 mg) in sample size causes an apparent increase in molar radioactivity greater than 1%.

The combustion of very large samples requires special techniques. One method suitable for producing one-half mole quantities of carbon dioxide is described by Freeland.[145] Naturally, the combustion requires a long time (2 to 3 hr). Liquid samples are injected through an 18-gage syringe needle; solids are added as an aqueous slurry from a pressure-equalizing separatory funnel. The carbon dioxide in the effluent gas is trapped in sodium hydroxide solution, subsequently released, and permitted to react with phenylmagnesium bromide.

SEALED-TUBE COMBUSTION Quantitative oxidation of organic compounds in the absence of a stream of oxygen is described by Hackspill and D'Huart,[146] who used copper oxide and copper powder to oxidize organic samples placed in the closed end of a combustion tube. By first heating the copper and copper oxide and then the sample, it was possible to manometrically determine carbon, hydrogen, and nitrogen.

Wilzbach and Sykes[147] describe a somewhat similar system for the convenient determination of carbon-14. The procedure is very much like that described by Wilzbach, Kaplan, and Brown[148] for the conversion of tritium compounds to a form suitable for measurement in an ionization chamber. In the carbon-14 procedure a disposable combustion tube is prepared from 34-cm-long by 11-mm-OD Pyrex 1720 glass tubing.[149] The tube is drawn out at the midpoint to form two tubes with break tips. To each tube is added $\frac{3}{4}$ g of 60-mesh copper oxide, $\frac{1}{4}$ g of 60-mesh copper, and 1 to 10 mg of sample. The tube is constricted, evacuated, and sealed off. Volatile samples are introduced in a sealed ampoule, which is broken by sharply jarring the evacuated and sealed combustion tube. Several such combustion tubes—separated so that the explosion of one tube, if it occurs, will not damage another—can be placed (horizontally) in the combustion furnace at one time. The combustion tubes are heated at 640 ± 10° for 30 min. After the tubes have cooled, they are placed in an evacuated apparatus that permits freezing out the water vapor at −95° and the carbon-14 dioxide at −195°. The carbon-14 dioxide trap is warmed to permit expansion of the gas into an ionization chamber; alternatively, all the labeled gas can be transferred to the ionization chamber by sweeping with tank carbon dioxide.

Other analysts have found the Wilzbach-Sykes procedure to be inadequate for the oxidation of many substances. Simon, Daniel, and Klebe[150] observe that copper oxide provides negligible oxygen vapor pressure at 650° and must therefore be in direct contact with organic material to oxidize it. They therefore recommend that substances which contain carbon, oxygen, and hydrogen be heated with potassium perchlorate. If nitrogen, halogen, or sulfur is present, then copper oxide is added. If the sample contains alkaline or alkaline-earth salts, it is necessary to add vanadium pentoxide to the mixture.

Buchanan and Corcoran[151] report that sealed-tube combustions with copper oxide alone give low and inconsistent recoveries with some compounds. They recommend Vycor combustion tubes and an oxidizing mixture consisting of copper oxide, manganese dioxide, and anhydrous cupric chloride in the ratio 5:1:1. Combustion requires heating at 850° for 30 min. Buchanan and Corcoran describe and illustrate an apparatus for the collection, manometric measurement, and determination (proportional gas counter) of carbon-14 dioxide.

Sealed-tube combustions are useful for burning samples without the introduction of extraneous carbon dioxide. With suitable apparatus[150] it is possible to not only assay carbon-14 and tritium but also to determine the carbon and hydrogen content as well. Such versatility is possible only in a complicated apparatus having 25 to 30 stopcocks, which must be manipulated and maintained. If regular determinations of carbon-14 are made, then a simple apparatus is much preferred. For scintillation counting, the sealed-tube combustions have the advantage that large numbers of combustions made over a period of several days can be counted in sequence; thus errors from instrument drift are minimized.

If measurements are made in an ionization chamber, then sealed-tube combustions have no advantage over the modified Pregl combustion procedure described earlier. What little advantage is gained in heating several tubes at one time is lost because of the time required to fabricate and fill them. If transfer of labeled gas to the ionization chamber is to be complete, it is necessary with the sealed-tube procedure to maintain a supply of liquid nitrogen. A further disadvantage is the limited maximum sample size (about 10 mg).

HEMPEL-SCHÖNIGER OXYGEN-FLASK COMBUSTION

Hempel[152] was the first to describe a technique for burning organic samples in an oxygen flask. The combustion procedure was further developed by Schöniger[153,154] and has become widely popular for preparing samples for liquid-scintillation counting, as well as for converting organic compounds that contain halides, phosphorus, sulfur, and metals to soluble inorganic derivatives. Usually, the combustion vessel is an Erlenmeyer flask (500- to 2000-ml) having an interchangeable ground-glass head. The sample is enclosed in a specially selected filter paper, packaged in cellophane, or simply folded in a fiber-glass mat. The sample is placed in a basket attached to the head of the flask. Liquid samples can be sealed in small thin-walled ampoules, which are then wrapped in filter paper. Ignition of the filter paper produces enough heat to rupture

the bulbs.[155] The ignition is accomplished either through heating by a resistance wire built into the basket or through the use of a concentrated beam of infrared light from a projection lamp located outside the flask. A simple shield can be devised[156] to eliminate the hazard of explosions or implosions. A complete ignition assembly, including the *essential* safety shield, is available commercially.[156] Either an absorbent such as aqueous sodium hydroxide solution can be added before ignition or an organic base such as ethanolamine can be added after the ignition is complete.[158] Organic solvents such as alcohol, dioxane, acetone, etc., should never be used to wash the combustion flask unless the flask is rinsed subsequently with water. Failure to completely remove such organic solvents prior to a combustion will result in a violent explosion that may not be contained by the usual safety shield.[73a]

A study[159] of the combustion products formed in the oxygen flask showed that chlorine remains ionic, whereas bromine and iodine are oxidized to the free forms. To obtain reproducible results by this method, for substances that contain bromine and iodine, Dobbs[160] recommends that the postcombustion procedure be modified. For scintillation counting, the modification consists in adding 10 vol % of 2-pentene to the phosphor and then delaying the counting for 2 hr after the phosphor is injected into the oxygen flask.

The oxygen-flask method is not directly useful for filling gas-filled counters but does have the advantage of being suitable for large samples (up to 300 mg total dry weight). Such a combustion procedure is very useful for biological samples whose radioactivity can be determined by scintillation counting once conversion to a soluble carbonate is made. Oxygen-flask combustions are not as quantitative as are other oxidation procedures; authors often admit that only 95 to 97% of the carbon-14 is recovered as carbon-14 dioxide.

The Parr oxygen bomb, long established in calorimetry measurements, is well adapted to burning relatively large samples (about 1 g). It is a compact, durable, and safe apparatus when properly used. Sheppard and Rodegker[161] describe a Parr bomb combustion of tissues for subsequent carbon-14 and tritium analysis. The carbon-14 dioxide is absorbed in sodium hydroxide solution and is then converted to barium carbonate-^{14}C for liquid-scintillation counting.

WET COMBUSTION   There is only one generally applicable wet combustion procedure in use at the present time. Organic compounds, with a few exceptions, are readily oxidized in an anhydrous boiling mixture of sulfuric, phosphoric, iodic, and chromic acids. The combination is commonly known as the Van Slyke–Folch oxidizing mixture.[162,163] The reagent is prepared by adding to a 1-liter Erlenmeyer flask 25 g of chromium trioxide, 5 g of crushed potassium iodate, 167 ml of phosphoric acid (density 1.7), and 333 ml of fuming sulfuric acid (20% free sulfur trioxide); the mixture is heated at 150° to dissolve the solids. The anhydrous phosphoric acid can be prepared by boiling 85% phosphoric acid or by adding 30 g of phosphorus pentoxide for every 70 g of 85% phosphoric acid. After it has cooled, the oxidizing mixture is transferred to a glass-stoppered bottle for storage. Figure 11-15 shows an apparatus for the oxidation of organic compounds with the Van Slyke–Folch reagent. Before the combustion is initiated, the ionization chamber is alternately filled with tank carbon dioxide and evacuated. After the third evacuation, the chamber is attached to the combustion line at G. Tube C is filled with the oxidizing solution, the sample (in a boat if it is a solid;

FIG. 11-15   Apparatus for Van Slyke–Folch oxidation of organic compounds. (A, reservoir for Van Slyke–Folch reagent; B, sample flask; C, Van Slyke–Folch reagent; D, stannous chloride; E, active manganese dioxide; F and G, fritted-disk pressure regulator.)

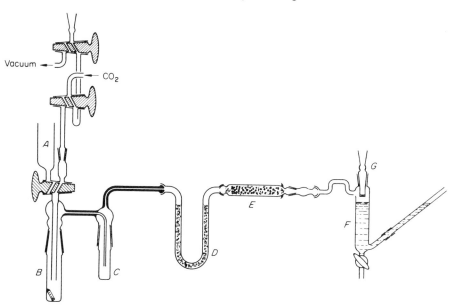

in an open-ended ampoule if it is a volatile liquid) is placed in B along with 15 to 25 mg of potassium iodate. The Van Slyke–Folch reagent is then added to the combustion tube. Most organic compounds dissolve instantly, thus permitting the sample to be oxidized immediately by heating with a Bunsen burner until the combustion is complete (usually 5 to 10 min). The combustion gases are then swept into the ionization chamber with tank carbon dioxide. Compounds that are volatile or that yield volatile oxidation-resistant products should be given time to dissolve, or the heating should be done very gently to prevent the escape of unoxidized carbon-14-labeled products. Simultaneous heating of the oxidizing mixture in C tends to reduce the loss of volatile liquids and unoxidized gases. Quaternary ammonium salts, acetic acids, compounds that yield acetic acid on combustion, and polymers such as polystyrene are oxidized with great difficulty. Dauben and Gee[164] noted, for example, that labeled choline hydrochloride undergoes only 52% oxidation by wet combustion. Isotope effects do accompany the partial wet combustion of aliphatic acids and alcohols;[165,166] under conditions that include no extraneous carbon dioxide sweep, the carbon dioxide from the combustion will not have a molar radioactivity that is representative of the sample. Vigorous heating of the combustion mixture often yields large and variable amounts of oxygen. Since the density of carbon dioxide is greater than that of carbon dioxide–oxygen mixtures, the apparent efficiency of the usual small (250-ml) chamber is greatest when the chamber is filled with 100% carbon dioxide. The efficiency decreases as the percentage of oxygen in it is increased. The use of an ionization chamber of at least 250-ml capacity will tend to minimize the effect of variable amounts of oxygen generated during the combustion. Such capacity is also desirable to ensure that all the carbon-14 dioxide will be swept into it by carrier

carbon dioxide. The stannous chloride trap removes halogens (including iodine from the oxidation procedure) from the effluent gases; precipitated manganese dioxide in E removes oxides of nitrogen at room temperature, a convenient replacement for the usual lead peroxide trap, which must be heated. Sample sizes are usually in the range from 5 to 15 mg and for that reason must be of moderate to high specific radioactivity. In spite of the shortcomings mentioned above, this method can be used with great precision.[167,168] However, reproducible results are more readily attained with the dry-combustion procedure.

Most of the other methods for the wet combustion of organic materials have limited usefulness for the combustion of pure organic compounds. Among these is the persulfate method in which the sample, in aqueous solution, is added to solid potassium persulfate. A drop of sulfuric acid is added, followed by the addition of silver nitrate solution to start the reaction. Carbon dioxide is then trapped in caustic solution for subsequent scintillation counting. The procedure is slow and is not necessarily quantitative. Sometimes a specific oxidation is possible. Bloom[169] found, for example, that the terminal group of glucose can be oxidized to formaldehyde, which is converted to the dimedon derivative for scintillation counting in toluene-based scintillator solution.

DECOMPOSITION OF BARIUM CARBONATE Sulfuric, phosphoric, or perchloric acid can be used to decompose carbon-14-labeled carbonates. For filling ionization chambers, the liberated gas is swept into the chamber (through a drying agent) with nonlabeled carbon dioxide. If the Van Slyke–Folch oxidation procedure is normally used for oxidizing organic compounds, the same apparatus and reagent can be used for decomposing labeled carbonates. The amount of carbon dioxide that dissolves in the above acids is a significant part of the gas evolved from a few milligrams of barium carbonate. By sweeping the heated solution with non-labeled carbon dioxide, most of the dissolved gas can be removed. Very small amounts (a few micrograms) of barium carbonate-^{14}C that are complexed with the ethylenediamine-tetraacetate cannot be decomposed and swept quantitatively into an ionization chamber.

A procedure is described[170] in which finely divided barium carbonate is decomposed by heating (30 min at 650°) it with a 50 mole % excess of anhydrous copper sulfate in a sealed tube. This procedure is a modification of the Wilzbach and Sykes method described in this section. Carbon dioxide may also be generated by heating barium carbonate with ten times its weight of fused lead chloride.[171] The mixture is heated slowly. Decomposition begins at 180°, but even at 400° the reaction is only about 96% complete after 4 hr. Silver chloride can be added to lower the fusion temperature, but in any case the tube or flask must not be filled to its greatest diameter or it may crack when it is cooled. Small amounts of hydrogen chloride are often generated during the fusion; this contamination together with the slowness of the reaction make it unsatisfactory for use in carbon-14 determination. However, fused lead chloride is a very satisfactory, easily controlled reagent for generating carbon-14 dioxide in the vacuum-line syntheses of labeled organic compounds.

SAMPLE WEIGHING   Samples for wet or dry combustion are most readily weighed in platinum boats. It is convenient to prepare a number of boats of similar weight (for example, 450 ± 20 mg) from platinum foil. Open-end platinum boats are also useful for weighing samples for scintillation counting. The weighed material is simply washed into the counting vial with the scintillation solution. Many volatile organic compounds will fail to distil from the usual vial that is closed at one end. One procedure for handling

samples that are difficult to volatilize, such as the benzyl halides, is described by Roth.[172] One end of a Pyrex tube (~4 mm OD) is drawn out and is sealed preparatory to making an ampoule. Potassium chlorate crystals are then packed in, and the thick end is drawn out and is cut off. The ampoule is weighed; it is then warmed to permit its being filled as it cools. The ampoule is placed inside a platinum cylinder rolled from foil and is introduced into the dry combustion tube, the open end of the ampoule being toward the furnace. Usually, the combustion occurs without breakage of the ampoule. A reusable, 5-cm-long quartz weighing pipet, designed expressly for dry combustion of aqueous solutions, is described by Jones.[173] Samples that contain as little as 0.01 mg of carbon-14 can be handled by a standard semimicro combustion apparatus. A weighing tube for small amounts of volatile liquid samples is described by Mitsui and Furuki.[174] The tube is a quartz capillary (70 mm long, 0.5 mm ID) with a hairpin of platinum wire (0.07-mm diam) folded back on itself and inserted to the center of the tube. Although the authors do not recommend it, it is possible to use capillary tubes whose diameter is as great as 0.75 mm. Liquid samples for scintillation counting can be weighed in open-ended melting-point capillaries. Filling of these tubes (including the quartz capillary) is conveniently done with a syringe of the type used to add a sample to a gas chromatograph. Samples for scintillation counting can be flushed into counting vials with part of the scintillator solution aliquoted for the vials.

II-6 CARBON-14 STANDARDS

Carbon-14 counting standards are available from both national and commercial agencies. Calibration accuracy is not high and is often claimed to be only within $\pm 10\%$ of the absolute beta disintegration rate. However, the relative calibration of a number of sources supplied by one agency is often very good.

In the United States commercial firms supply standards in the form of labeled barium carbonate, benzoic acid, and a solution of sodium carbonate. The National Bureau of Standards[175] sells labeled barium carbonate, benzoic acid (toluene solution), and sodium carbonate. In the United Kingdom[176] standards sold are the labeled compounds polymethylmethacrylate, hexadecane, and sodium carbonate (solution). Calibrated samples of labeled glycine, sodium carbonate (aqueous solution), and benzoic acid (toluene solution) are available in France.[177]

Labeled benzoic acid is not an ideal scintillation-counting standard, because it causes a small amount of quenching.[178] The toluene solution of labeled benzoic acid is also an unsatisfactory standard, because the toluene is much too volatile to permit accurate weighing. Also, gradual loss of toluene results in an increase in the specific activity of the remaining solution. This standard will be replaced by hexadecane which, because it is homogeneously labeled and less volatile than toluene, should be a much more satisfactory standard for scintillation counting. Toluene is popular as an internal standard for scintillation counting, and both carbon-14-labeled and tritium-labeled toluene are available from a commercial supplier[178a] whose calibration against the NBS standard is claimed to be accurate to within $\pm 3\%$. Additions of 100-μl portions of this secondary standard can become expensive. Some workers therefore prepare a toluene standard by purchasing 1 mc of uniformly labeled toluene, which they dilute to a suitable volume and calibrate against the NBS labeled benzoic acid (in toluene) standard. The addition of an internal standard by pipetting, rather than by weighing, is often accompanied by an error of $\pm 2\%$.

A barium carbonate-^{14}C disk prepared from standard barium carbonate or sodium carbonate is suitable as a semipermanent standard only if care is taken to minimize exposure of it to moist air. Exposure of such a barium carbonate-^{14}C sample to humid, inactive CO_2 was found to cause a 3.5% decrease in sample activity in $2\frac{1}{4}$ hr.[179]

11-7 LOW-LEVEL RADIOACTIVITY MEASUREMENT

The impetus for the development of low-level counting of carbon-14 was the discovery[180] that cosmic-ray-produced radiocarbon might provide a useful means of age determination. About 60 laboratories are engaged in the counting of carbon-14 at natural-abundance levels for the purpose of dating specimens that are of interest to climatologists, archeologists, geochemists, and geologists. The usefulness of carbon-14 for dating purposes is based on the assumptions that the half-life of carbon-14 is accurately established, that the specific activity of living organic materials has remained constant over the 60,000 years (more or less) which the dating method purports to measure, and that the biological samples have not exchanged carbon with reservoir carbon since their time of death. de Vries, de Vries, and Harris[181] found a remarkable correlation between climatic temperature fluctuations and changes in carbon-14 activity ($\pm 1\%$, with respect to the average over the last 400 years). During the past 2000 years the "modern" concentration of carbon-14 is believed to have varied as much as 2%, accounting for an uncertainty of about ± 150 years.[182] The determination of carbon-14 in large numbers of samples of known age, for example, from the annual rings of the sequoia tree, will help to establish a proper value for contemporary carbon at any given period in history. Wood from the bristlecone pine (the oldest living tree) will make possible the correlation of carbon-14 data with tree-ring studies on wood more than 6000 years old.[182a] Unfortunately, few historical events that occurred earlier than 3000 years ago can be dated with certainty by historians. Radiocarbon dates do agree, within the error of measurement, with archaeological finds that date back to 5000 years ago.[183] Libby[183] discusses the apparent discrepancies among radiocarbon dates. As a result of carbon-14 measurement, we know much about the circulation of the atmosphere and about the degree of mixing of the oceans. The dilution effect of carbon dioxide from fossil-fuel combustion and the enhancement of radioactivity caused by the testing of nuclear weapons have each contributed to our knowledge of short-term changes in the biosphere. The 18% increase of carbon-14 in the atmosphere of the southern hemisphere in the period 1954 to 1959 was used by Wilson[184] as a dating system to determine the origin of heartwood in the pine tree. Wilson suggested that the phenomenon of increase of carbon-14 in the atmosphere could provide a valuable short-term dating system for biological and other problems. Because of above-ground nuclear testing, the amount of atmospheric radiocarbon is about double the natural reference level of 1890 (14 dpm per gram of carbon).[184a] It is thought that by the year 2000 the concentration of atmospheric carbon dioxide will decrease slowly from the present high value (about 25 dpm per gram of carbon) to a constant value 12 to 15% above the reference level. This estimate presupposes cessation of above-ground nuclear testing. It has been proposed[185] that carbon-14 measurements be made on organic contaminants extracted from streams to show the degree of pollution by industrial waste and domestic sewage.

It is practically never necessary in organic chemistry to make investigations of carbon-14 at its natural-abundance level ($\sim$14 dis/min/g). However, carbon-14 can be measured with an error of less than 1% at that level. The fact that carbon-14 is available at a level of radioactivity as great as 8×10^{12} dis/min/g adds great flexibility to isotope-dilution studies and to the study of very slow reaction rates in radiation-sensitive systems.

INSTRUMENTATION AND SAMPLE PREPARATION   The most sensitive counting techniques require the use of Geiger-Müller, proportional, or liquid-scintillation counting systems, all with internal fillings. Methane, acetylene, and carbon dioxide are all good filling gases. A sample-conversion and counting apparatus that uses methane as a counting gas is available commercially.[186] The sample is burned in a quartz combustion tube. Hydrogenation of the resulting carbon dioxide over a ruthenium catalyst produces methane in yields that approach 100%. The total sample-conversion time is reported to be 4 to 5 hr. The danger of an explosion is thought to attend the use of acetylene at pressures above 1.5 atm; its synthesis requires one more step than does the methane synthesis. Carbon dioxide is the filling gas most readily prepared from any sample. It must be rigorously purified to remove such electronegative species as chlorine which, even in normally undetectable amounts, alter counting characteristics significantly. Very efficient installations have been built that utilize carbon-dioxide-filled gas counters operating in the proportional region. Such counters are usually ringed by cosmic-ray Geiger-Müller detectors; the entire assembly is shielded by materials chosen for their low background activity.

Most of the cooperating laboratories that submit data to *Radiocarbon*[187] use gas-filled counters. However, the development of scintillation counting of natural radiocarbon has advanced to a position competitive with other techniques. The liquid-scintillation counter has the advantage that it can accept a large sample within a small detecting system. The advantage of liquid-phase over gas-phase counting is apparent when it is realized that a 5-liter chamber filled to 5 atm with carbon dioxide contains about the same amount of carbon that is present in 20 ml of benzene, which is used in a scintillation-counting vial. High background count rate can be reduced by pulse-height discrimination and by a careful choice of multiplier phototubes operated in coincidence circuits. The sensitivity of the scintillation-counting method is limited by the amount of original specimen available and by the need for converting that specimen to an organic liquid that is efficiently counted. The most suitable liquid would be one that is already established as a good primary solvent in scintillation counting. Compounds such as benzene, toluene, and ethylbenzene are ideal, whereas methanol, methyl borate, paraldehyde, and ethyl alcohol all quench in various degrees. Benzene is the most useful from the standpoint of quenching and relative ease of synthesis. Carbon dioxide from wet or dry combustion of the sample is absorbed in alkali[188] for eventual preparation of benzene by the following series of reactions

$$^{14}CO_2 + SrCl_2 \longrightarrow Sr^{14}CO_3$$

$$Sr^{14}CO_3 + Mg \longrightarrow Sr^{14}C_2$$

$$Sr^{14}C_2 + H_2O \longrightarrow {}^{14}C_2H_2$$

$$^{14}C_2H_2 \xrightarrow[\text{(or silica-alumina)}]{600°} {}^{14}C_6H_6$$

The conversion of carbonate to carbide can proceed with yields of 90 to 98%.[189] The synthesis of benzene from acetylene at elevated temperatures[190] is not as good, but the polymerization of acetylene over a catalyst affords pure benzene in 75% yield.[191] In the catalytic process, acetylene is passed over silica-alumina pellets[192] activated by diborane gas.[193] The reactions leading to benzene have not been studied to determine the carbon-14 isotope effect. If the reactions do result in an overall depletion of carbon-14, such an effect could presumably be monitored by evaluating the change in $^{13}C/^{12}C$ ratios. The chemical and counting advances in liquid-scintillation radiocarbon dating are discussed by Noakes, Kim, and Stipp.[193a] Commercial equipment is available[194] that will convert samples as large as 20 g into benzene. Only the addition of a scintillator is needed for counting. Figure 1-116 is a diagram of the apparatus (called a "Benzene Synthesizer"). The procedure recommended for the conversion of carbon-14-containing samples is as follows. Carbonates are acidified

to produce carbon dioxide; organic samples are burned to carbon dioxide in a stream of oxygen. At this point, the carbon dioxide can be stored for future use, or it can be directed to the next stage, in which it is introduced into an evacuated chamber that contains molten lithium at 650°. When the conversion to lithium carbide is complete, the chamber is cooled to room temperature, the carbide is hydrolyzed to acetylene, and nitrogenous contaminants are removed from the acetylene in a special column. The acetylene is polymerized by first freezing it into a transfer trap and then, as the trap warms up, permitting the gas to expand into an evacuated catalyst column or columns. As the reaction proceeds the catalyst becomes slightly warm and purple. When the reaction is complete, the catalyst is heated to 100° under reduced pressure to remove the benzene. The amount of benzene collected varies from 2 to 4 ml, an amount sufficient for counting any but the oldest archaeological samples.

LOW-LEVEL RADIOCARBON STANDARD. The effect of relatively recent additions of both carbon-12 and carbon-14 to the radiocarbon reservoir is overcome by choosing, as a standard, wood that is over 100 yr old. The National Bureau of Standards, Washington, D.C., maintains a supply of oxalic acid, which is available as an inexpensive, universal reference standard for carbon-14 at the natural-abundance level. By international agreement, 95% of the radioactivity of this NBS oxalic acid corresponds with the natural carbon-14 activity of "recent wood," which is equivalent to wood grown in 1950 A.D., after corrections are made for isotopic fractionation and for the combustion of fossil fuel. The activity reported[194a] for NBS oxalic acid is 14.27 ± 0.07 dpm per gram of carbon. The activity of 95% NBS oxalic acid is therefore 13.56 ± 0.07 dpm per gram of carbon. The latter value—recent wood—corresponds to $(1.176 \pm 0.010) \times 10^{-10}\%$ carbon-14. For this calculation the half-life value of 5730 ± 40 years[1] was used.

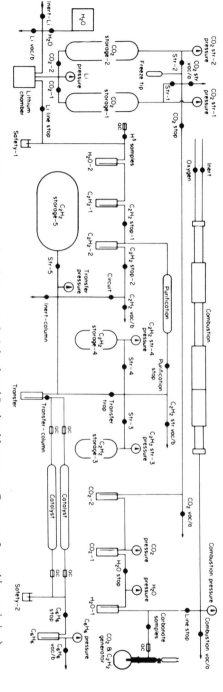

FIG. 11-16 The "Benzene Synthesizer." (*From A. G. Schrodt and Packard Instrument Company, Inc., with permission.*)

All data published in *Radiocarbon*[187] are based on the Libby value, 5570 ± 30 y, for the half-life; 1950 is accepted as the standard reference year for all dates whether they are in the B.P., that is, before present (1950), or in the A.D.–B.C. system.

11-8 STATISTICS OF COUNTING

The disintegration of radioactive atoms is a completely random process. It is impossible to predict the time at which any particular atom will disintegrate; the rate of decay is proportional to the number of unstable nuclei present at any instant. The radioactive-decay law is expressed by the fundamental relation

$$-\frac{dN}{dt} = \lambda N$$

or its integrated form

$$N_t = N_0 e^{-\lambda t}$$

where N_t is the number of radioactive atoms present at time t, N_0 is the number of nuclei present when $t = 0$, e is the base of natural logarithms, and λ is the disintegration constant.

The disintegrations observed in a radioactive sample are events that follow statistical law (Poisson statistics), which is used to determine the probability with which the observed rate corresponds to the true average rate. The application of statistics to nuclear measurements is covered in several references.[195–200] The actual disintegration rate, $-dN/dt$, fluctuates about an average value that depends on the *observed* counts and not on the number of disintegrations occurring during the interval concerned. Thus, only $\frac{1}{20}$th as much time may be required to accumulate a certain number of counts with one detector as with another less efficient detector. By application of statistics, it is possible to correlate the observed rate of counting with the most probable rate of counting of a radioactive sample. If the errors observed are much larger than can be assumed on the basis of a random disintegration process, it is often possible to ascribe such erratic measurements to failure of the measuring instrument.

The half-life of carbon-14 is long compared with the time devoted to the measurement; therefore, calculations do not require half-life corrections. The probability of recording any given count is calculated from the Poisson distribution

$$P_n = \frac{e^{-\bar{x}}(\bar{x})^n}{n!}$$

where n is the observed number of counts, and $\bar{x}$ is the mean of a large number of counts (true average). It is instructive to consider the probability of recording a certain count. For example, we may calculate the probability that 12 counts be obtained in a one-minute counting of a sample whose true average count rate is 20 counts/min. If proper values are inserted in the Poisson equation, then

$$P_n = \frac{(10^{-20/2.3})(20^{12})}{(1)(2)\cdots(12)} = 0.0176$$

For every 1000 measurements, about 18 will have the value 12 counts or less.

Ordinarily one does not do as was done above, that is, assume an error and then calculate the probability that such a deviation will be observed. Instead, it is customary to set a limit for the probability and then to calculate the limits of error in the reported result. The error, ϵ, is usually defined by the equation[197,199]

$$\epsilon = K\sqrt{\bar{x}}$$

where ϵ is the deviation of the observed count from the true average count. Within this interval or "confidence limit" there is a certain probability of finding the recorded value. K is a number that corresponds to a probability that any one determination will fall within ϵ; it is the "number of standard deviations," and the probability it represents is called the "confidence limit." Errors having probability limits of 0.10, 0.05, and 0.01 are called the nine-tenths error, the ninety-five hundredths error, and the ninety-nine hundredths error, respectively. Often these values are expressed as confidence limits, for example, 95% confidence limit. Table 11-2 lists the most important error limits and shows the numerical relation of the error, ϵ, to the probability constant, K. To use the simpler formula, $\epsilon = K \sqrt{\bar{x}}$, for the error, it is necessary to assume a Gaussian approximation to the Poisson distribution. Therefore, the values for K listed in Table 11-2 should not be used when the true average count of a determination is less than 10 counts.[195]

Errors are expressed as standard deviations more often than as other confidence limits, perhaps because the standard deviation is conveniently obtained by simply recording the square root of the number of observed events. It has been recommended[197] that *standard deviation* be used to refer to deviations in the original observations and that the term *standard error* be used to describe deviations in the means of *series* of original observations. Since the standard deviation may be exceeded in about 32% of the observations, it is often desirable to be more conservative in quoting an error. For example, one may prefer to use the 95% confidence interval for which the error is almost two standard deviations.

To have a normal distribution of data and to be able to calculate the standard error reliably, it is necessary to have at least 20 measurements. Since such a large set of data is seldom available, it is necessary to find other means for determining the precision of data. Such an estimate of deviation, called *variance*, is defined in the equation

$$S^2 = \frac{\sum_{i=1}^{n} (x_i - \bar{x})^2}{n - 1}$$

where S^2 is the variance, n is the number of observations x, and $\bar{x}$ is the average of the observations, or the observed mean, since the true mean is not known. The standard error for such a limited number of observations is obtained by taking the square root of the variance. An example of such a computation is shown in Table 11-3.

The combined error that results from the addition or subtraction of quantities is not obtained by summing the individual errors. Because of the probability that the individual errors may partially cancel, the combined error will be less than the simple sum and can be determined from the relation

$$S = \sqrt{S_1{}^2 + S_2{}^2}$$

where S, S_1, and S_2 can be the standard error, relative error, or any other of the commonly used expressions for error. For quantities

Table 11-2   Variation in confidence limits with change in K

K	Confidence limit corresponding to K	Percent error when total count is 100	Percent error when total count is 1000
0.00	0.000	0.0	0.0
0.50	0.383	5.0	1.58
0.68	0.500 (probable error)	6.8	2.14
1.00	0.683 (standard deviation)	10.0	3.16
1.65	0.900 ("reliable" error)	16.5	5.20
1.96	0.950 ("⁹⁵⁄₁₀₀" error)	19.6	6.20
2.58	0.990 ("⁹⁹⁄₁₀₀" error)	25.8	8.14

Table 11-3   Calculation of standard deviation

Measured value, x	Deviation from mean, $(x_i - \bar{x})$	$(x_i - \bar{x})^2$
124	+4	16
110	−10	100
130	+10	100
116	−4	16
$\bar{x} = 120$	$\sum (x_i - \bar{x}) = 0$	$\sum (x_i - \bar{x})^2 = 232$

$$S^2 = {}^{232}\!/\!_3 = 77.3$$
$$\text{Standard deviation} = \sqrt{77.3} = 8.8$$

A, B, C, etc., whose errors are respectively a, b, c, etc., the error of the sum is

$$(A \pm a) + (B \pm b) + \cdots$$
$$= (A + B + \cdots) \pm \sqrt{a^2 + b^2 + \cdots}$$

Similar expressions are used to calculate the appropriate error of a difference, the error of a product, and the error of a quotient. Calculations of the type described above are used to apply background calculations to counting data. Thus, the results for a sample that gave 2500 counts in 10 min and whose background count was 225 counts in 5 min could be reported as follows

Count rate (sample plus background) = $(2500 \pm \sqrt{2500})/10 = 250 \pm 5$ counts/min.

Count rate (background) = $(225 \pm \sqrt{225})/5 = 45 \pm 3$ counts/min.

Standard deviation = $S = \sqrt{3^2 + 5^2} = 6$
Net counting rate = 205 ± 6 counts/min.

In the above example the individual quantities were readily reduced to comparable units, namely, counts/min. When this cannot be done easily, the errors should be expressed in terms of percent of the observed quantities.

It is possible to calculate an optimum division of time between the counting of the sample and the counting of background. For a sample counting rate of N_s and a background counting rate of N_b, the most efficient distribution of sample counting

time (t_s) and background counting time (t_b) is given by the equation

$$\frac{t_s}{t_b} = \left(\frac{N_s}{N_b} \right)^{1/2}$$

whose derivation is given by Jarrett.[195] The simple nomograph described by Tittle[198] is also useful.

A problem encountered occasionally in evaluating counting data is the occurrence of extreme values that are either too high or too low. The extreme value can be rejected if there is evidence that the experiment was accompanied by an unusual occurrence, such as voltage variation, failure of shielding, improper readout of a timer, etc. If no such evidence exists, it may still be desirable to discard a divergent reading. The rejection is especially desirable if the variation occurs as one of a series of a small set of determinations, because its influence on the best value of the determination may be unduly large. Chauvenet's criterion is a statistical approach to the problem of rejecting suspected observations. The criterion provides for the rejection of any reading in a series of n readings when its deviation from the mean is of such magnitude that the probability of occurrence of any error that large or larger is less than $1/(2n)$. Table 11-4 (from Jarrett[195]) lists values for the ratio, p (deviation/standard error), acceptable within the limits of the standard error for a series of n observations. For more conservative probability levels, the value of p is much higher. For $n = 5$, the value of p for the 95% confidence level is 2.79; for the 99% confidence level, it is 4.55.

The following example will illustrate the use of Chauvenet's criterion. The molar radioactivity of a carbon-14-labeled sample was determined in five separate measurements; the results in mc/mole were: 4.20, 4.21, 4.19, 4.13, 4.22. Should the value 4.13 be rejected? The mean value, including the suspected 4.13, is 4.19 mc/mole. From the variance ($S^2 = 0.00125$) the calculated standard error is 0.0354. The deviation 0.06 of the

Table 11-4   Chauvenet's criterion for the retention or rejection of extreme values

n	p	n	p	n	p	n	p
2	1.15	8	1.86	25	2.33	100	2.81
3	1.38	9	1.91	30	2.40	200	3.02
4	1.54	10	1.96	35	2.45	250	3.09
5	1.65	12	2.04	40	2.50	400	3.23
6	1.73	15	2.13	50	2.58	500	3.29
7	1.80	20	2.24	75	2.71	1000	3.48

n = number of determinations.
p = ratio of the deviation to the standard deviation.

suspected observation divided by the standard error is 1.70. Because this value exceeds the limiting value 1.65 given in Table 11-4, the observation may be rejected, thus leaving 4.20_5 as the average of the remaining four values. Often, for a limited number of determinations, the median has advantages over the average when large errors are suspected. For the above example, the median value of 4.20 is very near the mean value calculated after rejection of the lowest value, 4.13.

CITED REFERENCES

[1] H. Godwin, *Nature*, **195**, 984 (1962).

[2] E. E. Hughes and W. B. Mann, *Intern. J. Appl. Radiation Isotopes*, **15**, 97 (1964).

[3] D. Strominger, J. M. Hollander, and G. T. Seaborg, *Rev. Mod. Phy.*, **30**, 605 (1958).

[4] S. Shemizu, H. Nakamura, and I. Kumabe, *Bull. Inst. Chem. Res., Kyoto Univ.*, **26**, 65 (1951); *Chem. Abstr.*, **48**, 6852 (1954).

[5] B. M. Tolbert and W. E. Siri in A. Weissberger, "Technique of Organic Chemistry," 3d ed., vol. I, part IV, pp. 3416–3422, Interscience Publishers Inc., New York, 1960.

[6] M. Calvin, C. Heidelberger, J. C. Reid, B. M. Tolbert, and P. F. Yankwich, "Isotopic Carbon," pp. 101–126, John Wiley & Sons, Inc., New York, 1949.

[7] Anonymous, "How to Prepare Radioactive Samples for Counting Planchets," Technical Bulletin No. 7, Nuclear-Chicago Corp., Des Plaines, Ill., 1960.

[8] S. Aronoff, "Techniques of Radiobiochemistry," pp. 48–49, The Iowa State College Press, Ames, Iowa, 1956.

[9] M. A. L'vova and V. V. Bochkarev, *Metody Polucheniya i Izmeren. Radioaktivn. Preparatov, Sb. Statei*, 239–260 (1960).

[10] A. N. Wick, H. N. Barnet, and N. Ackerman, *Anal. Chem.*, **21**, 1511 (1949).

[11] S. A. Berson and R. S. Yalow, *Science*, **131**, 606 (1960).

[12] From *Science* and the authors, with permission.

[13] M. C. Kordecki and M. B. Gandy, *Intern. J. Appl. Radiation Isotopes*, **10**, 210 (1961).

[14] M. Calvin, C. Heidelberger, J. C. Reid, B. M. Tolbert, and P. F. Yankwich, "Isotopic Carbon," pp. 104–114, John Wiley & Sons, Inc., New York, 1949.

[15] W. Seaman and D. Stewart, Jr., *Anal. Chem.*, **33**, 963 (1961).

[16] R. H. Hamilton and D. E. Moreland, *Anal. Chem.*, **34**, 717 (1962).

[17] V. I. Maĭmind, M. I. Lerman, and L. A. Neĭman, *Zhur. Anal. Khim.*, **15**, 371 (1960).

[18] A. Marcó, J. C. Scott, J. C. Elwood, and J. T. Van Bruggen, *Anal. Chem.*, **31**, 1746 (1959).

[19] C. C. McCready, *Nature*, **181**, 1406 (1958).

[20] E. M. Pearce, F. DeVenuto, W. M. Fitch, H. E. Firschein, and U. Westphal, *Anal. Chem.*, **28**, 1762 (1956).

[21] J. D. Moyer and H. S. Isbell, *Anal. Chem.*, **29**, 393 (1957).

[22] H. S. Isbell, H. L. Frush, and N. B. Holt, *J. Res. Natl. Bur. Std.*, **64A**, 363 (1960).

[23] P. C. Tompkins, L. Wish, and W. T. Burnett, Jr., *Anal. Chem.*, **22**, 672 (1950).

[24] L. A. Walker and R. Lougheed, *Intern. J. Appl. Radiation Isotopes*, **13**, 95 (1962).

[25] G. A. Ropp, V. F. Raaen, and A. J. Weinberger, *J. Am. Chem. Soc.*, **75**, 3694 (1953).

[26] E. C. S. Little, *Nature*, **184**, suppl. no. 12, 900 (1959).

[27] B. M. Tolbert and W. E. Siri in A. Weissberger, Ed., "Technique of Organic Chemistry," 3d ed., vol. I, part IV, pp. 3418–3421, Interscience Publishers Inc., New York, 1960.

[28] T. T. Hutchens, C. K. Claycomb, W. J. Cathey, and J. T. Van Bruggen, *Nucleonics*, **7**(3), 41 (1950).

[29] G. S. Saucier, L. P. Dugal, and A. Léveillé, *Can. J. Biochem. Physiol.*, **37**, 721 (1959).

[30] H. J. Perkins and M. D. MacDonald, *Science*, **138**, 1259 (1962).

[31] W. G. Verly, S. Bricteux-Grégoire, G. Koch, and E. Demey, *Proc. Intern. Conf. Peaceful Uses At. Energy, 2nd, Geneva, 1958*, **21**, 131 (1958).

[32] R. H. Müller, *Anal. Chem.*, **31**(4), 73A (1959).

[33] *Chem. Abstr.*, **55**, 11120c (1960); M. A. L'vova and V. V. Bochkarev, *Metody Polucheniya i Izmeren. Radioaktivn. Preparatov, Sb. Statei*, 239 (1960).

[34] B. Kalab and E. Broda, *Intern. J. Appl. Radiation Isotopes*, **13**, 191 (1962).

[35] D. R. Christman and A. P. Wolf, *Anal. Chem.*, **27**, 1939 (1955).

[36] S. C. Brown and W. W. Miller, *Rev. Sci. Instr.*, **18**, 496 (1947).

[37] W. H. Melhuish, *New Zealand J. Sci.*, **3**, 549 (1960).

[38] S. Apelgot, A. Roumegous, G. Patureau, and E. Moustacchi, *Bull. Soc. Chim. Biol.*, **37**, 1363 (1955).

[39] W. B. Mann, H. H. Seliger, W. F. Marlow, and R. W. Medlock, *Rev. Sci. Instr.*, **31**, 690 (1960).

[40] B. Kalab, *J. Sci. Instr.*, **38**, 253 (1961).

[41] R. F. Glascock, "Isotopic Gas Analysis for Biochemists," p. 63, Academic Press, Inc., New York, 1954.

[42] See discussion in Glascock, pp. 62–68; W. Bernstein and R. Ballentine, *Rev. Sci. Instr.*, **21**, 158 (1950).

[43] E. Broda and B. Kalab, *Mikrochim. Acta*, 128 (1962).

[44] J. D. Davidson and P. Feigelson, *Intern. J. Appl. Radiation Isotopes*, **2**, 2 (1957).

[45] C. G. Bell, Jr., and F. N. Hayes, Eds., "Liquid Scintillation Counting," Pergamon Press, New York, 1958.

[46] S. Rothchild, Ed., "Advances in Tracer Methodology," vol. I, pp. 69–166, Plenum Press, New York, 1963.

[47] R. Autrata, *Chem. Listy*, **58**(4), 381 (1964).

[48] E. Petrozzi, *Minerva Nucl.*, **7**(3), 91 (1963).

[49] A. S. Figuera and A. Serra, *Comit. Nazl. Ric. Nucl.*, **CNC-34**, 46 pp. (1960).

[50] E. Rapkin, *Intern. J. Appl. Radiation Isotopes*, **15**, 69 (1964).

[51] E. Schram and R. Lombaert, "Organic Scintillation Detectors," Elsevier Publishing Co., New York, 1963.

[52] J. C. Birks, "The Theory and Practice of Scintillation Counting," The Macmillan Company, New York, 1964.

[53] R. J. Dern in "Liquid Scintillation Counting," C. G. Bell, Jr., and F. N. Hayes, Eds., p. 205, Pergamon Press, New York, 1958.

[54] G. T. Okita, J. J. Kabara, F. Richardson, and G. V. LeRoy, *Nucleonics*, **15**(6), 111 (1957).

[55] J. J. Kabara, N. R. Spafford, M. A. McKendry, and N. L. Freeman in S. Rothchild, Ed., "Advances in Tracer Methodology," vol. I, pp. 76–85, Plenum Press, New York, 1963.

[56] R. J. Herberg, *Anal. Chem.*, **33**, 1308 (1961).

[57] E. T. Bush, *Anal. Chem.*, **36**, 1082 (1964).

[57a] D. L. Horrocks, *Intern. J. Appl. Radiation Isotopes*, **17**, 441 (1966).

[58] H. Kallmann and M. Furst, *Phys. Rev.*, **79**, 857 (1950).

[59] H. Kallmann and M. Furst, *Nucleonics*, **8**(3), 32 (1951).

[60] F. N. Hayes, B. S. Rogers, and P. C. Sanders, *Nucleonics*, **13**(1), 46 (1955).

[61] *Chem. Abstr.*, **55**, 19831b (1961); N. A. Kas'yanova and E. P. Nesynov, *Zhur. Priklad. Khim.*, **34**, 950 (1961).

[62] Available commercially from Rohm and Haas Co., Philadelphia, Pa. 19105.

[63] G. T. Reynolds, F. B. Harrison, and G. Salvini, *Phys. Rev.*, **78**, 488 (1950).

[64] H. Kallmann, *Phys. Rev.*, **78**, 621 (1950).

[65] C. Leger and M. A. Tamers, *Intern. J. Appl. Radiation Isotopes*, **14**, 65 (1963).

[66] Wheaton Glass Company, Millville, New Jersey, U.S.A.

[67] E. Rapkin and J. A. Gibbs, *Intern. J. Appl. Radiation Isotopes*, **14**, 71 (1963).

[68] Buchler Instruments, Inc., Fort Lee, N. J.; Ace Glass, Inc., Vineland, N.J.

[69] E. Rapkin, "Hydroxide of Hyamine 10-X," Technical Bulletin, Packard Instrument Company, Inc., Downers Grove, Ill., June 1961.

[70] J. M. Passmann, N. S. Radin, and J. A. D. Cooper, *Anal. Chem.*, **28**, 484 (1956).

[71] R. A. Oppermann, R. F. Nystrom, W. O. Nelson, and R. E. Brown, *Intern. J. Appl. Radiation Isotopes*, **7**, 38 (1959).

[72] H. Jeffay and J. Alvarez, *Anal. Chem.*, **33**, 612 (1961).

[73] F. H. Woeller, *Anal. Biochem.*, **2**(5), 508 (1961).

[73a] J. D. Davidson and V. T. Oliverio, *Atomlight*, no. 60, 1 (1967).

[74] R. M. Dowben, *U.S. Atomic Energy Commission Report* **AF-SAM-57-102**, 1957.

[75] W. J. Kaufman, A. Nir, G. Parks, and R. M. Hours, "Tritium in the Physical and Biological Sciences," vol. 1, p. 249, International Atomic Energy Agency, Vienna, 1962.

[76] F. A. Loewus, *Intern. J. Appl. Radiation Isotopes*, **12**, 6 (1961).

[77] G. A. Bruno and J. E. Christian, *Anal. Chem.*, **33**, 1216 (1961).

[78] G. A. Bray, *Anal. Biochem.*, **1**, 279 (1960).

[79] F. E. Kinard, *Rev. Sci. Instr.*, **28**, 293 (1957).

[80] J. A. Baxter, L. E. Fanning, and H. A. Swartz, *Intern. J. Appl. Radiation Isotopes*, **15**, 415 (1964).

[81] B. L. Funt and A. Hetherington, *Science*, **125**, 986 (1957).

[82] C. G. White and S. Helf, *Nucleonics*, **14**(10), 46 (1956).

[83] D. G. Ott, C. R. Richmond, T. T. Trujillo, and H. Foreman, *Nucleonics*, **17**(9), 106 (1959).

[84] C. F. Gordon and A. L. Wolfe, *Anal. Chem.*, **32**, 574 (1960).

[85] D. S. Jenkinson, *Nature*, **186**, 613 (1960).

[86] D. Steinberg in S. Rothchild, Ed., "Advances in Tracer Methodology," vol. 1, p. 93, Plenum Press, New York, 1963.

[87] Manufactured by Pilot Chemicals, Inc., Watertown, Mass.

[88] H. J. Cluley, *Analyst*, **27**(1032), 4 (1962).

[89] Bush Beach and Segner Bayley Ltd., Marlow House, Lloyds Avenue, London, E.C.3.

[90] L. Gilly and R. Bisci, *Comm. Energie At. (France), Rappt.*, no. **2318** (1963).

[91] F. A. Blanchard and I. T. Takahashi, *Anal. Chem.*, **33**, 975 (1961).

[92] M. Vaughan, D. Steinberg, and J. Logan, *Science*, **126**, 446 (1957).

[93] W. O. Brown and H. G. Radman, *Biochem. J.*, **78**, 571 (1961).

[94] J. D. Davidson in C. G. Bell, Jr., and F. N. Hayes, Eds., "Liquid Scintillation Counting," p. 88, Pergamon Press Inc., New York, 1958.

[95] R. J. Herberg, *Science*, **128**, 199 (1958).

[95a] G. E. Francis and J. D. Hawkins, *Intern. J. Appl. Radiation Isotopes*, **18**, 223 (1967).

[96] E. A. Shneour, S. Aronoff, and M. R. Kirk, *Intern. J. Appl. Radiation Isotopes*, **13**, 623 (1962).

[97] F. S. Feates, *J. Sci. Instru.*, **41**, 641 (1964); one of us (V. F. R.) is grateful to Dr. D. Dominey, AERE, Harwell, for informing him of the work and demonstrating the apparatus.

[98] F. N. Hayes, B. S. Rogers, and P. C. Sanders, *Nucleonics*, **13**(1), 46 (1955).

[99] M. Helmick, *Atomlight*, p. 6 (1960).

[100] H. E. Dobbs, *Nature*, **197**, 788 (1963).

[101] S. Helf and C. White, *Anal. Chem.*, **29**, 13 (1957).

[102] R. J. Herberg, *Anal. Chem.*, **32**, 42 (1960).

[103] H. M. Fales, *Atomlight*, no. 25, 8 (1963).

[104] C. T. Peng, *Anal. Chem.*, **32**, 1292 (1960).

[105] M. Toporek, *Intern. J. Appl. Radiation Isotopes*, **8**, 229 (1960).

[106] L. A. Baillie, *Intern. J. Appl. Radiation Isotopes*, **8**, 1 (1960).

[107] R. J. Herberg, *Anal. Chem.*, **32**, 1468 (1960).

[108] G. A. Bruno and J. E. Christian, *Anal. Chem.*, **33**, 650 (1961).

[109] E. T. Bush, *Anal. Chem.*, **35**, 1024 (1963).

[110] E. T. Bush, *Nuclear-Chicago Technical Bulletin no. 10* (1962).

[111] C. H. Wang, *Atomlight*, no. 21, 1 (1962).

[112] H. H. Ross, *Intern. J. Appl. Radiation Isotopes*, **15**, 273 (1964).

[113] B. L. Funt and A. Hetherington, *Intern. J. Appl. Radiation Isotopes*, **13**, 215 (1962).

[114] D. L. Horrocks, *Nature*, **202**, 78 (1964).

[115] T. Higashimura, O. Yamada, N. Nohara, and T. Shidei, *Intern. J. Appl. Radiation Isotopes*, **13**, 308 (1962).

[116] D. G. Fleishman and V. V. Glazunov, *Pribory i Tekhn. Eksperim.*, no. 3, 55 (1962); English translation in *Instr. Exptl. Tech. (USSR) (English Transl.)*, pp. 474–482 (1960).

[117] A. G. Schrodt, J. A. Gibbs, and R. E. Cavanaugh, "Quench Correction by Automatic

External Standardization," presented at American Nuclear Society meeting, San Francisco, Cal., December 3, 1964.

[118] Packard Instrument Company, Inc., Downers Grove, Illinois 60515.

[119] B. M. Tolbert, "Ionization Chamber Assay of Radioactive Gases," United States Atomic Energy Commission Report UCLA-3499 (March 5, 1956).

[120] B. M. Tolbert and W. E. Siri in A. Weissberger, Ed., "Technique of Organic Chemistry," 3d ed., vol. I, part IV, pp. 3355–3371, Interscience Publishers Inc., New York, 1960.

[121] W. E. Grummitt, R. M. Brown, A. J. Cruikshank, and I. L. Fowler, *Can. J. Chem.*, **34**, 206 (1956).

[122] D. R. Christman and C. M. Paul, *Anal. Chem.*, **32**, 131 (1960).

[123] "Radioactivity," Recommendations of the International Commission on Radiological Units and Measurements, Handbook 86, pp. 17–22, Superintendent of Documents, U.S. Government Printing Office, Washington, D.C., November 29, 1963.

[124] W. Franzen and L. W. Cochran in A. H. Snell, Ed., "Nuclear Instruments and Their Uses," vol. I, pp. 3–30, John Wiley & Sons, Inc., New York, 1962.

[125] W. P. Jesse and J. Sadauskis, *Phys. Rev.*, **97**, 1668 (1955); *ibid.*, **107**, 766 (1957).

[126] Keithley Instruments, Inc., 12415 Euclid Ave., Cleveland, Ohio.

[127] E. Fairstein in A. H. Snell, Ed., "Nuclear Instruments and Their Uses," vol. I, pp. 194–234, John Wiley & Sons, Inc., New York, 1962.

[128] Applied Physics Corporation, Monrovia, California; Nuclear-Chicago Corporation, Des Plaines, Illinois 60018.

[129] B. M. Tolbert and W. E. Siri in A. Weissberger, Ed., "Technique of Organic Chemistry," 3d ed., vol. I, part IV, p. 3370, Interscience Publishers Inc., New York, 1960.

[130] Anonymous, *Anal. Chem.*, **31**, 88A (1959).

[131] API Instruments Co., Chesterland, Ohio 44026.

[132] I. M. Whittemore, E. A. Ludwigsen, and B. M. Tolbert, United States Atomic Energy Commission Report UCRL-3595 (October 15, 1956), pp. 14–15.

[133] B. M. Tolbert and W. E. Siri in A. Weissberger, Ed., "Technique of Organic Chemistry," 3d

ed., vol. I, part IV, pp. 3431–3432, Interscience Publishers Inc., New York, 1960.

[134] M. Večeřa and L. Synek, *Mikrochim. Acta*, 208 (1960).

[135] J. Horacek, J. Koerbl, and V. Pechanec, *Mikrochim. Acta*, 294 (1960).

[136] M. Večeřa, D. Šnobl, and L. Synek, *Collection Czech. Chem. Commun.*, **25**, 281 (1960) and preceding publications; *Chem. Abstr.*, **54**, 13989h and 13989i (1960).

[137] M. Večeřa and D. Šnobl, *Collection Czech. Chem. Commun.*, **25**, 2013 (1960); *Chem. Abstr.*, **54**, 20671a (1960).

[138] G. Kainz and J. Mayer, *Mikrochim. Acta*, 241 (1962).

[139] J. Attenburrow, A. F. B. Cameron, J. H. Chapman, R. M. Evans, B. A. Hems, A. B. A. Jansen, and T. Walker, *J. Chem. Soc.*, 1094 (1952).

[140] Laboratory Equipment Corporation, St. Joseph. Michigan 49085.

[141] Y. A. Gawargious and A. M. G. MacDonald in N. D. Cheronis, Ed., "Microchemical Techniques," p. 401, John Wiley & Sons, Inc., New York, 1962.

[142] C. S. Yeh, *Microchem. J.*, **7**, 303 (1963).

[143] T. S. Ma and M. Gutterson, *Anal. Chem.*, **38**, 186R (1966).

[144] V. F. Raaen, unpublished observation.

[145] L. T. Freeland, *Anal. Chem.*, **36**, 2055 (1964).

[146] L. Hackspill and G. D'Huart, *Bull. Soc. Chim. France*, **35**, 800 (1924).

[147] K. E. Wilzbach and W. Y. Sykes, *Science*, **120**, 494 (1954).

[148] K. E. Wilzbach, L. Kaplan, and W. G. Brown, *Science*, **118**, 522 (1953).

[149] Corning Glass Works, Corning, New York.

[150] H. Simon, H. Daniel, and J. F. Klebe, *Angew. Chem.*, **71**, 303 (1959).

[151] D. L. Buchanan and B. J. Corcoran, *Anal. Chem.*, **31**, 1635 (1959).

[152] W. Hempel, *Angew. Chem.*, **5**, 393 (1892).

[153] W. Schöniger, *Mikrochim. Acta*, 123 (1955).

[154] W. Schöniger, *Mikrochim. Acta*, 869 (1956).

[155] R. Bennewitz, *Mikrochim. Acta*, 54 (1960).

[156] P. Gouverneur and C. D. F. Eerbeek, *Anal. Chim. Acta*, **27**, 303 (1962).

[157] F & M Scientific Corporation, 1202 Arnold Ave., N.C.C. Air Base, New Castle, Del.

[158] H. P. Baden, *Anal. Chem.*, **36**, 960 (1964).

[159] C. E. Childs, E. E. Meyers, J. Cheng, E.

Laframboise, and R. B. Balodis, *Microchem. J.*, **7**(3), 266 (1963).

[160] H. E. Dobbs, *Anal. Chem.*, **36**, 687 (1964).

[161] H. Sheppard and W. Rodegker in S. Rothchild, Ed., "Advances in Tracer Methodology," vol. 1, pp. 192–194, Plenum Press, New York, 1963.

[162] D. D. Van Slyke and J. Folch, *J. Biol. Chem.*, **136**, 509 (1940).

[163] M. Calvin, C. Heidelberger, J. C. Reid, B. M. Tolbert, and P. F. Yankwich, "Isotopic Carbon," pp. 92–94, John Wiley & Sons, Inc., New York, 1949.

[164] W. G. Dauben and M. Gee, *J. Am. Chem. Soc.*, **74**, 1078 (1952).

[165] I. Zlotowski and M. Zielinski, *Nukleonika*, **4**, 5 (1959).

[166] E. A. Evans and J. L. Huston, *J. Chem. Phys.*, **19**, 1214 (1951).

[167] V. F. Raaen and G. A. Ropp, *Anal. Chem.*, **25**, 174 (1953).

[168] C. J. Collins and G. A. Ropp, *J. Am. Chem. Soc.*, **77**, 4160 (1955).

[169] B. Bloom, *Anal. Biochem.*, **3**, 85 (1962).

[170] I. M. Whittemore, E. A. Ludwigsen, and B. M. Tolbert, United States Atomic Energy Commission Report UCRL-3595 (October 15, 1956), p. 12.

[171] N. Zwiebel, J. Turkevich, and W. W. Miller, *J. Am. Chem. Soc.*, **71**, 376 (1949).

[172] H. Roth, "Pregl-Roth Quantitative Organische Mikroanalyse," 7th ed., p. 56, Springer-Verlag, Vienna, 1958.

[173] A. R. Jones, *Rev. Sci. Instr.*, **24**, 230 (1953).

[174] T. Mitsui and C. Furuki, *Mikrochim. Acta*, 169 (1960).

[175] National Bureau of Standards, Washington, D.C. 20234.

[176] The Radiochemical Centre, Amersham, Buckinghamshire, England.

[177] Commissariat à l'Energie Atomique, Centre d'Etudes Nucléaires, Saclay, France.

[178] M. Helmick, *Atomlight*, p. 6, February, 1960.

[178a] New England Nuclear Corporation, Boston, Mass. 02118.

[179] G. Samos, *Science*, **110**, 663 (1949).

[180] W. F. Libby, *Phys. Rev.*, **69**, 671 (1946).

[181] H. de Vries, A. E. de Vries, and A. Harris, *Science*, **128**, 472 (1958).

[182] E. K. Ralph and R. Stuckenrath, *Nature*, **188**, 185 (1960).

[182a] M. Stuiver and H. E. Suess, *Radiocarbon*, **8**, 534 (1966).

[183] W. F. Libby, *Science*, **140**, 278 (1963).

[184] A. T. Wilson, *Nature*, **191**, 714 (1961).

[184a] R. Berger, W. F. Libby, G. V. Alexander, J. F. Mead, and J. F. Ross in S. Rothchild, Ed., "Advances in Tracer Methodology," vol. 3, pp. 321–329, Plenum Press, New York, 1966.

[185] A. A. Rosen and R. Meyer, *Science*, **143**, 1164 (1964).

[186] Sharp Laboratories, La Jolla, California.

[187] A yearly journal (first issue in 1959) published by the *The American Journal of Science*. It describes the equipment and lists the radiocarbon data of approximately 60 contributing laboratories.

[188] G. J. Fergusson [*Rev. Sci. Instr.*, **34**, 403 (1963)] described the use of Linde type 4A molecular sieve for collection of atmospheric carbon dioxide. The carbon dioxide was regenerated by heating the molecular sieve to 380° at 1 mm pressure. Molecular sieves should prove useful also for storage of high-level carbon-14 dioxide for subsequent regeneration in the syntheses of labeled compounds.

[189] *Chem. Abstr.*, **55**, 12367a (1961); V. P. Shishkov, G. A. Anorova, and T. N. Shatkina, *Metody Polucheniya i Izmeren. Radioaktivn. Preparatov, Sb. Statei*, 140 (1960).

[190] M. A. Tamers, J. J. Stipp, and J. Collier, *Geochim. Cosmochim. Acta*, **24**, 266 (1961).

[191] J. E. Noakes, D. W. Hood, and A. F. Isbell, paper presented to the Oak Ridge Institute of Nuclear Studies, Oak Ridge, Tennessee, November 1961.

[192] Houdry Process Co., 1528 Walnut Street, Philadelphia 2, Pa.

[193] Callery Chemical Co., Marketing Division, 9600 Perry Highway, Pittsburg 37, Pa.

[193a] J. E. Noakes, S. M. Kim, and J. J. Stipp, pp. 68–92 in "Proceedings of the Sixth International Conference Radiocarbon and Tritium Dating," Pullman, Washington; June 7–11, 1965; USAEC Report CONF-650652.

[194] Packard Instrument Company, Inc., Box 428, Downers Grove, Illinois 60515.

[194a] I. Karlen, I. U. Olsson, P. Kallberg, and S. Killicci, *Arkiv Geofysik*, **4**(22), 465 (1965).

[195] A. A. Jarrett, "Statistical Methods Used in the Measurement of Radioactivity (Some Useful

Graphs)," United States Atomic Energy Commission Report AECU-262, June 1946.

[196] G. Friedlander, J. W. Kennedy, and J. M. Miller, "Nuclear and Radiochemistry," 2d ed., pp. 166–190, John Wiley & Sons, Inc., New York, 1964.

[197] A. C. Kuyper, *J. Chem. Educ.*, **36**, 128 (1959).

[198] C. W. Tittle, "How to Apply Statistics to Nuclear Measurements," Technical Bulletin 14, Nuclear-Chicago Corp., Des Plaines, Illinois, 1962.

[199] M. Calvin, C. Heidelberger, J. C. Reid, B. M. Tolbert, and P. F. Yankwich, "Isotopic Carbon," pp. 283–291, John Wiley & Sons, Inc., New York, 1949.

[200] G. D. Chase and J. L. Rabinowitz, "Principles of Radioisotope Methodology," 2d ed., pp. 64–90, Burgess Publishing Company, Minneapolis, Minn., 1962.

GENERAL REFERENCES

(*a*) M. Calvin, C. Heidelberger, J. C. Reid, B. M. Tolbert, and P. F. Yankwich, "Isotopic Carbon," John Wiley & Sons, Inc., New York, 1949.

(*b*) B. M. Tolbert and W. E. Siri in A. Weissberger, Ed., "Technique of Organic Chemistry," vol. I, part IV, 3d ed., chap. L, Interscience Publishers, Inc., New York, 1960.

(*c*) E. Schram and R. Lombaert, "Organic Scintillation Detectors," Elsevier Publishing Company, New York, 1963.

(*d*) D.-E. Watt and R. Ramsden, "High Sensitivity Counting Techniques," The Macmillan Company, New York, 1964.

(*e*) E. Broda, "Radioactive Isotopes in Biochemistry," Elsevier Publishing Company, New York, 1960.

(*f*) M. D. Kamen, "Isotopic Tracers in Biology," 3d ed., Academic Press Inc., Publishers, New York, 1957.

(*g*) C. G. Bell, Jr., and F. N. Hayes, Eds., "Liquid Scintillation Counting," Pergamon Press Inc., New York, 1958.

(*h*) R. F. Glascock, "Isotopic Gas Analysis for Biochemists," Academic Press Inc., Publishers, New York, 1954.

(*i*) A. H. Snell, Ed., "Nuclear Instruments and Their Uses," vol. 1, John Wiley & Sons, Inc., New York, 1962.

(*j*) S. Rothchild, Ed., "Advances in Tracer Methodology," Plenum Press, New York; vol. 1, 1963; vol. 2, 1965; and vol. 3, 1966.

(*k*) M. C. Nokes, "Radioactivity Measuring Instruments," Philosophical Library, New York, 1958.

(*l*) G. H. Daub, F. N. Hayes, and E. Sullivan, Eds., "Proceedings of the University of New Mexico Conference on Organic Scintillation Detectors, August 15–17, 1960," U.S. Atomic Energy Commission Report TID-7612 (1961).

PROBLEMS

11-1. A carbon-14 sample is mounted inside an ionization chamber. Assume that a 0.20-μc sample is used and that the 45-Kev particles all expend their energy in the carbon dioxide filling. Calculate (*a*) the saturation current and (*b*) the current caused by the primary beta-particle emission.

11-2. What would be the objection to mounting the sample described in Problem 1 on a well-insulated probe within the chamber?

11-3. Primary and secondary scintillator solutes were added to a 12.00-g sample of *p*-cymene (from contemporary terpene fractions). If the specific activity of contemporary carbon is 15 dpm, calculate (*a*) the expected number of disintegrations per minute for the *p*-cymene sample. If the sample is counted with an efficiency of 90% and if the background count is 36 counts/min, then (*b*) what will be the optimum distribution of time between counting the background and counting the sample?

11-4. The discriminators on a liquid-scintillation spectrometer are adjusted so that the number of counts from a typical sample will be roughly equal for adjacent channels ("windows"). The ratios in the two channels differ substantially, which fact suggests that at least one of the two samples is a strong quencher. The effect of adding 50 μl of an internal standard (1.2×10^5 counts/min/ml) to each sample and to the blank provided additional evidence for quenching.

| | *Radioactivity, counts/min* (*lower channel/upper channel*) | |
Sample No.	Sample	Sample plus standard
Blank	20/8	2410/2718
1	2208/1802	4180/3850
2	1920/2180	4320/4894

(a) Calculate the overall efficiency for counting carbon-14.

(b) In which sample did quenching occur?

(c) Calculate the net activity (disintegrations per minute) for the two samples.

11-5. A carbon-14 standard was prepared by adding 3.000 g of a National Bureau of Standards solution of benzoic acid-7-^{14}C in toluene (1.65 × 10^4 dis/sec/g) to 0.1023 g of pure benzoic acid contained in a sublimation apparatus. After dissolution was complete, the toluene was removed by distillation at reduced pressure; the benzoic acid was then sublimed. The amount of benzoic acid present in the original toluene solution was 0.14 mg. Calculate the molar radioactivity of the sublimed benzoic acid.

11-6. Three samples of the benzoic acid prepared as described in Problem 5 were burned successively in a dry-combustion apparatus, and the carbon dioxide from each was swept into an ionization chamber. The rate-of-charge method was used in such a way that readings were recorded in seconds required to charge a condenser to a given potential. Samples whose weights were 10.615, 11.980, and 12.355 mg gave average charge periods of 119.1, 105.4, and 102.3 sec, respectively. About 25 g of tracer-level benzoic acid-7-^{14}C was then prepared and was purified for use as a secondary standard. Samples of this secondary standard that weighed 9.035, 9.615, and 10.060 mg gave charge periods of 63.45, 59.65, and 56.92 sec. Calculate the molar radioactivity of the benzoic acid to be used as a secondary standard.

11-7. Eight samples of carbon-14-labeled p-toluic acid, all of equal weight, were oxidized in a wet-combustion apparatus. The carbon dioxide that was generated was swept with inactive carbon dioxide into a 250-ml ionization chamber. The rate-of-charge method was used to determine the molar radioactivities: 1.999, 1.996, 2.006, 2.006, 2.010, 2.012, 2.013, 2.006 mc/mole. Calculate the average molar radioactivity, showing (a) the average deviation, (b) the standard deviation, and (c) the 0.95 confidence limit.

12
CHROMATOGRAPHY

Many excellent general references on chromatography exist[1-15,15a,15b] that are of value in chromatographic work with carbon-14-labeled compounds. Extensive and useful information is available on the applications of the various kinds of chromatography to unlabeled organic compounds[2,3a,3b,5a-e,7a,9,10,13,14] and on radiochromatographic techniques.[1,2,3,9,10,16,17,18] At the end of each issue of the *Journal of Chromatography*, there appear tabulations entitled "Chromatographic Data" and also a bibliography, which is annotated under the heading "Radioactive Compounds," as well as according to type of compound. These tabulations are a most convenient source of recent chromatographic information.

Chromatography is particularly useful in the rapid isolation, identification, and quantitative determination of the compounds involved in organic reactions. It is used extensively by manufacturers of carbon-14-labeled organic reagents to check the purity of their products and to isolate quantities of them in pure form. Tracer compounds that contain carbon-14 are usually prepared in small batches (0.1 to 1.0 g) and are costly, especially so if the specific activity is high; the sizes of test portions must be limited accordingly. Chromatography is invaluable in the separation, analysis, and purification of compounds that impose these difficulties. A unique application of the technique is the storage of a labeled compound on the solid chromatographic supporting medium (e.g., paper, ion-exchange resin, clay, or zeolite) in order to minimize its radiation decomposition.[19]

Paper partition chromatography is one of the most frequently used chromatographic techniques for isolating carbon-14-labeled compounds. No applications of foam and emulsion chromatography[3] to carbon-14 compounds have been found described in the literature.

12-1 PARTITION CHROMATOGRAPHY

12-1a PAPER PARTITION CHROMATOGRAPHY

Paper partition chromatography of unlabeled organic compounds is treated extensively by Block, Durrum, and Zweig.[20] They provide an index to R_f tables, which is arranged alphabetically according to the name of the substance chromatographed, and also a subject-classified bibliography. This index and bibliography are references equally useful in paper partition chromatography of carbon-14-labeled organic compounds. *The Journal of Chromatography* contains a section "Bibliography of Paper Chromatography." The bibliographic entries are taken from 60 periodicals, in which most of the original papers on paper chromatography are published, and five reference journals. The subject matter included in the bibliography is arranged under 35 headings; the bibliography began with papers published in 1961. Pocchiari and Rossi[21] comprehensively review quantitative radio paper chromatography. Applications and techniques of paper chromatography of organic substances that contain carbon-14 are summarized by Lissitzky and Michel.[22] Carbon-14 was the radionuclide chosen by Fink and Fink[23] in their evaluation of filter-paper partition chromatography as a tool in biological studies with radioactive elements that show a more general distribution and a less penetrating radiation than does iodine-131. They were the first to separate and identify carbon-14-labeled organic compounds by means of paper partition chromatography and to demonstrate the potential value of the tool.

The technique has several **advantages** that make it widely used in work with carbon-14 compounds. It is an excellent way to ensure radiopurity. In the separation of α-aminoadipic acid from contaminative glutamic acid, it was used to guarantee radiopurity when the criterion of constant specific activity by recrystallization was not satisfactory.[24] The

isotopic purities of DL-valine-1-^{14}C and DL-leucine-1-^{14}C have been established by paper chromatography and autoradiography.[25] The synthesis of 1,1-dimethylbiguanide-^{14}C has been controlled stepwise with respect to radioactivity by means of paper chromatography.[26] The presence of volatile, as well as nonvolatile, radioactive impurities can be detected if the proper procedures are followed to prevent loss of the suspected volatile impurity from the paper chromatogram.[27,28] It is possible with many types of paper chromatography to isolate the carbon-14-labeled derivative in good yield without the addition of carrier. Paper chromatography becomes a highly sensitive quantitative method when a scintillator is used in conjunction with it or when the technique of photoradio-chromatography is used. The limits of quantitative measurements by means of these techniques are discussed below.

Several possible **pitfalls** should be considered in the paper partition chromatography of carbon-14-labeled compounds.[28,29] It is first necessary to separate the carbon-14-labeled compound of interest from all other compounds that contain radioactivity, because the techniques for radioassay are not specific. Thus, if any spot contains more than one carbon-14 compound, each compound will contribute to the total radiation emanating from the spot; the total radioactivity therefore cannot be a quantitative measure of a singly labeled component. The paper itself may absorb a large part of the radiation from carbon-14, the extent of absorption varying with variation in the thickness and density of the paper. For carbon-14, the proportion of beta particles unabsorbed by paper of mean density 8.785 mg/cm^2 is 0.366; the variation of the self-absorption correction factor that corresponds to a variation of $\pm 10\%$ in paper density is $\pm 7.4\%$.[30] If a chromogenic reagent is used to locate the spots, some of the carbon-14 atoms may be removed by the reagent. Asymmetric drying of the paper can cause the carbon-14-labeled material to be distributed unevenly in the paper. It is reported that the radioactivity on paper chromatograms can be measured accurately with a Geiger counter only if the chromatograms are dried in still air, because drying in a draft causes substances in the spots to concentrate erratically at the surface of the paper and thus to result in an error in counting that is as large as 25%.[31] Although unsymmetrical drying may cause trouble, it can be used to advantage when properly controlled. van Tubergen and Markham[32] improved the method for the detection of tritium-labeled thymidine of low specific activity on paper chromatograms by spraying the chromatograms with a suitable solvent and then quickly heating them on one side only. The radioactivity of the heated surfaces was three times greater than that of untreated chromatograms. Also, residual solvent may absorb weak beta radiation. Some compounds that usually are considered to be nonvolatile will evaporate from paper.[33] Decomposition of unstable compounds may occur during chromatography and cause decomposition products to be considered erroneously as impurities.[33] The pH of the paper and of the development solvents apparently are the important factors in glycine-2-^{14}C breakdown during paper chromatography.[34] "Streaking" or "tailing" can cause difficulty in quantitative work.[33] The "carrier effect" is also a possible source of error. It was observed by Catch[33] for labeled mixtures of glucose and fructose and for leucine and isoleucine in the solvent system tert-amyl alcohol–diethylamine–water when L-isoleucine-^{14}C was present. In another reference,[35] Catch comments generally on the possible errors of paper chromatography. Losses from elution and plating[36] often result when a compound is removed from a chromatogram; therefore, under some conditions, it may be advisable to make the quantitative measurement of the labeled compound directly on the chromatogram. Cognizance of these pitfalls is the first step

in preventing them. Satisfactory ways have been worked out for avoiding many of them.[28,37]

Quantitative measurement of carbon-14-labeled compounds isolated by paper partition chromatography is made by any one of several procedures. If there is no need to preserve the chromatogram as such, one of the following two general procedures is used. In the first, the chromatogram is cut into pieces, and the radioactivity on each piece is measured. In the second, the labeled compounds are located by means of a chromogenic reagent or by scanning the chromatogram for beta radiation. The loci are cut from the chromatogram and either the radioactivity of each is determined directly or the labeled material is extracted from each and is then measured in the extract or in the residue obtained by evaporating the extract. Also, the labeled compound may be eluted from the undivided chromatogram and determined in the eluate. Often it is desirable to preserve the chromatogram, for example, for the purpose of comparison with other chromatograms or as a means of storing the labeled material. In this case, the quantitative measurement is made directly from the chromatogram by manual or automatic scanning and counting, by autoradiography, or by photoradiochromatography. Each of these methods of quantitative measurement is discussed below.

Numerous *scanning devices* for the detection and measurement of radioactivity on paper chromatograms are described. The survey by Pocchiari and Rossi[21] is excellent; their discussion of automatic apparatuses for measurement of radiochromatograms is thorough and well organized. References to many scanning devices are given by Lederer and Lederer,[38] by Block, Durrum, and Zweig,[39] and by Moses and Edwards.[40] Several instruments for the automatic scanning of paper radiochromatograms are made commercially.[41,42,43]

For *manual scanning*, the Scott type

Geiger-Müller tube is very useful. It is described by Fuller[44] and is discussed at length by Moses and Edwards,[40] who give much information about the measurement of carbon-14 with it.

In view of the existence of apparatus for *automatic scanning*, the tedious manual measurement of chromatograms is seldom necessary. The Scott type tube is equally useful as a component of an apparatus for automatic scanning. The simple and highly sensitive Forro manual chromatogram scanner was adapted by Eisenberg and Leder[45] to automatic paper-strip scanning. The automatic modification is also simple and easily constructed. It exhibits a reproducible and strictly linear relationship between corresponding points on the chromatogram and the record. To illustrate the sensitivity and resolution obtainable with this scanner, Eisenberg and Leder use the record scan of a chromatogram on which a carbon-14-labeled compound was isolated. An automatic apparatus with which as little as 4×10^{-4} μc of a carbon-14 compound can be detected on a paper strip is described by Dubini and Fanteschi.[46] The activity is detected by means of a flow-type proportional counter having a narrow window of 1.2-mg/cm^2 thickness and is indicated by peaks on the recording paper. The paper strip is fastened to the surface of a cylinder, which rotates in front of the counter window; cylinders of various diameters are used. Spots having edges as close together as 3 mm can be distinguished.

A 2π windowless gas-flow proportional counter for scanning paper chromatograms for beta emitters is described by Dobbs.[46a] The chromatogram strip, attached to a plate, passes through a hemispherical counting chamber. The paper traverses the sensitive volume of the counter at a speed that can be varied. The area of chromatogram counted at any instant is defined by means of a sliding plate, located between the chamber and the strip, that contains rectangular slits of various

dimensions. Counting gas is introduced at two points inside and two points outside the sensitive volume. Dobbs has shown that the gas flow rate, build up of static charge, volatilization of the sample, and face of the chromatogram scanned affect the reproducibility of results. On the basis of these findings, a satisfactory procedure is recommended.

Shipotofsky[46b] designed a simple radiochromatogram scanner to provide maximum sensitivity and versatility at low cost. The device contains easily constructed Geiger flow-through tubes and may be operated either as a windowless detector for maximum sensitivity or with ultra-thin windows to maintain a high level of sensitivity and yet minimize contamination.

To improve the sensitivity in scanning unidimensional radiochromatograms of compounds labeled with weak beta emitters, Salomon[47] devised a detecting system that simultaneously scans the upper and lower surfaces of the chromatogram. A photograph and a diagram that shows the structural detail of the scanner are given. Radiochromatographic profiles for carbon-14 are used to compare the performance of the instrument with its prototype, with a helium-organic quenched 1.5-mg/cm^2 commercial Geiger-Müller tube, and with a commercial windowless flow counter. A 4π chromatogram scanner of this type is made commercially.[41] By paper chromatography, Licser and Elias[48] studied isomerization among the isomers of 1,2,3,4,5,6-hexachlorocyclohexane. They describe a special 4π flow counter to measure carbon-14 in the separated isomers.

The continuous automatic registration of the radioactivity of a large number of paper chromatograms is possible with the apparatus of Vigne and Lissitzky.[49] The chromatogram passes over an adjustable slit in front of an end-window beta counter. The output from the counter is integrated and recorded; the speeds of the chromatogram and chart are synchronized. The apparatus can be used to measure a wide range of activities, because the best slit width for a given chart speed can be calculated and the sensitivity of the integrator can be varied over a range of ratios from 1 to 10. The error for the complete sequence of operations is claimed to be no greater than 5%. A simple and inexpensive automatic scanner for paper chromatograms is described by Eisler, Chorney, and Kisieleski.[50] The electronic system of this scanner consists of a strip recorder, count-rate meter of range from 20 to 10,000 counts/sec, and the combination of a scaler with a variable high-voltage power supply. Inclusion of the scaler allows integrated counts to be taken for measurements of specific activity at any point along the chromatogram. A special marking mechanism makes possible the determination of R_f values directly from the recording chart. Minimal concentrations of carbon-14 of the order of 10^{-5} $\mu c/cm^2$ in Whatman No. 1 paper can be detected. An automatic scanning apparatus for one- and two-dimensional radio paper chromatograms is described by Frank and co-workers.[51] The apparatus has alternative counting devices. One uses a scaler and mechanical counter, which is photographed periodically. The other uses an electronic decade counter, each computing tube of which is connected to a voltmeter; the voltmeter readings are photographed periodically. Measurements are taken at set distances regulated at 0.5 to 1 cm; the duration of a measurement varies automatically with the intensity of the radiation.

A unit identical with a graphic recorder is used by Fouarge[51a] to move radioactive chromatograms on paper strips under a counter tube. An endless strip of cellulose acetate carries as many as 15 paper strips.

The automatic direct quantitation of radioactivity on paper chromatograms is possible with instrumentation described by Ludwig and coauthors.[52] From commercially available equipment, modified slightly, they obtained an instrument that scans a paper strip for radioactivity, records the rate on a moving chart, and records the total number of counts in each peak of radioactivity on the strip regardless of the counting rate. A number of strips can be taped together up to a length of 50 ft, and the instrument will function without attention for two days. For poorly resolved peaks, it is possible to print out the counts in fixed intervals of time. A block diagram of the instrument is shown.

An array of Geiger counters is described by Gilbert and Keene[53] for measuring very rapidly the distribution of radioactivity, particularly the weak beta from carbon-14, along a 30-cm chromatogram. Instead of one counter alone, an array of thirty beta-sensitive Geiger counters at 1-cm spacing in a single envelope is used. The whole of a 30-cm-long chromatogram with spots of minimum beta activity as low as 10^{-5} μc can be measured accurately with a single exposure in a few hours; moderate amounts of radioactivity can be measured in a few minutes. The unique feature of the apparatus is the simple method for determining the count rate of each counter. A part of the electrical charge passed by each counter is collected by a probe and is stored on a condenser of high insulation. At the end of the exposure, the voltages of the thirty condensers are read by an electrometer. The readings are proportional to the activities under each counter. The design principle of the apparatus can be applied to either one- or two-dimensional distributions.

An improved two-dimensional scanner for radiochromatograms was developed by Perkins and Tyrrell,[54] who also discuss briefly several earlier two-dimensional scanners. Permanent facsimiles are printed on electrosensitive paper in considerably less time than is required to obtain a corresponding x-ray film autoradiograph. The radiochromatogram can be any size up to 21 in. × 21 in. The limit of detection for carbon-14 is of the order of 35 counts/min above background, although compact spots that assay as low as

20 counts/min can be readily detected visually on the facsimile. A facsimile made from a 21 in. × 21 in. radiochromatogram of glucose-U-^{14}C in a 62-hr scanning time is shown in comparison with an autoradiograph of the same radiochromatogram made in 192 hr.

A semiautomatic device for measuring radioactivity on two-dimensional paper chromatograms was developed by Moses and Lonberg-Holm.[55] Positions of radioactive compounds on chromatograms are determined by autoradiography, and the appropriate areas are cut out. The areas are sandwiched between two continuous bands of thin plastic polyester film in an apparatus designed for the purpose. In another apparatus, the accumulated double band of film bearing the excised areas is passed automatically in a discontinuous manner between two detector tubes for a predetermined counting period. For each spot, the number of counts and elapsed time are printed out automatically.

The specific activity of radioactive substances is determined by Price and Hudson.[56] They used a counting tube with gas-phase sensitivity to beta radiation and cathode sensitivity to ultraviolet photon radiation to measure these radiations from identical areas of paper chromatograms. By comparing the radioactivity curve with the optical-density curve, radiochemical contamination is easily recognized.

Other apparatus for the automatic recording and measurement of carbon-14 on paper chromatograms is described.[57-60] Automatic scanning devices for the determination of tritiated compounds on paper chromatograms are described by Eisler, Chorney, and Kisieleski[50] and by Carleton and Roberts;[61] these devices should be equally useful for carbon-14-labeled compounds.

The method of *photoradiochromatography*, developed by Baptista, Ramalho, and de Matos Fernandes,[62] is unique and is particularly suitable for scanning radioactive chromatograms of low activity. It is highly sensitive and simple and is a useful substitute for direct autoradiography. The method is based on the fact that a photographic film is sensitive enough to record the light emitted during the operation of a halogen-filled Geiger-Müller counter. The film and chromatogram are mounted side by side and are made to traverse a collimating slit under an end-window counter. The G-M counter acts as an amplifier to enhance the sensitivity of the photographic film in the photographic recording of light corresponding to limited radioactive zones in the chromatogram. By means of a calibration chart that shows optical density of the film as a function of the counting rate, the method can be made quantitative. Counting rates very little above background can be registered easily. The usefulness of the method as a substitute for the direct autoradiography of chromatograms is shown by Figs. 12-1 and 12-2.

The use of *liquid-scintillation counting* to measure quantitatively carbon-14-labeled compounds isolated on filter paper has certain advantages. The counting efficiency and precision achieved for carbon-14 with liquid-scintillation counting are much greater than that possible with a conventional Geiger-Müller counter. The counting range is very wide (20 to 200,000 cpm in adjacent spots),[63] it is not always necessary to elute the carbon-14 activity from the paper, sample preparation is simple, and insolubility of the carbon-14 compound is sometimes an asset.

A variety of techniques have been used for the liquid-scintillation counting of carbon-14-labeled compounds in paper chromatograms. Roucayrol, Oberhausen, and Schuler[64] impregnated the filter paper with a liquid scintillator and thereby caused some of the energy of the beta particles that would otherwise be lost in the paper to give rise to scintillations. Since the liquid scintillator causes the paper to become fairly transparent, the scintillations are easily detected with a multiplier phototube when the paper strip traverses it. The count rate is a linear function

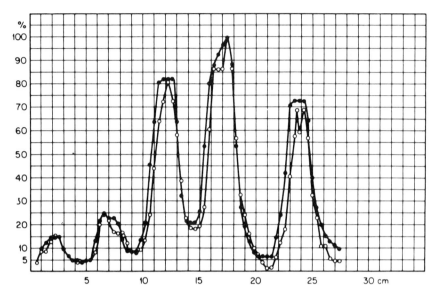

FIG. 12-1   Radioactive distributions (normalized) obtained from a photoradiochromatogram (●) and the corresponding radiochromatogram (○). (*From A. M. Baptista, A. J. G.
Ramalho, and A. M. de Matos Fernandes*, INTERN. J. APPL. RADIATION ISOTOPES, **5**, 289 (1959)
with permission from that journal and the authors.)

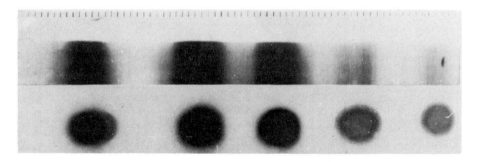

FIG. 12-2   Above: an autoradiogram of a chromatogram (exposure time, 7 days).
Below: the corresponding photoradiochromatogram (30 min).
(*From A. M. Baptista, A. J. G. Ramalho, and A. M. de Matos Fernandes*, INTERN. J. APPL. RADIATION
ISOTOPES, **5**, 289 (1959) *with permission from that journal and the authors.*)

of activity and is reproducible. Under the best conditions, the sensitivity to beta particles of carbon-14 is about one hundred times greater than that of a Geiger-Müller tube with a mica end-window of less than 2 mg/cm² thickness and at 5 mm from the sample. Carbon-14 can be counted in the presence of phosphorus-32 or iodine-131 with slightly less sensitivity. The count rate varies as much as 30% with variation in quality of filter papers. To prevent displacement of activity along the paper, Roucayrol, Oberhausen, and Schuler added a high polymer to the liquid scintillator.

Wang and Jones[65] immersed segments of filter-paper strips into holders that were built into specially made vials, delivered the liquid-scintillation mixture into the vials, and counted the carbon-14 activity in a Tri-Carb liquid-scintillation spectrometer. The counting efficiencies and reproducibilities they achieved in counting carbon-14-labeled compounds are indicated in Table 12-1. Subsequently to the work of Wang and Jones, Geiger and Wright[66] presented data to show that the use of special vials was not necessary and that the angle of rotation of the paper section as seen by the phototubes need not be controlled. They used a scintillation spectrometer equipped with an automatic sample changer for the liquid-scintillation counting. Loftfield,[63] however, disagrees with the conclusions of Geiger and Wright and gives data to show that the counting efficiency *is* influenced by the orientation of the paper strip with respect to the phototube. He recommends that best precision is achieved when the strip is rolled into a cylindrical form, although some loss of efficiency occurs. Also, he found that if paper strips are not oven-dried there is a variable lowering of counting efficiency and that variations in the concentration of eluting buffer used in his work caused variations in counting efficiency.

Table 12-1   Counting efficiencies and reproducibility for the liquid-scintillation counting of paper chromatograms[65],f

Labeled compound	Radioactivity, dpm	Net counting rate,ᵃ cpm	Efficiency, percent	Precision,ᵇ percent
Benzoic acid-7-¹⁴Cᶜ	4795	4076	85	2
Benzoic acid-7-¹⁴Cᵈ	4795	4059	85	1
Na-benzoate-7-¹⁴C	4795	2610	54	2
Glucose-U-¹⁴C	5472	3124	57	2
K-gluconate-U-¹⁴C	9969	5334	54	2
Glutamic acid-2-¹⁴C	24640	13347	54	2
Amino acids-¹⁴Cᵉ	8881	4884	55	2

ᵃ Net counting rate refers to the observed counting rate less the background counting rate. Countings were carried out to a standard deviation of no more than 1 percent.

ᵇ Precision is expressed as percentage deviation from the mean of four replicate samples.

ᶜ Labeled compound dissolved in the scintillation solution without the insertion of filter paper.

ᵈ Labeled compound dissolved in the scintillation solution with the insertion of a piece of blank filter paper.

ᵉ Paper chromatogram of a mixture of ¹⁴C-labeled amino acids in a bacteria hydrolyzate was counted prior and after development in *sec*-butanol NH₃ solvent. Total recovery from fifteen 2.5 cm × 4 cm sections was 90 percent of the applied activity.

ᶠ Table taken from C. H. Wang and D. E. Jones, *Biochem. Biophys. Res. Commun.*, **1**, 203 (1959) by permission from Academic Press, Inc. and the authors.

Bousquet and Christian[67] attributed imprecise results in the liquid-scintillation counting of paper chromatograms not to orientation or to size of the paper strips but to a phosphorescent material of long decay time that was present in the scintillator solution. By using a scintillator system that dissolved aqueous acid and by acidifying the samples before counting them, they obtained an essentially linear relationship between applied and observed carbon-14 activities. They developed a valid procedure for the quantitative radioassay of carbon-14-labeled salicylic acid on paper chromatograms; the counting efficiency was about 25%. Improved methods for liquid-scintillation assay of carbon-14-labeled compounds isolated on paper chromatograms are described by Bartley and Abraham.[68] By persulfate oxidation, they release the carbon-14 as carbon-14 dioxide, which is then absorbed in a scintillator solution and counted in a liquid-scintillation spectrometer.

Sensitive autopositive photography was used in conjunction with the liquid-scintillation technique by Stitch and Oakey[69] for partial characterization of carbon-14-labeled oestrogen metabolites by paper chromatography following isotope dilution. An intense black image of the chromatogram spot on a light background is recorded by an autopositive photographic paper (Kodak Autopositive), the slow speed of which permits all photographic processing to be done in daylight.

The technique of wetting a filter paper that contains an active deposit with a liquid scintillator solution and counting it directly[64] was improved by Funt and Hetherington.[70] They overcame the problem of loss of solvent from the warm phototube surface by using monoisopropylbiphenyl as the scintillator solvent; at room temperature the vapor pressure of this solvent is about $\frac{1}{1000}$ that of toluene, a frequently used scintillator solvent. The linear dependence of counting rate on the activity of a sample of sodium carbonate-^{14}C[71] is shown in Fig. 12-3; the counting efficiency was 31.5%. From sections of paper chromatograms placed in counting vials, Takahashi, Hattori, and Maruo[72] extracted carbon-14-labeled amino acids and sugars into Hyamine hydroxide [p-(diisobutylcresoxyethoxyethyl)dimethylbenzylammonium hydroxide], added scintillator solution, and counted the extracts in a liquid-scintillation spectrometer. Excellent reproducibility and recovery of radioactivity are reported.

Investigators have used filter paper impregnated with alkali as an absorbing agent for carbon-14 dioxide. Wakil[73] moistened the strip with a methanolic solution of Hyamine, absorbed carbon-14 dioxide on the strip, and counted the strip in the way described by Wang and Jones.[65]

Baxter and Senoner[73a] describe the innovations of detecting carbon-14-labeled amino acid spots on paper chromatograms with the sodium salt of trinitrobenzene-1-sulfonic acid and of measuring the radioactivity by scintillation counting after burning the segments of the paper that contain the spots in an improved combustion apparatus and absorbing the carbon-14 dioxide. The reagent forms an intense yellow complex with most amino acids without removing carboxyl groups. However, the complex absorbs at a wavelength within the spectrum of the light emission used to activate the scintillation counter, thus preventing the direct scintillation counting of the spots on the paper. By this method the recoveries of radioactivity are reported to be in the range from 96 to 100%.

By persulfate oxidation, Bartley and Abraham[73b] have released carbon-14 dioxide from compounds on segments of paper chromatograms and absorbed it directly in a liquid scintillator for measurement. They tested the technique with carbon-14-labeled glucose, acetate, lactate, alanine, and succinate.

These experiments indicate that some of the factors to be considered in achieving

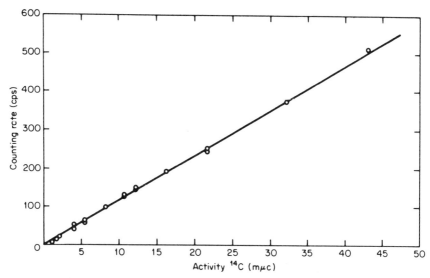

FIG. 12-3   Linear dependency of counting rate on activity of carbon-14 on filter paper. (*From B. L. Funt and A. Hetherington,* SCIENCE, **131,** *No.* 3413, 1608 (1960); *reprinted from* SCIENCE *by permission and also by permission from the authors.*)

maximum accuracy and precision in the liquid-scintillation counting of paper chromatograms containing carbon-14 are: the drying procedure, thickness and orientation of the paper, possible presence of long-lived phosphorescent contaminants in the liquid scintillator, and volatility of the scintillator solvent.

Submicroanalysis by a radiometric precipitation technique that includes paper chromatography and liquid-scintillation counting was accomplished by Welford, Chiotis, and Morse.[73c] They achieved a high sensitivity (0.0001 μg for calcium as calcium oxalate-^{14}C); they suggest that the technique is also applicable to the determination of any elements that can be precipitated as oxalate, carbonate, or any compound that can be labeled with carbon-14. Elements precipitated as compounds having sulfur-35 and phosphorus-32 labels were also separated and determined at high sensitivity by this technique.

Some liquid scintillator systems used in the counting of carbon-14 compounds isolated by paper chromatography are listed in Table 12-2.

Solid-scintillation counting of carbon-14 in paper chromatograms has been used only to a very limited extent. Seliger and Agranoff[74] sprayed 1-in. squares of paper that contained glucose-^{14}C with a saturated solution of scintillation-grade anthracene in benzene. After evaporation of the benzene, microcrystals of anthracene were thus deposited throughout the paper, the amount for highest efficiency in counting carbon-14 being about 1 mg/cm². The segments were counted at 12° on the face of a Dumont 6292 phototube in a lighttight enclosure "with a precision to ±5%." The counting efficiency ranged from 16 to 63% for net counts/sec from 32 to 126, respectively, depending on the discriminator settings. The authors state that good resolution was obtained, that tritium and carbon-14 could be identified in the same spot, and that

Table 12-2   Some liquid-scintillator systems used in the counting of carbon-14-labeled compounds isolated by paper chromatography

Liquid scintillator solution	^{14}C-Labeled material chromatographed	Reference
PBD^a(8 g)–toluene (1 liter)	Glucose-^{14}C, urea-^{14}C	64
PPO^b(4 g)–POPOP^c (50 mg)–toluene (1 liter)	See Table 12-1	65
Terphenyl (3 g)–POPOP (30 mg)–toluene (1 liter)	See Table 12-1	65
"Scintillation mixture cont'g 20% ethanol"^{d}	Sodium acetate-^{14}C	67
"Scintillation mixture using toluene"^{d}	Glucose-1-^{14}C	67
PPO(0.3%)–POPOP(0.03%)–toluene	Valine-^{14}C Valine-^{14}C hydroxamate	63
p-Terphenyl(4.0 g)–POPOP(0.1 g)–monoisopropylbiphenyl	Sodium carbonate-^{14}C	70
PPO(6.5 g)–POPOP(0.13 g)–naphthalene(102 g)–ethyl alcohol(300 ml)–dioxane(500 ml)–xylene(500 ml)	Salicylic-^{14}C acid	68
PPO(0.4%)–POPOP(0.05%)–toluene^e	Carboxylsalicylic-^{14}C acid	68
PPO(4.6 g)–POPOP(80 mg)–naphthalene(73 g)–toluene(350 ml)–dioxane(350 ml)–methanol(210 ml)^f	Hexa-N-acetyl neomycin B Hexa-N-acetyl neomycin C Tetra-N-acetyl neamine	78

^{a} PBD = phenylbiphenyloxadiazole.

^{b} PPO = 2,5-diphenyloxazole.

^{c} POPOP = 1,4-bis-2-(5-phenyloxazoyl)benzene.

^{d} Presumably of composition similar to that of the scintillator systems used by Wang and Jones.[65]

^{e} This scintillator system was reported to give spurious counts.[68]

^{f} This solution is called Diotol.

the sprayed strips were stable for weeks and could be re-counted with reproducible results.

A plastic-scintillator method for radioassay of carbon-14 compounds on filter paper was developed by Nakshbandi.[74a] A paper cleansing tissue soaked in a benzene solution of plastic scintillator (N.136 Nash and Thompson Ltd., London, England; about 200 g/liter) is placed on each side of the filter paper. The "sandwich" is held briefly in benzene vapor to prevent too rapid evaporation of the solvent and is then dried at ~60°. The dry sample is placed vertically in an empty vial and is counted in a Tri-Carb liquid-scintillation spectrometer. Exceptionally good results are reported for carbon-14 compounds; the maximum counting efficiencies for alanine-^{14}C in water (polar) and for hexadecane-^{14}C (nonpolar) were 55 and 58%, respectively.

Scintillation spectrometry techniques for counting radioactivity on paper strips are reviewed by Davidson.[75] Scintillation chromatograph scanners are made commercially;[76,77] one of them[77] is based on the method of Roucayrol, Oberhausen, and Schuler.[64]

Autoradiography, in conjunction with separation by paper chromatography, is used extensively for the identification of carbon-14-labeled compounds (see Table 12-3 below). It is discussed separately as an assay method in its own right (see Chap. 13).

Some carbon-14-labeled compounds isolated by paper partition chromatography are listed in Table 12-3. Those that have also been autoradiographed are so designated. The list does not begin to indicate the large number of compounds subjected to this experimental technique. By this means, many of the carbon-14 compounds available from commercial suppliers are checked for purity, stored to avoid self-decomposition, and even isolated in quantity. Trade brochures from suppliers provide the names of many other such compounds.

12-1b GAS-LIQUID PARTITION CHROMATOGRAPHY

The general literature on gas chromatography is reviewed critically and informatively by Desty.[79] He groups it into four classes: proceedings of symposia, compilations of abstracts, handbooks with a practical bias intended mainly for the beginner, and authoritative comprehensive texts. The scope and limitations of the literature in each of these classes are discussed concisely. There are other general references[80-84] not reviewed by Desty. Modern methods for the separation and continuous measurement in the gas phase of compounds labeled with radiocarbon are reviewed by Drawert and Bachmann.[84a]

The gas chromatography of radioactive substances is reviewed ably by Adloff,[85] who discusses techniques and applications in particular. More than half the 55 references cited by Adloff relate to work with carbon-14. In a still more specific review, Cacace[86] points out the significance of labeled organics in gas chromatography; carbon-14 is the isotope to which he gives greatest attention.

Gas-liquid partition chromatography has several **advantages** over the usual chromatographic techniques. It is more rapid, sensitive, and efficient and can be used to separate a large number of molecular species that may be present—even in extremely small amounts— in a very small volume of a volatile sample. Scharpenseel[87] discusses in detail the combined techniques of gas chromatography and measurement of the activity of carbon-14- and tritium-labeled substances in a flow-through ionization chamber and vibrating-reed electrometer, a proportional counter, and a liquid-scintillation spectrometer.

When carbon-14-labeled organic compounds are separated and both mass assay and radioactivity assay are made simultaneously on the separated components, the technique has many additional advantages. It is useful for the direct analysis of radioactive substances of high volatility, which would be impossible by paper chromatography. By the use of a suitable detector, the technique is likewise applicable to relatively nonvolatile compounds. Wolfgang and Rowland[88] enumerate several advantages offered when both thermal-conductivity and proportional-counter detectors are used. Among the advantages, the following[89] exist regardless of the method of radioassay: *1.* the activity and specific activity of each fraction are determined at no extra cost in time, *2.* there is small chance of missing portions of the activity that may be present in unexpected chemical forms, *3.* carrier-free radiocompounds can be handled by the same techniques used for macro quantities, and *4.* an excellent and rapid indication of radiochemical identity and purity is available by comparing the results

Table 12-3   Some carbon-14-labeled compounds isolated by paper chromatography
(*The asterisks designate those compounds that were also autoradiographed and the references on the autoradiography.*)

Class	Carbon-14-labeled compound	References
Alkaloids	Morphine-N-methyl*	1
	Nicotinic acid and its derivatives	2
Amines	DL-Adrenaline*	3
	DL-Aminomethyl-3,4-dihydroxybenzyl alcohol	4
	Choline analogs (seven)	5
Amino acids and their derivatives	Amino acids* (general)	6, 7*, 8*, 9*, 10, 11, 12
	Basic amino acids*	13
	Alanine*	13*, 14*
	α-Aminoadipic acid	15
	β-Aminopropionitrile	16
	Aspartates*	14
	Aspartic acid*	13
	Choline-methyl chloride	17
	α,γ-Diaminobutyric acid	15
	Glutamic acid*	13*, 14*, 15, 18*
	Glutamine*	14
	Glutathione*	14
	Glycine*	19*, 20, 21
	Glycine hydrochloride	17
	Isolucine*	22
	Lysine*	18*, 23, 24
	L-Lysine*	19
	L-Leucine*	19
	Methionine	25
	Norleucine	17
	Norvaline hydrochloride	17
	Ornithine	15
	Serine*	13
	Threonine*	13
	Thyroxine	17
	Valine	26
	Valine hydrochloride	17
Carbohydrates and their derivatives	Starch* (general)	27
	Sugars* (general)	7*, 8*, 9*, 28*
	Fructose*	21, 27*
	Galactose	29
	Glucose*	14*, 21, 27*, 29, 30, 31
	Glucose phosphate*	32
	Hexose phosphates*	13
	Lactates*	14
	Lactose	29

Table 12-3 (*Continued*)

Class	Carbon-14-*labeled* compound	References
	Pelargonidin 3-glucoside	33
	L-Rhamnose	30
Carboxylic acids and their derivatives	Carboxylic acids* (general)	7*, 8*, 9*, 34
	Acetic acid*	22
	Aconitic acid*	13
	Bromoacetic acid*	35
	Calcium glycolate	17
	Citrates*	14
	Citric acid*	13
	Fumarates*	14
	Fumaric acid*	13
	Glucuronic acid*	30, 36*
	β-Hydroxybutyrates*	14
	4-Hydroxyphenylpyruvic acid	37
	Isocitric acid*	13
	α-Ketoglutaric acid	31
	Maleates*	14
	Malic acid*	13
	Methyl malonate*	22
	Mono- and diphosphoglyceric acids*	38
	Oxalacetic acid	31
	Oxalic acid	39
	Phenylethylacetic acid*	36
	Phosphoglyceric acid*	13
	Phosphopyruvic acid*	13
	Propionic acid*	22
	Pyruvic acid	31
	Stearic acid	40
	Succinates*	14
	Succinic acid*	13*, 17
	Ureido succinic acid*	41
Heterocyclic compounds	Uracil*	42
Purines	Adenine sulfate	17
	8-Azaadenine	17
	8-Azaguanine	17
	Guanine hydrochloride	17
	Hypoxanthine	43
Steroids	Steroids (general)	44
	Aldosterone	45
	Aldosterone diacetate	45
	Cholesterol	17
Urea and its derivatives	Urea*	14*, 41*
	1,1-Dimethylbiguanide	46
	Phenobarbital	47

References for Table 12-3

[1] K. S. Anderson and L. A. Woods, *J. Org. Chem.*, **24**, 274 (1959).

[2] E. Leifer, L. J. Roth, D. S. Hogness, and M. H. Corson, *J. Biol. Chem.*, **190**, 595 (1951).

[3] R. W. Schayer, *J. Biol. Chem.*, **189**, 301 (1951).

[4] D. R. Howton, J. F. Mead, and W. G. Clark, *J. Am. Chem. Soc.*, **77**, 2896 (1955).

[5] R. M. Lemmon, M. A. Parsons, and D. M. Chin, *J. Am. Chem. Soc.*, **77**, 4139 (1955).

[6] R. M. Fink and K. Fink, "Radiocarbon and Filter Paper Partition Chromatography," United States Atomic Energy Report MDDC-1486, Oct. 27, 1947.

[7] W. Stepka, A. A. Benson, and M. Calvin, *Science*, **108**, 304 (1949).

[8] M. Calvin and A. A. Benson, *Science*, **109**, 140 (1949).

[9] A. A. Benson, J. A. Bassham, M. Calvin, T. C. Goodale, V. A. Haas, and W. Stepka, *J. Am. Chem. Soc.*, **72**, 1710 (1950).

[10] *Chem. Abstr.*, **55**, 7531f (1961); T. Wada, *Nippon Isotope Kaigi Hobunshu*, **2**, 513 (1958).

[11] R. B. Loftfield, *Atomlight*, no. 13, 1 (1960).

[12] Anon., *Chem. Eng. News*, **39**, 21 (1961).

[13] A. O. M. Stoppani, S. L. S. de Favelukes, L. Conches, E. Ramos, and M. M. Pigretti, *Proc. Intern. Conf. Peaceful Uses At. Energy, 2nd, Geneva, 1958*, **25**, 12 (1958).

[14] J. Katz and I. L. Chaikoff, *J. Biol. Chem.*, **206**, 887 (1954).

[15] M. Rothstein and D. M. Greenberg, *J. Am. Chem. Soc.*, **81**, 4756 (1959).

[16] T. Tuominen, K. Juva, and E. Kulonen, *Ann. Med. Exptl. Biol. Fenniae (Helsinki)*, **36**, 391 (1958).

[17] B. M. Tolbert, P. T. Adams, E. L. Bennett, A. M. Hughes, M. R. Kirk, R. M. Lemmon, R. M. Noller, R. Ostwald, and M. Calvin, *J. Am. Chem. Soc.*, **75**, 1867 (1953).

[18] H. Borsook, C. L. Deasy, A. J. Haagen-Smit, G. Keighley, and P. H. Lowy, *J. Biol. Chem.*, **173**, 423 (1948).

[19] P. N. Campbell and O. Greengard, *Proc. Intern. Conf. Peaceful Uses At. Energy, 2nd, Geneva, 1958*, **25**, 129 (1958).

[20] J. Dancis, N. Braverman, and J. Lind, *J. Clin. Invest.*, **36**, 398 (1957).

[21] L. P. Shubnyakova and I. N. Bukharov, *Metody Polucheniya i Izmeren. Radioaktivn. Preparatov, Sb. Statei*, 94 (1962).

[22] D. D. Feller, *Proc. Intern. Conf. Peaceful Uses At. Energy, 2nd, Geneva, 1958*, **25**, 44 (1958).

[23] L. L. Miller and W. F. Bale, *J. Exptl. Med.*, **99**, 125 (1954).

[24] L. L. Miller, C. G. Bly, and W. F. Bale, *J. Exptl. Med.*, **99**, 133 (1954).

[25] C. H. Edwards, E. L. Gadsden, L. P. Carter, and G. A. Edwards, *J. Chromatog.*, **2**, 188 (1959).

[26] J. M. Dubert, P. Gros, J. Coursaget, and M. Macheboeuff, *Bull. Soc. Chim. Biol.*, **33**, 1692 (1951).

[27] S. Udenfriend and M. Gibbs, *Science*, **110**, 708 (1949).

[28] C. K. Hordis and G. N. Kowkabany, *Anal. Chem.*, **30**, 1210 (1958).

[29] H. R. Roberts and F. J. Carleton, *Anal. Chem.*, **28**, 11 (1956).

[30] P. D. Hoeprich and J. N. Whitesides, *Anal. Chem.*, **34**, 1350 (1962).

[31] G. A. Abdel-Tawab, E. Broda, and G. Kellner, *J. Chromatog.*, **2**, 99 (1959).

[32] L. Longinotti and F. Pocchiari, *Gazz. Chim. Ital.*, **84**, 1171 (1954).

[33] G. E. Livingston and P. Markakis, *Science*, **124**, 28 (1956).

[34] F. A. Isherwood, *Biochem. J.*, **40**, 688 (1946).

[35] M. Quintiliani and M. Boccacci, *Proc. Intern. Conf. Peaceful Uses At. Energy, 2nd, Geneva, 1958*, **25**, 85 (1958).

[36] G. Milhaud, B. Silver, and J. P. Aubert, *Proc. Intern. Conf. Peaceful Uses At. Energy, 2nd, Geneva, 1958*, **25**, 27 (1958).

[37] G. Billek and E. F. Herrmann, *Monatsh. Chem.*, **90**, 89 (1959).

[38] S. Aronoff, *Arch. Biochem. Biophys.*, **32**, 237 (1951).

[39] H. Götte, R. Kretz, and H. Baddenhausen, *Angew. Chem.*, **69**, 561 (1957).

[40] A. Kornberg and W. E. Pricer, Jr., *J. Am. Chem. Soc.*, **74**, 1617 (1952).

[41] S. Takeyama, T. Noguchi, Y. Miura, and M. Ishidate, *Pharm. Bull. (Tokyo)*, **4**, 492 (1956).

[42] "Catalog and Price List, April, 1959," New England Nuclear Corporation, Boston, Mass., p. 5.

[43] G. R. Greenberg, *J. Biol. Chem.*, **190**, 611 (1951).

[44] D. L. Berliner, O. V. Dominquez, and G. Westenskow, *Anal. Chem.*, **29**, 1797 (1958).

[45] B. Kliman and R. E. Peterson, *J. Biol. Chem.*, **235**, 1639 (1960).

[46] M. Herbert and L. Pichat, *Bull. Soc. Chim. France*, 21 (1960).

[47] L. J. Roth, E. Leifer, J. R. Hogness, and W. H. Langham, *J. Biol. Chem.*, **178**, 963 (1949).

of the mass assay with those of the radio-activity assay.

In gas-liquid chromatography of carbon-14-labeled materials, regardless of how the effluent is radioassayed, a low-level sample should not be assayed following a high-level sample. Many compounds are not recovered completely from the column; therefore, cross contamination can be significant if this precaution is not taken.

The **quantitative measurement** of carbon-14-labeled compounds isolated by gas-liquid chromatography is done with an ionization chamber, beta-proportional counter, or Geiger-Müller counter or by means of liquid or solid scintillators. Discontinuous or continuous measurement is possible with each. Of these, the ionization chamber and scintillators are used most extensively. To collect and subsequently radioassay fractions is laborious and is done conveniently only when a peak is detected. Therefore, very small amounts of radioactive intermediates may not be collected as separate fractions. On the other hand, when the column effluent is radioassayed continuously, the full resolving power of gas-liquid chromatography is retained throughout the radioassay, the information gained is more reliable, and much time is saved. Both Adloff[85] and Cacace[86] give excellent summaries of some of the various techniques of measurement. The ionization-chamber method is well suited for the measurement of beta emitters in gaseous samples.[90,91] If the beta emitter is a liquid or solid—which may be the case if the carbon-14-labeled component of the gaseous effluent is converted to such for radioassay—the liquid-scintillation method is more sensitive than the ionization-chamber method. Guinn

and Wagner[92] discuss the advantages and disadvantages of each method in a variety of typical situations selected for use in their systematic comparison of the two methods.

The *ionization-chamber counting* has the advantage of detecting all the radioactive components of the mixture to be analyzed and hence constitutes a powerful means for the separation and determination of labeled compounds.[93]

Counting in the ionization-chamber region has the limitations of being applicable only to those gases that have suitable ionization characteristics and of being critically dependent on the purity of the gases to be assayed.[94] Winkelman and Karmen[95] determined that the sensitivity of an ionization chamber when used in a flowing-gas system is limited, because it responds to relatively large fractions of unlabeled material in the gas stream. The response varies with the kind and quantity of the material and can be obtained without polarizing the chamber. They developed a method, discussed below, in which this limitation is avoided.

The gas chromatography–ionization chamber method for determining carbon-14-labeled compounds, as well as other beta emitters, has been modified from time to time with a resulting increase in the versatility and sensitivity of the method. The ionization chamber of the design described by Riesz and Wilzbach[96] was modified by Nystrom,[97] who mounted the chamber adjacent to the thermistor and used it in the temperature range from 20 to 100°. In an experiment in which carbon-14-labeled toluene was used, he determined that the minimum quantity of carbon-14 detectable in a peak is 0.05 μc. Nystrom analyzed a sample of methanol-^{14}C prepared by the lithium aluminum hydride reduction of radioactive carbon dioxide. The main peak was identified as methanol-^{14}C and the minor peak as methyl formate-^{14}C. The methyl formate-^{14}C was mixed with carrier material and degraded. Labeling was found in both carbons of the methyl formate; the reaction conditions were then modified to eliminate the methyl formate.

The ionization chambers used by Riesz and Wilzbach[96] and by Nystrom[97] both have a ceramic insulator. At the elevated temperatures (200 to 250°) required for gas chromatography of fatty-acid esters, ceramic insulators give rise to stress currents, which thus limit their applicability.

An ionization chamber suitable for high-temperature (240°) gas chromatography was constructed by Mason, Dutton, and Bair.[98] The main insulator is fabricated of Teflon; brass tubing is used to prevent the Teflon from sagging. The chamber has its own heating element and can be used externally to the gas chromatograph.

A technique for the measurement of radioactivity independent, within a wide range, of any particular gas chromatographic conditions was developed by Cacace and Inam-ul-Haq.[93] After the effluent gases are passed through a conventional thermal-conductivity cell, they are diluted with a current of carrier gas. The dilution is so made that the total flow rate can be adjusted to a certain fixed value at which the ionization chamber is calibrated. Thereby, the radioactivity measurements are independent of flow rate of carrier gas in the chromatograph, and the necessity of heating the ionization chamber to prevent condensation of high-boiling compounds is eliminated. The sensitivity of this device for the continuous measurement of the radioactivity is proportional to the ratio between the chamber volume and the gas flow rate. However, resolution of elution peaks is also a function of chamber volume. The satisfactory compromise conditions chosen by Cacace and

Inam-ul-Haq were a 100-ml ionization chamber calibrated at 10-liters/hr flow rate of carrier gas. The sensitivity achieved under these conditions was measured with tritiated compounds; the detection of compounds having a minimum activity of some milli-microcuries and the measurement of about 20 mμc of activity were possible. Satisfactory quantitative analyses were made on standard samples under a wide variety of chromatographic conditions: temperature from 70 to 135°, flow rate from 0.5 to 3.5 liters/hr, and sample size from 0.1 to 10 mg. Cacace and Inam-ul-Haq recommend that the method, without modification, can be extended to volatile organic compounds labeled with carbon-14.

Very high sensitivity for measuring carbon-14 in gas chromatographic effluents by use of an ionization chamber was achieved first by Cacace, Guarino, and Inam-ul-Haq[99] and later by Winkelman and Karmen.[95] The response of the chamber to unlabeled material in the gas stream is avoided. The column effluent is burned over copper oxide, a procedure which James and Piper[100] also used together with a proportional counter instead of an ionization chamber. The water produced is either trapped or reacted with heated iron to release hydrogen gas for tritium assay. The gas entering the ionization chamber is only carbon dioxide (or hydrogen) and carrier gas. The composition of gas in the chamber is kept essentially constant by use of an ionization chamber of relatively large volume and by the addition of a brisk dilution flow of carrier gas directly to the ionization chamber. Winkelman and Karmen[95] state that the sensitivity of the method is such that 202 $\mu\mu$c of carbon-14 in a compound emerging 8 min after injection can be distinguished from baseline fluctuations. The method has many advantages in addition to high sensitivity. It is applicable to the analysis of a wide variety of organic substances—low- and high-boiling, low- and high-specific-activity, polar and inert. The problem of fabricating a suitable insulator does not exist. The composition of the gas in the chamber is changed relatively little by the entrance of a fraction that is unlabeled carbon dioxide. Diphasic signals are almost entirely eliminated. The assay of the column effluent for tritium, as well as carbon-14, is possible. The large volume of the ionization chamber permits highly efficient assay.

The method was modified by Karmen and co-workers[101] to provide for the determination of tritium; the modification is also useful for carbon-14 determination, as well as for the simultaneous determination of both tritium and carbon-14. The amounts of these radioisotopes in the components separated determine whether they are measured in an ionization chamber or by scintillation counting.

Cacace, Cipollini, and Perez[101a] describe a technique for the continuous elemental analysis and radiometric analysis of carbon-14-labeled compounds separated by gas chromatography. The eluates are converted to carbon dioxide and hydrogen, which are separated on another column. The activity of the carbon dioxide is assayed by a flow ionization chamber or an internal-flow proportional counter, depending on the specific activity of the sample. Both the total activity and the specific activity of a compound can be determined in a single operation. Simultaneous assay for carbon-14 and tritium in doubly labeled molecules is possible, because the hydrogen and carbon contained in each compound are separated.

The gas-chromatography–ionization chamber method has been used by Nystrom[97] to check the purity of products arising from the Wilzbach titration method, from hot-atom chemistry investigations, from radiochemical preparations, and from organic mechanism studies, as well as in the analysis of methanol-^{14}C prepared from the lithium aluminum hydride reduction of radioactive carbon dioxide. The method was used by Cacace and Guarino[102] in studying the radiation labeling

with carbon-14 of aliphatic hydrocarbons; they analyzed mixtures of carbon-14-labeled hydrocarbons that contained C_2 through C_6 compounds. Also in this way, Cacace, Guarino, and Inam-ul-Haq[99] separated and radioassayed high-boiling substances labeled with carbon-14. Winkelman and Karmen[95] analyzed mixtures of carbon-14-labeled methyl esters and methyl esters of soap; Karmen and co-workers[101] analyzed a mixture that contained tritium-labeled methyl, ethyl, and propyl acetates and carbon-14-labeled butyl acetate. Examples of the use of preparatory gas chromatography in the manufacture of labeled molecules are given by Pichat and co-workers.[103] With very little alteration, gas chromatography has been used for the purification of 1- to 10-mmole quantities of carbon-14-labeled molecules and their separation from complex reaction mixtures. Labeled products having boiling points up to 180° and in quantities of about 100 mg to 1 g have been separated. Their radioactivities were measured separately by ionization-chamber counting. Some carbon-14 compounds thus purified are acetone, benzene, and methyl and ethyl acrylate.

Commercial gas chromatograph–ionization chamber systems are available.[104,105]

The *scintillation-counting* method of assay of carbon-14-labeled compounds in gas chromatographic effluents can be the best assay method. The method has many advantages. It is highly sensitive, equally suitable for the assay of all beta emitters, and adaptable to the simultaneous assay of two radioisotopes.[106] Because the radioactivity can be observed for long periods at the operator's convenience, the method is statistically very reliable; the ionization-chamber method is less reliable statistically, since the disintegration rate can be assessed only while the compound is in the detector.[107] Usually, the apparatus and sample preparation are simple, and the method is adaptable for routine use.[108,109]

The scintillation method of assay is

limited to compounds that neither quench nor absorb the fluorescence of the scintillator and are miscible with the solution of scintillator if a solution is used.[94] Organic solvents are necessary in liquid counting, and a relatively colorless sample is required.[109] Other limitations and also advantages may be associated with particular apparatus or techniques.

Both liquid and solid scintillators are used in many forms to assay radioactive fractions emerging from a gas-liquid chromatograph. Scintillator crystals are deposited on the walls of a gas detector chamber, imbedded in grooves in the face of a cell, placed in glass tubes and coated with a stationary phase, or suspended in a solution that contains the fraction. The solid scintillator may be a plastic. Solid and liquid scintillators are used in solutions in suitable solvents. Scintillating gels are also used. They are made by mixing a liquid scintillator with a thixo-tropic gelling agent, such as finely divided silicon dioxide[110] or a castor oil derivative.[111]

Numerous methods are described that are either adaptable to or designed specifically for the continuous assay of gas-liquid chromatographic effluents by scintillation counting. Hanle, Hengst, and Schneider[112] layered one wall of a gas chamber with anthracene crystals and detected scintillations due to carbon-14 dioxide with a multiplier phototube. Difficulties with this method are that the anthracene evaporates readily under vacuum and that the radioactive gas is adsorbed on the scintillator when the phototube is cooled to reduce the thermal background. Stranks[94] applied the same ideas in a scintillation gas-counter assembly in which a plastic scintillator (Pamelon) was one wall of the chamber. The chemical form of the isotopic species is immaterial so long as it does not react with the plastic scintillator. The specific activities of duplicate samples are reproduced

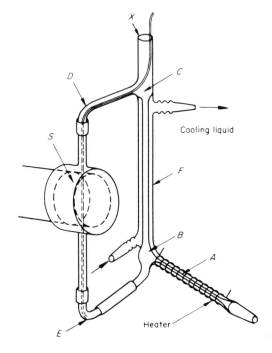

FIG. 12-4 Instrument for measuring radioactivity of vapors. (*After A. E. Lowe and D. Moore*, NATURE, **182**, 133 (1958) *by permission from* NATURE *and the authors.*) *A*: Capillary tube through which vapors and carrier gas flow (heated electrically to temperature of the column). *BCDE*: Circuit for the circulation of the liquid phosphor. *F*: Jacket for circulation of cooling liquid. *X*: Opening for insertion of thin polyethylene tube, through which the phosphor is introduced, and for escape of carrier gas. *S*: Counting cell.

to $\pm 0.5\%$, and the absolute counting efficiency is adequate. Light sensitivity of Pamelon and the need to orient the cell on top of the multiplier phototube each time a sample is counted induced Greenfield[113] to use a flow-through Pamelon cell positioned within a lead castle in such a way that the cell can be filled, emptied, and washed without being removed from the counter. Greenfield used the assembly to measure sulfur-35, but it is equally useful for carbon-14.

Popják suggested a technique for counting the carbon-14 content of vapors emerging from a gas-liquid chromatographic apparatus simultaneously with the recording of the analytical chromatograph output. The effluent vapors are condensed into a circulating liquid phosphor that is a solution of diphenyloxazole in toluene or xylene. The scintillations excited in the phosphor by the carbon-14 are detected with a multiplier phototube. A range-changing device automatically keeps the record of count rate on the scale of the recorder. The record obtained is of the integral type. The prototype of the instrument is described briefly by Lowe and Moore;[114] Fig. 12-4 shows it diagrammatically. The improved form is described and discussed extensively by Popják and co-workers.[115] The instrument was designed to measure the radioactivity of carbon-14–fatty acids emerging as vapors from a gas-liquid chromatographic column. It differentiates between the radioactive fractions with a resolving power that is as great as that of the column used. The radiochromatograms together with the corresponding analytical record obtained with a gas-density balance (Fig. 12-5) illustrate the performance of the instrument. A still more advanced instrument was developed to take two multiplier phototubes on two opposite sides of the counting chamber and thus to benefit from coincidence circuit ryand to measure two isotopes simultaneously. The advanced instrument is described by Popják, Lowe, and Moore.[116] The efficiencies of carbon-14 and tritium

counting are essentially the same for the single- and double-photomultiplier instruments, that is, about 50% for carbon-14 and about 20% for tritium. The advanced

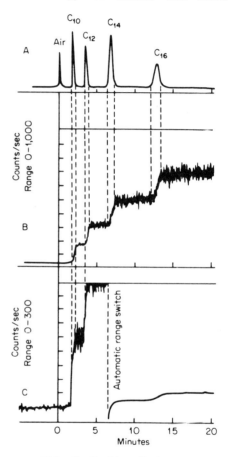

FIG. 12-5 Gas-liquid radiochromatogram obtained from the analysis of the methyl esters of four ^{14}C-labeled fatty acids on ethylene glycolpolyadipate ester column at 197°C. A, analytical record; B and C, simultaneous records of radioactivity made at two levels of sensitivity. Total load 1.25 mg of esters containing 1362 disintegrations/sec. Analytical record taken with one-tenth the normal sensitivity of the gas density balance. (*After G. Popják, A. E. Lowe, D. Moore, L. Brown, and F. A. Smith,* J. LIPID RES., **1,** 29 (1959) *by permission from the* JOURNAL OF LIPID RESEARCH *and the authors.*)

instrument has greater sensitivity, because it gives a background counting rate one-tenth that seen with the simple instrument. It gives excellent precision; the maximum variation observed in the counting of a standard mixture of carbon-14-labeled fatty acid esters during one year was $\pm 3\%$, much of which variation is attributed to probable imprecision in pipetting.[116] Popják and collaborators[116] have used the instrument for determining the purity of synthetic isotopically labeled substrates, for biosynthetic experiments, for turnover studies, and for analysis of cell constituents of photosynthetic organisms grown in the presence of carbon-14 dioxide. Carboxylic acids and higher alcohols were determined. The Series 319 Flow Detector[117] is an instrument of the double-photomultiplier type suggested by Popják.[116] A possible disadvantage of the Popják instrument is that fast-moving materials of high specific activity can cause the instrument to switch to low sensitivity unless the cell is emptied and refilled during the operation.[100]

Scharpenseel and Menke[118] describe a procedure for the direct recording of activity from tritium while the column effluent passes through a tube that contains anthracene and 2,2'-p-phenylene-bis-(5-phenyloxazole) (POPOP) scintillators. The method should also be applicable to carbon-14.

A system for either the manual or automatic collection of effluent from a gas-liquid chromatographic column in vials of scintillation solvent is used by Dutton.[119] The apparatus is so designed that adequate heat is supplied up to the point of the hot gas–solvent interface, a critical factor in a condensation procedure, because cool areas condense and accumulate radioactive eluants.

An efficient device was developed by Karmen and Tritch[120] for continuous or discontinuous trapping of carbon-14-labeled materials from gas chromatographic effluents. Short sections of glass tubing that contained anthracene crystals coated with a stationary phase (silicone oil) are located at the exit port

of an analytical column. The carbon-14 activity of methyl esters of fatty acids trapped from a column effluent on the coated anthracene is assayed, without further manipulation, by substituting the trap for the sample of liquid scintillator solution in a liquid-scintillation spectrometer. Continuous scintillation counting of a single trap permits the high resolution and convenience afforded by simultaneously recording component elution and radioactivity. The design of the Series 318 Flow Detector[121] is based on the original observations of Karmen and Tritch. In the continuous recording, an integrated step-function record of total activity versus time is obtained.

The discontinuous method of collecting fractions was used by Nystrom[97] in conjunction with the recording of thermal conductivity. He trapped the effluent gas in vials of scintillator solution for 30-sec periods; the results were qualitative only, because each radioactivity measurement was averaged over a 30-sec period. Karmen and co-workers[101] extended the use of essentially the same technique to the simultaneous scintillation counting of carbon-14 and tritium in column effluents.

A flame ionization detector is used by Cramer and associates[121a] as a combustion chamber in combination with absorbers of special design to measure radioactivity in effluents of a gas chromatograph. The combustion products, carbon dioxide and water, are recovered quantitatively from the detector. Special absorbers, connected to the detector, trap the carbon dioxide. Carbon-14 radioactivity in the absorbing liquid (15 wt% sodium hydroxide solution plus a small amount of detergent) is measured by heterogeneous scintillation counting with a coincidence counting system. (The system is the same as that described by Schram and Lombaert,[149] which is discussed below in Sec. 12-1c.) It is reported that total carbon-14 activities of 10^{-11} c/fraction can be determined with $\pm 15\%$ accuracy in a 1-hr counting time. The procedure is recommended for combustible carbon-14-labeled organic compounds. The method is illustrated with results of the analysis of the products of gamma radiolysis of *n*-pentane that contained about 0.6% 1-pentane-4-^{14}C (specific activity 3.7 mc/mole). Its possible usefulness for other isotopes (e.g., tritium and sulfur-35) is suggested, since absorbers suitable for water and sulfur dioxide could be used in place of that for carbon dioxide.

The scintillation-counting method of assay of carbon-14-labeled compounds in gas chromatographic effluents has been applied in numerous studies. During their study of the labeling of benzene with a carbon-14 ion beam, Lemmon and associates[122] used the method to determine the specific radioactivity of the benzene and toluene fractions isolated from irradiated benzene. The phenolic components of cigarette smoke were identified and determined quantitatively by Spears;[123] he used carbon-14 labeling, gas-liquid chromatography, and liquid scintillation counting to determine the concentrations of phenols.

Beta proportional counting as a method of radioassay of carbon-14-labeled compounds in gas chromatographic effluents is especially sensitive. Wolfgang and Rowland[124] indicate that with their flow-proportional counter as little as 10^{-9} to 10^{-8} curie of total activity can readily be detected and resolved.

Proportional counters of early designs were used in conjunction with gas chromatography to only a limited extent, because amplifier-scalers of sufficient sensitivity and reliability were lacking and the behaviors of the gas counters themselves were undependable.[125] The counters readily developed noise, became contaminated easily, and were nearly impossible to decontaminate effectively.[125] The inherent limitations of proportional counters for application to gas chromatography are the difficulty of constructing counters capable of operating at temperatures up to 250°, change in the operating characteristics as a result of the

expansion of the center wire, poisoning of the center wire by stationary phase that is stripped from the column, and deposition within the cell of long-chain fatty acids when the gas stream from the detector is diluted with cold gas.[100]

Proportional counters free of the problems associated with those of the early designs were developed by Wolfgang and Mackay;[125] their counters were noise-free, not easily contaminated, and easily decontaminated. A diagram of the gas chromatographic–radioassay apparatus used by Wolfgang and Rowland[124] is shown in Fig. 12-6; a detailed diagram of the flow proportional counter used with it is shown in Fig. 12-7.

Later, Schmidt-Bleek and Rowland[125a] designed a brass-Teflon internal proportional flow counter for radio-gas chromatography that is more inert toward possible components of the flow stream than are the glass counters with silver cathodes. Figures 12-8 and 12-9 give the detailed design. The counter is inexpensive (less than $100), useful at elevated temperatures (tested to 160°), has a low background without further shielding, can be disassembled easily, provides for variation in counting volume, and is virtually indestructible. Schmidt-Bleek and Rowland suggest that when the counter is used with chromatographic columns operated at temperatures above 200°, it is often more convenient to pyrolyze or ignite the emerging components and to operate the counter at 100° or less than to operate it at higher temperatures.

James and Piper[100] recognized the inherent limitations of beta proportional counters for the radioassay of gas chromatographic effluents. In their procedure, which follows, the limitations do not exist. Argon is used as carrier gas, all organic compounds in the effluent are burned over copper oxide, water is removed by passing the gas stream over magnesium perchlorate, carbon dioxide is injected to give a final concentration of 5%, and the gas is passed at room temperature into a proportional counter of the simplest construction (Fig. 12-10). The combustion train is attached to the outlet of a conventional gas chromatograph. The apparatus is now available commercially.[126] Later,[127] they designed a new apparatus that is a metal or glass chromatographic column wound on a heated aluminum former. The column is attached directly to a quartz combustion train that contains copper oxide and iron powder. All organic compounds in the effluent are burned to carbon dioxide and water. The water is reduced by the iron to hydrogen. The hydrogen is detected with a miniature katharometer. Carbon dioxide is injected to give a final concentration of 5%, and the mixed gases are counted in a simple proportional counter that can count the beta radiation from either carbon-14 or

tritium with efficiencies of almost 100% for carbon-14 and 60% for tritium. Means can be provided for the simultaneous counting of carbon-14 and tritium. A similar radioactivity monitoring system is available commercially as the Barber-Coleman radioactivity monitoring system.[127a] Swell modified the combustion unit of this system to determine satisfactorily carbon-14 and tritium in sterols and steroids[127b] and in cholesterol esters.[127c] The procedure gives excellent reproducibility and good resolution of radioactive peaks.

Instrumentation is also available commercially[127d] that will simultaneously record the composition of the effluent, as measured by a thermal-conductivity detector, and the component radioactivity; the results of the quantitative radioactivity measurements can be printed out as differential, integral, or differential/integral modes.

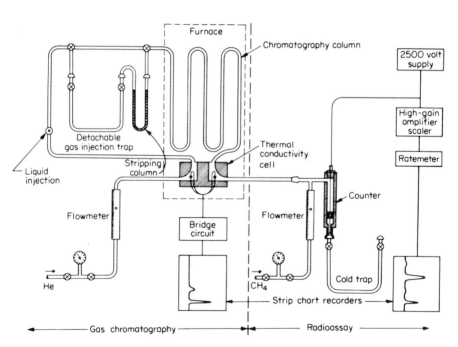

FIG. 12-6 Diagram of gas chromatographic—radioassay apparatus. (*After R. Wolfgang and F. S. Rowland,* ANAL. CHEM., **30**, 903 (1958); *courtesy of* ANALYTICAL CHEMISTRY *and the authors.*)

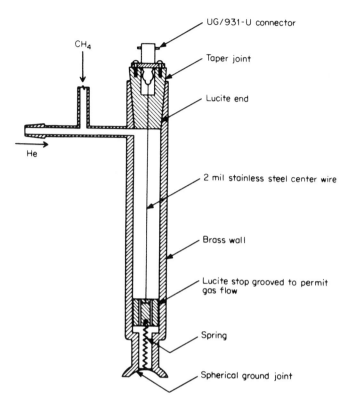

CH₄

He

UG/931-U connector

Taper joint

Lucite end

2 mil stainless steel center wire

Brass wall

Lucite stop grooved to permit
gas flow

Spring

Spherical ground joint

FIG. 12-7 Flow-proportioned
counter for gas chromato-
graph (counter case grounded
to scaler). (*After R. Wolfgang
and F. S. Rowland*, ANAL.
CHEM., **30**, 903 (1958); *courtesy
of* ANALYTICAL CHEMISTRY *and
the authors.*)

FIG. 12-8   Detailed design for brass-Teflon proportional counter. (*After F. Schmidt-Bleek
and F. S. Rowland*, ANAL. CHEM., **36**, 1695 (1964); *courtesy of* ANALYTICAL CHEMISTRY *and
the authors.*)

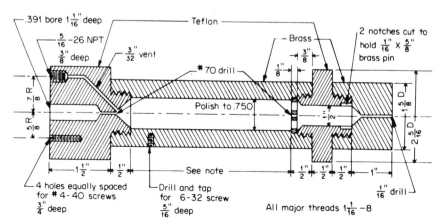

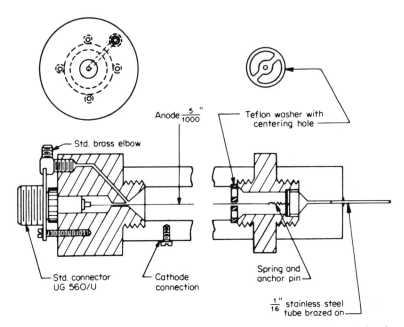

FIG. 12-9   Construction of Teflon ends for proportional counter. (*After F. Schmidt-Bleek and F. S. Rowland,* ANAL. CHEM., **36,** 1965 (1964); *courtesy of* ANALYTICAL CHEMISTRY *and the authors.*)

The gas-chromatographic–beta-proportional-counting method was used by Wolfgang[128] in the analysis for the labeled products formed by the reaction of recoil carbon-14 as a result of the irradiation of methane and ethane that contained 5 to 10% nitrogen, which was the source of 40-kev carbon-14 atoms. Low-level assay techniques with near-perfect discrimination against tritium were required, the tritium being formed from trace impurities in the containers. The product mixture, with or without carriers,

FIG. 12-10   Section of proportional counter. *A*: Tungsten wire 0.002 in. diameter. *B*: Polythene plug. *C*: Brass insert. *D*: Copper tube ½ in. diameter. (*After A. T. James and E. A. Piper,* J. CHROMATOG., **5,** 265 (1961); *by permission from the* JOURNAL OF CHROMATOGRAPHY *and the authors.*)

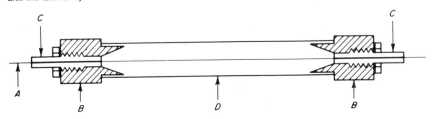

was chromatographed in helium on silica gel or other columns. Mass assay of the separated products was made with a thermal-conductivity device.

Yang and Wolf[129] studied the gas-phase reactions of recoil carbon-14 in anhydrous ammonia by gas chromatographic flow counting; a window flow counter, as described by Wolfgang and Mackay,[125] was the detector at the exit of the column. They have tabulated the yields of radioactive species as a result of the $^{14}N(n,p)^{14}C$ nuclear transformation in gaseous ammonia, as well as in methylamine. James and Piper,[100] with their simple proportional flow counter, analyzed fatty acids isolated from yeast grown in the presence of 2-stearic-^{14}C acid that contained labeled palmitic and heptadecanoic contaminants; mass assay was done with a gas-density meter. They also analyzed a mixture of lauric, myristic, palmitic, and stearic acids. The use of their new apparatus is demonstrated by results of the analysis of a mixture of linolenic, linoleic, oleic, stearic, palmitic, and myristic acids.[127] The decomposition of liquid and gaseous isobutane-^{14}C by cobalt-60 radiation was studied over the temperature range from -20 to $+50°$ by Kivel and Voigt.[130] For mass assay, they used a thermal conductivity cell; radioassay was done with a proportional counter assembly similar to that described by Wolfgang and Rowland.[124] Visser and co-workers[131] used gas-liquid chromatography to purify toluene-^{14}C that was produced by the thermal neutron irradiation of a mixture of benzene and 2-methylpyrazine; activity measurements were made according to the beta-proportional-counting method described by Christman and co-workers.[132] For measuring yields of radicals in the radiolysis of liquid hydrocarbons, Holyrod and Klein[132a] determined the total radioactivity in each component with a flow counter connected to the effluent of a gas chromatographic detector. Stocklin, Cacace, and Wolf[132b] applied an improved radio-gas chromatographic tech-

nique to the analysis of carbon-11 and carbon-14 recoil products in aliphatic hydrocarbons and amines by using a proportional window (4π-sandwich) as a flow counter. Their system takes into account changes in flow rate that occur after the injection of a large sample and that must be considered when the radioactivity of the gas is monitored with a flow counter. The flow meter is used for continuous recording and is independent of the viscosity of the gas. In their work with volatile organic compounds that contained carbon-14, Drawert, Rapp, and Ziegler[132c] led the effluent fractions from the gas chromatographic column through a reaction tube that contained Raney nickel at 420° where the organic compounds are cracked to methane in a hydrogen carrier gas stream. A quenching gas arrangement follows, from which the gas passes through a soft-beta-ray counter. By means of a direct-injection valve located at the inlet to the catalytic converter, the total mixture, without prior separation, can be injected onto the hot catalyst bed and the total count obtained. Drawert, Bachmann, and Steffan[132d] describe the combination of a combustion vial with a simple vacuum apparatus for the determination of carbon-14 compounds that are difficult to vaporize. An apparatus that consists of a vapor-phase chromatograph and a flow proportional counter that may be used up to 200° is described by Bruzzi, Castelli, and Cervellati.[132e] The whole device allows the carrying out of the gas chromatographic separation and continuous measurement of radioactivity of organic molecules labeled with carbon-14 and tritium; for carbon-14, the sensitivity is reported to be 0.2 mμc.

For radioassay of gas chromatographic effluents, *Geiger-Müller counting* has the advantage that it is relatively simple. However, the interpretation of the specific activity of a single component from data taken with a Geiger-Müller counter may be difficult.

A flow type Geiger counter was used in conjunction with gas chromatography by

Kokes, Tobin, and Emmett[133] in showing that the microcatalytic-chromatographic technique is an effective means of studying reactions with the help of radioactive tracers. A reactor unit is attached to the top of a chromatographic column, small quantities of reactant are injected into a suitable carrying gas, the mixture is passed over a catalyst, and the exit gas from the reactor is passed directly into the chromatographic column. They illustrated the technique by identifying the products of the catalytic cracking of 2,3-dimethylbutane. Van Hook and Emmett[134,135] used essentially the same technique and carbon-14 as a tracer to study the catalytic cracking of n-hexadecane over a silica-alumina catalyst. Product and radioactivity analyses were made through C_{12} hydrocarbons. Two separate counting techniques were used. One was a modified form of the method reported by Blyholder and Emmett.[136] The modifications were as follows: the effluent gas was burned to carbon dioxide, which was then introduced into the counting chamber; the chamber and nitrogen reservoir were brass, not Pyrex; and one eluent peak at a time was counted. In the other technique, static gas counting was done with a Tracerlab TGC-14 thin-window (aluminized Mylar) counting tube. Some 48 products of the catalytic cracking of n-hexadecane were isolated, and several of the secondary reactions that occur during the cracking were identified. The nature of carbonium-ion-forming steps and the exchange of hydrocarbons with radioactive coke were studied.

A schematic diagram of the Geiger counter–cell described by Blyholder and Emmett[136] and also by Blyholder[137] is shown in Fig. 12-11. In this liquid-nitrogen trapping method, the effluent from the gas chromatograph is led into the cell, where the components are condensed onto the cooled surface. The counting rate increases by one step each time a radioactive component is condensed. The difference between two successive steps is a measure of the radio-

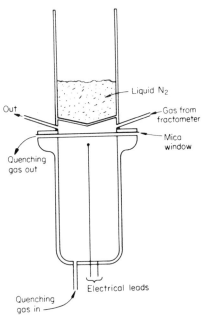

FIG. 12-11 Geiger counter–cell used in conjunction with a gas chromatographic apparatus. (*After G. Blyholder*, ANAL. CHEM., **32**, 572 (1960); *courtesy of* ANALYTICAL CHEMISTRY *and the author.*)

activity of a component. With this Geiger counter–cell, the integrated activity of a fraction of gas is measured regardless of the width of its associated chromatographic peak or the residence time of the fraction in the counter. The specific activity of the gas in the fraction can thereby be determined without the necessity of previous calibration with a sample of that component having a known specific radioactivity. The mechanism of the Fischer-Tropsch synthesis was studied by Blyholder and Emmett[136] by means of the counter-cell.

In their studies of the distribution of radioactivity in recoil-labeled toluene-^{14}C, Visser and co-workers[131] used a Geiger-Müller counter with an anticoincidence circuit to count the carbon-14 dioxide, as $Ba^{14}CO_3$, that resulted from the degradation of toluene-^{14}C. The toluene-^{14}C had been

The labels on the figure read: Liquid N₂, Out, Gas from fractometer, Mica window, Quenching gas out, Quenching gas in, Electrical leads.

prepared from a mixture of benzene and 2-methylpyrazine by thermal neutron irradiation; it was purified by repeated passes through a gas-liquid chromatographic column.

Gas chromatography in conjunction with radioassay is used in a somewhat different way by Behrendt.[138] He introduced the method of gas chromatographic detection based on treatment of the chromatographed vapors with a labeled reagent and adapted the method to use in gas-liquid partition chromatography. The organic effluent is burned over copper oxide, and the product carbon dioxide is labeled by exchange reaction with hot (200°) sodium carbonate-^{14}C. Behrendt suggests that: "This unchanged detector should become over 10^6 times more sensitive than the thermal conductivity cell, by the use of carrier-free $Na_2^{14}CO_3$ and of adequate counting equipment."

12-1c COLUMN PARTITION CHROMATOGRAPHY

In column partition chromatography, a column of a solid material supports a liquid (the stationary phase); the eluant is the mobile phase. The solid may be cellulose powder, silica gel, starch, cotton linters, asbestos, alumina, or any such material that can hold the stationary phase. Lederer and Lederer[139] give a general discussion of partition chromatography on columns, including reversed-phase chromatography. The technique has advantage for the isolation of relatively large quantities of carbon-14-labeled compounds; otherwise, paper and gas-liquid partition chromatography are used more extensively.

Certain **pitfalls** attend the use of this chromatographic technique.[140] Sometimes the solid support varies from batch to batch. Trailing may occur during development of the column. The behavior of a single substance in the mixture chromatographed may not be independent of the presence of other

substances. A number of the pitfalls that exist for paper partition chromatography (see Sec. 12-1a) may also occur in partition on columns, particularly cellulose columns. Schram and Lombaert[141] warn that a cell satisfactory for use in the continuous recording of the radioactivity of column eluates must have two characteristics: (1) the absence of mixing, which could impair the resolution attained in the chromatographic step, and (2) a volume large enough to give a sufficient number of counts but not larger than the fractions of effluent usually collected for chemical analysis. If a scintillator is being used to detect carbon-14 radioactivity in a column eluate, attention should be given to the possibility of adsorption of labeled compounds, especially the more complex ones, on the surface of the scintillator.[142] Such effects have been observed and are not easily predicted. They can cause a continual increase in background radioactivity.

For the **quantitative measurement** of carbon-14-labeled compounds in column eluates, use of *liquid and solid scintillators* is important and is ever increasing. Schram and Lombaert[143,144,145] continuously detected carbon-14 radioactivity in chromatographic aqueous effluents with a scintillating-plastic cell through which the effluent flows in a very thin layer (0.3 × 4 mm). The cell is coupled to auxiliary counting equipment that consists of two multiplier phototubes, a high-voltage supply, two wide-band amplifiers, a coincidence circuit, an integrator, and a recorder. The apparatus has the following characteristics: no contamination, good reproducibility, low flow resistance, possibility of recording high counting rates, efficiency higher than a thin end-window counter in the absence of self-absorption background of about 2.5 counts/sec without shielding. Efficiency for carbon-14 is 6%. Funt and Hetherington[146] likewise used a plastic scintillator but in the form of a tightly wound spiral (about 1 m long, $1\frac{3}{4}$ in. OD) capillary (1.5 mm OD, 0.6 mm ID, 0.269 cm^3 volume). The capillary is encapsulated in silicone fluid. The scintillation counting assembly consists of a multiplier phototube and conventional electronic circuits, linear amplifier, and integral discriminator. For solutions of $^{14}CO_3^{2-}$ (maximum particle energy, 0.156 Mev) the relation between counting rate and radioactivity is linear; counting efficiency for carbon-14 is 5.7%. For carbon-14 dioxide gas, the detection efficiency is 58.3%. This technique has certain noteworthy features: for inorganic solutions or biological fluids sample preparation is not required, the detector's efficiency is constant, gamma background is low, 4-π geometry is used, colored solutions can be counted, and counting rate is independent of rate of flow of effluent.

An efficient method for scintillation counting in a liquid-solid system was introduced by Steinberg.[147] He demonstrated that highly purified crystalline anthracene suspended in a radioactive aqueous solution is a superior scintillator for the measurement of radioactivity of the solution. For small volumes of carbon-14 samples, efficiencies are as high as 54%; for a 3-ml sample, about 20%. He compared anthracene with several other solid fluors, including the plastic scintillator Pilot Scintillator B. Schram and Lombaert,[148] aware of Steinberg's demonstration, constructed an improved apparatus for continuous measurement of carbon-14 in chromatographic column effluents. Micro crystals of anthracene are embedded in zigzag grooves in the face of a Teflon block, which forms part of the cell through which the effluent flows. Results vary with the type of grooves used and the state of subdivision of the anthracene. In a further refinement of the technique of using anthracene crystals, Schram and Lombaert[149] constructed a cell that consists of a length (about 60 cm) of transparent polyethylene tubing, which is filled with anthracene powder of calibrated size and formed into a spiral, and a flat Lucite vial that contains the spiral and is filled with silicone oil. The vial is of such dimensions that it can be used with a single refrigerated multiplier phototube, with phototubes applied on both sides of the cell, and with phototubes placed at right angles. The cell fits into most commercially available units for liquid scintillation counting of weak beta emitters. Both flow resistance and counting efficiency increase with decrease in size of the anthracene crystals. Crystals of about 300-μ size are used for carbon-14; the efficiency attained is 55%. The use of anthracene was evaluated further and extended by Scharpenseel and Menke,[150] by Rapkin and Packard,[151] and by Piez.[152] The work of Scharpenseel and Menke was done with tritium-labeled amino acids; they used 9:1 anthracene–POPOP as a scintillator. Rapkin and Packard confirmed Steinberg's[147] work; they used six levels of radioactivity of carbon-14-labeled benzoic acid in aqueous solution. Also, they evaluated a plastic scintillator (Pilot "B" beads) for the same purpose as the anthracene and showed that with it the efficiency for carbon-14 is only about one-third that obtainable with anthracene. For the determination of carbon-14 and tritium in the effluent of the amino acid analyzer, Piez constructed a quartz flow cell that contained crystalline anthracene. The cell can be used with standard scintillation counters permitting efficiencies for carbon-14 of 27 and 38% at 7 and 18 counts/min background. Carbon-14 radioactivity of about 1000 counts/min can be determined with a 5% standard error; above 3000 counts/min the error is 1 to 3%. Anthracene crystals are used in commercially available instrumentation for the flow monitoring of chromatographic column eluates that contain carbon-14.[153,154] The use of anthracene has certain disadvantages. Many organic compounds become absorbed on anthracene. Also, it dissolves in most organic eluates from chromatographic columns, which therefore could not be analyzed by this technique.

Geiger-Müller counting has also been used for the continuous monitoring of carbon-14-containing eluates from a chromatographic column. Berthet[155] gives design and performance information about a recording rate-meter for measuring radioactivity in chromatographic effluents. The apparatus is stable, and the response is linear. The range of sensitivity is from 300 to 30,000 counts/min; errors are below 2%. Four scales of sensitivity are provided; compensation is made automatically for counts lost during recovery time of the Geiger tube. Bangham[156] describes a simple helium-ethanol flow counter of increased sensitivity achieved by running the liquid as a thin film in contact with a thin mica window of area about seven times the usual area of an end-window Geiger-Müller tube. Dobbs[157] describes a simple arrangement, using a Geiger-Müller tube, that will satisfactorily detect carbon-14 at levels as low as 0.0025 μc/ml in organic solution. He used it for long periods of time to detect carbon-14-labeled alcohols. Corfield and co-workers[158] designed an apparatus to collect effluent fractions of equal volume from a chromatographic column, evaporate them to dryness, count them in turn beneath an end-window Geiger-Müller counter, and provide a record of the counts obtained. The apparatus was not evaluated with carbon-14 as a label; nevertheless, it should be useful for eluates that contain this radioisotope.

Carbon-14 labeled amino acid mixtures were separated on ion-exchange columns by Schormueller and Stan[158a] and were then measured continuously with a scintillation tube. Elwyn[158b] continuously analyzed column eluates from amino acid analyzers by passing the eluate into an anthracene-packed plastic counting cell.

The use of a *moving paper strip* as a collector for column chromatographic effluents is described.[159,160] Although this technique was not studied with carbon-14, it should be useful for its measurement.

Some carbon-14-labeled compounds that have been isolated by column partition chromatography include uniformly labeled L-amino acids,[161] morphine and neomor-

phine on powdered cellulose,[162] morphine-N-methyl-^{14}C on neutral alumina,[162] and fatty acids on acid-treated Florisil.[162a]

Not only is the technique of column partition chromatography useful in work with carbon-14-containing materials, but carbon-14 itself is a tool for studying the process of partition column chromatography, for example, in elucidating the mechanism of the partitioning step, in detecting tailing, in determining the behavior of singly labeled substances relative to others present in the mixture chromatographed, and in detecting irreversible phenomena.

12-2 ADSORPTION CHROMATOGRAPHY

Adsorption chromatography is discussed very thoroughly by Lederer and Lederer.[163]

12-2a LIQUID ADSORPTION CHROMATOGRAPHY

The application of liquid adsorption chromatography in work with carbon-14-labeled compounds has been limited. By means of an activated alumina column developed with benzene(75%)-hexane(25%), Wolf and Anderson[164] isolated anthracene-^{14}C that had been produced by neutron irradiation of the nitrogen analog, acridine. Carbon-14-labeled alcohols were separated from an ether solution on adsorption chromatographic columns by Dobbs.[157] Rappoport and Hassid[165] used a Sowden-Fischer procedure and cellulose column chromatography to prepare and isolate L-arabinose-1-^{14}C. In a similar way, Murray and Butler[166] prepared D-ribose-1-^{14}C and D-arabinose-1-^{14}C; the column was developed with acetone.

The techniques for **quantitative measurement** of carbon-14-labeled compounds in eluates from partition column chromatographs (see Sec. 12-1c) are equally applicable to the liquid eluates from adsorption columns.

12-2b   GAS ADSORPTION CHROMATOGRAPHY

Little or no use has been made of gas adsorption chromatography in work with carbon-14 compounds.

12-3   ION-EXCHANGE CHROMATOGRAPHY

Lederer and Lederer[167] give a thorough discussion of ion-exchange chromatography.

The possibility of isotopic separation of ^{12}C—^{14}C mixtures by ion-exchange chromatography was shown by Davidson, Mann, and Sheline.[168] They used the systems hydroxide–hydrogen cyanide–hydrogen chloride and acetate–formic acid–hydrogen chloride on the strongly basic resin Dowex 2. In the former case, the resin was loaded with a solution of carbon-14-labeled HCN (about 0.26 M); displacement was effected with HCl solution (about 0.125 M). Carbon-14 enrichment occurred in the cyanide band, the enrichment factor being about 3.5. The carbon-14-enriched cyanide appeared at the front of the band. In the latter case, carbon-14-labeled formic acid solutions were used. The degrees of enrichment achieved demonstrated the practicality of the ion-exchange approach to isotope fractionation.

A cellulose derivative, diethylaminoethyl cellulose (DEAE-cellulose), was used as an anion exchanger by Straub, Garzó, and Ullman[169] to isolate glycine-1-^{14}C, which is adsorbed on the ion exchanger. They were studying the formation of labeled protein precursors in tissue slices during the course of biosynthesis of amylase.

The effect of carbon-14-labeling on the ion-exchange chromatography of amino acids was studied by Piez and Eagle. In three cases,[170,171,172] the partial resolution of labeled from unlabeled amino acids was observed. This anomaly is discussed in Sec. 12-5.

Khym and Cohn[173] have shown that monosaccharides such as glucose, fructose, and galactose form borate complexes that are readily separable on ion-exchange columns. Kamen[174] suggests that such complexes can be applied to the separation of carbon-14 labeled sugars.

In a study of primordial organic chemistry, Palm and Calvin[175] subjected methane-^{14}C, together with a number of other presumed primordial gases of the earth's atmosphere, to electron bombardment. They examined the products by ion-exchange chromatography, among other techniques. Several minor molecules were identified and urea was found as a major component in the absence of added phosphine, which inhibits urea formation.

The preparation of phthaloylglycine-1-^{14}C and some simple glycyl-1-^{14}C peptides was achieved by Banfi, Teplan, and Otvos[176] with a Dowex-50(H$^+$) ion-exchange column.

Fluorescent ion-exchange resins (both anion and cation) have been made[177] in which the properties of ion exchange and fluorescence coexist. The polymer of the resin is formed from the mixture vinyl-toluene-divinylbenzene-ethylvinylbenzene (83: 10:7 mole % ratio). p-Terphenyl is the primary fluorescent compound used (at 3.5% of the weight of the monomers); 9,10-diphenylanthracene is the wavelength shifter (0.1% of the monomer weight). Cation-exchange groups are introduced into the resin by treating it with 5% sulfuric acid that contains 1% silver sulfate as catalyst. Anion-exchange properties are introduced by chloromethylation followed by amination. The counting efficiency for carbon-14 on the anion resin is 35%; the anion resin will efficiently absorb and count carbon-14 as carbonate. Fluorescent ion-exchange resins have the advantages of ease of sample preparation and recovery, permitting beta emitters to be counted in the presence of gamma emitters, nondestruction of amines or biological acids, and conforming to the shape of any counting vessel. Resins of this type were described by Heimbuck, Gee, and Bould.[178]

Ion-exchange column chromatography is used extensively by manufacturers of carbon-14-labeled compounds in the preparation, purification, and isolation of the compounds; references to the many techniques and procedures used are available.[179]

Chromatography on papers impregnated with ion-exchange resins is also useful in work with carbon-14 compounds. An example is the method described by Loftfield and Eigner.[180] In their study of amino-acid-activating enzymes, they separated the carbon-14 forms of the amino acids on $\frac{3}{4}$ by 5 in. strips of paper impregnated with Amberlite IR-120 (sulfonic acid resin, Na+ form). They describe a typical experiment in which valine-^{14}C, isoleucine-^{14}C, and alloisoleucine-^{14}C were used.

The **quantitative measurement** of carbon-14-labeled eluates from ion-exchange columns or papers is not different from that described for other types of columns (see Sec. 12-1c) and for papers (see Sec. 12-1a).

Table 12-4 indicates a few of the many carbon-14-labeled compounds that have been separated by ion-exchange chromatography.

12-4 THIN-LAYER CHROMATOGRAPHY

The chromatographic technique of greatest potential in work with carbon-14 compounds may possibly be thin-layer chromatography. In this method, a thin layer of adsorbent deposited on a glass or plastic plate serves as either the solid stationary phase or the solid support for the liquid stationary phase. In their review of thin-layer chromatography, Maier and Mangold[181] give an interesting tabular summary of its early history. Although first used in 1938, the technique was not perfected until 1956–1958. Its use up to that time warranted very little discussion by Lederer and Lederer[182] in their comprehensive review of chromatography, where it appears under the heading The "Chromatostrip." There are a number of books on thin-layer chromatography.[183,183a,184,184a,185,186,187]

Table 12-4   Some carbon-14-labeled compounds isolated by ion-exchange chromatography

Carbon-14-labeled compound	Ion exchanger	Reference
Amino acids	Dowex 50	170
	Amberlite IR-120 (paper)	180
Carbonate	Fluorescent anion-exchange resin	177
Formic acid	Dowex 2	168
Glucose	Dowex 50	170
Glutamine	Dowex 50	170
Glycine	DEAE-cellulose	169
Glycyl peptides	Dowex 50	176
Hydrogen cyanide	Dowex 2	168
Phthaloylglycine	Dowex 50	176
Urea		175

The review by Maier and Mangold[181] lists seventeen other reviews and 310 original publications on the subject. Extensive subject-indexed bibliographies are available on request from industries.[187] Mangold[184] discusses thin-layer chromatography with radioisotopes; Otto docs also.[187a] von Arx and Neher[188] give useful information on furnishing a laboratory for thin-layer chromatography.

The **advantages** of thin-layer chromatography are numerous and are being increasingly exploited in qualitative, quantitative, and preparative work with carbon-14 compounds. The technique is rapid (usually less than 1 hr is required), simple, sensitive, and reliable. Its resolving power is generally greater than that of column chromatography. The adsorbent layers have high capacity. Thin-layer chromatography is exceedingly versatile. It permits the use of many types of adsorbents (either alone or as mixtures), corrosive spray reagents, and a wide range of developing temperatures; it is applicable to samples of size in the range from 0.02 μg to 10 mg. The counting efficiency for carbon-14 is high. Often, thin-layer chromatography is a means to quantitative work that otherwise might not be accomplished.

Many of the same **sources of error** inherent in column chromatography are also characteristic of thin-layer chromatography. Maier and Mangold[181] mention several. An adsorbent may alter a compound during the chromatography; alumina and silica gel are such adsorbents. The developing solvent and sample may react. Wollish, Schmall, and Hawrylyshyn[189] and also Mangold, Kammereck, and Malins[190] point out that R_f values are not always reproducible in thin-layer chromatography and suggest that standards be run simultaneously with samples for comparison.

The **quantitative assay** of thin-layer chromatograms for carbon-14 compounds has been done by a variety of radiochemical techniques. Rosenberg and Bolgar[191] describe the rapid scanning of thin-layer chromatoplates with a scanner that consists of an end-window *Geiger tube*, ratemeter, and recorder. The efficiency of the method for carbon-14 compounds is stated to be about 2% depending on coating thickness of the plate and on slit width and time constant of the scanner. Performance of the method is illustrated with chromatoplates of oleic acid-1-^{14}C and both impure and purified triolein-1,1′,1″-^{14}C. Mangold, Kammereck, and Malins[192] also mention the effectiveness of the use of a Geiger counter for measuring radioactivity on chromatoplates.

The usefulness of *gas-flow counting* also is indicated by Mangold, Kammereck, and Malins.[192] A methane gas-flow counter of special design is described by Schulze and Wenzel[193] for the automatic continuous measurement of carbon-14- and tritium-containing compounds in a thin-layer chromatogram. A radiochromatogram scanner is available commercially[194] that uses a gas-flow detector with an ultrathin window (<100 $\mu g/cm^2$) for maximum carbon-14 efficiency. This scanner is suitable for two-dimensional scanning of a number of plates of area

totalling not more than 8×8 in. Results are presented on an X-Y recorder.

Autoradiography has been used frequently in the assay of thin-layer chromatograms for carbon-14 compounds. This technique is discussed in Chap. 13.

The use of *zonal scraping* followed by *liquid scintillation counting* for the direct assay of thin-layer chromatographic adsorbents is described in several publications by Snyder and co-workers.[195–199] They developed both a manual[197] and an automatic[199,200] device for the rapid quantitative transfer of extremely small zones of adsorbent from a narrow glass plate into counting vials. The manual scraper[196] served as the prototype for the completely automatic scraper and sample collector (see Fig. 12-12).[199,200] The scraper accommodates chromatoplates that are $20 \times 2 \times 0.4$ cm. Silica Gel G and Adsorbisil 1 have been used as adsorbents. The scraper removes adsorbent zones that are 1, 2, or 5 mm wide and deposits them into polyethylene counting vials (24 to a tray). Liquid scintillator is added to the vials. The tray of vials can be placed in a Packard series 4000 Tri-Carb for radioassay, or the samples can be radioassayed separately in any liquid-scintillation spectrometer. By proper programming of the spectrometer, the data can be graphed automatically. This automatic zonal scraper and sample collector developed by Snyder and his associates has many advantages. It is rapid; 24 samples can be scraped and collected in one minute. It is quantitative; essentially 100% of total carbon-14- and tritium-labeled lipids so separated were recovered. The resolution is high; segments of the chromatostrip as narrow as 1 mm can be removed. High sensitivity (detection of as little as 100 dis/min in a chromatographic peak) is achieved by proper choice of suspension medium and liquid scintillator system. The scraping technique precludes the necessity for elution. Graphical presentation of results can be achieved automatically. The labeled compounds are recoverable from the liquid scintillation

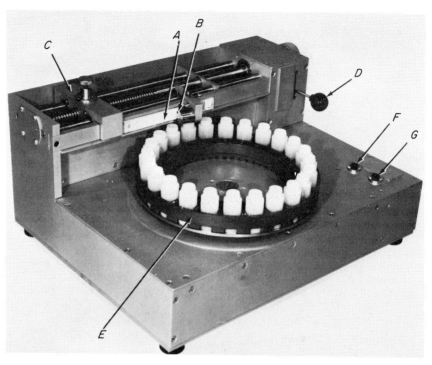

FIG. 12-12   Front view of automatic zonal scraper and sample collector. *A*: Thin-layer chromatography plate (2-cm wide). *B*: Spring loaded scraper blade. *C*: Carriage. *D*: Lever used to adjust movement of TLC strip (1-, 2-, and 5-mm increments). *E*: Turntable collecting tray which holds 24 liquid scintillation vials. *F*: Start button. *G*. Stop button. (*From F. Snyder, pp. 521–533 in "Radioisotope Sample Measurement Techniques in Medicine and Biology," International Atomic Energy Agency, Vienna, 1965; with acknowledgement to the Medical Division, Oak Ridge Institute of Nuclear Studies, Inc. under contract with the United States Atomic Energy Commission.*)

counting medium. The scraper-sample collector is relatively inexpensive.

A *gelatinous scintillator* was incorporated by Roucayrol and Taillandier[201] into the adsorbent as a means of measuring beta activity on chromatostrips with a phototube and associated photoelectric equipment.

The extension of the analytical usefulness of labeled reagents, including carbon-14 compounds, by means of thin-layer chromatography is discussed by Koss and Jerchel.[202] It is suggested that the thin-layer chromatographic separation of lipids be made following their acetylation with carbon-

14-labeled acetic acid and of fatty acids after their esterification with diazomethane-[14]C. Also, the separation of hydroxy and amino compounds might be done with thin-layer chromatography following their conversion to labeled esters and amides with carbon-14-labeled acetic anhydride.

The use of thin-layer chromatography as a practical means of achieving enrichment in carbon-14 has been suggested.[203] It was reported that in the thin-layer chromatography of unlabeled and carbon-14-labeled sodium formate the R_f values for the labeled compound were greater than for the unlabeled.

However, others[203a] found that the alkaline zone on the chromatogram, originally thought to be unlabeled sodium formate, was sodium hydroxide; therefore, no isotopic enrichment occurred.

Thin-layer chromatography and radio scanning were used by Dicarlo, Hartigan, and Phillips[204] to study the hydrolysis of carbon-14-labeled pentaerythritol tetranitrate by 1 N HCl in 75% aqueous dioxane. By thin-layer chromatography, the hydrolysis mixtures were resolved into the four nitrate esters and pentaerythritol; the compounds were located by radio scanning.

Some of the carbon-14-labeled organic compounds that have been isolated by thin-layer chromatography are listed in Table 12-5.

Aids to work with thin-layer chromatography of radioactive substances are described in the literature;[205] they include a cassette for autoradiography and related apparatus and an aspirator for removal of the radioactive material from the plate. Special apparatus for thin-layer chromatography of radioactive materials is available commercially from a number of suppliers.[206]

12-5 ANOMALIES IN THE CHROMATOGRAPHY OF CARBON-14-LABELED COMPOUNDS

Contradictory to a basic assumption made in isotope tracer work, the slight separation of carbon-14-labeled molecules from the corresponding unlabeled molecules has been reported in several cases. Piez and Eagle[207] chromatographed protein hydrolyzates from cells fed carbon-14-labeled glucose or glutamine. The peak of radioactivity in the effluent did not precisely coincide with the amino acid peaks located by the ninhydrin color reaction but always followed them closely. The heterogeneity was the result of partial resolution of labeled from unlabeled amino acids. The presence of carbon-14 in an amino acid resulted in slower movement on the ion-exchange column. In further studies[208] of the

ion-exchange chromatography of amino acids labeled with carbon-14, they observed that labeling the carbon atom adjacent to an ionized atom, such as the 1 or 2 position in an α-amino acid, slowed movement of the labeled molecules on the column. The result was that the specific radioactivity of successive fractions within the amino acid band increased. The ion-exchange behavior was not affected by the presence of carbon-14 in a position separated from a charged center, as in serine-3-^{14}C and in valine-4-^{14}C. They discuss the possibility that an inductive effect related to carbon-14 is responsible for the observed differences. In this work the length of the column of ion-exchange resin used (Dowex 50) was much greater than is generally used; thus, the resolution achieved was better than usual. The same effect was observed again by Piez[209] in studies of the continuous scintillation counting of carbon-14 and tritium in the effluent of the automatic amino acid analyzer; a relatively large effect was observed with phenylalanine-1-^{14}C.

An effect related to that observed for amino acids was found during the countercurrent distribution of certain sugars. Marshall and Cook[210] reported that D-arabinose-1-^{14}C and L-arabinose-1-^{14}C migrate less rapidly than do their unlabeled counterparts. Marshall and Magee[211] observed that D-lyxose-1-^{14}C behaves in the same way. They point out that because of such an isotope effect a considerable error can result, both in chromatography as well as in countercurrent distribution, if a single fraction rather than the peak is selected for the determination of specific activity.

Additional evidence of the existence of such an isotope effect is provided in the work of Klein.[212] He co-chromatographed a mixture of cholesterol acetate-2-^{3}H and cholesterol acetate-1-^{14}C on Davison Code 12 silica gel and obtained the ^{3}H/^{14}C ratio for successive fractions across the chromatographic peak by conventional liquid-scintillation counting techniques. The ratio was

Table 12-5 Some carbon-14-labeled compounds isolated by thin-layer chromatography

Compound	Developing solvent system	Reference
n-Cetane-1-^{14}C	Petroleum ether–diethyl ether or	1
	Petroleum ether–diethyl ether–acetic acid	1
Cholesterol-4-^{14}C	Petroleum ether–diethyl ether or	1
	Petroleum ether–diethyl ether–acetic acid	1
Cholesteryl-4-^{14}C arachidonate	Hexane–isopropyl ether	2
Cholesteryl-4-^{14}C linolenate	Hexane–isopropyl ether	2
Cholesteryl oleate-^{14}C		3
Coniferine		4, 5
Dinitrophenylamino-^{14}C acids	Toluene–pyridine–2-chloroethanol–ammonium hydroxide and	6
	Chloroform–benzyl alcohol–ethyl alcohol	6
Fatty acids and lipids		7, 8
Isoflavones		9, 10
Isoprenoids		11
Oleic acid-1-^{14}C	Ligroin–diethyl ether–acetic acid	12
Oleyl aldehyde-^{14}C	Petroleum ether–diethyl ether or	1
	Petroleum ether–diethyl ether–acetic acid	1
Palmitic-1-^{14}C acid	Hexane and	13
	Hexane–diethyl ether	13
Pentaerythritol	Ethyl acetate (H_2O-sat.)	14
	Ethyl acetate–toluene	14
	Ethyl alcohol–water	14
	Ethyl alcohol–chloroform	14
	1-Butanol–ammonium hydroxide–water	14
Pentaerythritol nitrates (mono-, di-, tri-, and penta-)	(As for pentaerythritol)	14
Steroids-^{14}C		15
Terpenes		16
Testosterone-4-^{14}C		17
Triolein-1,1′,1″-^{14}C (unpurified and purified)	Ligroin–diethyl ether–acetic acid	12
Tripalmitin-1-^{14}C	Petroleum ether–diethyl ether or	1
	Petroleum ether–diethyl ether–acetic acid	1
Tripalmitin-^{14}C and other ^{14}C-labeled lipids	Petroleum ether–diethyl ether–glacial acetic acid	13, 18
	Hexane–diethyl ether–acetic acid	19

References for Table 12-5
[1] H. K. Mangold, R. Kammereck, and D. C. Malins, 'Thin-Layer Chromatography as an Analytical and Preparative Tool in Lipid Radiochemistry,' in N. D. Cheronis, Ed., "Microchemical Techniques," pp. 697–714, John Wiley & Sons, New York, 1962.
[2] *Marked Molecules*, MM 3/64 (April 15, 1964), Euratom, 51–53 rue Belliard, Brussels, Belgium.
[3] V. Mahadevan and W. O. Lundberg, *J. Lipid Res.*, **3**, 106 (1962).
[4] K. Kratzl and G. Puschmann, *Holzforschung*, **14**, 1 (1960).
[5] K. Kratzl, *Holz Roh- Werkstoff*, **19**, 219 (1961).
[6] F. Drawert, O. Bachmann, and K. H. Reuther, *J. Chromatog.*, **9**, 376 (1962).
[7] G. A. Dhopeshwarkar and J. F. Mead, *Proc. Soc. Exp. Biol. Med.*, **109**, 425 (1962).
[8] G. A. Dhopeshwarkar and J. F. Mead, *J. Lipid Res.*, **3**, 238 (1962).
[9] H. Grisebach and N. Doerr, *Z. Naturforsch.*, **15b**, 284 (1960).
[10] H. Grisebach and L. Patschke, *Chem. Ber.*, **93**, 2326 (1960).
[11] H. Wagner, *Mitt. Gebiete Lebensm. Hyg.*, **51**, 416 (1960).
[12] J. Rosenberg and M. Bolgar, *Anal. Chem.*, **35**, 1559 (1963).
[13] F. Snyder, *Atomlight*, no. 38, 7 (June, 1964).
[14] F. J. Dicarlo, J. M. Hartigan, Jr., and G. E. Phillips, *Anal. Chem.*, **36**, 2301 (1964).
[15] G. S. Richardson, I. Weliky, W. Batchelder, M. Griffith, and L. L. Engel, *J. Chromatog.*, **12**(1), 115 (1963).
[16] J. Battaille and W. D. Loomis, *Biochim. Biophys. Acta*, **51**, 545 (1961).
[17] P.-E. Schulze and M. Wenzel, *Angew. Chem.*, **74**(20), 777 (1962).
[18] F. Snyder and N. Stephens, *Anal. Biochem.*, **4**, 128 (1962).
[19] F. Snyder and H. Kimble, *Blueprints of an Automatic Zonal Scraper and Sample Collector*, United States Atomic Energy Commission Report ORINS-47, November, 1964.

examined for evidence of difference in mobility of the two compounds. A significant difference existed, the ratio being 40% higher at the trailing edge than at the leading edge of the peak. This difference was attributed to differences in isotopic labeling.

These few observations suggest that such isotope effects in chromatographic separations, which are thought possibly to be anomalies, should not be ignored. As further refinements are made in separation processes and in methods of radioassay, it will no doubt be possible to better understand such effects and to use them in mechanisms studies. On the other hand, apparent (but unreal) isotope effects may seem to accompany such processes as distillation, crystallization, extraction, and chromatography. These effects can be the result of anomerization reactions that proceed with isotope effects.[213] They may also result from dilution of a labeled compound in such a way that one stereochemical form contains relatively more carbon-14 than the other stereochemical form.

CITED REFERENCES

[1] S. Aronoff, "Techniques of Radiobiochemistry," pp. 16–34 and 39–43, The Iowa State College Press, Ames, Iowa, 1956.
[2] R. J. Block, E. L. Durrum, and G. Zweig, "A Manual of Paper Chromatography and Paper Electrophoresis," 2d ed., Academic Press, Inc., New York, 1958; esp. pp. 68–75 and 110–390.
[3] H. G. Cassidy, "Fundamentals of Chromatography," Interscience Publishers, Inc., New York, 1957; e.g. pp. 349–350.
[3a] R. Stock and C. B. F. Rice, "Chromatographic Methods," Reinhold Publishing Corp., New York, 1963.
[3b] C. E. Hedrick and J. S. Fritz, "Bibliography of Reversed-Phase Partition Chromatography," U.S. Atomic Energy Commission Report IS-950, July, 1964.
[4] V. J. Coates, H. J. Noebels, and I. S. Fagerson, "Gas Chromatography," Academic Press, Inc., New York, 1958.
[5] D. H. Desty, Ed., "Gas Chromatography 1958," Academic Press, Inc., New York, 1958.
[5a] A. B. Littlewood, "Gas Chromatography. Principles, Techniques and Applications," Academic Press Inc., New York, 1962.

[5b] M. Schröter and K. Metzner, "Gas-Chromatographie 1961," Akademie-Verlag, Berlin, 1962.

[5c] A. Goldup, Ed., "Gas Chromatography 1964," Elsevier Publishing Company, Amsterdam, 1965.

[5d] L. Fowler, Ed., "Gas Chromatography," 4th International Gas Chromatography Symposium, Michigan State University, June 17–21, 1963, Academic Press Inc., New York, 1963.

[5e] R. Kaiser, "Gas Phase Chromatography;" Vol. I, 'Gas Chromatography;' Vol. II, 'Capillary Chromatography;' translated by P. H. Scott, Butterworths, London, 1963.

[6] I. M. Hais and K. Macek, "Handbuch der Papierchromatographic," Band I, 'Grundlagen und Technik,' Gustav Fisher Verlag, Jena, 1958.

[7] I. M. Hais and K. Macek, Eds., "Paper Chromatography. A Comprehensive Treatise," Academic Press, New York, and Publishing House of the Czechoslovak Academy of Sciences, Prague, 1963.

[7a] K. Macek and I. M. Hais, Eds., "Stationary Phase in Paper and Thin-Layer Chromatography," Proceedings of the 2nd Symposium Held at Liblice June 10–12, 1964, Elsevier Publishing Co., New York, 1965.

[8] A. I. M. Keulemans, "Gas Chromatography," Reinhold Publishing Corp., New York, 1957.

[9] M. Lederer, Ed., "Chromatographic Reviews," vols. 1, 2, and 3, Elsevier Publishing Co., New York, 1959, 1960, and 1961; esp. vol. 1, pp. 21–34; vol. 2, pp. 1–169; and vol. 3, pp. 24–157.

[10] E. Lederer and M. Lederer, "Chromatography, A Review of Principles and Applications," 2d ed., Elsevier Publishing Co., New York, 1957; esp. pp. 116–120 and 143–146, chaps. 6 and 14, and div. IV.

[11] F. C. Nachod, Ed., "Ion Exchange: Theory and Application," Academic Press, Inc., New York, 1949.

[12] R. L. Pecsok, Ed., "Principles and Practice of Gas Chromatography," John Wiley & Sons, Inc., New York, 1959.

[13] H. H. Strain "Chromatographic Adsorption Analysis," Rev. Reprint, Interscience Publishers, Inc., New York, 1945; esp. chap. VIII.

[14] E. Heftmann, Ed., "Chromatography," Reinhold Publishing Corp., New York, 1961; esp. chaps. 14–24, and 27. See also 2d ed., 1967.

[15] L. Savidan, "La Chromatographie," Dunod, Paris, France, 1958.

[15a] J. C. Giddings, "Dynamics of Chromatography. Part I. Principles and Theory," Marcel Dekker, Inc., New York, 1965.

[15b] "Chromatography—1962. An Experiment in Specialized Bibliographies," April 1, 1963, American Chemical Society.

[16] E. B. Chain, "Methods of Quantitative Radiochromatography as Applied to the Study of Intermediate Metabolism," Blackwell Scientific Publications, Oxford, England, 1956.

[17] M. D. Kamen, "Isotopic Tracers in Biology," 3d ed., Academic Press, Inc., New York, 1957; esp. apx. 3.

[18] I. Smith, Ed., "Chromatographic and Electrophoretic Techniques," 2d ed., vol. 1, 'Chromatography,' William Heinemann Medical Books Ltd., London, 1960; esp. chap. 25.

[19] B. M. Tolbert, *Nucleonics*, **18**, 74 (1960).

[20] R. J. Block, E. L. Durrum, and G. Zweig, "A Manual of Paper Chromatography and Paper Electrophoresis," 2d ed., Academic Press, Inc., New York, 1958.

[21] F. Pocchiari and C. Rossi, *J. Chromatog.*, **5**, 377 (1961); see also F. Pocchiari and C. Rossi in M. Lederer, Ed., "Chromatographic Reviews," vol. 4, pp. 1–18, Elsevier Publishing Company, New York, 1962.

[22] S. Lissitzky and R. Michel, *Bull. Soc. Chim. France*, 891 (1952).

[23] R. M. Fink and K. Fink, "Radiocarbon and Filter Paper Partition Chromatography," United States Atomic Energy Commission Report MDDC-1486 (Oct. 27, 1947).

[24] M. Rothstein and D. M. Greenberg, *J. Am. Chem. Soc.*, **81**, 4756 (1959).

[25] M. F. Bühler, J. P. A. Castrillón, A. E. A. Mitta, and M. A. Danket, *Arg., Rep., Com. Nacl. Energia At., Informe* nos. 42, 48 (1960).

[26] M. Herbert and L. Pichat, *Bull. Soc. Chim. France*, 21 (1960).

[27] R. M. Lemmon, *Nucleonics*, **11**(10), 45 (1953).

[28] "How to Use Radioactivity in Paper Chromatography," Technical Bulletin No. 4, Nuclear-Chicago Corp., Chicago, Ill., 1959.

[29] V. Moses and R. W. H. Edwards, 'Chromatography of Radioactive Substances,' chap. 25, p. 484, in I. Smith, Ed., "Chromatographic

and Electrophoretic Techniques," vol. I, 'Chromatography,' William Heinemann Medical Books Ltd., London, 1960.

[30] F. P. W. Winteringham, A. Harrison, and R. G. Bridges, *Analyst*, **77**, 19 (1952).

[31] R. G. S. Bidwell, *Can. J. Botany*, **39**, 607 (1961).

[32] R. P. van Tubergen and R. Markham, *Angew. Chem. Intern. Ed. Engl.*, **1**(2), 125 (1962).

[33] J. R. Catch, *Anal. Chem.*, **29**, 1726 (1957).

[34] A. K. Huggins and V. Moses, *Nature*, **191**, 668 (1961).

[35] J. R. Catch, "Carbon-14 Compounds," pp. 85–86, Butterworth, Inc., Washington, D.C., 1961.

[36] D. L. Berliner, O. V. Dominquez, and G. Westenskow, *Anal. Chem.*, **29**, 1797 (1958).

[37] "How to Use the Radioisotopic Derivative Method in Quantitative Analysis," Technical Bulletin No. 3, Nuclear-Chicago Corp., Chicago, Ill., 1958.

[38] E. Lederer and M. Lederer, "Chromatography. A Review of Principles and Applications," 2d ed., pp. 143–146, Elsevier Publishing Co., New York, 1957.

[39] R. J. Block, E. L. Durrum, and G. Zweig, "A Manual of Paper Chromatography and Paper Electrophoresis," 2d ed., pp. 71–74, Academic Press, Inc., New York, 1958.

[40] V. Moses and R. W. H. Edwards, 'Chromatography of Radioactive Substances,' chap. 25, pp. 487–506, in I. Smith, Ed., "Chromatographic and Electrophoretic Techniques," vol. I, 'Chromatography,' William Heinemann Medical Books Ltd., London, 1960.

[41] The Scanogram II, available from Atomic Accessories, Inc., 111 West Merrick Road, Valley Stream, N.Y.

[42] The Actigraph III, available from Nuclear-Chicago Corporation, Des Plaines, Illinois 60018.

[43] The Model 7201 Radiochromatogram Scanner, available from Packard Instrument Company, Inc., Downers Grove, Illinois 60515.

[44] R. C. Fuller, *Science*, **124**, 1253 (1956).

[45] F. Eisenberg, Jr., and I. G. Leder, *Anal. Chem.*, **31**, 627 (1959).

[46] M. Dubini and R. Fanteschi, *Comit. Nazl. Ricerche Nucleari*, CNI-32 (1960) (in English); *Chem. Abstr.*, **54**, 21878 (1960).

[46a] H. E. Dobbs, *J. Chromatog.*, **15**(1), 29 (1964).

[46b] S. H. Shipotofsky, *Anal. Biochem.*, **7**(2), 233 (1964).

[47] L. L. Salomon, *Science*, **131**, 415 (1960).

[48] K. H. Lieser and H. Elias, *Z. Anal. Chem.*, **181**, 560 (1961).

[49] J. Vigne and S. Lissitzky, *J. Chromatog.*, **1**, 309 (1958).

[50] W. Eisler, W. Chorney, and W. E. Kisieleski, 'An Automatic Scanner for Tritiated Compounds in Paper Chromatograms,' "Biological and Medical Research Division Semiannual Report, January through June, 1957," Argonne National Laboratory, pp. 143–146, ANL-5732 (July, 1957).

[51] M. Frank, F. Ugolini, F. Pocchiari, C. Rossi, and E. B. Chain, *Congr. Intern. Biochim.*, 3ᵉ, *Brussels, 1955*, 146; in English.

[51a] J. Fouarge, *J. Chromatog.*, **9**, 96 (1962).

[52] H. Ludwig, V. R. Potter, C. Heidelberger, and C. H. de Verdier, *Biochim. Biophys. Acta*, **37**, 525 (1960) (in English); *Chem. Abstr.*, **54**, 13239e (1960).

[53] C. W. Gilbert and J. P. Keene in vol. I, 'Research with Radioisotopes in Physics and Industry,' pp. 698–706 of R. C. Extermann, Ed., "Radioisotopes in Scientific Research," Pergamon Press, New York, 1958.

[54] H. J. Perkins and C. Tyrrell, *Can. J. Biochem. Physiol.*, **39**, 1183 (1961).

[55] V. Moses and K. K. Lonberg-Holm, *Anal. Biochem.*, **5**, 11 (1963).

[56] T. D. Price and P. B. Hudson, *Nucleonics*, **13**(3), 54 (1955).

[57] H. F. Linskens, *J. Chromatog.*, **1**, 471 (1958).

[58] L. Weise, *Chemiker Ztg.*, **83**, 51 (1959).

[59] W. Diller, *Arzneimittel-Forsch.*, **9**, 181 (1959).

[60] N. Martalogu, T. Nascutiu, and N. Scinteie, *Rev. Chim. (Bucharest)*, **12**, 346 (1961).

[61] F. J. Carleton and H. R. Roberts, *Intern. J. Appl. Radiation Isotopes*, **10**, 79 (1961).

[62] A. M. Baptista, A. J. G. Ramalho, and A. M. de Matos Fernandes, *Intern. J. Appl. Radiation Isotopes*, **5**, 289 (1959).

[63] R. B. Loftfield, *Atomlight*, no. 13, 1 (1960).

[64] J. C. Roucayrol, E. Oberhausen, and R. Schuler, *Nucleonics*, **15**(11), 104 (1957).

[65] C. H. Wang and D. E. Jones, *Biochem. Biophys. Res. Commun.*, **1**, 203 (1959).

[66] J. W. Geiger and L. D. Wright, *Biochem. Biophys. Res. Commun.*, **2**, 282 (1960).

[67] W. F. Bousquet and J. E. Christian, *Anal. Chem.*, **32**, 722 (1960).

[68] J. C. Bartley and S. Abraham in S. Rothchild,

Ed., "Advances in Tracer Methodology," vol. 3, p. 69, Plenum Press, New York, 1966.

[69] S. R. Stitch and R. E. Oakey, *Biochem. J.*, **81**, 12P (1961).

[70] B. L. Funt and A. Hetherington, *Science*, **131**, 1608 (1960).

[71] B. L. Funt, private communication, April 23, 1962.

[72] *Chem. Abstr.*, **56**, 7639d (1962); H. Takahashi, T. Hattori, and B. Maruo, *Anal. Biochem.*, **2**, 447 (1961).

[73] S. Wakil, private communication; reported by E. Rapkin in Packard Technical Bulletin Number 7, Jan., 1962, Packard Instrument Company, Inc., Downers Grove, Illinois 60515.

[73a] C. F. Baxter and I. Senoner, *Atomlight*, no. 33, 1 (1963).

[73b] J. C. Bartley and S. Abraham, *Atomlight*, no. 49, 1 (1965).

[73c] G. A. Welford, E. L. Chiotis, and R. S. Morse, *Anal. Chem.*, **36**, 2350 (1964).

[74] H. H. Seliger and B. W. Agranoff, *Anal. Chem.*, **31**, 1607 (1959).

[74a] M. M. Nakshbandi, *Intern. J. Appl. Radiation Isotopes*, **16**, 157 (1965).

[75] E. A. Davidson, "Packard Technical Bulletin," Packard Instrument Company, Inc., Downers Grove, Illinois 60515, June, 1961.

[76] Tri-Carb Spectrometer, available from Packard Instrument Company, Inc., Downers Grove, Illinois 60515.

[77] DMSL-1 Liquid Scintillation Paper Chromatograph Scanner, available from Numec Instruments and Controls Corporation, Apollo, Pa.; see R. H. Müller, *Anal. Chem.*, **34**, 77A (1962).

[78] D. G. Kaiser, *Anal. Chem.*, **35**, 552 (1963).

[79] D. H. Desty, *Nature*, **194**, 822 (1962).

[80] S. Dal Nogare and R. S. Juvet, Jr., "Gas-Liquid Chromatography, Theory and Practice," Interscience Publishers, New York, 1962.

[81] A. I. M. Keulemans, "Gas Chromatography," 2d ed., Reinhold, New York, 1959.

[82] A. B. Littlewood, "Gas Chromatography: Principles, Techniques, and Applications," Academic Press, New York, 1962.

[83] H. A. Szymanski, Ed., "Lectures on Gas Chromatography 1962," Plenum Press, New York, 1963.

[84] M. van Swaay, Ed., "Gas Chromatography 1962," Butterworth Inc., Washington, D.C., 1962.

[84a] F. Drawert and O. Bachmann, *Angew. Chem. Intern. Ed. Engl.*, **2**(9), 540 (1963).

[85] J. P. Adloff, *J. Chromatog.*, **6**, 373 (1961), (in French); also in M. Lederer, Ed., "Chromatographic Reviews," vol. IV, pp. 19–23, Elsevier Publishing Company, New York, 1962 (in English).

[86] F. Cacace, *Nucleonics*, **19**(5), 45 (1961).

[87] H. W. Scharpenseel, *Angew. Chem.*, **73**, 615 (1961).

[88] R. Wolfgang and F. S. Rowland, *Anal. Chem.*, **30**, 903 (1958).

[89] Adapted from Wolfgang and Rowland; courtesy of *Analytical Chemistry* and the authors.

[90] V. P. Guinn and C. D. Wagner, *Carygraph*, **1**(4), 4 (no date).

[91] K. E. Wilzbach, *Carygraph*, **1**(4), 9 (no date).

[92] V. P. Guinn and C. D. Wagner in S. Rothchild, Ed., "Advances in Tracer Methodology," vol. 1, p. 160, Plenum Press, New York, 1963.

[93] F. Cacace and Inam-ul-Haq, *Science*, **131**(3402), 732 (1960).

[94] D. R. Stranks, *J. Sci. Instr.*, **33**, 1 (1956).

[95] J. Winkelman and A. Karmen, *Anal. Chem.*, **34**, 1067 (1962).

[96] P. Riesz and K. E. Wilzbach, *J. Phys. Chem.*, **62**, 6 (1958).

[97] R. F. Nystrom, "Detection of Carbon-14 and Tritium Labeled Compounds by the Gas Chromatography–Ionization Chamber Techniques," a paper presented at the Symposium on Ionization Chamber Measurements of Radioactivity and Radiation, San Francisco, Calif., Nov. 13, 1959.

[98] L. H. Mason, H. J. Dutton, and L. R. Bair, *J. Chromatog.*, **2**, 322 (1959).

[99] F. Cacace, A. Guarino, and Inam-ul-Haq, *Ann. Chim.* (Rome), **50**, 915 (1960).

[100] A. T. James and E. A. Piper, *J. Chromatog.*, **5**, 265 (1961).

[101] A. Karmen, I. McCaffrey, J. W. Winkelman, and R. L. Bowman, *Anal. Chem.*, **35**, 536 (1963).

[101a] F. Cacace, R. Cipollini, and G. Perez, *Anal. Chem.*, **35**, 1348 (1963).

[102] F. Cacace and A. Guarino, *Nature*, **186**(4725), 632 (1960).

[103] L. Pichat, C. Baret, J.-P. Guermont, and M.

Audinot, pp. 145–155 in "Radioisotopes in the Physical Sciences and Industry," Copenhagen, September, 1960, vol. 3, International Atomic Energy Agency, Vienna, 1962.

[104] Cary-Loenco Chromatograph–Radioactivity Analysis System, available from Applied Physics Corporation, Monrovia, Calif.

[105] E-180 Actichromatograph, available from Radiation Equipment & Accessories Corporation, Lynbrook, N.Y.

[106] G. Popják, A. E. Lowe, and D. Moore, in S. Rothchild, Ed., "Advances in Tracer Methodology," vol. 1, p. 128, Plenum Press, New York, 1963.

[107] H. J. Dutton in S. Rothchild, Ed., "Advances in Tracer Methodology," vol. 1, p. 151, Plenum Press, New York, 1963.

[108] J. W. Harlan in S. Rothchild, Ed., "Advances in Tracer Methodology," vol. 1, p. 115, Plenum Press, New York, 1963.

[109] D. A. Buyske, R. Kelly, J. Florini, S. Gordon, and E. Peets in S. Rothchild, Ed., "Advances in Tracer Methodology," vol. 1, p. 185, Plenum Press, New York, 1963.

[110] This material is available commercially as Cab-O-Sil from Godfrey L. Cabot, Inc., 125 High St., Boston 10, Mass.

[111] Such a derivative is Thixin, available from Baker Castor Oil Co., Inc., 40 Avenue A, Bayonne, N.J.

[112] W. Hanle, K. Hengst, and H. Schneider, Z. Naturforsch., **76**, 633 (1952).

[113] S. Greenfield, Analyst, **83**, 114 (1958).

[114] A. E. Lowe and D. Moore, Nature, **182**, 133 (1958).

[115] G. Popják, A. E. Lowe, D. Moore, L. Brown, and F. A. Smith, J. Lipid Res., **1**(1), 29 (1959).

[116] G. Popják, A. E. Lowe, and D. Moore, in S. Rothchild, Ed., "Advances in Tracer Methodology," vol. 1, p. 127, Plenum Press, New York, 1963.

[117] Manufactured by Packard Instrument Company, Inc., La Grange, Ill.

[118] H. W. Scharpensell and K. H. Menke, Tritium Phys. Biol. Sci., Proc. Symp. Detection Use, Vienna, Austria, 1961, **1**, 281 (Pub. 1962).

[119] H. J. Dutton in S. Rothchild, Ed., "Advances in Tracer Methodology," vol. 1, p. 147, Plenum Press, New York, 1963.

[120] A. Karmen and H. R. Tritch, Nature, **186**, 150 (1960).

[121] Manufactured by Packard Instruments Company, Inc., Downers Grove, Illinois 60515.

[121a] W. A. Cramer, J. P. W. Houtman, R. O. Koch, and G. J. Piet, Intern. J. Appl. Radiation Isotopes, **17**, 97 (1966).

[122] R. M. Lemmon, F. Mazzetti, F. L. Reynolds, and M. Calvin, J. Am. Chem. Soc., **78**, 6414 (1956).

[123] A. W. Spears, Anal. Chem., **35**, 320 (1963).

[124] R. Wolfgang and F. S. Rowland, Anal. Chem., **30**, 903 (1958).

[125] R. Wolfgang and C. F. MacKay, Nucleonics, **16**(10), 69 (1958).

[125a] F. Schmidt-Bleek and F. S. Rowland, Anal. Chem., **36**, 1695 (1964).

[126] From Pye Scientific Instruments, Cambridge, England.

[127] A. T. James and E. A. Piper, Anal. Chem., **35**, 515 (1963).

[127a] Radioactivity Monitoring System, Model 5190, available from Barber-Coleman Company, Rockford, Ill.

[127b] L. Swell, Anal. Biochem., **16**(1), 70 (1966).

[127c] L. Swell, Proc. Soc. Exp. Biol. Med., **121**, 1290 (1966).

[127d] The BIOSPAN model 4998 gas radiochromatography system and the model 8735 digital integrator, available from Nuclear Chicago, 333 Howard Ave., Des Plaines, Ill., 60018.

[128] R. Wolfgang, Proc. Intern. Conf. Peaceful Uses At. Energy, 2nd, Geneva, 1958, **29**, 326 (1958).

[129] J. Y. Yang and A. P. Wolf, J. Am. Chem. Soc., **82**, 4488 (1960).

[130] J. Kivel and A. F. Voigt, Intern. J. Appl. Radiation Isotopes, **10**, 181 (1961).

[131] R. Visser, C. R. Redvanly, F. L. J. Sixma, and A. P. Wolf, Rec. Trav. Chim., **80**, 533 (1961).

[132] D. R. Christman, N. E. Day, P. R. Hansell, and R. C. Anderson, Anal. Chem., **27**, 1935 (1955).

[132a] R. A. Holyrod and G. W. Klein, Intern. J. Appl. Radiation Isotopes, **13**, 493 (1962).

[132b] G. Stocklin, F. Cacace, and A. P. Wolf, Z. Anal. Chem., **194**, 406 (1963).

[132c] F. Drawert, A. Rapp, and A. Ziegler, Chem. Ingr.-Tech., **35**(12), 853 (1963).

[132d] F. Drawert, O. Bachmann, and H. Steffan, Chem. Ingr.-Tech., **35**(12), 854 (1963).

[132e] L. Bruzzi, A. Castelli, and A. Cervellati, Nucl. Instr. Methods, **26**(2), 305 (1964).

[133] R. J. Kokes, H. Tobin, and P. H. Emmett, *J. Am. Chem. Soc.*, **77**, 5860 (1955).

[134] W. A. Van Hook and P. H. Emmett, *J. Am. Chem. Soc.*, **84**, 4410 (1962).

[135] W. A. Van Hook and P. H. Emmett, *J. Am. Chem. Soc.*, **84**, 4421 (1962).

[136] G. Blyholder and P. H. Emmett, *J. Phys. Chem.*, **63**, 962 (1959).

[137] G. Blyholder, *Anal. Chem.*, **32**, 572 (1960).

[138] S. Behrendt, *Z. Physik. Chem.*, *New Series* (*Frankfurt*), **20**, 367 (1959).

[139] E. Lederer and M. Lederer, "Chromatography. A Review of Principles and Applications," 2d ed., chap. 16, Elsevier Publishing Co., New York, 1957.

[140] "How to Evaluate an Analytical Method with the Aid of Radioisotopes," Technical Bulletin No. 5, Nuclear-Chicago Corp., Chicago, Ill., 1959.

[141] E. Schram and R. Lombaert, "Organic Scintillation Detectors," Elsevier Publishing Company, New York, 1963, p. 100.

[142] E. Rapkin, *Intern. J. Appl. Radiation Isotopes*, **15**, 69 (1964).

[143] E. Schram and R. Lombaert, *Biochem. J.*, **66**, 20P (1957).

[144] E. Schram and R. Lombaert, *Anal. Chim. Acta*, **17**, 417 (1957).

[145] E. Schram and R. Lombaert, "Radioisotopes in Scientific Research," vol. I, 'Research with Radioisotopes in Physics and Industry,' Pergamon Press, New York, 1958, pp. 626–635.

[146] B. L. Funt and A. Hetherington, *Science*, **129**, 1429 (1959).

[147] D. Steinberg, *Anal. Biochem.*, **1**, 23 (1960).

[148] E. Schram and R. Lombaert, *Arch. Intern. Physiol. Biochim.*, **68**, 845 (1960).

[149] E. Schram and R. Lombaert, *Anal. Biochem.*, **3**, 68 (1962).

[150] H. W. Scharpenseel and K. H. Menke, "Tritium in the Physical and Biological Sciences," vol. 1, p. 281, International Atomic Energy Agency, Vienna, 1962.

[151] E. Rapkin and L. E. Packard in G. H. Daub, F. N. Hayes, and E. Sullivan, Eds., "Proceedings of the University of New Mexico Conference on Organic Scintillation Detectors, August 15–17, 1960," United States Atomic Energy Commission Document TID-7612 (1961).

[152] K. A. Piez, *Anal. Biochem.*, **4**, 444 (1962).

[153] "Packard Tri-Carb Flow Monitor/Flow Detector," Packard Instrument Company, Inc., Downers Grove, Illinois 60515, December, 1961.

[154] "Continuous Scintillation Counting of Weak Beta Emitters in Flowing Aqueous Streams," Technical Bulletin No. 15, Nuclear-Chicago Corp., Des Plaines, Illinois 60018, 1963.

[155] J. Berthet, *Biochim. Biophys. Acta*, **15**, 1 (1954).

[156] D. R. Bangham, *Biochem. J.*, **62**, 552 (1956).

[157] H. E. Dobbs, *J. Chromatog.*, **2**, 572 (1959).

[158] M. C. Corfield, S. Dilworth, J. C. Fletcher, and R. Gibson, *Intern. J. Appl. Radiation Isotopes* **5**, 42 (1959).

[158a] J. Schormueller and H. J. Stan, *Z. Anal. Chem.*, **211**(4), 274 (1965).

[158b] D. H. Elwyn, *Atomlight*, no. 37, 5 (1964).

[159] H. Schlierf, *Z. Anal. Chem.*, **159**, 118 (1957).

[160] E. A. Bell, *Nature*, **180**, 190 (1957).

[161] *Atomlight*, no. 21, 14 (1962).

[162] K. S. Anderson and L. A. Woods, *J. Org. Chem.*, **24**, 274 (1959).

[162a] K. K. Carroll, *J. Lipid Res.*, **3**, 388 (1962).

[163] E. Lederer and M. Lederer, "Chromatography. A Review of Principles and Applications," 2d ed., div. I, Elsevier Publishing Co., New York, 1957.

[164] A. P. Wolf and R. C. Anderson, *J. Am. Chem. Soc.*, **77**, 1608 (1955).

[165] D. A. Rappoport and W. Z. Hassid, *J. Am. Chem. Soc.*, **73**, 5524 (1951).

[166] D. H. Murray and G. C. Butler, *Can. J. Chem.*, **37**, 1776 (1959).

[167] E. Lederer and M. Lederer, "Chromatography. A Review of Principles and Applications," 2d ed., div. II, Elsevier Publishing Co., New York, 1957.

[168] C. N. Davidson, C. K. Mann, and R. K. Sheline, *J. Am. Chem. Soc.*, **83**, 2389 (1961) and *J. Phys. Chem.*, **67**(7), 1519 (1963).

[169] F. B. Straub, T. Garzó, and Á. Ullman, *J. Am. Chem. Soc.*, **78**, 751 (1956).

[170] K. A. Piez and H. Eagle, *Science*, **122**, 968 (1955).

[171] K. A. Piez and H. Eagle, *J. Am. Chem. Soc.*, **78**, 5284 (1956).

[172] K. A. Piez, *Anal. Biochem.*, **4**, 444 (1962).

[173] J. S. Khym and W. E. Cohn, *J. Am. Chem. Soc.*, **75**, 1153 (1953).

[174] M. D. Kamen, "Isotopic Tracers in Biology,"

3d ed., p. 182, Academic Press, Inc., New York, 1957.

[175] C. Palm and M. Calvin, *J. Am. Chem. Soc.*, **84**, 2115 (1962).

[176] D. Banfi, I. Teplan, and L. Otvos, *Acta Chim. Acad. Sci. Hung.*, **35**, 213 (1963).

[177] *Chem. Eng. News*, p. 50 (April 8, 1963).

[178] A. H. Heimbuck, H. Gee, and H. Bould, Tracerlab, Richmond, Calif.

[179] See the radiochemical product data sheets provided by the vendors of carbon-14-labeled compounds; a list of vendors is given in Apx. II.

[180] R. B. Loftfield and E. A. Eigner, *J. Am. Chem. Soc.*, **81**, 4753 (1959).

[181] R. Maier and H. K. Mangold, 'Thin-Layer Chromatography' in C. N. Reilley, Ed., "Advances in Analytical Chemistry and Instrumentation," vol. 3, pp. 369–477, John Wiley & Sons, Inc., New York, 1964.

[182] E. Lederer and M. Lederer, "Chromatography. A Review of Principles and Applications," 2d ed., pp. 12–13, Elsevier Publishing Co., New York, 1957.

[183] J. M. Bobbitt, "Thin-Layer Chromatography," Reinhold, New York, and Chapman & Hall Ltd., London, 1963.

[183a] K. Randerath, "Dünnschicht-Chromatographie," Verlag Chemie, Weinheim, 1962; English translation by D. D. Libman, "Thin-Layer Chromatography," Academic Press, New York and London, 1963; 2d ed., 1966.

[184] E. Stahl, Ed. "Dünnschicht-Chromatographie, Ein Laboratoriumshandbuch," Springer-Verlag, Berlin-Göttingen-Heidelberg, 1962; esp. 'Allgemeiner Teil, G. Isotopentechnik' by H. K. Mangold, Academic Press, New York and London, 1964.

[184a] E. Stahl, Ed., "Thin-Layer Chromatography, a Laboratory Handbook," by H. R. Bolliger and others. [English translation by Cambridge Consultants] Berlin, New York, Springer-Verlag, 1965.

[185] E. V. Truter, "Thin Film Chromatography," Cleaver-Hume Press, Ltd., London, 1963.

[186] L. J. Morris and A. T. James, Eds., "New Biochemical Separations," van Nostrand Co., London, 1964.

[187] For example: Camag; Gilman Instrument Co.; Arthur H. Thomas Co.; G. K. Turner; Kensington Scientific Corp.; Brinkmann Instruments Inc.; Colab Laboratories, Inc.; M. Woelm; Mallinckrodt Chemical Works.

[187a] P. PH. H. L. Otto, 'Thin-Layer Chromatography of Radioactive Substances,' pp. 98–110 in J. Krugers and A. I. M. Keulemans, Eds., "Practical Instrumental Analysis," Elsevier Publishing Company, New York, 1965.

[188] E. von Arx and R. Neher, 'Furnishing a Laboratory for Paper and Thin-Layer Chromatography,' in M. Lederer, Ed., "Chromatographic Reviews," Vol. 5, pp. 46–57, Elsevier Publishing Co., New York, 1963.

[189] E. G. Wollish, M. Schmall, and M. Hawrylyshyn, *Anal. Chem.*, **33**, 1138 (1961).

[190] H. K. Mangold, R. Kammereck, and D. C. Malins in N. D. Cheronis, Ed., "Microchemical Techniques," p. 703, John Wiley & Sons, New York, 1962.

[191] J. Rosenberg and M. Bolgar, *Anal. Chem.*, **35**, 1559 (1964).

[192] H. K. Mangold, R. Kammereck, and D. C. Malins in N. D. Cheronis, Ed., "Microchemical Techniques," p. 705, John Wiley & Sons, New York, 1962.

[193] P.-E. Schulze and M. Wenzel, *Angew. Chem. Intern. Ed. Engl.*, **1**, 580 (1962); *Angew. Chem.*, **74**, 777 (1962).

[194] Model RSC-239 "Duo-Scan 1," available from Atomic Accessories Inc., 811 West Merrick Rd., Valley Stream, N.Y.

[195] F. Snyder and N. Stephens, *Anal. Biochem.*, **4**, 128 (1962).

[196] F. Snyder, T. J. Alford, and H. Kimble, "Radioassay of Thin-Layer Chromatograms. Blueprints for Zonal Scraper," United States Atomic Energy Commission Report ORINS-44 (April, 1964).

[197] F. Snyder, *Atomlight*, no. 38, 7 (June, 1964).

[198] F. Snyder and H. Kimble, *Anal. Biochem.*, **11**, 510 (1965).

[199] F. Snyder and H. Kimble, "Blueprints of an Automatic Zonal Scraper and Sample Collector for Radioassay of Thin-Layer Chromatograms," United States Atomic Energy Commission Report ORINS-47, November, 1964.

[200] F. Snyder, 'Quantitative Radioassay Methods for Thin-Layer Chromatography: Zonal and Autoradiographic Scans,' pp. 521–533 in

"Radioisotope Sample Measurement Techniques in Medicine and Biology," International Atomic Energy Agency, Vienna, 1965.

[201] J.-C. Roucayrol and P. Taillandier, *Compt. Rend.*, **256**, 4653 (1963).

[202] F. W. Koss and D. Jerchel, *Radiochim. Acta*, 3(4), 221 (1964).

[203] K. V. Viswanathan, *Intern. J. Appl. Radiation Isotopes*, **16**, 60 (1965).

[203a] J. Morávek and L. Lešetický, *Intern. J. Appl. Radiation Isotopes*, **17**, 607 (1966).

[204] F. J. Dicarlo, J. M. Hartigan, Jr., and G. E. Phillips, *Anal. Chem.*, **36**, 2301 (1964).

[205] K. H. Erismann, *J. Chromatog.*, **20**, 600 (1965).

[206] For example: Baird-Atomic, 33 University Road, Cambridge, Mass., 02139; Gelman Instrument Company, Ann Arbor, Mich., 48106; Kensington Scientific Corporation, 1165–67th Street, Oakland, Calif., 94608; Laboratorium Prof. Berthold, 7547 Wildbad, West Germany; Packard Instrument Company, Inc., 2200 Warrenville Road, Downers Grove, Ill., 60515.

[207] K. A. Piez and H. Eagle, *Science*, **122**, 968 (1955).

[208] K. A. Piez and H. Eagle, *J. Am. Chem. Soc.*, **78**, 5284 (1956).

[209] K. A. Piez, *Anal. Biochem.*, **4**, 444 (1962).

[210] L. M. Marshall and R. E. Cook, *J. Am. Chem. Soc.*, **84**, 2647 (1962).

[211] L. M. Marshall and D. Magee, *J. Chromatog.*, **15**, 97 (1964).

[212] P. D. Klein, *Atomlight*, no. 41 (Oct., 1964). Also, isotope fractionation during analytical separations is discussed in detail in the following references:

a. P. D. Klein, 'The Occurrence and Significance of Isotope Fractionation During Analytical Separations of Large Molecules,' pp. 3–65 in J. C. Giddings and R. A. Keller, Eds., "Advances in Chromatography," Marcel Dekker, Inc., New York, 1966.

b. P. D. Klein and P. A. Szczepanik, "Fine Structure of Isotopically Labeled Amino Acids Determined by Ion Exchange Chromatography," *Anal. Chem.*, **39**, 1276 (1967).

[213] F. Weygand, H. Simon, K. D. Keil, H. S. Isbell, and L. T. Sniegoski, *Anal. Chem.*, **13**, 1753 (1962).

CHAPTER
13
AUTORADIOGRAPHY

Autoradiography (also called radioautography) has been defined[1] as the production of a two- or three-dimensional image in a photographic emulsion by the radiations from a radioactive substance. This highly sensitive technique is useful in locating labeled molecules in a great variety of samples. Usually, the physical form of the sample does not limit the applicability of autoradiography as either a qualitative or quantitative analytical tool. The advantages of this tool are numerous. The equipment needed is relatively simple, and the procedures are easily understood. In the detection of radiation by autoradiography, the spatial resolution of the distribution of activity is high, response is stable for long times, type and energy of radiation can be discriminated, and tracks of individual events can be viewed.[2] Autoradiography is an alternative to counting, the resolution achieved being far greater than that of counting. An autoradiograph is a permanent record; the data desired can be taken from it at will.

A number of excellent general references on autoradiography exist. Boyd's[3] comprehensive and very readable book contains parts on theory, techniques, and bibliography. The information given in it is not limited to biology and medicine, as the title might indicate; most of it is equally useful in other disciplines. Yagoda's[4] book emphasizes the photographic emulsion as a means of investigating radioactive radiations and includes an entire chapter on the principles of beta-particle autoradiography. One objective of the book is to impart an understanding of the registration mechanism and its interferences. Chapters are devoted to autoradiography in the books by Francis, Mulligan, and Wormall,[5] by Faires and Parks,[6] by Wang and Willis,[7] and by Roth.[8] These chapters include discussions of the history, nature, general principles, and types of autoradiography; emulsion characteristics; techniques; and applications. The bibliographies and references given are helpful. In several other books[9–14] shorter discussions are to be found. The bibliographies that accompany these chapters are excellent sources of additional references. Still shorter discussions are available in a number of articles.[15–22] A bibliography resulting from a literature search on autoradiography also exists.[22a]

Carbon-14 is a radioisotope especially suitable for autoradiographic purposes, because its emission is weak and its half-life is long. The classified subject index given by Boyd[23] lists 56 references to autoradiographic studies made with the element carbon before 1954.

13-1 FILMS AND EMULSIONS SUITABLE FOR AUTORADIOGRAPHY OF CARBON-14

Films suitable for autoradiography of beta emitters, including carbon-14, consist of a substance (often silver bromide) sensitive to beta radiation, a medium for suspending this substance (gelatin), and a support for the resulting emulsion (cellulose acetate or glass). Usually 80% or more of the emulsion is silver bromide. In contact autoradiography, the support is relatively thick. In contour, liquid-emulsion, and stripping-film autoradiography, the emulsion is thin; therefore, the scattering of beta radiation is not important and resolution is good.

It is of interest to know that Cobb and Solomon[24] used carbon-14 to study the properties of the early available films having possible use for detection of beta radiation and were able to resolve individual beta tracks from the carbon-14. The films they recommended are still in use for beta-ray recording and autoradiography. The results of their studies are tabulated by Yagoda.[25] The emulsions include some made by the Ansco, Cramer, Eastman, and Ilford companies. The table gives absolute values for background, sensitivity, contrast, and granularity.

A concise and very informative discussion of the more recently produced autoradiographic and photographic emulsions is given by Overman and Clark.[26] They present a table of pertinent general information about Kodak emulsions commonly used in gross autoradiography, in microscopic autoradiography, and for special purposes. The Eastman No-Screen and other x-ray films are listed for application in gross autoradiography, and the NT series for microscopic autoradiography.

For carbon-14 autoradiography, single-coated films are, in general, preferred to double-coated films because the background is lower. For autoradiograms of carbon-14 on paper chromatograms, No-Screen x-ray films are most suitable.

The possibility of using color film to obtain autoradiograms of mixtures of two isotopes, provided one has a weak-beta emission and no accompanying gamma radiation, is mentioned by Smith.[27,28] A differential coloring should result from the difference between the penetrations of the beta particles from the different isotopes.

In a particular problem that requires autoradiography of carbon-14, the selection of the most suitable emulsion is affected by several factors. These include the geometry and surface characteristics of the material to be autoradiographed, the amount and the degree of localization of the carbon-14, the presence and proximity of other radionuclides, the limits of sensitivity and resolution imposed by the problem, and the maximum background that can be tolerated. Of these factors, the sensitivity and resolution desired are possibly the most significant.

Before the autoradiographic work with carbon-14 compounds is begun, the suppliers of materials for autoradiography should be consulted for information about the characteristics and availability of their most recent products. Often their information will include a useful bibliography of selected references.[28a]

13-2 SENSITIVITY AND RESOLUTION

Not all the properties of an emulsion that result in high sensitivity are those that also give high resolution. However, it is not necessary that a suitable emulsion have both these characteristics; the emulsion chosen usually represents a compromise. Sensitivity increases with increase in grain size and in grain concentration and is greater for double-coated than for single-coated films. Conversely, resolution decreases with increase in grain size and in emulsion thickness and is greater for single-coated films. Resolution, as well as sensitivity, increases with increase in grain concentration.

The *sensitivity* of a film has been defined by Cobb and Solomon[24] as the base-ten logarithm of the number of beta particles per square centimeter required to produce a photographic density 0.6 above background fog. The granularity of a film can be estimated by developing the images of the film to an approximate density of 0.6 and measuring microscopically the approximate diameter of the clumps of silver grains.

By means of Cobb and Solomon's definition of sensitivity, Boyd[29] has calculated for four films the number of disintegrations from carbon-14 required per square centimeter of film to give a photographic density of 0.6 above background fog. The values follow:

Kodak film[a]	Disintegrations per cm^2 of film $\times 10^{-6}$
X-ray double-coated No-Screen	17.4
X-ray double-coated type K	20.4
X-ray single-coated type M stripping	245.5
Nuclear single-coated NTB stripping	257.0

^a Data taken from Table 1 of reference 29.

From the same definition of sensitivity, Herz[16] calculated that a density of 0.6 on Kodak No-Screen x-ray film would be produced after a 15-day exposure by 0.38 × 10^7 beta particles (0.154-Mev) from carbon-14 of 3.6 × 10^{-4}-$\mu c/cm^2$ initial activity. The significance of the sensitivity of carbon-14 autoradiography of tissue sections is conveyed by Fitzgerald and co-workers,[30] who have calculated that satisfactory autoradiographs can be obtained on x-ray film with 10-μ thick sections in 15 days exposure with carbon-14 at concentrations of 0.05 μc per gram of tissue.

The sensitivities of certain emulsions and films have been determined with beta-emitters other than carbon-14 (phosphorus-32, sulfur-35, calcium-45, and iodine-131). Kikuchi and Oishi[31] studied the Fuji Photo Film Company's ET-2E, ET-6B, and ET-7A nuclear plates and Process plate and the Konishiroku Photo Industry Company's MR-NI nuclear plates and No-Screen x-ray film. With the same beta-emitters, Poddar[32] investigated the sensitivity of Kodak autoradiographic stripping film to beta radiation (average energies from 0.04 to 0.70 Mev) in terms of the average number of grains developed per incident beta particle. He discusses the significance of the energy dependence of the sensitivity with reference to the estimation of the average energy necessary to render a photographic grain developable. The results of these studies should be applicable to autoradiography with carbon-14.

To increase the sensitivity of autoradiography, Yagoda[33] suggests that the effect of sensitizers is worthy of study. He mentions that fluorescent materials (petroleum, mineral oil, lubricating oil, Vaseline, dyes) have been used by several other investigators as sensitizers.

Resolution has been defined, in terms of single image, as the distance between the point of maximum density and the point at which the density is half the maximum density.[34] In terms of two point sources of activity, it is the minimum distance between them that just allows them to be distinguished from each other in the developed film.[35]

In addition to grain size, grain density, emulsion thickness, and single- or double-coating, other factors that affect resolution with a particular emulsion in carbon-14 autoradiography are separation between specimen and emulsion, thickness of sample, and time of exposure and of development. The resolution achievable with beta particles is severely limited by their small size, which results in their being greatly scattered by atoms in their paths, and by their relatively long path lengths. In the emulsion, the maximum path length of betas from carbon-14 is about 90 μ, whereas that of betas from tritium is about 4 μ. Aronoff[36] illustrates the significance of resolution with respect to geometry and gives mathematical expressions for the relationship. Stevens[37] has designed a test for resolution that is useful in comparing emulsions. According to Faires and Parks,[38] the resolutions (in microns) generally attainable are:

stripping film   1–3
coating technique   5–7
x-ray film (contact)   25–30

Perfection of contact between sample and emulsion is perhaps the most important factor in attaining maximum resolution. The very high resolution of the stripping film arises from its extreme thinness as well as its excellent contact.

The autoradiographic resolution of doubly labeled compounds has been achieved by Kempner and Miller;[39] autoradiography with two sheets of x-ray film resolves isotopes in a doubly labeled compound or a mixture of labeled compounds when the electrons emitted have sufficient energy differences. For example, only the closer film is affected by carbon-14 or sulfur-35, whereas phosphorus-32 affects both films.

13-3 EXPOSURE TECHNIQUES

A nomogram for calculating autoradiographic exposures was published by Duncombe.[40]

It permits equalization of exposures and is applicable to any radioisotope. The following considerations are used:

$$N_0 = \text{number of radioactive species at time } t_0$$
$$N_0 e^{-\lambda t_1} = \text{atoms remaining at end of } t_1$$
$$\lambda = \text{decay constant for isotope in question}$$
$$\text{etc. for } t_2, t_3, \text{ and } t_4$$
$$N_0(e^{-\lambda t_1} - e^{-\lambda t_2}) = \text{number of atoms that have decayed in } (t_2 - t_1).$$

The condition that two autoradiographs obtain the same total radiation dose is:

$$N_0(e^{-\lambda t_1} - e^{-\lambda t_2}) = N_0(e^{-\lambda t_3} - e^{-\lambda t_4})$$
$$e^{-\lambda t_1} - e^{-\lambda t_2} = e^{-\lambda t_3} - e^{-\lambda t_4}$$

This last equation is the basis of the nomogram. Obviously, the nomogram is not needed for obtaining autoradiographs of carbon-14 alone, but is useful if short-lived isotopes (e.g., phosphorus-32, sulfur-35) are present together with carbon-14, for example, in doubly labeled compounds.

Estimation of the proper exposure time is based on a number of factors including the nature of the sample, its specific radioactivity, and the use to be made of the results. Estimates of the proper dosage required to give adequate exposure vary from 10^6 to 10^9 beta particles per square centimeter of emulsion.[41,42] An empirical approach to the estimation of proper exposure time is taken by Faires and Parks,[43] who assume that for close contact between the sample and a stripping-film emulsion and for a specific activity of 1 μc per gram of sample uniformly distributed, an exposure of about 14 days would give a reasonable density. In view of the great variation among samples and of the various ways of obtaining an autoradiograph, the trial-and-error approach seems to be almost unavoidable.

Autoradiographic exposure systems and specific techniques are discussed in detail in several places; they will only be summarized here. In a brochure,[2] three exposure systems—controlled-gap, contact, and emulsion embedding—are described. The descriptions include a diagram of the arrangement of sample with respect to emulsion, information on emulsion forms, advantages and disadvantages of the systems, and suggested applications; typical autoradiograms are also shown. Wang and Willis[44] group specific autoradiographic techniques in two general methods, the temporary contact method and the permanent contact method. In the temporary contact method, the emulsion and sample are in contact only during the exposure time. In the permanent contact method, the sample is mounted permanently with the emulsion; modifications of the permanent contact method are designated mounting, coating, stripping-film, and "high-resolution" methods. Although Wang and Willis discuss these techniques with respect to tissue sections in particular, the information is generally applicable.

Occasionally, exact recommendations are made regarding the exposure period for a certain type of sample. Smith[45] states that for a spot, about 1-cm² area on a paper chromatogram, that emits about 5000 particles from carbon-14 per minute from the surface on each side of the paper, a barely detectable blackening of the film will be produced in one day and that at least ten times this activity, or ten times the exposure period, should be aimed for. Aronoff[46] recommends exposure conditions for one or more paper chromatograms that contain only carbon-14 or both carbon-14 and phosphorus-32. Aronoff also gives an equation whereby it is possible to calculate the number of electrons per square centimeter required to give a desired density within a known period of time for Kodak No-Screen x-ray film.

For the autoradiographic study of solutions that contained carbon-14, Ader[47] immersed in a liquid photographic emulsion a capillary tube that contained the sample; the emulsion was then developed and examined with a microscope. The amount of

radioactivity was determined by the number and length of the tracks. Broda[48] also discusses this technique, which he calls a "capillary" method, and notes that it was developed for carbon-14 by others.[49] Broda states that the fraction of beta particles detected is determined by calibration, but is always quite high, and that the sensitivity of detection of radiocarbon is excellent because the background is very small. The technique is particularly suited to the determination of small amounts of carbon-14 in small samples.

A quick and convenient liquid-emulsion technique is described by Joftes,[50] which has high resolution for use with carbon-14 and tritium. It also has the advantage of ease of processing large numbers of autoradiograms.

13-4 QUANTITATION OF AUTO-RADIOGRAMS OF CARBON-14

According to Stevens and Spracklen,[22] it is believed that quantitative autoradiography should not only prove to be a useful alternative to the employment of a counter, but in some cases should prove to be advantageous. Their article provides much information applicable in the quantitation of autoradiograms of carbon-14. Some of this information has been extracted and is presented here. In a tracer experiment the least amount of radioactive material used should be the smallest that permits adequate precision in the method of measurement. On the other hand, use of an excessive amount of radioactive material must be avoided to prevent too great a density or too large an exposed area in the photographic emulsion. Measurement of autoradiographs producing a density of 0.6 above fog gives precision of magnitude similar to that obtainable by a counter with a total of 1000 counts and negligible background. Films of high sensitivity to beta particles, such as high-speed No-Screen x-ray film, should be used. Under these conditions, a deviation not greater than a few percent is ensured. An experiment with sulfur-35 and iodine-131 showed that 1-in.-diameter samples, which gave 1000 counts/min with a conventional end-window Geiger-Müller counter, required a three-day exposure to produce a density 0.6 above fog on x-ray film. On this basis more than 4000 min of autoradiographic exposure is needed to give the same effectiveness as 1 min with an end-window counter. A greater quantity of radioactive material is not necessarily required for the autoradiographic method than for the counting method, because certain factors favor the autoradiographic method, namely, reduction of the area of the sample, increase of exposure time, and refinement of the method of assessment. Although placing the emulsion and sample very close together increases rate of blackening, special attention to uniformity of sample is required. Density produced on development of the emulsions should be kept within a definite range, for example, 0.3 to 1.2 above fog. Quantitative comparisons having different orders of precision can be made. Samples can be sorted in ascending order of activity. Semiquantitative results can be achieved by visual comparison against exposures made with sources of known strength with a standard deviation of 3 to 5%; use of a densitometer instead of the eye makes possible a standard deviation as small as 1%. The lower densities of emulsions exposed to beta rays are directly proportional to the exposure. For samples having very low activity, a densitometer permits accurate measurements; also, the number of developed grains per unit area of film can be counted, a technique used in high-resolution autoradiography.

For quantitative autoradiography, calibrated sources are useful. Stevens and Spracklen[22] suggest three ways of obtaining them: use of available samples whose activity has been determined in previous experiments; preparing sources on planchets by mixing portions from two solutions, one of a labeled and one of an inert compound, or from two solutions, each of a labeled compound but one compound having twice the specific radioactivity of the other; and preparing samples by the "toning" of silver in processed photographic emulsions, that is, depositing within the gelatin layer another atomic species in stoichiometric proportion to the amount of silver present, for example, radioactive carbon can be deposited in the form of silver ferrocyanide. The preparation of radioactive standards with step-type concentration of tracer is described in a EURATOM report;[51] carbon-14 is one of the four tracers for which the standards are prepared. The report gives a method of preparing radioactive standard films having uniform known thickness; photographic gelatin is the support for the tracer. A method is also given for the preparation of radioactive films having constant concentration and increasing thickness ("wedges"); these films are for use in determining the effect of thickness variation on the autoradiographic image blackening.

Quantitative autoradiography is the general subject of a group of papers presented at the Conference on Radiography sponsored by the American Cancer Society and the National Cancer Institute; these papers are published in *Laboratory Investigation*.[52–56] The quantitative technique of track or grain counting is discussed in three[52,53,56] of these papers. The technique is used when high-resolution autoradiography is required, as is especially the case in autoradiographic studies of biological cells. The technique requires an optical or electron microscope; with it, there is the possibility that resolution of the order of 0.1 μ is obtainable. A special optical system and direct-recording microscope for quantitative autoradiography of this type is described by Gullberg.[57] The automatic quantitation of microautoradiographs is discussed by Tolles[54] and by Pelc.[56] The basic matrix theory of quantitative histological autoradiography is presented by Odeblad.[55]

Some studies have been made toward increasing the reliability of the quantitation of autoradiographs. Herz[58] studied ways of processing stripping emulsions to minimize latent image fading during storage and to increase their sensitivity to electrons. Also, Matitsch[59] made experiments to determine methods of defogging beta-sensitive emulsions without sacrificing the beta sensitivity.

13-5 SOURCES OF ERROR

Attention should be given to the fact that the sources of error in autoradiography with carbon-14 are numerous. It is well to process with each sample autoradiographed a control sample that contains no carbon-14.

The sample itself is the source of errors resulting from

1 chemical fogging; for example, by volatile substances, chemical reducing agents, or luminescing materials

2 contaminant radioactivity from radionuclides other than carbon-14

The emulsion to be used may have become fogged if the cardboard used to pack it contained carbon-14.

During the exposure of the emulsion to the sample, errors may arise from the following sources, as well as directly from the sample:

1 pressure on the film, or bending or scratching it, all of which produce pseudophotographic effects

2 background fog from carbon-14 that was present in the cowhide used to make the gelatin from which the emulsion was prepared

3 background fog from the carbon-14 in the atmosphere and from other extraneous radiation

4 self-absorption

5 "cross-fire," that is, the film in contact with one sample is affected by the radiation from a neighboring sample[60]

6 light fogging of the emulsion

7 fingerprints

8 slippage or shrinkage of the sample and emulsion with respect to each other

9 leaching of carbon-14

10 exposures of too long duration

11 contamination from previously used autoradiographic equipment

In the development of the emulsion and thereafter, errors may be introduced from the following sources:

1 nonoptimum development time

2 photochemicals

3 nonuniform response of the emulsion to beta radiation

4 latent image fading

Other errors are mentioned in discussions of particular techniques of autoradiography, for example, if staining techniques are used in conjunction with autoradiography, silver grains can be removed by the staining.

Sources of error are enumerated by Boyd[61] and by Overman and Clark.[62]

13-6 ELECTRON MICROSCOPIC AUTORADIOGRAPHY

The technique of using electron microscopy together with grain or track counting to achieve high resolution has already been mentioned. Liquier-Milward[63] demonstrated that the technique was successful for the 0.3-Mev particles from cobalt-60 and suggested that it "is likely to be of great value in the case of the soft radiation of carbon-14, as the grains of the tracks are close enough to allow a very high magnification"—and it has indeed become so. Ross[64] reviews some of the factors that relate to the theory and application of autoradiography when used with either light or electron microscopy. In each case, the specimen and the photographic emulsion permanently attached to it are viewed as a unit in the microscope. Ullberg[65] discusses in some detail electron microscopic autoradiography, which he designates EMAR;

his discussion includes historic development, application of emulsion to the sample, exposure and photographic processing, resolution, sensitivity, and limitations. The discussions by both Ross and Ullberg are useful in acquiring an understanding of this new and promising method; they are supplemented with numerous references that include uses of carbon-14 in the method. Ross mentions the newer emulsions suitable for electron microscopic autoradiography, some of grain size from 0.03 to 0.05 μ with which there is the possibility of achieving a resolution of 0.1 μ. The technique, particularly useful in biological research, is being developed in the direction of the study of single grains of silver halide.

13-7 AUTORADIOGRAPHY COUPLED WITH CHROMATOGRAPHY

Autoradiography has been used fairly extensively in conjunction with chromatography, especially thin-layer and paper-partition chromatography, as a means of assaying chromatograms. Some of the many examples of the use of these coupled techniques are mentioned below. Thin-layer and paper-partition chromatography complement gas-liquid chromatography in that with each of the former it is possible to detect polymeric nonvolatile impurities that would normally be held up in the gas-liquid chromatograph. Conversely, volatile materials that are easily detected in gas-liquid chromatography could be readily lost by volatilization in thin-layer or paper-partition chromatography.

13-7a THIN-LAYER CHROMATOGRAPHY

The application of autoradiography of thin-layer chromatograms has been described by Kratzl[66] in a comprehensive review on the biogenesis of lignins.

The coupled techniques are useful as a means of checking the purity of carbon-14 compounds. The purity of synthetically produced cholesteryl oleate-^{14}C was proved in this way by Mahadevan and Lundberg.[67] Cholesteryl linolenate and cholesteryl arachidonate, each labeled with carbon-14 on position 4 (available from the European Atomic Energy Community), were checked for purity by autoradiography of the thin-layer chromatograms on silica gel.[68] In their study of thin-layer chromatography as a quantitative assay procedure for carbon-14, Snyder and Stephens[69] prepared autoradiograms of the chromatograms of four samples of carboxyl-labeled tripalmitin-^{14}C having different specific activities and demonstrated the usefulness of these coupled techniques in establishing the radiopurity of a compound.

The sensitivity possible for carbon-14 by autoradiography of thin-layer chromatograms is indicated from the work of Fray and Frey[70] and of Richardson and co-workers.[71] By placing a highly sensitive photographic film in direct contact with the thin-layer chromatogram for one hour, Fray and Frey detected as little as 0.01 to 0.05 μc of carbon-14 per square centimeter of chromatogram. With longer exposure the sensitivity increased, for example, after a 268-hr exposure, the detection limit was about 3×10^{-4} μc/cm^2. Richardson and associates reported that chromatography on a 250-μ layer of silica gel G and 9-day contact with Eastman Kodak Company's Royal Blue x-ray film detects 4×10^{-4} μc of carbon-14 in 0.5 cm^2; on a 1-day exposure, detection of 7.2×10^{-3} μc/cm^2 (5×10^6 accumulated counts/min/cm^2) can be expected.

In studies of lipid radiochemistry, Mangold, Kammereck, and Malins[72] prepared autoradiograms of thin-layer chromatograms of carbon-14-labeled lipids by exposing the chromatographic plates in the dark to Eastman No-Screen medical x-ray safety film for one week. The films were developed with Supermix developer[73] for 4 to 6 min and were fixed for 30 min with acid fixer. They caution that the glass plates used in autoradiography of chromatoplates should be carefully cleaned to avoid the appearance of "shadows" produced by residual material from earlier chromatograms of radioactive substances. They recommend prolonged application of chromic sulfuric acid solution as the most efficient method of cleaning plates. They also warn that contamination of the laboratory and darkroom with radioactive powdered silica must be strictly avoided.

Schwane and Nakon[74] describe a technique for removing thin-layer chromatograms of radioactive water-soluble substances from the chromatoplate for subsequent autoradiography and scanning. The technique is reported to be satisfactory when silica gel or kieselguhr is the adsorbent. A film of polystyrene is deposited from solution onto the chromatogram. The dried film is stripped off together with the adsorbent by means of a razor blade. The carbon-14 activity is radioassayed from the smooth side of the film to avoid differences in activity due to variations in polystyrene film thickness. Schwane and Nakon point out that the removed film can be sectioned and counted in a simple gas flow counter, whereas the chromatoplate must be assayed by an end-window type counter unless specialized equipment is available.

Certain techniques developed primarily for autoradiography of tritium-containing thin-layer chromatograms are also useful for chromatograms that contain carbon-14. Sheppard and Tsien[75] exposed thin-layer chromatograms that contained tritium-labeled substances to photographic plates prepared carefully with Kodak type NTB nuclear-track emulsion, which is widely used for autoradiography of tissue sections. They found that as little as 0.01 μc of tritium was detectable in a compact spot. Luthi and Waser[76] describe "thin layer fluorography" of tritium-labeled compounds, which consists in the inclusion of a scintillator (anthracene) in the adsorbent (silica gel) when the chromatoplate is prepared. The beta radiation from the tritium causes the anthracene to fluoresce, and the tritium-induced fluorescence produces

what Luthi and Waser prefer to call a "fluorograph" rather than an autoradiograph. It should be possible to use the techniques described by Sheppard and Tsien and by Luthi and Waser to increase the sensitivity of detection of carbon-14 on thin-layer chromatograms.

13-7b PAPER-PARTITION CHROMATOGRAPHY

One of the most satisfactory ways to locate a carbon-14 compound on a paper chromatogram is by autoradiography. It is this purely qualitative use to which autoradiography is most frequently put in conjunction with paper-partition chromatography. Autoradiography is particularly useful for locating spots on two-dimensional paper chromatograms. Catch[77] suggests that coarse autoradiography of a paper chromatogram is very simple and that an activity of 10^{-5} μc/cm^2 as an 'infinitely thin' film will give a perceptible image on a fast x-ray film in 24 hours. Innumerable applications have been made of this qualitative technique. Some carbon-14 compounds that have thus been located and identified are indicated in Table 12-3.

Paper-partition chromatography is followed by autoradiography as a means to check the radiochemical purity of carbon-14 compounds in preparative work.[78]

Autoradiographic resolution of the doubly labeled compounds adenosine diphosphate-^{32}P and adenosine-8-^{14}C diphosphate on a paper chromatogram was demonstrated by Kempner and Miller.[39]

Although scintillation autoradiography of tritium-labeled compounds on paper chromatograms is described,[79-82] the technique does not appear to have been used for carbon-14 compounds. With tritium, a scintillator is necessary, because the beta particles may not have sufficient energy to reach the photographic emulsion, whereas no scintillator is needed with carbon-14, because the beta particles from carbon-14 have a maximum energy ten times that of the tritium beta particles. The technique might be used to increase the sensitivity of detection of carbon-14, but detection does not depend on the use of it.

13-8 AUTORADIOGRAPHIC ELECTROPHORESIS

The unique method of thin-layer autoradiographic electrophoresis of carbon-14 and tritium compounds in buffered photographic gelatin is reported by Lambiotte.[83] X-ray film itself is used as the supporting medium for the electrophoretic separation, during which period the radioactive ions have no time to leave any track as they move in the photographic emulsion unless the specific activities of the compounds are very high. Glutamic-^{14}C acid, histidine-^{14}C, and valine-^{3}H were separated on Kodirex x-ray film that had been immersed in a buffer solution of pH 5.25 or 7.25 and then blotted dry; 20 to 30 v/cm was applied for 60 min. Glucose-^{14}C was used to show that the nonelectrophoretic migration due to electro-osmosis and evaporation was negligible under these conditions. The separations were sharp, and the diffusion was weak. As little as 0.001 μc of tritium-labeled compounds was detected in a 6-day exposure; the sensitivity for carbon-14 compounds is not stated.

13-9 APPLICATIONS OF CARBON-14 AUTORADIOGRAPHY IN OTHER DISCIPLINES

Thus far, this discussion of autoradiography of carbon-14 compounds has been devoted almost entirely to its use in organic chemistry. The technique has been of value in other disciplines as well, particularly biochemistry. Some of its uses in other fields are mentioned briefly below. A comprehensive review of these is beyond the scope of this book; the references cited are only those encountered at random in the course of the preparation of this book.

Excellent source references exist on the applications of autoradiography in biology[4,22a,81,85,86] and in medicine.[4,22a] These contain a large number of references to studies done with carbon-14.

Numerous studies of cell biochemistry are reported. The technical aspects of the application of autoradiography in the study of nucleic acid metabolism are discussed by Lajtha and Oliver[87] in reference to the use of phosphorus-32, carbon-14, and tritium as labels for nucleic acid metabolites; the advantages of thymidine-^{14}C over thymidine-^{3}H are enumerated. Boyd and co-workers[88] prepared autoradiographs of carbon-14 incorporated in individual blood cells. As an experimental tool in pharmacological research, whole animals have been autoradiographed; the fate of iproniazid-^{14}C in a mouse 2 and 24 minutes after injection was determined in this way by Nair and Roth.[89] Autoradiography of adenine-8-^{14}C was used by Pelc[90] to study the effect of x rays on the metabolism of cell nuclei of nondividing tissues and by Sirlin and Edwards[91] to study mouse sperm. Adenine-8-^{14}C was also used by Rabinovitz and Plaut[92] in cytochemical and autoradiographic observations of nuclear ribonucleic acid in amoeba proteins. By double-labeling with thymidine-^{14}C and thymidine-^{3}H, Pilgrim and Maurer[93] made an autoradiographic study of the constancy of the DNA-doubling duration in types of mouse and rat cells.

Studies of amino acids by labeling with carbon-14 and autoradiography are not unusual; the work of McFarlane[94] is an example.

Some other biochemical applications of the autoradiography of carbon-14 compounds are illustrated by the work of Vaněk and associates[95] on the biosynthesis of erythromysin, that of Keglević-Brovet and co-workers[96] on the metabolism of serotonin in vivo, and that of Waser and Luthi[97] on the fixation of curarizing and depolarizing drugs on mouse end plates.

The technique of counting under a microscope was used by Perumova and Pakulina[98] to measure the beta-track traces left in a 30-μ thick photoemulsion by carbon-14 in biological specimens.

The role of carbon dioxide in photosynthesis makes autoradiography with carbon-14 a natural technique for extensive use in botany. One of the earliest applications of the technique was that by Fink and Fink,[99] who identified the various amino acids and sugars in the green alga *chlorella*. The use of carbon-14 autoradiography in photosynthesis is discussed extensively by Calvin.[100]

The usefulness of the method in studying the uptake and distribution of compound by living plants and the possible reactions that occur in the plants is illustrated by the work of Bowden and Marion[101] with tryptophan-β-^{14}C, of Hoffmann and Latzko[102] with cyanamide-^{14}C, and of Greenshields[103] with uniformly labeled sucrose-^{14}C.

CITED REFERENCES

1 R. A. Faires and B. H. Parks, "Radioisotope Laboratory Techniques," 2d ed., p. 207, George Newnes Ltd., London, 1960.

2 Anon., "Services in Research," 'Autoradiography,' Isotopes Incorporated, 123 Woodland Ave., Westwood, N.J.

3 G. A. Boyd, "Autoradiography in Biology and Medicine," Academic Press, New York, 1955.

4 H. Yagoda, "Radioactive Measurements with Nuclear Emulsions," John Wiley & Sons, Inc., New York, 1949.

5 G. E. Francis, W. Mulligan, and A. Wormall, "Isotopic Tracers," 2d ed., chap. 10, The Athlone Press, University of London, 1959.

6 R. A. Faires and B. H. Parks, "Radioisotope Laboratory Techniques," 2d ed., chap. 19, George Newnes Ltd., London, 1960.

7 C. H. Wang and D. L. Willis, "Radiotracer Methodology in Biological Science," chap. 7, Prentice-Hall, Inc., Englewood Cliffs, N.J., 1964.

8 L. J. Roth, Ed., "Isotopes in Experimental Pharmacology," Part III 'Autoradiography,' The University of Chicago Press, Chicago, Ill., 1965.

9 S. Aronoff, "Techniques of Radiobiochemistry," chap. 3, sec. 3.2, The Iowa State College Press, Ames, Iowa, 1956.

10 M. D. Kamen, "Isotopic Tracers in Biology," 3d ed., chap. III, sec. H, Academic Press, Inc., New York, 1957.

11 E. Broda, "Radioactive Isotopes in Biochemistry," chap. VIII, sec. 11, Elsevier Publishing Company, New York, 1960.

12 R. T. Overman and H. M. Clark, "Radioisotope Techniques," chap. 2, sec. 2.4, McGraw-Hill Book Company, Inc., New York, 1960.

13 I. Smith, "Chromatographic and Electrophoretic Techniques," vol. I, chaps. 25 and 26, William Heinemann, Medical Books Ltd., London, 1960.

14 H. Piraux, "Radioisotopes and Their Industrial Applications," chap. 12, sec. 12.2, Charles C. Thomas, Springfield, Ill., 1964.

15 D. H. Axelrod, *Advan. Biol. Med. Phys.*, **2**, 131 (1951).

16 R. H. Herz, *Nucleonics*, **9**(3), 24 (1951).

17 A. Beiser, *Rev. Mod. Phys.*, **24**, 273 (1952).

18 P. J. Fitzgerald, *Lab. Invest.*, **2**, 181 (1953).

19 Y. Goldschmidt-Clermont, *Ann. Rev. Nucl. Sci.*, **3**, 141 (1953).

20 W. P. Norris and L. A. Woodruff, *Ann. Rev. Nucl. Sci.*, **5**, 297 (1955).

21 Papers presented at the "Conference on Autoradiography," sponsored by the American Cancer Society and the National Cancer Institute; published in *Lab. Invest.*, **8**, 59–330 (1959).

22 G. W. W. Stevens and D. Spracklen, "International Atomic Energy Agency Conference on the Use of Radioisotopes in the Physical Sciences and Industry, Copenhagen, 1960," vol. 2, p. 211, International Atomic Energy Agency, Vienna, Austria, 1962.

22a "Autoradiography, A Literature Search," PAEC(A)IN-645 (Dec. 1964), Phillipine Atomic Energy Commission, Manila, P.I.

23 G. A. Boyd, "Autoradiography in Biology and Medicine," p. 364, Academic Press, New York, 1955.

24 J. Cobb and A. K. Solomon, *Rev. Sci. Instr.*, **19**, 441 (1948).

25 H. Yagoda, "Radioactive Measurements with Nuclear Emulsions," Table 25, p. 221, John Wiley & Sons, Inc., New York, 1949.

26 R. T. Overman and H. M. Clark, "Radioisotope Techniques," pp. 76–81, McGraw-Hill Book Company, Inc., New York, 1960.

27 I. Smith, Ed., "Chromatographic and Electrophoretic Techniques," vol. I, 'Chromatography,' pp. 532–533, William Heinemann, Medical Books, Ltd., London, 1960.

28 I. Smith notes that the technique was suggested by Dr. H. B. Levine of the Naval Biological Laboratory, Department of Bacteriology, University of California, Berkeley 4, Calif.

28a For example, "Kodak Materials for Nuclear Physics and Autoradiography," Kodak Pamphlet No. P-64, Eastman Kodak Company, Rochester, N.Y., 14650.

29 G. A. Boyd, "Autoradiography in Biology and Medicine," p. 49, Academic Press Inc., New York, 1955.

30 P. J. Fitzgerald, E. Simmel, J. Weinstein, and C. Martin, *Lab. Invest.*, **2**, 181 (1953).

31 S. Kikuchi and Y. Oishi, *Résumés des Communications*, **1**, 17 (1957) (International Congress of Pure and Applied Chemistry, 16th, Paris).

32 R. K. Poddar, *Radiation Res.*, **11**, 498 (1959).

33 H. Yagoda, "Radioactive Measurements with Nuclear Emulsions," pp. 223–224, John Wiley & Sons, Inc., New York, 1949.

34 R. A. Faires and B. H. Parks, "Radiation Laboratory Techniques," 2d ed., p. 209, George Newnes Limited, London, 1960.

35 C. H. Wang and D. L. Willis, "Radiotracer Methodology in Biological Science," p. 145, Prentice-Hall, Inc., Englewood Cliffs, N.J., 1965.

36 S. Aronoff, "Technique of Radiobiochemistry," p. 40, The Iowa State College Press, Ames, Iowa, 1956.

37 G. W. W. Stevens, *Nature*, **161**, 432 (1948).

38 R. A. Faires and B. H. Parks, "Radiation Laboratory Techniques," 2d ed., p. 210, George Newnes Limited, London, 1960.

39 E. S. Kempner and J. H. Miller, *Science*, **135**, 1063 (1962).

40 W. G. Duncombe, *Intern. J. Appl. Radiation Isotopes*, **10**, 212 (1961).

41 M. D. Kamen, "Isotopic Tracers in Biology," 3d ed., p. 103, Academic Press, Inc., New York, 1957.

42 H. Piraux, "Radioisotopes and Their Industrial Applications," p. 245, Charles C. Thomas, Springfield, Ill., 1964.

43 R. A. Faires and B. H. Parks, "Radioisotope Laboratory Techniques," 2d ed., pp. 210–211, George Newnes Limited, London, 1960.

44 C. H. Wang and D. L. Willis, "Radiotracer Methodology in Biological Science," pp. 148–150, Prentice-Hall, Inc., Englewood Cliffs, N.J., 1964.

45 I. Smith, Ed., "Chromatographic and Electrophoretic Techniques," p. 492, William Heinemann, Medical Books, Limited, London, 1960.

46 S. Aronoff, "Techniques of Radiobiochemistry," p. 41, The Iowa State College Press, Ames, Iowa, 1956.

47 M. Ader, *J. Phys. Radium*, **13**, 110 (1952); *Chem. Abstr.*, **46**, 5986e (1952).

48 E. Broda, "Radioactive Isotopes in Biochemistry," pp. 85–86, Elsevier Publishing Company, New York, 1960.

49 M. Reinharz and G. Vanderhaeghe, *Nuovo Cimento*, **12**, 243 (1954); see also H. Levi and A. S. Hogben, *Kgl. Danske Videnskab. Selskab Mat. Fys. Medd.*, **30**(9), (1955).

50 D. L. Joftes, *Lab. Invest.*, **8**(1), 131 (1959).

51 L. Matteoli, P. Logi, and S. Salamanna, "Quantitative Autoradiography. Part I: Preparation of the Radioactive Standards with Step-type Concentration of Tracer" (translated title), EUR 1883.i, Istituto di Ricerche Breda S.p.A., Milan, Italy, 1964.

52 H. Levi and A. Nielsen, *Lab. Invest.*, **8**(1), 82 (1959).

53 J. E. Gullberg, *Lab. Invest.*, **8**(1), 94 (1959).

54 W. E. Tolles, *Lab. Invest.*, **8**(1), 99 (1959).

55 E. Odeblad, *Lab. Invest.*, **8**(1), 113 (1959).

56 S. R. Pelc, *Lab. Invest.*, **8**(1), 127 (1959).

57 J. E. Gullberg, *Exp. Cell. Res. Suppl.*, **4**, 222 (1957).

58 R. H. Herz, *Lab. Invest.*, **8**(1), 71 (1959).

59 T. Matitsch, *Öster. Akad. Wiess., Math.-naturw. Kl., Sitzber Abt. II*, **164**(5–7), 169 (1955); *Chem. Abstr.*, **49**, 5174f (1955).

60 G. W. W. Stevens and D. Spracklen, "International Atomic Energy Agency Conference on the Use of Radioisotopes in the Physical Sciences and Industry, Copenhagen, 1960," vol. 2, pp. 216–217, International Atomic Energy Agency, Vienna, Austria, 1962.

61 G. A. Boyd, "Autoradiography in Biology and Medicine," pp. 137–163, Academic Press, New York, 1955.

62 R. T. Overman and H. M. Clark, "Radioisotope Techniques," pp. 80–81, McGraw-Hill Book Company, Inc., New York, 1960.

63 J. Liquier-Milward, *Nature*, **177**(4509), 619 (1956).

64 R. Ross, *Atomlight*, no. 46, July, 1965.

65 S. Ullberg, 'Electron Microscopic Autoradiography (EMAR),' in L. J. Roth, Ed., "Isotopes in Experimental Pharmacology," chap. 12, The University of Chicago Press, Chicago, Ill., 1965.

66 K. Kratzl, *Holz Roh- Werkstoff*, **19**, 219 (1961).

67 V. Mahadevan and W. O. Lundberg, *J. Lipid Res.*, **3**, 106 (1962).

68 Anon., "Marked Molecules," Euratom Scientific and Technical Information, Brussels, April 15, 1964, MN 3/64.

69 F. Snyder and N. Stephens, *Anal. Biochem.*, **4**, 128 (1962).

70 G. Fray and J. Frey, *Bull. Soc. Chim. Biol.*, **45**(11), 1201 (1963).

71 G. S. Richardson, I. Weliky, W. Batchelder, M. Griffith, and L. L. Engel, *J. Chromatog.*, **12**(1), 115 (1963).

72 H. K. Mangold, R. Kammereck, and D. C. Malins in N. D. Cheronis, Ed., "Microchemical Techniques," pp. 697–714, Interscience Publishers, Inc., New York, 1962.

73 General Electric X-Ray Department, Milwaukee, Wisconsin.

74 R. A. Schwane and R. S. Nakon, *Anal. Chem.*, **37**, 315 (1965).

75 H. Sheppard and W. H. Tsien, *Anal. Chem.*, **35**, 1992 (1963).

76 U. Luthi and P. G. Waser, *Atomlight*, no. 50, January 1966.

77 J. R. Catch, "Carbon-14 Compounds," p. 102, Butterworths, Washington, D.C., 1961.

78 See, for example, the Research Radiochemical Product Data sheets published by Volk Radiochemical Company, Chicago, Ill.

79 A. T. Wilson, *Nature*, **182**, 524 (1958).

80 A. T. Wilson, *Biochim. Biophys. Acta*, **40**, 522 (1960).

81 A. W. Rogers, *Nature*, **184**, 721 (1959).

82 E. V. Parups, I. Hoffman, and H. R. Jackson, *Talanta*, **5**, 75 (1960).

83 M. Lambiotte, *Atomlight*, no. 45, p. 10, May, 1965.

84 M. E. Johnston, "A Bibliography of Biological Applications of Autoradiography, 1954 through 1957," U.S. Atomic Energy Commission Report UCRL-8400 (July, 1958).

85 M. E. Johnston, "A Bibliography of Applications of Autoradiography, 1958 through 1959," U.S. Atomic Energy Commission Report UCRL-8901 (August, 1959).

86 M. E. Johnston, "A Bibliography of Biological Applications of Autoradiography 1 July 1959 to 1 January 1961. Reviews and Lectures No. 117," U.S. Atomic Energy Commission Report NP-10597 (July 28, 1961); Naval Radiological Defense Laboratory, San Francisco, Calif.

87 L. G. Lajtha and R. Oliver, *Lab. Invest.*, **8**, 214 (1959).

88 G. A. Boyd, G. W. Casarett, K. I. Altman, T. R. Noonan, and K. Solomon, *Science*, **108**, 529 (1948).

89 V. Nair and L. J. Roth, *Atomlight*, no. 18, p. 7, May, 1961.

90 S. R. Pelc, *Nature*, **178**, 359 (1956).

91 J. L. Sirlin and R. G. Edwards, *Exptl. Cell Res.*, **9**, 596 (1955).

92 M. Rabinovitz and W. Plaut, *Exptl. Cell Res.*, **10**, 120 (1956).

93 C. Pilgrim and W. Maurer, *Naturwissenschaften*, **49**, 544 (1962); also available as Argonne National Laboratory Translation No. 31.

94 A. S. McFarlane, *Proc. Intern. Conf. Peaceful Uses At. Energy, 2nd, Geneva, 1958*, **25**(2), 100 (1958).

95 Z. Vaněk, J. Majer, A. Babický, J. Liebster, and K. Vereš, *Proc. Intern. Conf. Peaceful Uses At. Energy, 2nd, Geneva, 1958*, **25**(2), 143 (1958).

96 D. Keglević-Brovet, Z. Supek, S. Kveder, S. Iskrić, and S. K. Kečkeš, *Proc. Intern. Conf. Peaceful Uses At. Energy, 2nd, Geneva, 1958*, **25**(2), 125 (1958).

97 P. G. Waser and U. Luthi, *Nature*, **178**, 981 (1956).

98 N. D. Perumova and L. E. Pakulina, *Dokl. Akad. Nauk SSSR*, **152**(2), 461 (1963).

99 R. M. Fink and K. Fink, *Science*, **107**, 253 (1948).

100 M. Calvin, "Photosynthesis," U.S. Atomic Energy Commission Report UCRL-8278 (June, 1958).

101 K. Bowden and L. Marion, *Can. J. Chem.*, **29**, 1043 (1951).

102 E. Hoffmann and E. Latzko, *Z. Pflanzenernaehr. Dueng. Bodenk.*, **66**, 222 (1954); *Chem. Abstr.*, **48**, 13826d (1954).

103 R. N. Greenshields, *Nature*, **189**, 851 (1961).

CHAPTER
14
MASS SPECTROMETRY; CARBON-13, A SUPPLEMENTARY ISOTOPE TO CARBON-14

14-1 INTRODUCTION

Mass spectrometry has rarely been used to measure carbon-14, except in the determination of its half-life (see Chap. 1) and to measure simultaneously the isotope effects of both carbon-13 and carbon-14 and thereby to evaluate the ratio of the two isotope effects (see Sec. 5-6b).

Before carbon-14 became available, compounds enriched in carbon-13 were applied in chemical and biochemical studies that involved isotope-dilution analysis[1] (Chap. 2), location of carbon atoms (Chap. 3), etc. Carbon-14 is now preferred for these applications, because radioassay of carbon-14 compounds is simpler and less expensive (see Chap. 11) than is mass spectrometry of carbon-13 compounds. However, some specialized applications require carbon-13, and carbon-14 cannot be substituted in these cases. Mass spectrometry has long been used for carbon-13 measurement.

Carbon-13 is present to the extent of about 1.1 % in natural carbon (see Table 1-1); the exact percent varies somewhat with the source of the natural carbon. Carbon-13 can be enriched by chemical exchange reactions that involve either cyanide[2] or carbon dioxide.[3] Compounds labeled with carbon-13 at concentrations of 60 atom percent or more can now be purchased from chemical supply houses.

Carbon-13 has several properties that are advantageous compared with those of carbon-14. Since carbon-13 is a stable isotope, no hazard exists in its use in high concentrations. Furthermore, the cost in high concentrations is sufficiently low to permit practical experiments with compounds enriched to more than 50% in carbon-13. Such highly enriched compounds can be used in experiments with doubly labeled molecules. The percent of doubly labeled molecules is usually insignificantly small when carbon-14 is used at the tracer level but is much higher in all studies with carbon-13 (see Secs. 3-4c and 8-2). An example of the use of doubly labeled molecules is described in Sec. 14-3c.

14-2 SPECTROMETRY OF CARBON-13

14-2a MASS SPECTROMETRY

When a high-molecular-weight organic compound of carbon-13 is to be analyzed by mass spectrometry, the compound is usually degraded to a simpler gaseous compound of carbon, which is inserted in a mass spectrometer for determination of the $^{13}C/^{12}C$ ratio. Most often the simpler carbon compound is carbon dioxide. However, it is sometimes possible to place the original compound directly in the spectrometer.[4,5] In either case an isotope-ratio mass spectrometer is the instrument preferred for the measurement of carbon-13, although simpler instruments have been used with less accurate results. The principles of the isotope-ratio mass spectrometer and also of other instruments used for carbon-13 determination are well known[6,7] and will not be discussed here. Use of precision mass spectrometry to study carbon-13 isotope effects is discussed in Chap. 5; publications of Yankwich and co-workers, referred to from Table 5-5, contain information about precision mass spectrometry of low-molecular-weight carbon-13 compounds.

Carbon-13 isotope fractionation may occur when a carbon-13 compound is degraded for introduction into a mass spectrometer. The consequences of kinetic isotope effects that accompany degradations have already been discussed in relation to carbon-14 tracer studies (see Sec. 10-2c). If carbon-13 isotope fractionation occurs during the degradation, the carbon-13 concentration observed mass spectrometrically is normally lower than the true concentration of carbon-13 in the compound being assayed. In most cases the magnitude of the error is difficult to assess. One advantage of mass spectrometry of the undegraded compound[4,5] is that such isotope fractionation is avoided; un-

fortunately, under these conditions other difficulties are often encountered.[4,5]

14-2b INFRARED SPECTROPHOTOMETRY

For a few organic compounds, including $^{13}CO_2$, infrared spectra[8] can be used to determine the $^{13}C/^{12}C$ ratio. Generally, however, this method is far less accurate than is mass spectrometry.

14-2c NUCLEAR MAGNETIC RESONANCE SPECTROMETRY

In principle carbon-13, like hydrogen, oxygen-17, and other nuclides with odd mass numbers, can be determined by nuclear magnetic resonance (n.m.r.) spectrometry. Although its sensitivity for the measurement of carbon-13 is less than might be desired, this method has the great advantage that, in some tracer studies, it can bypass the need for degrading labeled compounds. The study of the rearrangement that occurs during the photochlorination of methyl-^{13}C-cyclopropane is an interesting example[9]

$$\triangleright\!\!-^{13}CH_3 \xrightarrow[h\nu]{\text{chlorination}} \triangleright\!\!-^{13}CH_2Cl$$
$$+ \,^{13}CH_2{=}CH{-}CH_2{-}CH_2Cl$$
$$+ \text{ products chlorinated in the ring}$$

The carbon-13-labeled products shown were determined in the product mixture, and other possible ^{13}C-position isomers were excluded. The n.m.r. spectra were taken at 60 Mc; tetramethylsilane was the *external reference*.

Spin-spin coupling of carbon-13 nuclei, present at the natural-abundance level, with the protons bonded to them can be measured by high-resolution n.m.r. spectrometry.[10] The coupling constant (125–250 cps) can be related to the amount of s character of carbon-hydrogen bonds. The variations in the degree of hybridization of carbon-hydrogen bonds are of special interest in determining the acidic character of protons on the bridgehead carbon atoms in strained polycyclic compounds.[11]

The possibility that the chemical shift of hydrogen in $-^{14}CH_2-$ might differ measurably from that in $-^{12}CH_2-$ has been investigated in a limited way.[12] 4-Methylbenzyl alcohol (85 atom % ^{14}C in the methylene carbon) in either carbon tetrachloride or benzene solution shows a single symmetrical hydrogen resonance for the benzyl hydrogens. The study of such secondary isotope effects may be more successful for other nuclei such as oxygen-17 and nitrogen-15 for which the chemical shifts are about 100 times greater than they are for protons.

14-3 SPECIAL USES FOR CARBON-13

Carbon-13 is used as a supplementary isotope to carbon-14. However, in certain studies it is not possible to use carbon-14 instead of carbon-13.

14-3a ISOTOPE-EFFECT STUDIES

Carbon-13 isotope-effect studies are discussed and are documented in Chap. 5; the advantages and disadvantages of carbon-13 in this application are discussed in Sec. 5-2c. In some applications to the investigation of reaction mechanisms, isotope-effect studies made with either carbon-13 or carbon-14 can serve the purpose. Usually, however, isotope-effect studies with these two isotopes are supplementary, and both are essential.

14-3b STUDIES OF REACTIONS IN THE MASS SPECTROMETER

There has been wide interest in "extra-analytical" studies with the mass spectrometer, that is, studies in which the mass spectrometer is used in a way other than simply as an analytical tool or as a means of determining isotope concentration. In such studies various types of mass spectrometers— usually not isotope-ratio spectrometers—are

used for fundamental physical and chemical research.[13,14] Information has been obtained about ionization potentials, ion-molecule reactions, reaction kinetics and mechanisms, radiation chemistry, and the like. In research of this type stable isotopes, which include carbon-13, deuterium, and nitrogen-15, are immensely helpful in the identification of mass spectrometric peaks of unknown origin.

A single example of the application of carbon-13 in a fundamental mass spectrometric investigation will suffice. A peak corresponding to a negative ion of mass 26 was observed when formic acid and nitrogen were introduced simultaneously into a modified magnetic-deflection type mass spectrometer.[15] When formic acid alone was introduced into the spectrometer, the negative-ion peak at mass 26 was not detected. Substitution of deuterated formic acid and nitrogen for formic acid and nitrogen caused no shift of the peak to a position of mass higher than 26. Instead, the peak corresponding to a negative ion of mass 26 remained in the same position; therefore, the negative ion of mass 26 did not contain hydrogen. When, in the formic acid–nitrogen system, nitrogen-15 was substituted for nitrogen or formic-^{13}C acid was substituted for formic acid, the peak at mass 26 shifted to mass 27. This shift indicated that the unknown peak was produced by a negative ion that contained both carbon and nitrogen. It was concluded that the negative ion of mass 26 must be the cyanide ion (CN^-).

14-3c DOUBLE LABELING

To confirm that the negative ion of mass 26 (see Sec. 14-3b) was CN^-, a simple experiment that involved double labeling was performed. Nitrogen-15 was substituted for nitrogen, and formic-^{13}C acid was substituted for formic acid in the same experiment. A shift of the peak from mass 26 to mass 28 resulted. This shift left no doubt that the negative ion of mass 26 was CN^-.

There are plausible arguments[15] that CN^- is formed in the mass spectrometer by a negative ion-molecule reaction, which can be written

$$HCOO^- + N_2 \rightarrow CN^- + \text{other products}$$

No other products were identified.

The usefulness of double labeling is by no means limited to fundamental studies performed *in* a mass spectrometer. However, when other types of double labeling are done, a mass spectrometer is usually needed to measure isotope concentrations. An example of the study of an isotope-exchange reaction by double labeling is described in Sec. 4-3c.

CITED REFERENCES

[1] R. N. Boos, S. L. Jones, and N. R. Turner, *Anal. Chem.*, **28**, 390 (1956).

[2] H. C. Urey and L. J. Greiff, *J. Am. Chem. Soc.*, **57**, 321 (1935).

[3] C. A. Hutchinson, D. W. Stewart, and H. C. Urey, *J. Chem. Phys.*, **8**, 532 (1940).

[4] K. Biemann, "Mass Spectrometry," chap. 5, McGraw-Hill Book Company, Inc., New York, 1962.

[5] F. W. McLafferty, Ed., "Mass Spectrometry of Organic Ions," Academic Press, New York, 1963.

[6] C. R. McKinney, J. M. McCrea, S. Epstein, H. A. Allen, and H. C. Urey, *Rev. Sci. Instr.*, **21**, 724 (1950).

[7] K. Biemann, "Mass Spectrometry," chap. 1, McGraw-Hill Book Company, Inc., New York, 1962.

[8] J. M. Milatz, J. C. Kluyver, and J. Hardebol, *J. Chem. Phys.*, **19**, 887 (1951).

[9] E. Renk, P. R. Shafer, W. H. Graham, R. H. Mazur, and J. D. Roberts, *J. Am. Chem. Soc.*, **83**, 1987 (1961).

[10] N. Muller and D. E. Pritchard, *J. Chem. Phys.*, **31**, 768 (1959).

[11] D. Seebach, *Angew. Chem. Intern. Ed. Engl.*, **4**(2), 121 (1965).

[12] V. F. Raaen and B. M. Benjamin, unpublished work.

[13] F. H. Field and J. L. Franklin, "Electron Impact Phenomena and the Properties of Gaseous Ions," Academic Press, Inc., New York, 1957.

[14] S. C. Lind, "Radiation Chemistry of Gases," chap. 12, Reinhold Publishing Corp., New York, 1961.

[15] C. E. Melton and G. A. Ropp, *J. Am. Chem. Soc.*, **80**, 5573 (1958).

PART

FOUR

USE OF CARBON-14
IN THE STUDY
OF ORGANIC
REACTIONS

CHAPTER
15
MODEL
EXPERIMENTS

15-1 INTRODUCTION

Numerous examples of applications of carbon-14 are discussed in earlier chapters of this book. To assist the reader in designing his own experiments, four additional examples are discussed in detail in this chapter. These examples were selected, because they are of general interest and have instructional value. Since they illustrate the use of principles explained in Part II, they are numbered to correspond to the numbering of the principles there. Thus, the principle described in Chap. 3 is illustrated in this chapter by model Exp. 15-3.

In all cases, standard laboratory equipment was used in these model experiments. Neither the equipment nor the laboratory procedures require detailed description in this chapter. All the detailed information needed for handling carbon-14 effectively and safely is given in Part III.

15-2 ISOTOPE-DILUTION ANALYSIS: DETERMINATION OF AMOUNTS OF MINOR BY-PRODUCTS FORMED IN THE NITRATION OF TOLUENE

The work of Roberts and associates[1,2,3] provides several interesting examples that demonstrate the carrier-addition method of carbon-14 isotope-dilution analysis (Sec. 2-3). These workers studied the yields of by-products formed during nitration of toluene. They logically chose carrier addition (that is, dilution with unlabeled species) instead of normal isotope addition (Sec. 2-2) to minimize the number of syntheses of labeled compounds and to gain the advantage of the weight added as carrier in isolating, purifying, and derivatizing labeled products. The individual studies performed were determinations of the yields of: (1) *m*-nitrotoluene produced during mononitration of toluene by mixed acids at four different temperatures,[1] (2) 3,4-dinitrotoluene produced during nitration of *p*-nitrotoluene with mixed acids at 65 to 75° with two different ratios of nitric acid to *p*-nitrotoluene,[2] and (3) 2,3-dinitro-toluene produced during nitration of *o*-nitrotoluene[3] under conditions similar to those used in Study 2. For convenience and brevity, these studies are designated (1), (2), and (3). Measurement of the yields of these minor by-products is greatly simplified by isotope-dilution analysis but is difficult by other analytical methods.

15-2a OUTLINE OF PROCEDURES

(*Study 1*) At each of four temperatures (0°, 30°, 45°, and 60°) toluene-1-^{14}C was nitrated with slightly less than the stoichiometric amount of nitric acid to minimize dinitration. The reaction was quenched, and labeled mononitrotoluenes were separated as a mixture from the other components by steam distillation. The percent of *m*-nitrotoluene in this mixture was measured by isotope dilution. An ~3-g sample of the mixture was weighed accurately and was diluted with about 8 g of inactive *m*-nitrotoluene, also weighed accurately. The diluted sample was carefully distilled. The *m*-nitrotoluene fraction was oxidized by chromic acid to *m*-nitrobenzoic acid. To prevent possible errors due to contamination by other isomers, the *m*-nitrobenzoic acid was recrystallized repeatedly until the melting point was sharp (141.2°) and the measured molar radioactivity was constant. Radioassays were performed by wet combustion and ionization-chamber measurement (Sec. 11-5). The percent *m*-nitrotoluene in the mixture of mononitrotoluenes was calculated by use of a modification of Eq. 2-4, that is,

$$m\text{-nitrotoluene, }\% = \frac{100D}{W[(S_0/S) - 1]} \qquad (15\text{-}1)$$

In Eq. 15-1, W is the weight of mixed mononitrotoluenes, and D is the weight of *m*-nitrotoluene added as carrier. In this application S_0 is the molar radioactivity of toluene-1-^{14}C, and S is that of *m*-nitrobenzoic-1-^{14}C acid. The radioactivities must be expressed on a molar basis, because these

compounds have different molecular weights (Sec. 9-2).

An independent tracer experiment was performed to determine the possibility of error in S caused by contamination of *m*-nitrobenzoic-1-^{14}C acid with *p*-nitrobenzoic-1-^{14}C acid and/or *o*-nitrobenzoic-1-^{14}C acid of higher radioactivities (Sec. 10-2). A synthetic mixture that contained *m*-nitrotoluene, *o*-nitrotoluene, and *p*-nitrotoluene-1-^{14}C was distilled by use of the same fractionating column as before. The *m*-nitrotoluene fraction was oxidized, as before, to *m*-nitrobenzoic acid, which was radioassayed and was found to be inactive. This test (Sec. 2-6f) proved that the method of separation used produced *m*-nitrobenzoic acid that was not contaminated with *p*-nitrobenzoic acid. A parallel experiment with *o*-nitrotoluene-1-^{14}C demonstrated that the method of separation produced *m*-nitrobenzoic acid that was not contaminated with *o*-nitrobenzoic acid

(*Study 2*) Mixed acid was used to nitrate *p*-nitrotoluene-1-^{14}C at 65 to 75° under two conditions: (*a*) by use (done in duplicate) of an amount of nitric acid 10% in excess of the theoretical amount required to form dinitrotoluene, and (*b*) by use of an amount of nitric acid 14.8% less than this theoretical amount. In the first of the duplicate experiments, the nitration product was recrystallized from ethyl alcohol–Skellysolve B under conditions such that the dinitrotoluene isomers were not separated. The yield (based on nitric acid) of mixed dinitrotoluenes was 87%. In the second of the duplicate experiments, methanol–water instead of ethyl alcohol–Skellysolve B was used for the preliminary purification, and the yield of mixed dinitrotoluenes was 96%. In experiment *b*, steam distillation instead of recrystallization was used for the preliminary purification; the yield (based on nitric acid) of mixed dinitrotoluenes was 91%.

In all three experiments an accurately weighed 2- to 3-g sample of the labeled dinitrotoluene product mixture was diluted with about two-thirds its weight of unlabeled 3,4-dinitrotoluene, also weighed accurately. The isotope-dilution analysis for 3,4-dinitrotoluene in each of the mixtures of labeled dinitrotoluenes involved reduction (Fe, HCl) of the nitro groups and precipitation of the phenazine derivative of 3,4-diaminotoluene from alcoholic acetic acid

$^{14}CH_3$ $\xrightarrow{\text{reduction}}$ $^{14}CH_3$ ... NO_2, NO_2 → NH_2, NH_2

$^{14}CH_3$ ... o-phenanthrenequinone   (15-2)

The 2,4-diaminotoluene cannot form a phenazine and remains in solution. In each experiment, the 7-methyl-^{14}C-1,2;3,4-dibenzophenazine was recrystallized from benzene acetone. Radioassays (Sec. 11-5) were performed as in Study 1. Unfortunately, the small amounts of the derivative produced in the duplicate experiments precluded recrystallization to constant radioactivity. The calculated percent 3,4-dinitrotoluene in the mixture of dinitrotoluenes was therefore reported as an upper limit; this percent was calculated by an equation analogous to Eq. 15-1.

(*Study 3*) In this study three mixed-acid nitrations of o-nitrotoluene-1-^{14}C at 65 to 77° were performed as follows: (*a*) with the theoretical amount of nitric acid for dinitration, (*b*) with 10% excess nitric acid, and (*c*) with 5% less than the theoretical amount of nitric acid and slightly greater dilution (an attempt to duplicate plant-scale conditions).

In experiments *a* and *b* preliminary purification of the mixture of labeled dinitrotoluenes (before addition of 2,3-dinitrotoluene carrier) was accomplished by reprecipitation from warm ethyl alcohol on addition of cold dilute sulfuric acid. In experiment *c* preliminary purification by recrystallization from methanol was necessary to remove unreacted labeled o-nitrotoluene from the mixture of labeled dinitrotoluene before 2,3-dinitrotoluene carrier was added to the latter. The phenazine derivative of labeled 2,3-dinitrotoluene formed in higher yields than did that of the labeled 3,4-dinitrotoluene described in Study 2. As a result, it was possible to recrystallize the labeled derivative 6-methyl-^{14}C-1,2;3,4-dibenzophenazine to constant radioactivity. Table 15-3 (given below) includes three interesting series of values that show the changes in the millimolar radioactivity effected by several successive recrystallizations. Because recrystallization of the derivative to constant radioactivity was achieved, it was possible to report with confidence the percent 2,3-dinitrotoluene in the mixture of dinitrotoluenes. The results of Study 3 are not to be taken merely as upper limits.

Radioassays (Sec. 11-5) were performed as in Studies 1 and 2. Samples of 50-mg size were burned for greater accuracy. The percent 2,3-dinitrotoluene in the mixture of dinitrotoluenes was calculated by use of an equation analogous to Eq. 15-1.

15-2b RESULTS

Data and results are listed in Tables 15-1, 15-2, and 15-3. Table 15-1 gives samples of data and results obtained[1] for nitrations at 0 and 30°; details of parallel experiments at 45 and 60° are given in the original publication.[1]

15-2c COMMENTS

Studies 1, 2, and 3 were planned carefully and executed skillfully. The design of the

Table 15-1 Data and results of studies of yields of m-nitrotoluene-1-^{14}C formed during mononitration of toluene-1-^{14}C

Temperature, °C	0	30
Total reaction time (including time for mixing), min	180	35
Total yield of mixed mononitrotoluenes, %	100	92
Labeled mixed mono-nitrotoluenes diluted, g	2.97	3.11
m-Nitrotoluene carrier added, g	11.08	8.09
Radioactivity, μc/mmole:		
toluene-1-^{14}C used	3.14	2.74
m-nitrobenzoic-1-^{14}C acid	0.0174	0.0357
maximum deviation	±0.0008	±0.0030
m-Nitrotoluene in mixed mononitrotoluenes, %	2.1	3.4
m-Nitrotoluene by infrared spectrophotometry, %	—	3.45

experiments was adequate for the problems at hand. Some details, however, require further comment:

I. RADIOASSAYS

A. METHOD Wet combustion followed by ionization-chamber assay of the carbon-14 dioxide (Sec. 11-5) was suitable for these studies. However, other assay techniques (Chap. 11) could have been used; the choice was probably determined by the equipment available.

B. LEVEL OF RADIOACTIVITY The materials nitrated were labeled at the tracer level (~3 to 6 μc/mmole). The molar radioactivities of the derivatives of the labeled products were necessarily two or more orders of magnitude lower. At this lower level of radioactivity, precise radioassays are much more difficult to obtain than at the tracer level even though larger-than-usual (50-mg) samples are burned. The reported precision of assaying product derivatives was poor in some of the studies (Table 15-1).

Table 15-2 Data and results of studies of yields of 3,4-dinitrotoluene-1-^{14}C formed during nitration of p-nitrotoluene-1-^{14}C at 65 to 75°

Experiment	a	a[a]	b
$\dfrac{\text{Moles of nitric acid (in mixed acid)}}{\text{Moles of p-nitrotoluene-1-}^{14}\text{C}}$	1.1	1.1	0.852
Total reaction time (including time for mixing), min	20.3	20.3	20.3
Total yield of mixed dinitro-toluenes, %	87	96	91 (based on nitric acid)
Labeled mixed dinitrotoluenes diluted, g	2.728	2.541	3.028
3,4-Dinitrotoluene carrier added, g	1.821	1.696	2.010
Radioactivity, μc/mmole:			
p-nitrotoluene-1-^{14}C used	5.50	5.50	5.50
phenazine	0.0035	0.0033	—
3,4-Dinitrotoluene in mixed dinitrotoluenes (upper limit), %	0.04	0.04	0.2

[a] Duplicate.

Table 15-3   Data and results of studies of yields of 2,3-dinitrotoluene-1-^{14}C formed during nitration of o-nitrotoluene-1-^{14}C at 65 to 77°

Experiment	a	b	c
Moles of nitric acid (in mixed acid) / Moles of o-nitrotoluene-1-[14]C	1.0	1.1	0.946
Total reaction time (including time for mixing), min	22	22	22
Total yield of mixed dinitro-toluenes, %	93	94	48
Labeled mixed dinitrotoluenes diluted, g	2.202	2.515	1.268
2,3-Dinitrotoluene carrier added, g	2.024	2.299	1.160
Radioactivity, μc/mmole (average value for two or more assays):			
o-nitrotoluene-1-^{14}C used	4.90	4.90	4.90
phenazine, 1 recrystn.	0.0210	—	—
2 recrystn.	0.0184	0.0207	0.0140
3 recrystn.	0.0182	0.0187	0.0124
4 recrystn.	0.0182	0.0184	0.0123
2,3-Dinitrotoluene in mixed dinitrotoluenes, %	0.34	0.35	0.23

It is worthwhile to estimate the added cost of increasing the radioactivity level tenfold in Study 1 to make possible greater precision of assays of diluted samples. If 55 mmoles of toluene-1-^{14}C having a radioactivity of 30 μc/mmole were used in each of four experiments, a total of 6.6 mc of toluene-1-^{14}C would be required. It should be possible to synthesize this labeled toluene, at 40% overall yield, from 16.5 mc of $Ba^{14}CO_3$ costing about $120 (Table 1-2). The additional labor cost resulting from the synthesis instead of purchase of labeled toluene would no doubt be cancelled by the time saved later in obtaining precise radioassays. After the probable cost of purchasing 16.5 mc of toluene-1-^{14}C is deducted from $120, the cost of increasing the level of carbon-14 radioactivity tenfold could not be greater than $50 to $100 for Study 1. This amount would be a small price for the increased precision of radioassays of the product derivatives that would be possible at the higher level of radioactivity. If the experiments were performed with reasonable care in an efficient hood, the equipment and techniques for nitrations and product separations could also be used safely at the 30-μc/mmole level without change.

With a tenfold increase in radioactivity, the use of larger ratios of carrier to compound diluted would also be possible. The practical advantage of working with a greater weight of product derivative would be realized, particularly in Study 2. In that study the paucity of the phenazine derivative permitted the calculation of the percent 3,4-dinitro-toluene as an upper limit only.

C. COMPOUNDS ASSAYED   In Study 1 toluene-1-^{14}C, a liquid, was radioassayed by wet combustion. Confirmation by infrared spectrophotometry (Table 15-1) of the result obtained in the experiment at 30° indicates that the measured molar radioactivity of the toluene-1-^{14}C was correct. Nevertheless, wet combustion of volatile labeled compounds should be avoided because of the possibility of loss of part of the sample by distillation before oxidation is complete (Sec. 11-5d). When wet combustion of a volatile labeled compound cannot be avoided, the oxidizing solution that contains the sample should be allowed to stand for some time at room temperature to permit the oxidation to proceed as far as it will in the cold. The solution should then be warmed slowly so that the oxidation will be completed at the lowest possible temperature.

The use in Study 1 of toluene-1-^{14}C as a form for radioassaying can be criticized on other grounds also. The percent m-nitrotoluene is calculated (Eq. 15-1) as a function of a ratio of molar radioactives, S_0/S. For several reasons, this ratio should be more accurate when S_0 and S are measured by assaying two samples of the same compound than when they are measured by assaying samples of two different compounds. Some assay errors, such as those due to incomplete combustion, can logically be expected to cancel in a ratio obtained by assaying two samples of the same compound. Therefore, it would have been better to use m-nitrobenzoic-1-^{14}C acid as the assaying form for determining S_0 as well as S. A sample of m-nitrobenzoic-1-^{14}C acid suitable for use in the determination of S_0 could be prepared without great difficulty. Toluene-1-^{14}C could be oxidized to benzoic-1-^{14}C acid, which could be nitrated with fuming nitric acid to m-nitrobenzoic-1-^{14}C acid that contains about 20% of the ortho and para isomers. Small amounts of ortho and para isomers remaining after purification of the m-nitrobenzoic-1-^{14}C acid would not alter the measured value of S_0.

Similarly, in Studies 2 and 3 it would have been better to determine S_0 as well as S by assay of the phenazine derivatives of 3,4-dinitrotoluene-1-^{14}C and 2,3-dinitrotoluene-1-^{14}C respectively. This technique would probably be impractical, because it would require too much additional preparative work.

II. POSSIBLE USE OF NORMAL ISO-TOPE-ADDITION METHOD

Although consideration is given (see Part IB) to the merits of increasing tenfold the level of carbon-14 radioactivity used in Study 1, the alternative possibility of using normal isotope addition (Sec. 2-2) should not be overlooked. As previously stated, the principal advantages of the carrier-addition method are that fewer syntheses of labeled compounds are required and that the extra weight added as carrier greatly facilitates the isolation of pure labeled products, or their derivatives, for isotopic assay. For Studies 1, 2, and 3 these two advantages are of such importance that normal isotope addition can hardly be considered practical. On the other hand, normal isotope addition would have distinct advantages if the necessary carbon-14-labeled compounds (m-nitrotoluene-1-^{14}C, 3,4-dinitrotoluene-1-^{14}C, and 2,3-dinitrotoluene-1-^{14}C) could be synthesized and if these products (or their derivatives) could be isolated from the reaction mixtures without the help of added carrier.

To illustrate the applicability of normal isotope addition, the data from Study 3c (Table 15-3) were revised; the revised data are presented in Table 15-4 to show how they might have appeared for a normal isotope-addition analysis. A modification of Eq. 2-2 was used

$$2,3\text{-Dinitrotoluene, }\% = \frac{100a}{W}\left(\frac{S_0}{S} - 1\right) \quad (15\text{-}3)$$

In Eq. 15-3, W is the weight of the sample of mixed dinitrotoluenes analyzed, a is the weight of 2,3-dinitrotoluene-1-^{14}C used for "spiking" the dinitrotoluene mixture, S_0 is the molar radioactivity of the 2,3-dinitrotoluene-1-^{14}C, and S is the molar radioactivity of the phenazine derivative of 2,3-dinitrotoluene-1-^{14}C. The convenient slang expression,

Table 15-4 Hypothetical use of normal isotope addition to determine the yield of 2,3-dinitrotoluene formed during nitration of o-nitrotoluene (under plant process conditions)

Experiment	3c (Revised)
$\dfrac{\text{Moles of nitric acid (in mixed acid)}}{\text{Moles of } o\text{-nitrotoluene}}$	0.946
Total reaction time (including mixing time), min	22
Total yield of mixed dinitrotoluenes, %	48
Mixed unlabeled dinitrotoluenes "spiked," g	200
2,3-Dinitrotoluene-1-^{14}C used for "spiking," g	1.00
Total radioactivity required, μc	16.4
Radioactivity, μc/mmole:	
2,3-dinitrotoluene-1-^{14}C used	3.00
phenazine recovered	2.05
2,3-Dinitrotoluene in mixed dinitrotoluenes, %	0.23

"spiked," is sometimes used to indicate the addition of a relatively small amount of a labeled compound to a mixture of unlabeled compounds that is being analyzed by the normal isotope-addition method.

The 200-g sample of mixed dinitrotoluenes referred to in Table 15-4 would have been recovered after nitration of o-nitrotoluene with the aid of steam distillation, just as previously described for experiment 3c.

From Table 15-4 it is apparent that the normal isotope-addition method requires relatively little carbon-14 radioactivity by comparison with the carrier-addition method when a minor by-product is being determined. Even more important is the fact that both the 2,3-dinitrotoluene-1-^{14}C and the labeled phenazine have sufficiently high millimolar radioactivities to permit each to be radioassayed with optimum accuracy. Further-

more, the labeled phenazine derivative cannot be contaminated by labeled impurities in the case of normal isotope dilution. In the carrier-addition method, by contrast, it is possible that traces of impurities with molar radioactivities many times that of the phenazine might contaminate the phenazine. An isotopic test to prove the absence of such high-specific-activity contaminants was necessary in connection with Study 1. Errors in measured specific activities due to traces of impurities of high specific activity present after isotope dilution were discussed earlier (Sec. 10-2a).

Finally, if normal isotope addition were used in Experiment 3c, the nitration could be performed on as large a scale as desired, because no carbon-14 would be present. Samples from commercial-scale nitrations could be analyzed by this method. In some studies of plant processes that are difficult to duplicate reliably in the laboratory, the use of the normal isotope-addition method to analyze samples is very helpful. Normal isotope addition would as a rule be more practical in determining major products of reactions rather than minor by-products, because the former are easier to isolate without the aid of carrier.

III. MAXIMUM ERROR EXPECTED IN STUDY 1 FROM AN ISOTOPE EFFECT

In Study 1 a slight error in the results could be caused by a carbon-14 isotope effect during derivatization by chromic acid oxidation of m-nitrotoluene (Eq. 15-4)

$$^{14}CH_3 \xrightarrow[80\% \text{ yield}]{3 \text{ O}} {}^{14}CO_2H + H_2O \quad (15\text{-}4)$$

An isotope effect may occur when a derivative is formed by a nonquantitative reaction at the labeled atom (Sec. 9-5).

As seen below, the maximum predicted error due the isotope effect is not appreciable in Study 1. However, in some yield determinations by isotope-dilution analysis, the error introduced by the isotope effect in a low-yield derivatization could be as large as 8% of the reported yield and could justify use of a correction factor.

In Reaction 15-4, the rate-determining step would probably be cleavage of one of the carbon-14-to-hydrogen bonds. Accordingly, the expected maximum value[4] of the carbon-14 isotope effect would probably not exceed 3% (i.e., $k_{12}/k_{14} \leq 1.03$). For $k_{12}/k_{14} = 1.03$ (or $k_{14}/k_{12} = 0.97$), Fig. 5-3 indicates that the derivative formed by 80% conversion would have a molar radioactivity about 1.2% less than the molar radioactivity of its precursor. This error is not large enough to justify a correction in the small percentages of m-nitrotoluene (2.1 and 3.4%) reported in Table 15-1.

IV. OBJECTION TO SEPARATIONS PRIOR TO CARRIER ADDITION Any mixture that is about to be analyzed obviously should not be subjected to a process that might cause fractionation of the components before the mixture is sampled. For the same reason, preliminary purification prior to the addition of carrier as was practiced consistently in Studies 1, 2, and 3 is, in general, objectionable. There is, however, no cause to believe that the results reported in Tables 15-1, 15-2, and 15-3 were affected by unwanted fractionation. The confirmation of the isotope-dilution results by infrared spectrophotometry (Table 15-1) allays any suspicion regarding the results of Study 1. A second argument[2] was given, namely, that in Study 2 fractionation did not affect the results. For Studies 2 and 3, results show that the percentages of minor by-products are very small; therefore, the overall conclusions reached would not be altered even if some fractionation were known to have occurred.

An alternative procedure could have been used to eliminate any doubts, however slight, that might remain about the possibility of errors due to fractionation in any particular experiment. The entire reaction mixture, after the reaction was quenched, could have been extracted continuously to obtain a homogeneous solution of all the organic components in a water-immiscible solvent. An aliquot of the solution could then have been analyzed for the minor by-product of interest (2,3-dinitrotoluene in the case of Study 3) by the carrier-addition method of isotope dilution. Another aliquot could have been evaporated and the components separated by methods described in Study 3 for determining percent total dinitrotoluenes. From the two results so obtained, the percent 2,3-dinitrotoluene in the mixture of dinitrotoluenes could have been computed.

15-3 LOCATION OF CARBON ATOMS: THE MECHANISM OF AMINATION OF HALOBENZENES

Roberts and co-workers[5,6,7] considered the nature of the amination of halobenzenes by sodium amide or potassium amide in liquid ammonia

$$R\text{—}\underset{}{\bigcirc}\!\!-\!\!X \xrightarrow{\ NH_2^-\ } R\text{—}\underset{}{\bigcirc}\!\!-\!\!NH_2 + X^- \quad (15\text{-}5)$$

and of the reaction of halobenzenes with lithium diethylamide in ether at room temperature

$$R\text{—}\underset{}{\bigcirc}\!\!-\!\!X \xrightarrow{\ N(C_2H_5)_2^-\ } R\text{—}\underset{}{\bigcirc}\!\!-\!\!N(C_2H_5)_2 + X^-$$

$$(15\text{-}6)$$

They concluded that these reactions might proceed *via* a "benzyne" intermediate. In the absence of the substituent R, the "benzyne" would be a symmetrical intermediate

A straightforward test with carbon-14 (Sec. 3-4b) could therefore be applied. In the absence of carbon-14 isotope effects, iodobenzene-1-^{14}C could yield equal amounts of aniline-1-^{14}C and aniline-2-^{14}C if the amination proceeded by 1,2-hydrogen halide elimination followed by addition of ammonia to the "triple bond" of the postulated "benzyne" intermediate (see equation below). This use of carbon-14 to *test for a symmetrical intermediate* was successfully applied; the methods and results are discussed in the sections below. For the results of this test to be conclusive, it was necessary to establish that all the carbon-14 in the labeled iodobenzene used was actually in the 1-position and that neither iodobenzene-1-^{14}C nor aniline-1-^{14}C rearranged to the respective 2-^{14}C compound under the reaction conditions. A workable scheme for degrading aniline had to be selected (Chap. 10) so that the distribution of carbon-14 among the carbon atoms of aniline could be determined after the amination reaction. The solution of these rather formidable problems with minimum experimentation left only one or two questions unanswered; they involve side issues and do not affect the validity of the overall conclusions.

15-3a OUTLINE OF PROCEDURES

I. SYNTHESIS OF IODOBENZENE-1-^{14}C
Labeled iodobenzene was prepared from commercial aniline-1-^{14}C by the Sandmeyer reaction. After the reaction, the iodobenzene-1-^{14}C was diluted with about 50% of its weight of unlabeled iodobenzene. The diluted product was purified by steam distillation and was fractionated by distillation through a short Vigreux column. The yield of distilled iodobenzene-1-^{14}C, exclusive of the weight of iodobenzene added as carrier, was about 75%.

II. AMINATION OF IODOBENZENE-1-^{14}C
Iodobenzene-1-^{14}C (110 mmoles) was added quickly, with efficient mechanical stirring, to potassium amide (600 mmoles) contained in 350 ml of anhydrous liquid ammonia. A Dry Ice reflux condenser was used. After 8 min, the reaction was quenched with ammonium chloride. Ether (100 ml) was added to displace the ammonia, which was permitted to evaporate as the mixture warmed to room temperature. Water and additional ether were added. The ether layer was extracted with hydrochloric acid. The acid was neutralized, and the solution was made strongly basic with sodium hydroxide. The basic solution was extracted with ether, and the extract was dried over barium oxide and was distilled. The yield of carbon-14-labeled aniline was 42%.

Chlorobenzene-1-^{14}C was aminated in a similar experiment.

III. DEGRADATIONS
A sample of the carbon-14-labeled aniline produced by amination of iodobenzene-1-^{14}C was converted in 80% yield to phenol *via* the diazonium salt, which was decomposed with boiling 10% sulfuric acid. The carbon-14-labeled phenol was hydrogenated at room temperature in

$$\text{(15-7)}$$

$$\text{(15-8)}$$

ethyl alcohol with a platinum catalyst and hydrogen at 3 atm to carbon-14-labeled cyclohexanol in 92% yield. The procedure for the degradation of the carbon-14-labeled cyclohexanol is outlined in Sec. 10-3, Item VI,B. Carbon atom 1 of the carbon-14-labeled aniline was isolated as carbon-14 dioxide, which was collected and radioassayed in the form of barium carbonate-^{14}C. Essentially all the rest of the carbon-14 was found in carbon atoms 2 and 6, which were assayed together as the dibenzamide of 1,5-diaminopentane-1-^{14}C. The total molar radioactivity of the 6-membered ring of the carbon-14-labeled aniline degraded was measured by radioassaying the 2,4-dinitrophenylhydrazone or semicarbazone of carbon-14-labeled cyclohexanone.

Labeled aniline formed by amination of chlorobenzene-1-^{14}C was also degraded. In addition, a sample of the aniline-1-^{14}C used to synthesize iodobenzene-1-^{14}C was degraded in the same manner as the carbon-14-labeled aniline produced by amination of the iodobenzene-1-^{14}C and chlorobenzene-1-^{14}C. The object was to prove the reliability of the methods used to degrade aniline and also to confirm that, within the limit of experimental error, the aniline-1-^{14}C used to synthesize iodobenzene-1-^{14}C was labeled in the 1-position only. The data (see Tables 15-5 and 15-6 presented below) show no cause to doubt either the reliability of the methods of degradation or the specificity of the aniline-1-^{14}C labeling. Because of contamination by atmospheric carbon dioxide, the specific radioactivity of the barium carbonate-^{14}C unfortunately is about 3% lower than would be expected (see Sec. 11-5).

During the reactions that occurred preliminary to the degradation of the labeled aniline recovered after the amination of iodobenzene-1-^{14}C, labeled cyclohexanol was diluted with about 0.6 part of unlabeled cyclohexanol. This dilution caused no problem, since it was made *before* the benzene ring was degraded. Isotope dilution during the degradation obviously would not be permissible unless the dilution ratio were known exactly and a correction factor could thus be applied to the measured specific activity of the degradation product.

Still another dilution with carrier was made at the glutaric acid stage. This dilution was not objectionable because the diluted labeled glutaric acid was treated, not as a degradation product, but rather as a starting material for a new degradation to carbon dioxide and 1,3-diaminopropane (see Table 15-6).

IV. RADIOASSAYS   Radioassays were done by wet combustion and ionization-chamber counting of the resulting carbon-14 dioxide (Sec. 11-5). Just as in the case of Exp. 15-2, other techniques of sample preparation and of carbon-14 counting could have been used as well. Liquid-scintillation counting, for example, could have adequately served the purpose. Solid counting of either barium carbonate-^{14}C or labeled organic compounds would probably not have given sufficient accuracy.

The handling of barium carbonate-^{14}C appears to have caused some difficulty, as can be seen by examining Table 15-5. However, the confidence intervals reported in Tables 15-5 and 15-6 are not broad. They indicate that there was no trouble in assaying compounds with sufficient accuracy for the purpose at hand. Assay errors did not limit the reliability of the main conclusions reached.

15-3b   RESULTS

Tables 15-5 and 15-6 summarize the results of radioisotopic assays of the degradation-product derivatives and of the derivatives of the cyclohexanone from which they were formed. For each radioactivity analysis summarized in Table 15-5, the top number is the specific radioactivity (μc/mmole); the lower number in parentheses is the percent of the total (cyclohexanone) specific radioactivity (which the degradation product makes up).

Table 15-5   Radioisotopic assays (averages) for products of degradation of carbon-14-labeled aniline

Labeled aniline sample degraded	Cyclohexanone derivative assayed	Assay of cyclohexanone derivative	Assay of barium carbonate [C₁]	1,5-Diamino-pentane derivative assayed	Assay of 1,5-diamino-pentane derivative [C₂, C₆]
Starting material for synthesis of iodo-benzene-1-^{14}C	2,4-Dinitro-phenylhydrazone	0.2502 (100)	0.2420^a (96.7 ± 1)^a	Dibenzene-sulfonamide	0.0004 (0.2 ± 1)
Product of amination of iodobenzene-1-^{14}C	Semicarbazone	0.3804 (100)	0.1764 (46.4 ± 0.1)	Dibenzamide	0.2015 (53.0 ± 0.2)
Product of amination of chlorobenzene-1-^{14}C	2,4-Dinitro-phenylhydrazone and semicarba-zone	0.4247 (100)	0.1831 (43.1 ± 1)^a	Dibenzene-sulfonamide and dibenzamide	0.2201 (51.8 ± 1)

^{a} These values were reported to be low due to contamination with atmospheric carbon dioxide.

The data of Tables 15-5 and 15-6 show that amination of either iodobenzene-1-^{14}C or chlorobenzene-1-^{14}C is accompanied by a redistribution of carbon-14. For either of the labeled halobenzenes, the carbon-14 becomes distributed approximately—but not exactly—equally between the 1-position and the 2-position (or 6-position). After amination of either iodobenzene-1-^{14}C or chlorobenzene-1-^{14}C, the final distribution of carbon-14 is approximately that which would result if the

reactions indicated by Eqs. 15-7 and 15-8 took place. It is also evident that no measurable part of the carbon-14 ends up in positions 3, 4, or 5 when iodobenzene-1-^{14}C is aminated.

15-3c AUXILIARY EXPERIMENTS AND ARGUMENTS

I. SPECIFICITY OF THE IODOBENZENE-1-^{14}C LABELING   Confidence that the iodo-benzene-1-^{14}C used in the amination reaction

Table 15-6   Radioisotopic assays (averages) for products of further degradation of aniline formed by amination of iodobenzene-1-^{14}C

Labeled compound	Cyclohexanone semicarbazone	Glutaric acid (di-p-bromo-phenacyl ester)	2 CO₂ (as BaCO₃)	1,3-Diamino-propane (dibenzamide)
Carbon atoms represented	[All ring C's]	[C₂, C₃, C₄, C₅, C₆]	[C₂, C₆]	[C₃, C₄, C₅]
μc/mmole	0.3804	0.0357	0.0353	0.00004
Radioactivity based on cyclohexanone, %	100	53.0^a	52.4 ± 0.3	0.05 ± 0.3
Radioactivity based on glutaric acid, %	—	—	99	0.1

^{a} Because carrier was added before the labeled glutaric acid was degraded further, this percent had to be taken as equal to that of the dibenzamide of 1,5-diaminopentane reported in Table 15-5.

was labeled only in the 1-position was founded on several facts and arguments. First, the precursor aniline-1-^{14}C was degraded, and essentially all of its carbon-14 was found to be in the 1-position (Table 15-5). Second, the chlorobenzene-1-^{14}C used for amination was shown to contain not more than 7% of chlorobenzene-2-^{14}C; this chlorobenzene-1-^{14}C was aminated to produce aniline that contained about the same distribution of carbon-14 (about 50% in the 1-position and 50% in the 2-position) as the aniline formed by amination of the iodobenzene-1-^{14}C. Third, the possibility that the precursor of the iodobenzene-1-^{14}C (that is, aniline-1-^{14}C) might have rearranged during the Sandmeyer reaction was excluded by a logical argument. Any contaminant iodobenzene-2-^{14}C in the iodobenzene-1-^{14}C would have resulted in the production of at least a small amount of aniline-3-^{14}C on amination according to Eqs. 15-9 and 15-10

$$\text{(15-9)}$$

$$\text{(15-10)}$$

As Table 15-6 indicates, the amination of iodobenzene-1-^{14}C produced only an insignificant amount of aniline-3-^{14}C.

The possibility that the Sandmeyer reaction might have been the only cause of rearrangement of carbon-14 as shown in Eq. 15-11 was barely mentioned. At least one

$$\text{(15-11)}$$

good argument can be presented against this possibility: the iodobenzene-1-^{14}C and the chlorobenzene-1-^{14}C from an independent source gave, on amination, about the same distribution of carbon-14 in the labeled aniline formed.

II. EXCLUSION OF IODOBENZENE-1-^{14}C AND ANILINE-1-^{14}C AS THE REARRANGING ENTITIES IN LIQUID AMMONIA

An argument similar to one given in Part 15-3cI proves both that iodobenzene-1-^{14}C does not rearrange to iodobenzene-2-^{14}C in liquid ammonia prior to the amination and also that aniline-1-^{14}C does not rearrange to aniline-2-^{14}C in liquid ammonia after the amination. If either of these rearrangements occurs, some aniline-3-^{14}C will be produced and presumably a small amount of aniline-4-^{14}C as well. Neither aniline-3-^{14}C nor aniline-4-^{14}C is formed in significant quantity (Table 15-6).

III. DEVIATION FROM THE COMPOSITION 50% ANILINE-1-^{14}C–50% ANILINE-2-^{14}C IN THE AMINATION PRODUCT

The assays reported in Table 15-5 reflect a small but real deviation from the composition 50% aniline-1-^{14}C–50% aniline-2-^{14}C, which would be predicted for the amination product resulting from a symmetrical intermediate like that shown in Eqs. 15-7 and 15-8. The deviation is of similar magnitude and in the same direction for the amination product of iodobenzene-1-^{14}C and the amination product of chlorobenzene-1-^{14}C. The exact magnitude of the deviation is difficult to assess, because several of the barium carbonate-^{14}C assays reported in Table 15-5 were admittedly imperfect as a result of contamination with atmospheric carbon dioxide. The direction of the deviation corresponds to a slightly greater carbon-14 content in the 2-position than in the 1-position. The deviation therefore cannot be attributed to incomplete equilibration of these two positions resulting from some type of kinetically controlled rearrangement.

The authors[6,7] ascribe the deviation to either an *intramolecular* carbon-14 isotope effect (Chap. 5) in the addition of ammonia (or amide ion) to the "benzyne" intermediate (Eq. 15-8) or an *intramolecular* carbon-14 isotope effect in one or more degradation reactions. In the first of these explanations, attack by nitrogen on one carbon atom of the "benzyne triple bond" is assumed to be the rate-controlling step in the addition to the "triple bond"; a *normal intramolecular* carbon-14 isotope effect would then mean that the frequency of formation of aniline-2-^{14}C molecules would be a few percent greater than that of the formation of aniline-1-^{14}C molecules. This explanation is satisfactory in principle, but it is not supported by the results of isotope-effect research; additions to carbon-14-labeled carbon-to-carbon multiple bonds that have been studied exhibit either a very small carbon-14 isotope effect[8,9] or no measurable carbon-14 isotope effect at all.[10]

The second possible explanation offered[6,7] for the deviation from the composition 50% aniline-1-[14]C–50% aniline-2-^{14}C in the amination product is that the deviation may be caused by *intramolecular* carbon-14 isotope effects in degradation reactions. Of the various reactions used to degrade carbon-14-labeled aniline (see Sec. 10-3, Item VIB), only the formation of 6-aminohexanoic acid from cyclohexanone could involve an *intramolecular* carbon-14 isotope effect. It is difficult to understand how an *intramolecular* carbon-14 isotope effect in that step could have caused the deviation. Since none of the steps in the degradation are quantitative, one or more of these steps might have involved an *intermolecular* carbon-14 isotope effect. *Intermolecular* carbon-14 isotope effects as a possible contributing cause of the deviation in question are discussed further in Sec. 15-3e.

IV. DEUTERIUM ISOTOPE EFFECTS The
results of preliminary experiments strongly suggested that the ortho hydrogens play a vital part in the amination of halobenzenes. Bromomesitylene, bromodurene, and 2-bromo-3-methylanisole, which have no hydrogen atoms *ortho* to the bromine atom, are unreactive toward sodium amide in liquid ammonia. This fact is in keeping with the dehydrohalogenation–ammonia addition mechanism indicated in Eqs. 15-7 and 15-8.

The 1,2-elimination of hydrogen halide from a phenyl halide to form "benzyne" (Eq. 15-7) might occur by either a stepwise or a concerted process. Since the strongly basic amide ion can abstract a proton, it is logical to conclude that the hydrogen is removed as a proton and the halogen as halide ion as indicated in Eq. 15-7.

Deuterium kinetic isotope effects were studied for several halobenzenes (x = F, Cl, Br) in their reactions with potassium amide in liquid ammonia and their reactions with lithium diethylamide in ether. Relative rates of reaction of halobenzenes and the corresponding *o*-deuterohalobenzenes were determined. Observed values of k_H/k_D varied from about 1 to 6. It was concluded that for the dehydrohalogenation (Eq. 15-7) the proton (or deuteron) may be removed rapidly and reversibly before the second step, the rate-determining loss of chloride ion, occurs. This stepwise mechanism leads to a measured value of $k_H/k_D = 1$, because the deuterium has been washed out of the organic halide into the solvent before the occurrence of the chloride-ion loss, which determines the rate. At the other extreme, the concerted process leads to a maximum deuterium kinetic isotope effect of about 6. In this case the proton (or deuteron) loss is rate-determining, and the chloride-ion loss follows without delay. Between these two extremes are intermediate cases in which the proton (or deuteron) loss is fast enough relative to the chloride-ion loss to permit partial but not complete washing-out of deuterium prior to the rate-determining step. These intermediate cases lead to the intermediate values of k_H/k_D (between 1 and 6) that were observed.

As would be expected, the deuterium isotope effect observed in the sodium amide–liquid ammonia aminations depended on whether the halogen was fluorine, chlorine, or bromine, since the choice of the halogen should determine the relative rates of the steps in the hydrogen-halide-elimination re-action. In the aminations by lithium diethyl-amide in ether, there is no exchangeable hydrogen in the solvent to wash the deuterium out of the halides; accordingly, all measured values of k_H/k_D approach the maximum value of 6.

Results of the deuterium isotope-effect studies are consistent with the existence of a benzyne intermediate in the amination of halobenzenes.

V. CONSIDERATION OF ALTERNA-TIVES TO THE MECHANISM INVOLV-ING A "BENZYNE" INTERMEDIATE

The nearly 50-50 distribution of carbon-14 between aniline-1-^{14}C and aniline-2-^{14}C in the product proves only that the amination of iodobenzene *could* take place *via a symmetrical intermediate*, "*benzyne*." The feasibility of other mechanisms that either do not involve a symmetrical intermediate or involve a symmetrical intermediate other than "ben-zyne" requires attention.

A. ALTERNATIVE MECHANISMS NOT INVOLV-ING SYMMETRICAL INTERMEDIATES   The nearly 50-50 distribution of carbon-14 between aniline-1-^{14}C and aniline-2-^{14}C in the amina-tion product might, under some circum-stances, be interpreted as the result of a fortuitous combination in a 1:1 ratio of the two displacement mechanisms indicated by Eqs. 15-12 and 15-13

$$\text{C}_6\text{H}_4{}^{14}\text{I} + \text{NH}_2{}^- \rightarrow \text{C}_6\text{H}_4{}^{14}\text{NH}_2 + \text{I}^- \quad (15\text{-}12)$$

$$\text{C}_6\text{H}_4{}^{14}\text{I} + \text{NH}_2{}^- \rightarrow {}^{14}\text{C}_6\text{H}_4\text{NH}_2 + \text{I}^- \quad (15\text{-}13)$$

Equation 15-12 describes a direct displace-ment by attack of amide ion on the number-1 carbon atom; the reaction results in no redistribution of carbon-14 in the aniline produced. Equation 15-13 describes an "ab-normal" displacement involving attack of amide ion on the number-2 carbon, a 2-1

hydride ion shift, and loss of the iodine as iodide ion; the reaction results in aniline in which all the carbon-14 is in the number-2 position.

A sound argument against this chance combination of two mechanisms in 1:1 ratio is based on the fact that aminations of iodobenzene-1-^{14}C and of chlorobenzene-1-^{14}C give essentially the same ratio of aniline-1-^{14}C to aniline-2-^{14}C. It is highly improbable that the percentage contribution from each of two different mechanisms would be the same for amination of chlorobenzene as for the amination of iodobenzene.

Even stronger evidence exists against a combination of a direct displacement and an "abnormal" displacement in 1:1 ratio.[11] The extent of rearrangement of iodobenzene-1-^{14}C-2,4,6-D_3 (i.e., with the *ortho* hydrogen atoms replaced by deuterium) during amina-tion was studied. The percent carbon-14 found in the 1-position and the 2-position of the product amine was 47 and 53%, respectively. These percents are essentially the same as those reported for iodobenzene-1-^{14}C (Table 15-5); they indicate that sub-stitution of deuterium in both *ortho* positions of iodobenzene does not alter the degree of rearrangement during the amination. This result is consistent with the elimination-addition mechanism (with "benzyne" as the intermediate). The *ortho* deuterium is elim-inated in the first step, which forms "ben-zyne"; the deuterium therefore can have no influence on the mode of addition of am-monia to the "triple bond" if any trivial secondary effect of the remaining deuterium is neglected.

This result[11] is, on the other hand, not consistent with a 1:1 combination of a direct-displacement mechanism (Eq. 15-12) and an "abnormal" displacement (Eq. 15-13). The reason is that the "abnormal" displacement would involve a large (primary) deuterium isotope effect, whereas the direct displacement would involve at most only a small (secondary) deuterium isotope effect. The ratio of the contributions made by the two types of displacement would therefore be drastically altered by deuterium in the *ortho* positions.

Another possible rearrangement path involves equilibration of two anions by shift of the position of the halogen atom. Equation 15-14 illustrates this scheme as it might occur on reversible abstraction of a proton during the amination of iodobenzene-1-^{14}C

$$\text{(15-14)}$$

Such a scheme could lead to the formation of aniline-3-^{14}C as well as aniline-1-^{14}C and aniline-2-^{14}C. Since no aniline-3-^{14}C is formed by amination of iodobenzene-1-^{14}C, this mechanism cannot correctly explain the redistribution of carbon-14 during the amination reaction.

B. CONCEIVABLE SYMMETRICAL INTERMEDIATES OTHER THAN "BENZYNE" The symmetrical intermediates

that might conceivably form after addition of ammonia to iodobenzene-1-^{14}C could explain the approximately 50-50 distribution of aniline-1-^{14}C and aniline-2-^{14}C in the amination product. However, the existence of such symmetrical intermediates is considered improbable, because the addition of ammonia is endothermic by about 24 kcal/mole. Also, with such intermediates it would be very difficult to explain either the deuterium isotope effects that were observed in the aminations or the failure of *ortho*-substituted deuterium[11] to alter the degree of rearrangement during amination of iodobenzene-1-^{14}C.

Other symmetrical intermediates are conceivable, but there appear to be valid objections to each.

VI. SUPPLEMENTARY EVIDENCE By-products, such as diphenylamine, formed in the amination of halobenzenes can be accounted for if "benzyne" is assumed to be a reaction intermediate. It is interesting that "benzyne" was postulated as a dienophile in the reaction between furan and *o*-bromofluorobenzene in the presence of lithium amalgam. Presumably, the amalgam removes the bromine and fluorine atoms from the *o*-bromofluorobenzene to form "benzyne," which then undergoes an ordinary Diels-Alder reaction.[12]

It is suggested that "benzyne" has an appreciable half-life. If the ring is assumed to be a regular hexagon, the resonance energy of "benzyne" could be about the same as that of benzene. The amount of angle strain of a triple bond in a six-membered ring is comparable with that in cyclopropene, a known compound.

The elimination-addition mechanism involving "benzyne" can be used to explain qualitatively the orientation of the entering amino group relative to the substituent when various substituted halobenzenes are aminated.[13]

15-3d CONCLUSIONS

The nearly 50-50 distribution of carbon-14 between aniline-1-^{14}C and aniline-2-^{14}C that results when either iodobenzene-1-^{14}C or chlorobenzene-1-^{14}C is aminated proves that the amination can proceed *via* a symmetrical intermediate. Measured deuterium isotope effects and other evidence strongly support the view that the mechanism is one of elimination addition in which "benzyne" is the symmetrical intermediate.

15-3e COMMENTS

For reasons given in Sec. 15-3c, Item III, the magnitude of the deviation from the composition 50% aniline-1-^{14}C–50% aniline-2-^{14}C in the amination product is difficult

$$\text{(structure)} \xrightarrow{\text{conc. H}_2\text{SO}_4} \text{(structure)} \qquad (15\text{-}15)$$

to estimate. The questionable barium carbonate-^{14}C assays (Table 15-5) are particularly disturbing in this connection. It is not possible to state with confidence what is the cause of the deviation.

One reasonable explanation may be that the deviation results from a combination of factors. Three possible factors are (1) errors in the barium carbonate assays (low values), (2) *intermolecular* carbon-14 isotope effects in the derivatization of cyclohexanone (Sec. 9-5), and (3) an *intermolecular* carbon-14 isotope effect in the degradation process which splits cyclohexanone into the degradation products, carbon dioxide and 1,5-diaminopentane. Factor (2) could make the assay of the cyclohexanone appear to be lower than twice the assay of the 1,5-diaminopentane (see Table 15-5); no isotope effect would be expected in the derivatization of the 1,5-diaminopentane, because derivatization does not directly involve the labeled carbon atom. Factors (1) and (3) could make the result of the barium carbonate assay even lower than that of the assay of the cyclohexanone derivative. However, the situation is too complex to permit its exact analysis.

15-4 ISOTOPE EXCHANGE: MECHANISM OF THE REARRANGEMENT OF THE REARRANGEMENT OF α-CINENIC ACID TO GERONIC ACID

In numerous cases carbon-14 isotope-exchange studies (Chap. 4) have provided essential information about chemical reactions. Although isotope-exchange rate measurements (Secs. 4-2, 4-3b) are necessary[14,15,16] in many instances, this is not always so. In some cases, for example, in the study of the rearrangement of α-cinenic acid (Eq. 15-15) by Meinwald and co-workers[17] surprisingly simple experiments yield significant results. In that research[17] a carbon-14 test for reversiblity (Sec. 4-3a) was applied.

15-4a BACKGROUND INFORMATION

The rearrangement of α-cinenic acid, a compound discovered in 1908, was long considered to be extraordinary, because it appeared to involve a highly unusual methyl-group migration. Later it was demonstrated that α-cinenic acid-(2-methyl)-^{14}C rearranges to geronic acid-(7-methyl)-[14]C (Eq. 15-16) as would be expected if the carboxyl group migrated[18] instead of the methyl group. If the methyl group migrated, geronic acid-(2-methyl)-^{14}C would be produced. In a parallel study[19] 6-carboxy-6-ethyl-2,2'-dimethyl-tetrahydropyran was shown to undergo a cinenic acid type rearrangement that could be rationalized only by an apparent carboxyl group migration.

The results of recent work suggested the possibility of a decarbonylation-recarbonylation mechanism for the rearrangement of α-cinenic acid to geronic acid. This would, in effect, be the equivalent of carboxyl-group

$$\text{(structure)} \xrightarrow{\text{conc. H}_2\text{SO}_4} \text{(structure)}$$

$$(15\text{-}16)$$

migration. Koch and Haaf[20] showed that carboxylic acids that are branched at the *alpha* carbon atom can be prepared in good yield by treatment of suitable alcohols or olefins in concentrated sulfuric acid with carbon monoxide formed *in situ* from added formic acid. Stork and Bersohn[21] prepared acids from olefins in sulfuric acid by using carbon monoxide under pressure. These reactions apparently proceed by a carbonylation mechanism[20,21] which is the reverse of that of the long-recognized decarbonylation of acids in concentrated sulfuric acid.[22,23] The olefin used (or formed by dehydration of the alcohol used) is protonated. The resulting carbonium ion adds carbon monoxide (Eq. 15-17) to form a new positive ion. When the sulfuric acid is quenched, this positive ion is converted to a carboxylic acid (Eq. 15-18)

$$\begin{matrix} & & \text{H} & + \\ & \diagup\!\!\!\!-\text{C}\!-\!\text{C}\!-\!\diagdown & & \end{matrix} + \text{CO} \;\rightleftharpoons\; \begin{matrix} & & \text{CO}^+ \\ & \text{H} & | \\ & \diagup\!\!\!\!-\text{C}\!-\!\text{C}\!-\!\diagdown \end{matrix}$$

$$\text{(15-17)}$$

$$\begin{matrix} & \text{CO}^+ \\ & \text{H} & | \\ & \diagup\!\!\!\!-\text{C}\!-\!\text{C}\!-\!\diagdown \end{matrix} + \text{H}_2\text{O} \;\rightarrow\; \begin{matrix} & \text{CO}_2\text{H} \\ & \text{H} & | \\ & \diagup\!\!\!\!-\text{C}\!-\!\text{C}\!-\!\diagdown \end{matrix} + \text{H}^+$$

$$\text{(15-18)}$$

Lundeen[24] found that trialkylacetic acids isomerize in 94.9% sulfuric acid, which causes very little decarbonylation of the trialkylacetic acids. A study with carbon-14 showed that this isomerization occurs at least in part by a decarbonylation-recarbonylation process. The carbonium ion formed on loss of the carboxyl group rearranges to a more stable carbonium ion, which then recovers the carbon monoxide in the recarbonylation step to form the new carboxylic acid.

15-4b EXPERIMENTS

I. PRELIMINARY OBSERVATIONS

The slight foaming observed when α-cinenic acid is dissolved in concentrated sulfuric acid was the first indication of a decarbonylation-recarbonylation mechanism for the rearrangement of α-cinenic acid to geronic acid. Stronger evidence of such a mechanism came from an experiment in which the rearrangement of α-cinenic acid was carried out while carbon monoxide was bubbled through the sulfuric acid medium in a steady stream. Dry carbon monoxide was passed through 20 ml of concentrated sulfuric acid, cooled in an ice bath, until the sulfuric acid was saturated with the gas. Three grams of α-cinenic acid was dissolved in the sulfuric acid solution, and carbon monoxide was bubbled through for 2.5 hr longer. After the red sulfuric acid solution had stood overnight at room temperature, it was poured over 150 g of ice. When the quenching reaction was complete, the aqueous solution was diluted to 200 ml with water. The solution was extracted with five 50-ml portions of diethyl ether. The combined ether extracts were extracted with five 100-ml portions of saturated sodium bicarbonate solution. The combined bicarbonate extracts were acidified, and the acid organic material was extracted with ether. The ether solution was dried over anhydrous magnesium sulfate. On evaporation of the ether, 2.65 g (83% yield) of geronic acid was recovered. This yield is about double that obtained when the rearrangement of α-cinenic acid is carried out without bubbling carbon monoxide through the sulfuric acid solution. The inference is strong that carbon monoxide gas takes part in the reaction that forms geronic acid.

II. REARRANGEMENT OF α-CINENIC ACID IN CONTACT WITH CARBON-14 MONOXIDE

Into an evacuated glass vessel were placed 20 ml of concentrated sulfuric acid and 0.11 mmole (3.1 mg, ~2.75 ml) of carbon-14 monoxide that contained 2 mc of carbon-14 (specific radioactivity, 18.2 mc/mmole). α-Cinenic acid (1290 mg, 7.50 mmoles) was stored in a sidearm of the vessel where it could be mixed with the sulfuric acid at will. After the vessel was sealed, the liquid was shaken for 1 hr to permit contact between the gaseous and liquid phases. Then the α-cinenic acid was mixed with the sulfuric acid, and the solution was shaken overnight. The reaction mixture was quenched with 150 ml of ice water and was extracted continuously with ether. By means of a procedure similar to that described in I, 680 mg (53% yield) of crude isotopically labeled geronic acid was isolated. The 2,4-dinitrophenylhydrazone ($C_{15}H_{20}O_6N_4$) was prepared and was recrystallized eight times to a constant specific radioactivity of 26.6 μc/mmole, which is about one-tenth the specific radioactivity (262 μc/mmole) that would have resulted if the α-cinenic acid had decarbonylated quantitatively and if the carbon monoxide released had had time to equilibrate with the carbon-14 monoxide before recombining to form labeled geronic acid. Presumably, only the *dissolved* carbon-14 monoxide would have time to equilibrate with the carbon monoxide released from α-cinenic acid before the recarbonylation would occur.

A neutral by-product, the lactone

which usually forms directly from α-cinenic acid in sulfuric acid, was recovered in 23% yield from the ether solution that remained after extraction with sodium bicarbonate solution. This lactone (310 mg, crude) was purified by vacuum sublimation, and the sublimate was identified by its infrared spectrum. A sample of the sublimate was diluted with six parts of nonradioactive lactone in ether solution. The diluted lactone was subsequently recrystallized twice from petroleum ether to yield crystals (m.p., 50 to 51°; specific activity, 0.10 μc/mmole). This specific activity is equivalent to 0.70 μc/mmole for the undiluted lactone, which is about 4% of the molar specific activity of the labeled geronic acid produced along with it.

III. TEST FOR EXCHANGE OF GERONIC ACID WITH CARBON-14 MONOXIDE
Concentrated sulfuric acid (20 ml) was shaken 1 hr in a sealed vessel in contact with carbon-14 monoxide (5.7 mg, 0.20 mmole, 3 mc). Geronic acid (530 mg, 3.1 mmoles), previously placed in a sidearm before the vessel was sealed, was then mixed with the sulfuric acid. The solution was shaken overnight and was then quenched with 150 ml of ice water. Geronic acid was recovered as described previously and was converted to the 2,4-dinitrophenylhydrazone. After seven recrystallizations from ethyl alcohol, the specific activity of the derivative was only 0.36 μc/mmole. Complete equilibration of the geronic acid with the carbon-14 monoxide would have resulted in a specific activity of about 900 μc/mmole for the 2,4-dinitrophenylhydrazone. Obviously, the rate of exchange of carbon-14 between carbon-14 monoxide and geronic acid is very slow.

15-4c CONCLUSIONS
The by-product lactone of α-cinenic acid had a molar specific activity only about 4% as great as that of the geronic acid formed simultaneously. This lactone can be considered merely as a convenient derivative (Chap. 9) of the α-cinenic acid. It follows that the radioactivity of the labeled geronic acid (Exp. II) was not the result of equilibration of carbon-14 between carbon-14 monoxide and α-cinenic acid *before the rearrangement* to geronic acid.

Experiment III proved that geronic acid did not acquire carbon-14 by exchange with carbon-14 monoxide *after the rearrangement*. The results of Exp. II must therefore mean that the rearrangement of α-cinenic acid to geronic acid proceeds, at least partly, by a decarbonylation-recarbonylation process.

The data of Exp. II cannot be interpreted quantitatively in terms of the percent of the reaction that proceeds *via* a decarbonylation-recarbonylation process. Probably diffusion of carbon-14 monoxide from the gas phase to the solution would be far too slow to permit much of the undissolved carbon-14 monoxide to participate in the recarbonylation step. This slow diffusion could be the reason that the molar specific activity of the labeled geronic acid was only about 10% as great as that calculated for complete equilibration of the carbon-14. Very possibly, if Exp. II were repeated with more rapid mixing of the gaseous and liquid phases, the labeled geronic acid recovered would then have a higher molar specific activity. This research[17] could be profitably extended to include quantitative studies of the incorporation of carbon-14 monoxide into the geronic acid during rearrangement of α-cinenic acid.

15-5 KINETIC ISOTOPE EFFECTS: STUDY OF ISOTOPE EFFECTS IN THE DIECKMANN CONDENSATION OF CARBON-14-LABELED DIETHYL PHENYLENEDIACETATES

Carbon-13 and carbon-14 isotope-effect studies, like deuterium and tritium isotope-effect studies, can often supply critical information about reaction mechanisms (Chap. 5). Because deuterium and tritium isotope effects are much larger than carbon isotope effects, the former are easier to measure experimentally and have, for that reason, been applied more frequently than the latter as diagnostic tools. However, deuterium and tritium isotope-effect studies are not substitutes for carbon isotope-effect studies. Isotope-effect studies with deuterium and tritium on one hand and with carbon-13 and carbon-14 on the other can supply different information; they may supplement each other, but neither can take the place of the other.

One example of the use of an *intermolecular* carbon-13 isotope-effect study to test a proposed reaction mechanism was described in some detail in Sec. 5-4g. An investigation of the Dieckmann condensation[25] by both *intermolecular* and *intramolecular* carbon-14 isotope-effect studies is described in this section.

The Dieckmann condensation of diethyl phenylenediacetate (Eqs. 15-19, 15-20, 15-21, and 15-22) to ethyl 2-hydrindone-1-carboxylate is in effect irreversible when an excess of condensing agent is present to convert the product to its enolate salt (Eq. 15-22). The first step (Eq. 15-19) is attack by base to convert the ester to its anion

$$+ C_2H_5O^- \rightleftharpoons$$

$$+ C_2H_5OH \quad (15\text{-}19)$$

The second step (Eq. 15-20) is an *intramolecular* reaction of the anion

$$\rightleftharpoons$$

$$(15\text{-}20)$$

The third step (Eq. 15-21) is loss of an ethoxyl ion

$$\rightleftharpoons$$

$$+ C_2H_5O^- \quad (15\text{-}21)$$

The fourth step (Eq. 15-22) drives the reaction to completion

$$+ C_2H_5O^- \rightleftharpoons$$

(excess)

$$+ C_2H_5OH \quad (15\text{-}22)$$

The isotope effects were studied under two sets of conditions, (a) at 80° with absolute ethyl alcohol as the solvent and sodium ethoxide as the condensing agent, and (b) at 100° with toluene as the solvent and powdered sodium as the condensing agent. The object was to determine which of the steps is rate-determining. For the Dieckmann condensation of diethyl phenylenediacetate-1-^{14}C, both *intermolecular* and *intramolecular* isotope effects were measured. For the condensation of diethyl phenylenediacetate-2-^{14}C, only the *intermolecular* isotope effect could be measured.

To study the *intramolecular* isotope effect in the condensation of diethyl phenylenedi-acetate-1-^{14}C, the condensation product had to be degraded (Chap. 10). This degradation was accomplished by saponification of the product, labeled ethyl 2-hydrindone-1-car-boxylate, and decarboxylation (Eq. 15-23) of the resulting labeled β-ketoacid

$$\underset{\text{CH}_2}{\underset{|}{\overset{\text{CH}-{}^{14}\text{CO}_2\text{H}}{\underset{{}^{14}\text{CO}}{\bigcirc}}}} \xrightarrow{\Delta}$$

$$\underset{\text{CH}_2}{\underset{|}{\overset{\text{CH}_2}{\underset{{}^{14}\text{CO}}{\bigcirc}}}} + {}^{14}\text{CO}_2 \quad (15\text{-}23)$$

The ratio of the molar specific radioactivity of the carbon-14 dioxide to that of the 2-hydrindone-2-^{14}C is a measure of the ratio of the concentration of carbon-14 in the carbethoxy group to the concentration of carbon-14 in the keto group of the condensation product. The molar-specific-activity ratio is therefore also a measure of the *intramolecular* isotope effect, which is the ratio of the rate constants for reaction at the unlabeled and labeled centers within the symmetrical reactant, diethyl phenylenediacetate-1-[14]C (Secs. 5-1a, 5-2b). General methods of measuring the *intermolecular* isotope effects have been discussed already (Sec. 5-2a). For the present application to the *intermolecular*

isotope effect in the condensation of diethyl phenylenediacetate-1-^{14}C, these methods must be modified to take into account the fact that an *intramolecular* isotope effect can be superimposed on the *intermolecular* isotope effect (Sec. 5-2b).

I5-5a EVALUATION OF ISOTOPE EFFECTS

The present discussion is limited to the isotopic studies of the Dieckmann condensation in ethyl alcohol with sodium ethoxide as the condensing agent [condition (a)]. The original paper[25] should be consulted for the description of a study of the Dieck-mann condensation in toluene with powdered sodium as the condensing agent [condition (b)]. There is little relation between the study made under condition (a) and that under condition (b), since the mechanisms are undoubtedly different.

I. *INTRAMOLECULAR* ISOTOPE EFFECT IN THE CONDENSATION OF DIETHYL PHENYLENEDIACETATE-1-[14]C   It is convenient to define rate constants (symbol k) in terms of the abbreviated equations shown in Fig. 15-1. It is also helpful to designate the various molecular species by upper-case letters for reference.

Equation 15-24

$$\frac{k_3}{k_2} = \frac{[I]/([I] + [C])}{[G]/([G] + [D])} = \frac{S_{CO_2}}{S_h} \quad (15\text{-}24)$$

is a concise statement of the method of calculating the *intramolecular* isotope effect k_3/k_2, which has already been described above; it is similar to Eq. 5-9. Bracketed letters indicate the number of moles, or the molar concentrations of the molecular species in Fig. 15-1 to which the letters refer. The symbols S_{CO_2} and S_h refer respectively to the molar radioactivities of the accumulated carbon-14 dioxide and 2-hydrindone-2-[14]C. Equation 15-24 is applicable at any time during the course of the condensation reaction; it is

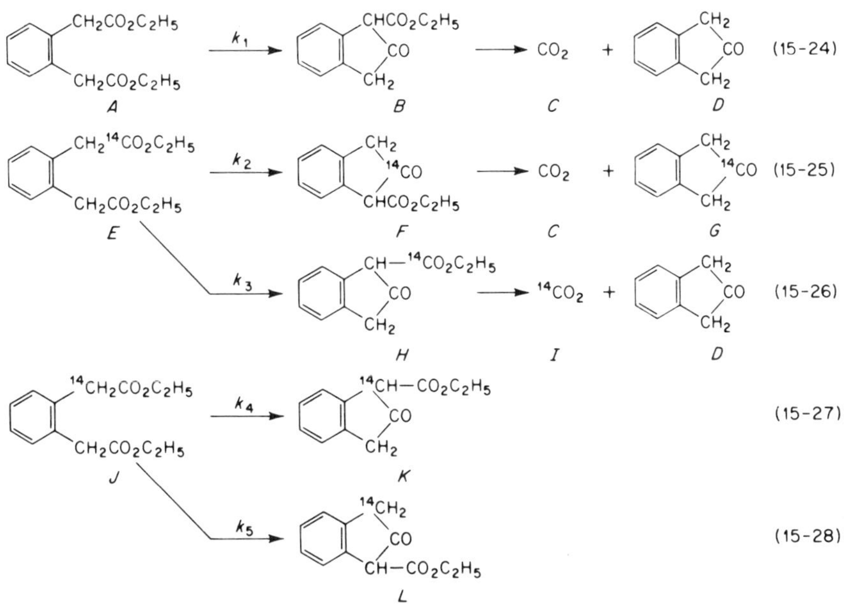

FIG. 15-1   Equations and rate constants used in the calculation of carbon-14 isotope effects in the Dieckmann condensation of diethyl phenylenediacetate-1-^{14}C.

not necessary to have the condensation reaction go to completion before this equation can be used; however, use of it could lead to an error in the calculated value for k_3/k_2 if either I, C, G, or D were also produced by a side reaction or introduced from any source other than the Dieckmann condensation of diethyl phenylenediacetate-1-^{14}C. In addition, proper use of Eq. 15-24 requires that both the ester saponification and the degradation reaction (Eq. 15-23) be quantitative so that no errors can be caused by *intermolecular* isotope effects in these two processes (Sec. 10-2a).

II. *INTERMOLECULAR* ISOTOPE EFFECT IN THE CONDENSATION OF DIETHYL PHENYLENEDIACETATE-1-^{14}C   To evaluate the *intermolecular* isotope effects, a variation of the "low-conversion approximation" method (Sec. 5-2a, Method II) was applied. The reactions were stopped at about 9% conversion. At or below 9% conversion,

the error inherent in the "low-conversion approximation" can be neglected.

The symbols used are those shown in Fig. 15-1. Equation 15-25 expresses the approximate value of the molar radioactivity of the product, carbon-14-labeled ethyl-2-hydrindone-1-carboxylate, accumulated at 9% reaction in terms of the reaction time, t, three rate constants, and the initial number of moles (indicated by bracketed letters with 0 subscripts) of labeled and unlabeled reactant

$$\frac{[F]+[H]}{[F]+[H]+[B]} =$$

$$\frac{[E]_0(1 - e^{-(k_2+k_3)t})}{[E]_0(1 - e^{-(k_2+k_3)t}) + [A]_0(1 - e^{-k_1 t})} \quad (15\text{-}25)$$

By an approximation based on the expansion of the exponential terms in a power series, Eq. 15-25 can be simplified to give Eq. 15-26

$$\frac{[F]+[H]}{[F]+[H]+[B]} \cong \frac{[E]_0(k_2 + k_3)}{[E]_0(k_2 + k_3) + [A]_0 k_1}$$

$$(15\text{-}26)$$

which can be further simplified, because at the carbon-14 tracer level the concentration of labeled molecules is very low in comparison with the concentration of unlabeled molecules. The terms $[F]$, $[H]$, and $[E]_0(k_2 + k_3)$ can therefore be dropped from the denominators. Furthermore,

$$k_3 \cong \frac{k_1}{2} \qquad (15\text{-}27)$$

because the unlabeled center in a labeled molecule can be assumed to react at nearly the same rate as an unlabeled center in an unlabeled molecule. The use of Eq. 15-27 is equivalent to neglecting any small secondary carbon-14 isotope effect that might occur in the Dieckmann condensation (Sec. 5-4f). These further simplifications result in Eq. 15-28

$$\frac{k_1}{2k_2} \cong \frac{[E]_0/[A]_0}{2\{([F] + [H])/[B]\} - [E]_0/[A]_0} \qquad (15\text{-}28)$$

It is apparent that Eq. 15-28, which states how the *intermolecular* isotope effect, $k_1/2k_2$, may be evaluated, can be rewritten as Eq. 15-34

$$\frac{k_1}{2k_2} \cong \frac{S_0}{2S_9 - S_0} \cong \frac{S_{100}}{2S_9 - S_{100}} \qquad (15\text{-}29)$$

For the purpose of Eq. 15-29, S_0 represents the initial molar radioactivity of the diethyl phenylenediacetate-1-^{14}C; S_0 should be equal to S_{100}, the molar radioactivity of the carbon-14-labeled ethyl 2-hydrindone-1-carboxylate accumulated at 100% reaction. The symbol S_9 represents the molar radioactivity of the carbon-14-labeled ethyl 2-hydrindone-1-carboxylate accumulated at or at less than 9% reaction. Since S_0 and S_9 are experimentally measurable quantities, the use of Eq. 15-29 to evaluate the *intermolecular* isotope effect, $k_1/2k_2$, is straightforward.

III. *INTERMOLECULAR* ISOTOPE EFFECT IN THE CONDENSATION OF DIETHYL PHENYLENEDIACETATE-2-^{14}C Equation 15-30, which is analogous to Eq. 15-29, was used to calculate the

intermolecular isotope effect in the condensation of diethyl phenylenediacetate-2-^{14}C

$$\frac{k_1}{2k_4} \cong \frac{S_0}{2S_9 - S_0} \cong \frac{S_{100}}{2S_9 - S_{100}} \qquad (15\text{-}30)$$

In Eq. 15-30, S_0 is the initial molar radioactivity of the diethyl phenylenediacetate-2-^{14}C, and S_9 is the molar radioactivity of the carbon-14-labeled ethyl 2-hydrindone-1-carboxylate accumulated at or below 9% reaction. In this case also, S_0 should be equal to S_{100}, the molar radioactivity of the carbon-14-labeled ethyl 2-hydrindone-1-carboxylate accumulated at 100% reaction.

15-5b EXPERIMENTAL DETAILS

I. SYNTHESIS Diethyl phenylenediacetate-1-^{14}C was synthesized by reaction of xylylene bromide with sodium cyanide-^{14}C and hydrolysis of the resulting phenylenediacetonitrile-1-^{14}C to phenylenediacetic-1-^{14}C acid. The acid was carefully purified until the melting point was 150 to 151° and was then refluxed in absolute ethyl alcohol that contained anhydrous hydrogen chloride to form the ester (b.p., 193 to 194° at 15 mm pressure).

Diethyl phenylenediacetate-2-^{14}C was prepared by a series of reactions beginning with the carbonation of *o*-tolylmagnesium bromide with carbon-14 dioxide. The resulting *o*-toluic-1-^{14}C acid was reduced with lithium aluminum hydride to *o*-methylbenzyl alcohol-1-^{14}C, which was converted to *o*-methylbenzyl-1-^{14}C bromide with phosphorus tribromide. The *o*-methylbenzyl-1-^{14}C bromide was brominated to *o*-xylylene-1-^{14}C bromide, which was recrystallized from chloroform and was then converted via the dinitrile and the dicarboxylic acid to diethyl phenylenediacetate-2-^{14}C.

Syntheses were performed on a macro scale. There was apparently no need to dilute with carrier during or after these syntheses.

II. DIECKMANN CONDENSATION Labeled diethyl phenylenediacetate (4.5 g, 18 mmoles), in 15 ml of absolute ethyl alcohol, was added to a solution of sodium ethoxide prepared from 0.42 g (18 mmoles) of sodium and 15 ml of absolute ethyl alcohol. The reaction solution was refluxed 15 min, cooled, diluted with cold water, and acidified with dilute hydrochloric acid. The yellow precipitate that formed was collected on a filter, was washed on the filter with water, and was recrystallized from ethyl alcohol. The yield of labeled ethyl-2-hydrindone-1-carboxylate was 2.58 g (70%); m.p., 65°.

III. DIECKMANN CONDENSATION AT ABOUT 9% REACTION

Labeled diethyl phenylenediacetate (17 g, 68 mmoles) was added in one portion to 140 mg (6.1 mmoles, 9% of the amount necessary for complete reaction) of sodium ethoxide dissolved in 50 ml of absolute ethyl alcohol. The solution was heated at reflux for 15 min, cooled, and diluted with 100 ml of ice water; the resulting solution was extracted with ether to remove unreacted ester. The aqueous layer was acidified with dilute sulfuric acid and was extracted with ether again. From the ether extract, 0.9 g of labeled ethyl 2-hydrindone-1-carboxylate was recovered. The amount represents 6.5% yield based on ester (72% yield based on sodium).

IV. SAPONIFICATION AND DECARBOXYLATION OF ETHYL 2-HYDRINDONE-1-CARBOXYLATE

In a typical degradation, 1.043 g of labeled ethyl 2-hydrindone-1-carboxylate was placed in the decarboxylation flask, and 10 ml of 20% sulfuric acid was placed above it in a dropping funnel. The flask was equipped with a reflux condenser, a trap cooled by Dry Ice–isopropyl alcohol, and a spiral bubbler filled with sodium hydroxide solution. The system was swept for 30 min with nitrogen, which by-passed the sodium hydroxide solution. The sulfuric acid was run into the decarboxylation flask, which was then heated on a steam bath for 5 hr while the nitrogen sweep was continued

to carry the released carbon dioxide into the sodium hydroxide solution. After the reaction was stopped, the sodium hydroxide was washed into an equal volume of 1 N ammonium chloride solution. Excess barium chloride solution was added. The barium carbonate was collected and dried. Its weight (1.005 g) represented 100.1% yield based on quantitative decarboxylation.

The apparatus was washed carefully with 10 ml of ethyl alcohol, which was then combined with the reaction solvent. The resulting solution was heated until all the hydrindone dissolved. The solution was cooled to 50° to effect precipitation of a small amount of a by-product, anhydro-bis-2-hydrindone (m.p., 170 to 175°), that formed during the decarboxylation. The cooled solution was filtered to remove this by-product, and the filtrate was then further cooled to 10° at which temperature the hydrindone (m.p., 57°) crystallized as white needles.

V. RADIOISOTOPIC ASSAYS

All labeled samples were oxidized to carbon-14 dioxide by wet combustion (Sec. 11-5d). The carbon dioxide was swept through an absorber, and barium carbonate-^{14}C was precipitated from the resulting solution. Since the weight of recovered barium carbonate-^{14}C was 100.2 to 101.0% of the calculated weight, the combustion was essentially quantitative. For each labeled sample combusted, 1.4000 g of barium carbonate-^{14}C was decomposed with sulfuric acid in a vacuum line, and the carbon-14 dioxide released was transferred to an ionization chamber. The same chamber was used for assaying all samples. The average counting error was reported to be about 0.5%.

This assay method results in a determination of the specific activity of the barium carbonate-^{14}C formed from the carbon-14 dioxide released during the wet combustion (Sec. 11-5d). Therefore, the specific activity of the organic compound combusted was calculated by multiplying the specific activity of the barium carbonate-^{14}C by the number of carbon atoms per molecule. The molar radio-activities listed in Tables 15-7, 15-8, and 15-9 are reported in units of drift rate, volts/minute. As used in this research, a drift rate of 1 v/min is about equivalent to 0.006 mc/mole.

15-5c RESULTS

Tables 15-7, 15-8, and 15-9 give the molar radioactivities (v/min) and the calculated isotope effects for twenty individual runs. The various isotope effects are reported in percent (Sec. 5-1a) rather than as ratios.

A radioactivity balance applied to each of the experiments listed in Table 15-7 means that S_e must equal $S_{CO_2} + S_h$. The data of columns 5 and 6 of Table 15-7 are in reasonably good agreement. This agreement provides a strong argument that the experimental

procedures and the counting techniques are reliable. Runs 20 and 21, which were made by use of diethyl phenylenediacetate-2-^{14}C in the same procedures, are additional sources of confidence. In these two runs the carbon dioxide was nonradioactive, and the values for S_h and S_e agree reasonably well with each other and with the molar radioactivity of the diethyl phenylenediacetate-2-^{14}C used.

For each of the individual runs reported in Tables 15-8 and 15-9, close agreement between S_0 and S_{100} indicates that the compounds assayed were essentially free of carbon-14-labeled impurities and other impurities.

Table 15-7 indicates that the mean value for the *intramolecular* isotope effect is about $5.6 \pm 0.7\%$. Tables 15-8 and 15-9 indicate that the two *intermolecular* isotope effects are about equal and are somewhat larger than

Table 15-7 Intramolecular isotope effect in the Dieckmann condensation of diethyl phenylenediacetate-1-^{14}C by sodium ethoxide in ethyl alcohol at 80°

Run No.	Reaction time, min	S_{CO_2}	S_h	$S_e{}^d$	$S_{CO2} + S_h$	Isotope effect $100[(k_3/k_2) - 1]$	Mean and average dev.
8	15	14.50	13.73	27.85	28.23	5.6	
9		14.49	13.73	28.42	28.22	5.5	
10		14.49	13.73	28.06	28.22	5.5	
11		14.33	13.79	28.13	28.12	3.9	5.1 ± 0.6
12	90	14.25	13.48	27.85	27.73	5.7	
13^a		13.39	12.83	26.26	26.22	4.4	
14^a		13.34	12.64	26.26	25.98	5.5	
15^a		13.55	12.65	26.39	26.20	7.1	5.7 ± 0.7
16	120^c	12.14	11.33	23.66	23.47	7.1	
17		11.77	11.23	—	23.00	4.8	
18		12.02	11.23	23.21	23.25	7.0	
19		11.90	11.29	23.21	23.19	5.4	6.1 ± 0.9
20^b	15	0.00	18.69	18.77	18.69		
21^b		0.00	18.78	19.01	18.78		

^{a} Molar radioactivity of the diethyl phenylenediacetate-1-^{14}C used was 26.12.

^{b} Used diethyl phenylenediacetate-2-^{14}C, molar radioactivity = 18.70.

^{c} 100% excess sodium ethoxide was used.

^{d} Molar radioactivity of the labeled ethyl 2-hydrindone-1-carboxylate.

Table 15-8 Intermolecular isotope effect in the Dieckmann condensation of diethyl phenylenediacetate-1-^{14}C by sodium ethoxide in ethyl alcohol at 80°

Run No.	S_0	S_9	S_{100}	Isotope effect, $100[(k_1/2k_2) - 1]$	
				Calculated from S_9 and S_0	Calculated from S_9 and S_{100}
27	23.27	22.10	23.30	11.2	11.4
28	23.07	22.39	23.30	6.3	8.5
29	23.17	22.39	23.28	7.2	8.3
Mean and average deviation				8.2 ± 2.0	9.4 ± 1.3

the *intramolecular* isotope effect. The mean *intermolecular* isotope effect with diethyl phenylenediacetate-1-^{14}C is about 8.7 ± 1.8%. The mean *intermolecular* isotope effect with diethyl phenylenediacetate-2-^{14}C is about 8.5 ± 1.5%.

15-5d CONCLUSIONS

I. THE MECHANISM OF THE DIECK-MANN CONDENSATION Large carbon-14 isotope effects are observed in the Dieckmann condensation of diethyl phenylenediacetate, both when the label is in a carboxyl group and also when the label is in a methylene group. The reasonable conclusion[25] is that

the rate-determining step is the formation of the bond between the carbon atoms of these two groups (Eq. 15-20). None of the other steps (Eqs. 15-19, 15-21, and 15-22) involve both the carboxyl group and the methylene group.

It is argued[25] that the formation of the new carbon-to-carbon bond (Eq. 15-20) and the loss of the ethoxyl ion (Eq. 15-21) cannot be concerted in a displacement reaction; the argument is based on the observation by Bigeleisen, Bothner-By, and Friedman[26] that no measurable carbon-13 fractionation occurs in the somewhat similar pyrolysis of barium adipate. That reaction is said to form cyclopentanone by a mechanism[26] having a

Table 15-9 Intermolecular isotope effect in the Dieckmann condensation of diethyl phenylenediacetate-2-^{14}C by sodium ethoxide in ethyl alcohol at 80°

Run No.	S_0	S_9	S_{100}	Isotope effect, $100[(k_1/2k_3) - 1]$	
				Calculated from S_9 and S_0	Calculated from S_9 and S_{100}
22	5.81	5.57	5.76	9.0	7.1
23	5.78	5.57	5.76	7.8	7.1
24	5.75	5.52	5.72	8.6	7.5
25	5.75	5.52	5.78	8.6	9.9
26	5.70	5.49	5.77	8.0	11.0
Mean and average deviation				8.4 ± 0.4	8.5 ± 1.5

concerted bond-breaking and bond-making process in the rate-determining step.

II. MAGNITUDES OF THE *INTER-* AND *INTRAMOLECULAR* ISOTOPE EFFECTS

The observed magnitudes of the carbon-14 isotope effects are discussed briefly[25] with reference to isotope-effect theory, but no definite conclusions are reached.

15-5e COMMENTS

The conclusions reached[25] about the reaction mechanism seem to be justified in general. However, the question of whether a carbon-to-carbon bond formation process alone can explain 5 to 9% carbon-14 isotope effects is debatable. A number of bond-forming processes have been shown to proceed with no measurable carbon-14 isotope effects.[8,9,10]

The authors' suggestion as a footnote[25] that activation in the rate-controlling bond formation (Eq. 15-20) may involve bond rupture at both the methylene and carbonyl carbon atoms has considerable merit. The activation process might, in fact, consist almost entirely in localization of the negative charge on the methylene carbon and simultaneous polarization of the carbonyl group as follows:

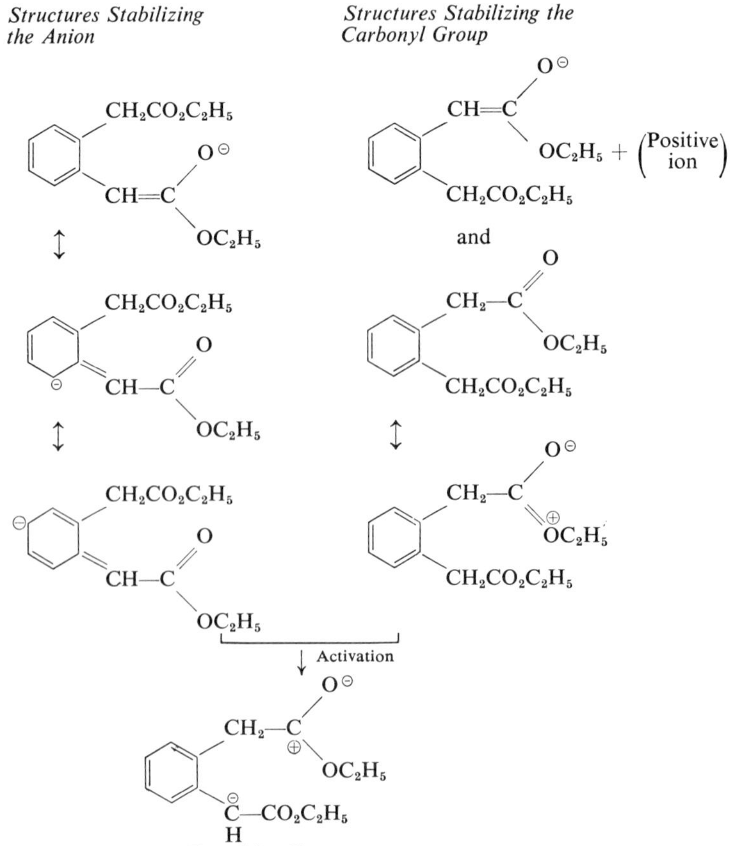

Structures Stabilizing the Anion

Structures Stabilizing the Carbonyl Group

$$CH_2CO_2C_2H_5$$

$$CH=C\stackrel{O^{\ominus}}{\underset{OC_2H_5}{}}$$

$$\updownarrow$$

$$CH_2CO_2C_2H_5$$

$$CH-C\stackrel{O}{\underset{OC_2H_5}{}}$$

$$\updownarrow$$

$$CH_2CO_2C_2H_5$$

$$CH-C\stackrel{O}{\underset{OC_2H_5}{}}$$

$$CH=C\stackrel{O^{\ominus}}{\underset{OC_2H_5}{}} + \left(\begin{array}{c}\text{Positive}\\\text{ion}\end{array}\right)$$

$$CH_2CO_2C_2H_5$$

and

$$CH_2-C\stackrel{O}{\underset{OC_2H_5}{}}$$

$$CH_2CO_2C_2H_5$$

$$\updownarrow$$

$$CH_2-C\stackrel{O^{\ominus}}{\underset{\overset{\oplus}{OC_2H_5}}{}}$$

$$CH_2CO_2C_2H_5$$

↓ Activation

$$CH_2-C\stackrel{O^{\ominus}}{\underset{\overset{\oplus}{OC_2H_5}}{}}$$

$$\overset{\ominus}{C}-CO_2C_2H_5$$
$$H$$

Transition State

It seems likely that the formation of the new carbon-to-carbon bond would have made little progress in the transition state,[27] since the formation of a strong new carbon-to-carbon bond in the transition state would probably reduce the expected carbon-14 isotope effect (Sec. 5-3a, Eq. 5-12) far below the observed level of 5 to 9%. Although such a discussion of the mechanism of the Dieckmann condensation is highly speculative, it illustrates how carbon-14 isotope effects can provide clues to the nature of transition states.

It is not practical to estimate from theoretical principles the magnitude of the carbon-14 isotope effects to be expected in the Dieckmann condensation. For such a complex reaction, the necessary information is lacking.

There seems to be no cause to suspect any large errors in the experimental values for the three isotope effects. However, the assumption of no secondary carbon-14 isotope effect (Eq. 15-27) may cause a measurable error in the calculated values for the two *intermolecular* isotope effects. Secondary carbon-14 isotope effects that approach 1% have been reported.[28,29]

CITED REFERENCES

[1] R. M. Roberts, P. Heiberger, J. D. Watkins, H. P. Browder, Jr., and K. A. Kobe, *J. Am. Chem. Soc.*, **80**, 4285 (1958).

[2] R. M. Roberts, H. P. Browder, Jr., and K. A. Kobe, *J. Am. Chem. Soc.*, **81**, 1165 (1959).

[3] R. M. Roberts, J. D. Watkins, and K. A. Kobe, *J. Am. Chem. Soc.*, **81**, 1167 (1959).

[4] G. A. Ropp and E. M. Hodnett, *J. Chem. Phys.*, **25**, 587 (1956).

[5] J. D. Roberts, H. E. Simmons, Jr., L. A. Carlsmith, and C. W. Vaughan, *J. Am. Chem. Soc.*, **75**, 3290 (1953).

[6] J. D. Roberts, D. A. Semenow, H. E. Simmons, Jr., and L. A. Carlsmith, *J. Am. Chem. Soc.*, **78**, 601 (1956).

[7] D. A. Semenow and J. D. Roberts, *J. Chem. Educ.*, **33**, 2 (1956).

[8] W. A. Bonner and C. J. Collins, *J. Am. Chem. Soc.*, **75**, 4516 (1953).

[9] J. G. Burr, Jr., *J. Am. Chem. Soc.*, **75**, 1990 (1953).

[10] G. A. Ropp, V. F. Raaen, and A. J. Weinberger, *J. Am. Chem. Soc.*, **75**, 3694 (1953).

[11] M. Panar and J. D. Roberts, *J. Am. Chem. Soc.*, **82**, 3629 (1960).

[12] G. Wittig and L. Pohmer, *Angew. Chem.*, **67**, 348 (1955).

[13] J. D. Roberts, C. W. Vaughan, L. A. Carlsmith, and D. A. Semenow, *J. Am. Chem. Soc.*, **78**, 611 (1956).

[14] W. P. Cain and R. M. Noyes, *J. Am. Chem. Soc.*, **81**, 2031 (1959).

[15] A. R. Amell, C. G. Houle, and W. A. Cilley, *J. Am. Chem. Soc.*, **81**, 4504 (1959).

[16] W. A. Bonner, *J. Am. Chem. Soc.*, **81**, 5171 (1959).

[17] J. Meinwald, H. C. Hwang, D. Christman, and A. P. Wolf, *J. Am. Chem. Soc.*, **82**, 483 (1960).

[18] J. Meinwald, *J. Am. Chem. Soc.*, **77**, 1617 (1955).

[19] J. Meinwald and J. T. Ouderkirk, *J. Am. Chem. Soc.*, **82**, 480 (1960).

[20] H. Koch and W. Haaf, *Ann.*, **618**, 251 (1958).

[21] G. Stork and M. Bersohn, *J. Am. Chem. Soc.*, **82**, 1261 (1960).

[22] L. P. Hammett, "Physical Organic Chemistry," p. 277, McGraw-Hill Book Company, New York, 1940.

[23] G. A. Ropp, *J. Am. Chem. Soc.*, **82**, 4252 (1960).

[24] A. Lundeen, *J. Am. Chem. Soc.*, **82**, 3228 (1960); apparently the research of Meinwald and co-workers[17] preceded this work.

[25] W. L. Carrick and A. Fry, *J. Am. Chem. Soc.*, **77**, 4381 (1955).

[26] J. Bigeleisen, A. A. Bothner-By, and L. Friedman, *J. Am. Chem. Soc.*, **75**, 2908 (1953).

[27] G. S. Hammond, *J. Am. Chem. Soc.*, **77**, 337 (1955).

[28] V. F. Raaen, A. K. Tsiomis, and C. J. Collins, *J. Am. Chem. Soc.*, **82**, 5502 (1960).

[29] V. F. Raaen, T. K. Dunham, D. D. Thompson, and C. J. Collins, *J. Am. Chem. Soc.*, **85**, 3497 (1963).

PROBLEMS

15-1. (*a*) By use of the cost data from Chap. 1 and yield data from Chap. 8, estimate the cost of the carbon-14 in 10 g of benzoic-7-^{14}C acid prepared at a specific radioactivity of 10 μc/mmole from barium carbonate-^{14}C. Ignore labor costs and laboratory expenses.

(b) Consult the most recent issue of the *Isotopes Index* to determine the cost if the benzoic-7-^{14}C acid were purchased from a commercial supplier.

15-2. Assume that the measured radioactivity (0.0184 μc/mmole) of the phenazine of 2,3-dinitrotoluene reported for Experiment 3b in Table 15-3 is thought to be in error because of the presence of 0.05 wt % of the starting material, *o*-nitrotoluene-1-^{14}C, as a contaminant in the phenazine. Calculate the corrected percent 2,3-dinitrotoluene in mixed dinitrotoluenes.

15-3. (a) Suggest a suitable derivative to replace the semicarbazone of cyclohexanone so as to avoid any primary carbon-14 isotope effect during derivatization (Sec. 15-3e, Table 15-5).

(b) Why would an ester of the precursor, phenol, be unsuitable as a derivative for this purpose?

15-4. Pivalic (trimethylacetic) acid was found to slowly exchange all of its ten hydrogen atoms with the deuterium atoms of an excess of concentrated deuteriosulfuric acid. Suggest a plausible mechanism for the exchange.

15-5. (a) By use of the method (Sec. 5-3a, Eq. 5-11) and the data (Table 5-3, Fig. 5-10) given in Chap. 5, compute the expected value for the *intermolecular* isotope effect for the Dieckmann condensation of diethyl phenylenediacetate-1-^{14}C at 80°C. Assume that carbon-14 is doubly bonded to the oxygen in the ground state and singly bonded to the oxygen in the transition state. Ignore the effect of the charges on the frequency in the transition state.

(b) Give one possible reason why this computed isotope effect is higher than the observed isotope effects (Sec. 15-5c).

CHAPTER
16
ADDITIONAL APPLICATIONS OF CARBON-14 TO THE STUDY OF REACTION MECHANISMS

16-1 INTRODUCTION

This chapter is a brief directory of a few typical mechanism studies, made with carbon-14, that were not mentioned in earlier chapters Table 16-1 is a guide to model experiments described in the literature. References to applications of carbon-14 in solving biochemical problems have, for the most part, been omitted throughout this book. However, biochemical uses of carbon-14 and strictly chemical uses have much in common, and a number of techniques are applicable to both. Biochemical studies with carbon-14 are documented elsewhere.[1]

16-2 CONJOINT USE OF THE CARBON-14 ISOTOPE TECHNIQUE AND ANOTHER TECHNIQUE

In some of the most effective research, the carbon-14 isotope technique has been used together with another technique. A notable example is described in Sec. 4-3b. The value of this approach should be considered carefully in the planning of an organic reaction mechanism study.

CITED REFERENCES

[1] For example see: R. S. Scharffenberg and J. K. Pollard, Jr., "Carbon-14, A Comprehensive Annual Bibliography of Applications in Chemistry, Biology, and Medicine," a CALBIOCHEM publication, Box 54282, Terminal Annex, Los Angeles 54, Calif., vol. 1, 1962. More recent volumes are also available.

Reactions investigated	Scope and description	Principal investigators	Leading references
Pinacol rearrangement; deamination reaction; etc.	Intensive studies of many acid-catalyzed rearrangements of carbon-14-labeled compounds; a useful source of detailed information about methods of synthesizing, purifying, degrading, and radio-assaying carbon-14 compounds; the contribution of symmetrical bridged-ion intermediates to the mechanism of several reactions is estimated.	W. A. Bonner C. J. Collins	*1* (a review), *2* (a review), *3, 4, 5*
Hydrocarbon rearrangements	Friedel-Crafts catalyzed rearrangements of alkyl-benzenes were studied. In a particularly interesting case, *n*-propyl-*β*-^{14}C-benzene was shown to yield *n*-propyl-benzene and di-*n*-propyl-benzenes that contained carbon-14 in the *alpha* and *beta* positions but not in the *gamma* positions.	R. M. Roberts	*6* (a review), *7, 8*
Claisen rearrangements	Mechanism of the Claisen rearrangement	H. Schmid	*9* (a review)
Hydrocarbon rearrangements, etc.	Pioneering studies of the occurrence of carbonium ions in molecular rearrangements	J. D. Roberts	Numerous papers since 1950 (see author index of the *Journal of the American Chemical Society*)
Reactions catalyzed by acids and Raney nickel	Mechanism of conversion of D-xylose to 2-fur-aldehyde; cleavage of 2,3,3-triphenyl-1-propanol by Raney nickel, etc.	W. A. Bonner	*10, 11* (see also C. J. Collins' work on molecular rearrangements)
Mechanisms of reactions involving free radicals	Polymerization mechanisms; mechanisms of rearrangements	W. B. Smith	*12, 13*
Rearrangement of bi-phenyl catalyzed by aluminum chloride	Demonstration that the carbon-14 label in a specifically labeled bi-phenyl becomes completely randomized	A. P. Wolf	*14*
Reactions of carbon-14-labeled carbohydrates	Isomerization of D-glucose-1-^{14}C catalyzed by strong-base resin is a typical study.	J. C. Sowden	*15*
Fischer-Tropsch synthesis	Use of carbon-14-labeled ethanol and carbon-14-labeled ketene as additives to synthesis gas to study the reaction mechanism	P. H. Emmett	*16, 17*

Table 16-1 (*Continued*)

Reactions investigated	Scope and description	Principal investigators	Leading references
Isomerization of carbon-14-labeled ethylcyclohexane over a nickel-silica-alumina catalyst	A carbonium ion mechanism is indicated by the distribution of carbon-14 in the products of isomerization.	H. Pines	18
Friedel-Crafts alkylation	Rearrangement during alkylation	J. W. T. Spinks C. C. Lee	19, 20
Rearrangement study (the 27th of a series of rearrangement studies made with carbon-14)	Investigation of the isotope position rearrangement in the norbornyl cation generated by the π route from the solvolysis of 2-(Δ^3-cyclopentenyl)-2-^{14}C-ethyl *p*-nitrobenzene-sulfonate	C. C. Lee L. K. M. Lam	21
Polymerization	Study of free-radical mechanism of polymerization using carbon-14-labeled initiators	J. C. Bevington	22, 23
Gaseous oxidation of hydrocarbons	Mechanism of oxidation of carbon-14-labeled 2-methyl-but-2-ene	C. F. Cullis	24
Degradation of carbon-14-labeled toluene	A method is described for determining the specific activity of each ring carbon atom.	F. L. J. Sixma	25
Oxidation of acetaldehyde; oxidation and dehydrogenation of hydrocarbons	Theoretical discussion and practical applications of the "Kinetic Isotope Method" of studying reaction mechanisms	M. B. Neiman	26–31
Friedel-Crafts type reactions and other catalytic processes	Mechanism studies	A. A. Balandin Y. A. Gorin V. N. Kondratyev V. D. Nefedov O. A. Rentov T. N. Shatkina N. N. Vorozhtsov	See treatise by Roginsky (27)
Exchange between nitrile and carboxyl groups; reaction of aromatic isocyanates and anhydrides; Dakin-West reaction	Mechanism of these reactions	L. Ötvös	32–34
High-temperature isotope exchange	Carbon-14 was used to study the exchange between lithium acetate and lithium phenylacetate.	A. E. A. Mitta	35
Nitration of desoxy-benzoin; isotope exchange under pyrolytic conditions	Mechanism studies	R. Nakai	36, 37

References for Table 16-1

[1] C. J. Collins, *Quart. Rev. (London)*, **14**, 357 (1960).

[2] C. J. Collins in V. Gold, Ed., "Advances in Physical Organic Chemistry," p. 1, chap. 1, vol. 2, Academic Press, New York, 1964.

[3] W. A. Bonner and C. J. Collins, *J. Am. Chem. Soc.*, **75**, 5372 (1953).

[4] C. J. Collins and W. A. Bonner, *J. Am. Chem. Soc.*, **75**, 5379 (1953).

[5] C. J. Collins and W. A. Bonner, *J. Am. Chem. Soc.*, **77**, 92 (1955).

[6] R. M. Roberts, *Chem. Eng. News*, **43**, 96 (1965).

[7] R. M. Roberts, G. A. Ropp, and O. K. Neville, *J. Am. Chem. Soc.*, **77**, 1764 (1955).

[8] R. M. Roberts and S. G. Brandenberger, *J. Am. Chem. Soc.*, **79**, 5484 (1957).

[9] H. Schmid, *Chimia (Aarau)*, **14**, 248 (1960).

[10] W. A. Bonner, *J. Am. Chem. Soc.*, **81**, 1181 (1959).

[11] W. A. Bonner and M. R. Roth, *J. Am. Chem. Soc.*, **81**, 5454 (1959).

[12] W. B. Smith and J. D. Anderson, *J. Am. Chem. Soc.*, **82**, 656 (1960).

[13] W. B. Smith and H. Gilde, *J. Am. Chem. Soc.*, **82**, 659 (1960).

[14] H. Wynberg and A. P. Wolf, *J. Am. Chem. Soc.*, **85**, 3308 (1963).

[15] J. C. Sowden and R. R. Thompson, *J. Am. Chem. Soc.*, **80**, 1435 (1958).

[16] R. J. Kokes, W. K. Hall, and P. H. Emmett, *J. Am. Chem. Soc.*, **79**, 2989 (1957).

[17] G. G. Blyholder and P. H. Emmett, *J. Phys. Chem.*, **64**, 470 (1960).

[18] H. Pines and A. W. Shaw, *J. Am. Chem. Soc.*, **79**, 1474 (1957).

[19] C. C. Lee and J. W. T. Spinks, *Can. J. Chem.*, **32**, 1005 (1954).

[20] C. C. Lee, M. C. Hamblin, and N. Jones, *Can. J. Chem.*, **36**, 1597 (1958).

[21] C. C. Lee and L. K. M. Lam, *J. Am. Chem. Soc.*, **88**, 2834 (1966).

[22] J. C. Bevington, D. E. Eaves, J. Toole, and L. Trossarelli, *Proc. U.N. Intern. Conf. Peaceful Uses At. Energy 2nd, Geneva*, **20**, 128 (1958).

[23] J. C. Bevington, *Makromol. Chem.*, **34**, 152 (1959).

[24] C. F. Cullis, A. Fish, and D. W. Turner, *Proc. Royal Soc. (London), Ser. A*, **267**, 433 (1962).

[25] H. Steinberg and F. L. J. Sixma, *Rec. Trav. Chim.*, **79**, 679 (1960).

[26] M. B. Neiman, *Zh. Fiz. Khim.*, **28**, 1235 (1954).

[27] S. Z. Roginsky, "Theoretical Principles of Isotope Methods for Investigating Chemical Reactions," p. 363, Academy of Sciences, U.S.S.R. Press, Moscow, 1956; AEC-tr-2873, available from the Office of Technical Services, Washington 25, D.C.

[28] M. B. Neiman, *Intern. J. Appl. Radiation Isotopes*, **3**, 20 (1958); (in English).

[29] M. B. Neiman and G. I. Feklisov, *Dokl. Akad. Nauk. SSSR*, **90**, 583 (1953).

[30] A. A. Balandin, M. B. Neiman, O. K. Bogdanova, G. V. Isagulyants, A. P. Shcheglova, and I. E. Popov, *Bull. Acad. Sci. U.S.S.R., Division of Chemical Sciences*, **1957**, 167 (in English).

[31] A. B. Nalbandyan, M. B. Neiman, and N. M. Emanuel, in R. C. Extermann, Ed., "Radioisotopes in Scientific Research," vol. II, p. 72, Pergamon Press, New York, 1958.

[32] L. Noszkó and L. Ötvös, *Acta Chim. Acad. Sci. Hung.*, **25**, 123 (1960); *Chem. Abstr.*, **55**, 21027i (1961).

[33] L. Ötvös, J. Márton, and J. Meisel-Ágoston, *Acta Chim. Acad. Sci. Hung.*, **24**, 327 (1960); *Chem. Abstr.*, **55**, 13309c (1961).

[34] L. Ötvös, J. Márton, and J. Meisel-Ágoston, *Acta Chim. Acad. Sci. Hung.*, **24**, 321 (1960); *Chem. Abstr.*, **55**, 13309a (1961).

[35] M. F. Buhler, J. A. Castrillon, and A. E. A. Mitta, *Proc. U.N. Intern. Conf. Peaceful Uses At. Energy, 2d, Geneva*, **20**, 95 (1958).

[36] M. Sugii and R. Nakai, *J. Org. Chem.*, **22**, 288 (1957).

[37] R. Nakai, M. Sugii, and H. Nakao, *J. Am. Chem. Soc.*, **81**, 1003 (1959) (see also Sec. 10-2).

ANSWERS
TO PROBLEMS

CHAPTER 2

2-1. (*a*) 50%.
  (*b*) +5.94%.
2-2. 3.83 g.
2-3. 3.86 mmoles.
2-4. (*a*) 144.8.
  (*b*) 289.6.
2-5. 23,300.
2-6. (*a*) 18.2 mmoles.
  (*b*) 5.65 mc/mole.

CHAPTER 3

3-1. (*a*) 20 μc/mmole.
  (*b*) 5 μc/mmole.
  (*c*) 123 μc.
3-2. 0.62 c/mole.
3-3. 0.02%. There are six labeled positions and fifteen combinations of pairs of labeled positions. The value for *f* (the fraction of ^{14}C atoms in carbon atoms of each methyl group) is about 7.8 × 10^{-5}.
3-4. (*a*) Essentially 0.
  (*b*) 2.1%.
  (*c*) In the absence of other information, it might be assumed that the catalyst sets free ethyl "carbonium ions," which may rearrange by a slow hydride-ion shift and which may be removed by relatively rapid attack at the *ortho* and *para* positions of ethylbenzene molecules to form diethylbenzenes. This hypothetical mechanism would account for the slight rearrangement detected in the diethylbenzene and the absence of rearrangement in the recovered ethylbenzene.
3-5. The mechanism described in the answer to Problem 3-4(c) involves competition between the rate of an *intramolecular* hydride-ion shift and the rate of an *intermolecular* attack of a positive ethyl fragment on the ethylbenzene nucleus. If the proposed mechanism is correct, the degree of rearrangement of the *beta* carbon atom to the *alpha* position (as determined by the amount of carbon-14 found in the terephthalic-^{14}C acid) should be enhanced by any change in the reaction conditions that would slow down the *intermolecular* process more than the *intramolecular* process. For example, diluting the reaction mixture with a nonparticipating solvent, such as nitrobenzene, might be expected to increase the amount of carbon-14 found in the terephthalic-^{14}C acid.

CHAPTER 4

4-1. *12.1 g.*

4-2. Interfering side reactions are possible. It was believed that the aluminum isopropoxide caused condensation of some of the acetone-2-^{14}C to higher ketones, which interfered with the formation of a pure 2,4-dinitrophenylhydrazone derivative of the acetone-2-^{14}C.

4-3. Phthalic acid.

4-4. (*a*) 327 μc/mole.

    (*b*) 8.1 μc per gram of Ba^{14}CO$_3$.

    (*c*) 0.171

    (*d*) 0.270

4-5. Alternatively, the test for reversibility could have been performed by mixing carbon-14-labeled adduct with unlabeled β-nitrostyrene and subjecting the mixture to a temperature of 130° as a melt for 24 hr. The detection of radioactivity in the recovered β-nitrostyrene might then have been taken as evidence for reversibility of the Diels-Alder reaction. However, it is barely possible that this test might have led to an erroneous conclusion if the Diels-Alder adduct happened to break down irreversibly at 130° to yield β-nitrostyrene and a polymer of 2,3-dimethylbutadiene.

    Although there is no reason to suspect this type of breakdown of the adduct of β-nitrostyrene and 2,3-dimethylbutadiene, the argument is made here to emphasize the care necessary to avoid misinterpreting experimental results observed in tracer experiments.

CHAPTER 5

5-1. *1.075% carbon-13.* Use Eq. 5-4. Since

$$k_{12}/k_{13} = 1.032,$$

$$\frac{k_{13}}{k_{12}} = 0.969 = r = \frac{S_3}{1.11}$$

and $S_3 = 1.075$.

5-2. *Slightly greater than 1.075.* Since the magnitude of kinetic isotope effects decreases with increasing temperature, $k_{12}/k_{13} < 1.032$ and $r > 0.969$.

5-3. (*a*) *1.089%.* Since $k_{13}/k_{12} = 0.969$ at 92°, use of Fig. 5-3 gives $r \cong 0.981$; therefore, the percent carbon-13 for the accumulated carbon dioxide is (1.11)(0.981) = 1.089. (*b*) *1.143%.* From Fig. 5-4 at $1 - f = 0.4$, $r' = 1.03$, and the

percent carbon-13 for the residual mesitoic acid is (1.11)(1.03) = 1.143.

5-4. *By making a total carbon-13 balance.* The weight of carbon-13 in the sample of mesitoic acid decarboxylated must equal the sum of the weights of the carbon-13 in the carbon dioxide and in the residual acid:

$$(100)(0.0111) = (60)(0.01089) + (40)(0.01143)$$

$$1.11 = 1.11$$

5-5. *42.5 μc/g.* Use Fig. 5-5. For last 4%, $r' = 1.43$; for last 3%, $r' = 1.475$; therefore, the corresponding specific radioactivities of carbon monoxide are:

$$S(\text{last } 4\%) = (1.43)(20)(^{46}\!/_{28}) = 47.0 \ \mu\text{c/g}$$

$$S(\text{last } 3\%) = (1.475)(20)(^{46}\!/_{28}) = 48.5 \ \mu\text{c/g}$$

By total radioactivity balance:

$$4S(\text{last } 4\%) = S(96 \text{ to } 97\%) + 3S(\text{last } 3\%)$$

$$4(47.0) = S(96 \text{ to } 97\%) + 3(48.5)$$

$$S(96 \text{ to } 97\%) = 188.0 - 145.5 = 42.5.$$

5-6. *42.4 μc/g.* This answer should be the same as the answer to Question 5-5. Use of Fig. 5-7 at $f = 0.965$ and $k^*/k = 0.889$ gives $r'' = 1.29$; therefore,

$$S(96 \text{ to } 97\%) = (1.29)(20)(^{46}\!/_{28}) = 42.4.$$

5-7. *The SN1 reaction.* If it is assumed that all other factors are equal in the two reactions, the SN2 reaction might be expected to exhibit the smaller carbon-14 isotope effect, because the new bond to the labeled atom in the transition state could offset the partial loss of the original bond to the labeled atom.

5-8. *Yes.* Table 5-3 gives the value 1.005 for the ratio of the square root of the reduced masses of the atoms attached in the ^{14}C—H and ^{12}C—H bonds that are cleaved. By comparison, the corresponding ratio for cleavage of carbon-14-labeled carbon-to-carbon bonds is 1.038. The expected kinetic isotope effect, k_{12}/k_{14}, depends strongly on this ratio.

5-9. Many factors enter into the selection of a suitable process for the separation of isotopes on a practical scale. A primary consideration is that the process be capable of continuous operation. Continuous operation is ordinarily much more readily achieved with a reversible chemical system than with a unidirectional process.

CHAPTER 9

9-1. 1.13×10^4 counts/min/mg.

9-2. 2.40 mc/mole.

9-3. Value (*a*) probably should be ignored, because chloroacetic acid is a poor weighing form and might contain water. Value (*b*) should be discarded, because the oxidation is probably accompanied by an isotope effect. Values (*c*) and (*d*) are probably reliable, because they agree closely; apparently the malonic acid synthesis does not involve a measurable ^{14}C-isotope effect. The average of (*c*) and (*d*), 1.245 mc, therefore should be a satisfactory estimate.

9-4. 5 liters.

9-5. 5 liters, theoretically. In practice, much more air probably would be needed, depending on the rate of the exchange reaction.

CHAPTER 10

10-1. (*a*) 43.5 mc/mole.

    (*b*) 223 μc/g.

10-2. (*a*) 15.5 μc/g.

    (*b*) By decarboxylation to styrene, derivatization, and extraction with bicarbonate solution to remove the benzoic acid contaminant.

10-3. 15.6 μc/g.

10-4. (*a*) 2.86%.

    (*b*) 1.05%.

10-5. (*a*) R-Substituted nucleus, 45.0% migration; R'-substituted nucleus, 55.0% migration.

    (*b*) The measured specific radioactivity of the carbon-14 dioxide would be slightly low. Correcting for this would result in an increase in the calculated percent migration of the R-substituted nucleus.

10-6. (*a*) Degradation can be accomplished by decarboxylation at 275°. The molar radioactivity of a pure derivative of the benzophenone produced is divided by the molar radioactivity of a pure sample of the initial *o*-benzoylbenzoic acid. The quotient gives the fraction of the carbon-14 in the carbonyl group of the acid.

    (*b*) Because of stabilization of the ring that contains the nitro-substituent, degradation can be effected by oxidation of the other two rings. The most probable product would be 3-nitrophthalic acid. The fraction of the total carbon-14 present in position 1 could be obtained by dividing the molar radioactivity of the 3-nitrophthalic acid by that of the 1-nitroanthracene.

    (*c*) In this case, both rings are partially stabilized by electronegative substituents. The best degradation would probably involve quantitative reduction to 4-(*p*-aminophenyl)benzoic acid and oxidation to phthalic acid. The electron-donating amino substituent should render the *p*-aminophenyl group susceptible to cleavage. The fraction of the total radioactivity present in the ring that contains the carboxyl substituent would be calculated by dividing the molar radioactivity of the phthalic acid by that of the 4-(*p*-nitrophenyl)benzoic acid.

10-7. See *J. Am. Chem. Soc.*, **79**, 2651 (1957).

10-8. (*a*) See *J. Am. Chem. Soc.*, **77**, 92 (1955).

    (*b*) Prolonged oxidation of the mixture can result in some oxidation of the ring-labeled benzophenone to benzoic acid. Thus, a small error in the calculated distribution of carbon-14 among the rings would result. The net effect of the error usually would be to make the distribution of carbon-14 among the rings appear to be more nearly even than it truly is. However, the direction of the error could differ depending on the relative amounts of carbon-14 in the different rings.

CHAPTER 11

11-1. (*a*) 1.6×10^{-12} amp. (*b*) 1.2×10^{-15} amp.

11-2. The continuous loss of beta particles will cause the sample to build up a high potential and will soon result in improper operation of the ionization chamber.

11-3. (*a*) 161 dpm. (*b*) $t_b/t_s = \sqrt{N_b/N_s} = {\sim}0.5$.

11-4. (*a*) 85%.

    (*b*) Sample no. 1. Quenching causes a downward shift of the pulse-height spectrum. There is therefore an increase in the ratio of count rate observed in the lower channel compared with the count rate in the upper channel. Moreover, the efficiency for counting the internal standard decreased from 85% in the nonquenching sample to 67% in sample no. 1.

    (*c*) Sample no. 1: $(4010/0.67) - 28 = 5950$ dpm. The effect of quenching on the background is not known in sample no. 1. Sample no. 2: $(4100 - 28)/0.85 = 4790$ dpm.

11-5. 1.594 mc/mole.

11-6. 2.03 mc/mole.

11-7. (*a*) 2.0060 ± 0.003 mc/mole.

    (*b*) 2.0060 ± 0.002 mc/mole.

    (*c*) 2.0060 ± 0.004 mc/mole.

CHAPTER 15

15-1. (*a*) About $6.50.

15-2. 0.29%.

15-3. (*a*) Cyclohexanol, the precursor of the cyclohexanone, could be converted to a solid ester such as the tosylate by a reaction not involving the labeled carbon atoms.

(*b*) Unlabeled cyclohexanol was added as carrier after hydrogenation of the phenol.

15-4. Pivalic acid would probably undergo slow decarbonylation and recarbonylation (see Ref. 24). An intermediate *t*-butyl carbonium ion, once formed, would likely exchange all of its nine hydrogen atoms with an excess of deuteriosulfuric acid–deuterium oxide by proton transfer. The deuterated *t*-butyl carbonium ion could then undergo carbonylation to form perdeuterated pivalic acid, since the tenth (acidic) hydrogen atom of pivalic acid should exchange almost instantaneously.

15-5. (*a*) $k_1/2k_2 = 1.044[1 + 0.108 - 0.037]$

$$= 1.118.$$

(*b*) The factor 1.044 (outside the brackets) might be too large. Use of a value of $\nu_{1L}{}^{\ddagger}/\nu_{2L}{}^{\ddagger}$ calculated from the masses of the molecular fragments (Sec. 5-6h) would lead to a ratio of $k_1/2k_2$ of about 1.07 to 1.08.

APPENDIXES

APPENDIX

I

NOMENCLATURE OF ORGANIC COMPOUNDS LABELED WITH CARBON-14 OR CARBON-13

At present there is no universally accepted system of naming organic compounds labeled with carbon-14 or carbon-13. In the United States, the suggestions of Collins, Crompton, Ronzio, and Tolbert[1] have generally been followed to name carbon-14 compounds. According to their suggestions, the capital C with a superscript following, C^{14}, is used as the isotope symbol; this symbol immediately follows that part of the compound name to which it refers. When a locant number or Greek letter is necessary, this locant is placed between the name and the isotope symbol. The name, the locant, and the isotope symbol are separated by hyphens. When necessary, parentheses are used to avoid ambiguity. If the position of the labeled atom is doubtful, the lower-case letter "x" is used as the locant. If two postions are labeled with carbon-14, a right-hand subscript 2 follows the isotope symbol.

These suggestions of Collins and co-workers[1] are followed in this volume with one exception: the superscript precedes rather than follows the isotope symbol. This location of the superscript to the left of the isotope symbol is recommended by the I.U.P.A.C. and is now the accepted practice in the United States; it has been the accepted practice in Britain since 1950.

A few examples will suffice to illustrate simple applications of these rules:

Formula	*Name*
$H^{14}CO_2H$	Formic-^{14}C acid
—$^{14}COCH_3$	(Aceto-1-^{14}C)-phenone
$CH_3{}^{14}CH_2OH$ mixed with $^{14}CH_3CH_2OH$	Ethyl-$^{14}C_2$ alcohol *or* Ethanol-$^{14}C_2$
—$CO_2C_2H_5$ labeled in ring at an unknown position	Ethyl(benzene-x-^{14}C)carboxylate

Formula	Name
CH₃CO₂C₃H₇	Propyl-x-¹⁴C acetate

$CH_3CO_2C_3H_7$ labeled at an unknown position in the propyl group — Propyl-x-^{14}C acetate

Other systems of nomenclature of labeled compounds are discussed by Catch[2] and by Murray and Williams.[3] These are generally more comprehensive than the suggestions of Collins and co-workers.[1] However, as Catch[2] suggests, the usefulness of any exhaustively complete system of nomenclature might be questioned inasmuch as most users of labeled organic compounds are not primarily organic chemists and doubtlessly will persist in using trivial names for labeled compounds instead of names based on systematic organic nomenclature.

Three of the nomenclature problems that the suggestions of Collins and co-workers do not consider are:

1 Accepted systems of nomenclature of organic compounds often give no number to any carbon atom at which substitution is impossible. Consequently, if such an un-numbered carbon atom is labeled with carbon-14, some new number or letter must be applied to locate that labeled position.

2 When carbon-14 is distributed uniformly among the carbon atoms, some workers consider it desirable to include a symbol such as "U.L." as part of the name. Compounds are described as being generally labeled (G.L.) when some selectivity occurs in the distribution of radioactivity on the various labeled positions. Biosynthesis from a simple labeled precursor does not ensure that the label will be distributed uniformly. One supplier makes the reasonable assumption that compounds isolated from algal sources are uniformly labeled if the increase in weight during growth (based on carbon-14 dioxide) is greater than threefold. Unfortunately, there is no general agreement on choice of a symbol or on the exact meaning of such a symbol when it is used.

3 There is no general agreement as to whether or not the names of carbon-14-labeled compounds should take into account the abundances of carbon-14 at various labeled positions.

CITED REFERENCES

[1] C. J. Collins, C. Crompton, A. R. Ronzio, and B. M. Tolbert, United States Atomic Energy Commission Report ORNL-1084, October 1, 1951.
[2] J. R. Catch, "Carbon-14 Compounds," Butterworth Inc., Washington, D.C., 1961, p. 72.
[3] A. Murray and D. L. Williams, "Organic Syntheses with Isotopes," part I, Interscience Publishers Inc., New York, 1958, p. 2.

APPENDIX
▌▌
SOME SUPPLIERS OF CARBON-14 COMPOUNDS

Two excellent sources of information on suppliers of carbon-14 compounds exist; they are:

1 "International Directory of Radio-isotopes," 2d ed., International Atomic Energy Agency, Vienna, 1962; esp. pp. 319–548.

2 J. L. Sommerville, Ed., "The Isotope Index 1963–1964," 7th ed., Scientific Equipment Company, P.O. Box 19086, Indianapolis, Indiana, 1963; esp. pp. 13–119.

These references are revised frequently. They tabulate alphabetically the available carbon-14 compounds and, for each compound, give information on supplier, supplier code, specific activity, and price. "The International Directory of Radioisotopes" also gives pertinent supplementary information such as chemical and radiochemical purity, medium, availability, and a listing of standard sources.

A list, by country, of some suppliers of carbon-14 compounds follows:

BELGIUM

Belgonucléaire
35, rue des Colonies
Brussels, Belgium

Center d'Etudes de l'Energie Nucléaire
Department des Radio-Isotopes
Mol-Donk, Belgium

European Atomic Energy Community
EURATOM
Direction Générale Recherches et Enseignement
Radioisotopes
51/53 rue Belliard
Brussels, Belgium

CANADA

Atomic Energy of Canada Limited
Commercial Products Division
P.O. Box 93
Ottawa, Canada

Merck, Sharp & Dohme of Canada, Ltd.
P.O. Box 899
Montreal 3, Quebec
Canada

CZECHOSLOVAKIA

Omnia Foreign Trade Corporation
Washingtonova, 11
Prague 3
Czechoslovak Socialist Republic

ENGLAND

The Radiochemical Centre
Amersham, Buckinghamshire
England

FRANCE

Commissariat á l'Energie Atomique
Department des Radioelements
B.P. No. 2, Gif-sur-Yvette
Seine-et-Oise, France

Institut Pasteur
Laboratoire des Isotopes
rue du Dr. Roux
Paris 15, France

GERMANY

Farbwerke Hoechst A. G.
Frankfurt/Main—Hoechst
Federal Republic of Germany

Kernreaktor Bau- und Betriebsgesellschaft
  mbH,
Karlsruhe, Weberstrasse 5
Federal Republic of Germany

Schering A. G.
Berlin-West N 65
Müllerstrasse 170/172
Federal Republic of Germany

HUNGARY

Hungarian Institute of Isotopes
National Atomic Energy Commission
Budapest, 114, POB 77
Hungary

Hungarian Trading Company for Pharma-
  ceutical Products
Budapest, 502, POB 34
Hungary

JAPAN

Daiichi Pure Chemicals Co., Ltd.
No. 1, 3-Chome
Edobashi, Nihonbashi, Chuo-ku
Tokyo, Japan

THE NETHERLANDS

N. V. Philips Duphar
Appollolaan 151
Amsterdam
Netherlands

RUSSIA

Soyuzchemexport
Smolenskaia-Semaia Square 32/34
Moscow G-200
USSR

SPAIN

Junta de Energia Nuclear
Centro Nacional de Energia Nuclear
"Jaun Vignón"
Madrid (3), Spain

UNITED STATES OF AMERICA

Atomic Accessories, Incorporated
811 West Merrick Road
Valley Stream, New York

Atomic Corporation of America
14725 Arminta Street
Panorama City, California

Bio-Rad Laboratories
1259 South 32nd Street
Richmond, California

Calbiochem
P.O. Box 54282
Los Angeles, California 90054

Hazelton-Nuclear Science Corporation
4062 Fabian Way
Palo Alto, California 94303

International Chemical and Nuclear Corporation
13332 East Torch Street
City of Industry, California

Isotopes, Incorporated
123 Woodland Avenue
Westwood, New Jersey 07675

Isotopes Specialties Company
P.O. Box 688
111 W. Chestnut
Burbank, California

Isoserve, Incorporated
131 Portland Street
Cambridge 39, Massachusetts

The Matheson Company, Incorporated
P.O. Box 85
East Rutherford, New Jersey 07073

National Bureau of Standards
Radioactivity Section
U.S. Department of Commerce
Washington, D.C. 20234

New England Nuclear Corporation
575 Albany Street
Boston, Massachusetts 02118

NICHEM, Incorporated
147 Scranton Ave.
Lynbrook, New York 11735

Nuclear-Chicago Corporation
333 East Howard Avenue
Des Plaines, Illinois 60018

Nuclear Research Chemicals, Incorporated
100 N. Crystal Lake Drive
P.O. Box 6458
Orlando, Florida 32803

Nuclear Science and Engineering Corporation
P. O. Box 10901
Pittsburgh, Pennsylvania 15236

Oak Ridge National Laboratory
Union Carbide Nuclear Company
Isotopes Sales Department
P.O. Box X
Oak Ridge, Tennessee 37830

Research Specialties Company
200 South Garrard Boulevard
Richmond, California

Schwarz Bio Research, Incorporated
Mountain View Avenue
Orangeburg, New York 10962

Tracerlab, Incorporated
1601 Trapelo Road
Waltham, Massachusetts 02154

U.S. Nuclear Corporation
801 N. Lake Street
P.O. Box 208
Burbank, California 91503

APPENDIX

III

SOME SUPPLIERS OF FILMS SUITABLE FOR AUTORADIOGRAPHY OF CARBON-14 COMPOUNDS

Agfa-Gevaert A. G.
509 Leverkusen-Bayerwerk
West Germany

General Aniline & Film Corporation (Ansco)
Photo and Reproduction Division
Department KK
Binghamton, New York

E. I. du Pont de Nemours and Company, Incorporated
Photo Products Department
Parlin, New Jersey

Eastman Kodak Company
Special Applications Sales
Rochester, New York 14650

Gevaert-France
4, rue Paul-Cezanne
Paris 8e, France

Gevaert Photo-Producten N. V.
Septestraat, 27
Mortsel/Antwerp
Belgium

Ilford Incorporated
2/4 Clements Road
Ilford, Essex
England

APPENDIX
IV
SUPPLIERS OF
SCIENTIFIC INSTRUMENTS

It is impossible and also unnecessary to attempt to provide a complete list of equipment applicable to work with carbon-14. However, publishers of technical journals have prepared such reference lists of scientific instruments and their manufacturers. Three such guides, designed for broad scientific readership and published annually, are:

1 "Laboratory Guide to Instruments, Equipment, and Chemicals," *Analytical Chemistry*.

2 "Buyers' Guide," *Nucleonics*.

3 "Guide to Scientific Instruments," *Science*.

NAME
INDEX

SUBJECT INDEX

R

|

JAN 24 1905